For those at Mobile House
who taught Merlin
lateral thinking.

Chris [illegible] 10/9/02

# I MERLIN

# I MERLIN

*An Historical Recreation*

Christopher Davson

The Book Guild Ltd
Sussex, England

The Book Guild Ltd
25 High Street,
Lewes, Sussex

First published 2000


Set in Sabon
Typesetting by Keyboard Services, Luton

Origination, printing and binding
in Singapore
under the supervision of
MRM Graphics Ltd, Winslow, Bucks

A catalogue record for this book is
available from the British Library

ISBN 1 85776 480 3

# CONTENTS

# LIST OF PLATES

# LIST OF FIGURES

# FOREWORD

## *by the Rt. Hon. The Earl of Halsbury,* F.R.S.

Around the commencement of our present Christian era, following some climatic change in the steppes of central Asia, nomadic hordes of Mongolians etc. started their remorseless trek westwards in search of pasture and water, pushing their terrified neighbours before them.

By AD361, when my cousin's book begins, the Western frontier was under nearly continuous threat from refugee Goths, Alemani, Vandals and Swabes – themselves fleeing before the Huns. For the next hundred years, most of which he describes, waves of Barbarians were sometimes repelled, but more often absorbed into Roman lands, and above all, into the Roman Army.

It is only natural that memories of these tumultuous times should have become enshrined in folk-memory, whether as myths, legends, or saga; also that they should have condensed into the forms in which we know them by concentrating on one or another of their aspects.

For British and American readers, King Arthur and the Holy Grail, his Knights, his Round Tables, and his Amours are still very much on today's stage; nor can they forget Lancelot and Guinevere, or indeed Merlin himself. But Francophones have their own treasures in the *Chansons de Geste* of Charlemagne and his Paladins, and of the Song of Roland. Nor will Richard Wagner readily let Germans and Scandinavians forget Tristan, Isolde, and King Mark; Parsifal, Kundry and Amfortas; Siegfried, Brünnhilde and Wotan.

All these, and more, are to be found in this book, in which my cousin Sir Christopher Davson contends that the originals of these cyclical folk memories are to be sought in the entourage of the Emperor Theodosius the Great, AD378–395; particularly in his larger-than-life family with its operatically dramatic quirks of piety and heroism, adultery and incest.

He has devoted eighteen years of his life to studying how the various myths, suitably analysed, correlate with the historical events that presumably triggered them off. I found his account so fascinating that I have just finished reading it, and perusing the accompanying Indexes, over a concentrated twenty-four hour period during which I could not lay it down.

I was not new to the subject as my sister, Lady Flavia Anderson, had also spent a lifetime studying and writing on the legend of the Holy Grail – her thesis being that it was not a drinking vessel but a water-filled lens used to light the sacred fire on prehistoric altars. Her study of geometrical optics began with Archimedes, the Sicilian applied-scientist, to whom Davson also turned in his inquiries. He went on to read the great Marcellin Berthelot's collection of the earliest Greek alchemical manuscripts, and also that popular historical study of them by the late Dr F. Sherwood Taylor, director of the Science Museum, of whose Council I was Chairman.

It is for all these reasons that I have the greatest pleasure in congratulating him on a task well and truly accomplished and in recommending his book to all students of the subject.

We [Sir Christopher and I] are descended from two remarkable sisters, our grandmothers, now in the Elysian Fields.

On my side, from Lucy Duff-Gordon, grande couturière of the Edwardian epoch, inventor of the bra, and populariser of the mannequin show and dress parade. On his side, from Elinor Glyn, romantic novelist and uncrowned Queen of social Hollywood.

That his grandmother and great aunt may both take pride in his work is the fervent prayer of his second cousin,

Halsbury

# ACKNOWLEDGEMENTS

There's no way I can sufficiently thank my wife Kate for consenting for nigh twelve years to share our bed and our lifestyle with a train of Guineveres. Not only was she the first to point out to me the significance of the sign 'STELLA ARTOIS' on a passing lorry in Belgium; not only has she typed much of the manuscript; not only has she lent me her computer to complete the task myself; not only has she endured strange holidays, seminars and missions whose purpose I could not then disclose; but, to crown it all, she has actually voyaged for me and brought back for me, courtesy of the Biblioteca Marciana, Venice, my very own facsimile copy of the *Liber Gradalis*, or *Book of the Holy Grail*. It is from that copy that I have taken the labyrinth which forms the Frontispiece of this book. Now, who's my 'bestest Guinevere'? Pippa Lewis' reputation as illustrations 'sleuth' proved well founded. In addition, one Ian has helped me with photography, another Ian with typing, and my son George has not only typed a quarter of the book himself, but has succeeded in making his father apparently 'hands-on' computer literate. Without all this help I could not have done it. Nor without the steadfast patience and trust of the Librarian of the London Library, who has enabled me to write with all my sources on the table in front of me. Chief among these has been the ever-blessed Tillemont, the 'historians' historian' if ever there was one. Finally I must thank Conrad, who warned; Andrew, who encouraged opportunely; and Bill and Bob, who enabled. For the result I alone must take responsibility.

I am also extremely grateful to the following for their permission to reproduce copyrighted material:

Save as shown below, all illustrations are from the author's own photographs, or from line drawings prepared for him, or from his own commissioned microfilm of Codex MS 299 in the Biblioteca Marciana, Venice, or else from 'Collection des anciens Alchimistes Grecs'; M. Berthelot; Georges Steinheil, Paris, 1888.

The author and publishers are grateful to the following for permitting the use of illustrations of which they are the copyright owners:

Trustees of the British Museum, Plate 4 & Figs 1–5, 10, 13–15, 21, 30, 31, 35, 39.

National Museums & Galleries on Merseyside, Walker Art Gallery, Liverpool L69 3LA, Plate 13.

Manx National Heritage, Douglas, Isle of Man, IM1 3LY, Plate 15 & Figs 42, 55.

National Museum of Ireland, Collins Barracks, Dublin 7, Ireland, Fig 60.

Mairie de Toulouse, Musée des Augustins, 21 rue de Metz – 31000 Toulouse, France, Fig 27.

Bildarchiv Foto Marburg, Wolffstraße D–35037 Marburg, Germany, Plate 14.

'Edizioni Poligraf', soc. coop. a.r.l, Via Bernabei, 25/b Palermo, Sicilia, Italy, Plates 5, 6, 9, 10 & Figs 6–9, 22, 28, 58.

Staatliche Kunstsammlung, Mathematisch–Physiker Salon, Zwinger, 01067 Dresden, Germany, Fig 20.

Fratelli Alinari, S.p.A., Largo Fratelli Alinari, 15 – 50123 Firenze, Italy, Figs 24, 25, 32.

Veclano Franco & C. S.n.C., 25019 Sirmione, Italy, Fig 11.

Edizione Poiatti, c/o Kina Italia S.p.A. 201131 Milano, Italy, Fig 33.

Istituto Archeologico Germanico, 1–00187 Roma, Italy, Plate 18.

Soprintendenza Archaeologica delle Province di Napoli e Caserta, Piazza Museo 19, 80135 Napoli, Italy, Plate 17.

Prof (Em.) J Mertens, B1970 Wezembeek, Belgium, Fig 29.

Prof Raymond Brulet, Dept d'Archaelogie, Université Catholique de Louvain, Louvain–la–Neuve, Belgium, Figs 36, 59.

The Heraldry Society, owners of the former Tabard Press, PO Box 32, Maidenhead, Plate 16.

# WHY THIS BOOK?

## *A Very Personal Introduction*

[NB: * indicates a reference in the Commentary]

Stand in that Crypt below St Mary's Chapel at Glastonbury which is still called Joseph's. Stand there in the morning, innocent, alone: above all, alone. Gape vaguely in the direction of the altar, expecting nothing. Then wait. Just wait.

This I did, some forty years ago. Here is what I saw. In the NE corner to the left of the altar, on or just above the ground, I saw a small flame like a candle flame, or perhaps only a night-light. This small flame was flickering; no, guttering, as if a wind was blowing it sideways – that is, southwards. As the flame leant over it would go blue, as a flame does *in extremis*. Then it would recover. Another gust would blow it again sideways, and it would again go blue, near asphyxiated. It shrank and shivered as I watched its death struggle. 'Don't let it die,' I found myself saying aloud. 'Please God don't let it die.' It didn't die. It recovered its upright position and its healthy yellow hue. Then it gently faded, as if withdrawn to a great distance by an unseen hand, and I saw it no more. But I was interested to learn from the Guidebook that the spot where I saw the flame was over the supposed tomb of St Indracht, an Irish Saint of whom I then knew nothing, but was later, amazingly, to learn was none other than Merlin himself (see page 64 and Comm. p. 278, 64.6).

I made the huge mistake of telling my mother, who had by now joined me, that I thought I had 'seen something'. On our return from our West Country holiday she intended me for the lion of the cocktail circuits. 'Tell them, dear boy, about our vision at Glastonbury. Tell them how you saw Joseph of Arimathea himself, with a long white beard standing on the altar holding the Holy Grail in his hands.' So she urged me on, but I cringed with embarrassment and fury, and sulked, and said I had seen nothing really, and tried to mean it. But I did see something, as I have told you.

Twenty years later my mother was dead, and I inherited from her some family heirlooms and papers. The heirlooms were her father's, and included armorial china and bookplates bearing her arms, which in her right I now quarter. The papers included her father's genealogy stretching back to the ninth century. I settled down to look into these relics. I was referred by the Harleian Society to Bartrum's recently published *Early Welsh Genealogical Tracts*, which I commenced studying. Let no one say it wasn't a tough read, but I persisted. There I found my own genealogy, and was able to learn that it was of above average reliability.

But Bartrum was able to take this genealogy another four centuries backwards. This, if true, would bring us to the fourth century, when the Romans still ruled Britain. What was I to make of this? I have spent the intervening twenty, or so, years in solid research which has taken me to many surprising and delightful places. Armed with this book, my readers will now be able to go on their own 'Merlin Tours' and to see for themselves the very real sites and extant remains.

Merlin will comment that there seems to be a strange sort of pattern in his life. Mine too. Let me just say that the first five books of *I Merlin* were transcribed from Merlin's scribes' sweating hands direct onto 'floppy discs' by my son George, working in his house on the site of that very St George's College (later Osney Abbey), where eight hundred and fifty years earlier Walter II, Archdeacon of Oxford, had 're–begotten' the whole story for the Romancers.

My qualifications for writing this book are therefore much the same as those of the supposed writer of the *Estoire de Saint Graal*, who, by his own account, wrote in AD750 or thereabouts, and who could well be Ferghal of Aghaboe, later Bishop of Salzburg and Apostle of Carinthia. His personal quest for the Holy Grail and its meaning started with a perusal of his own family tree. So did mine. Like me, he then pursued his researches in various European countries and, after what appears to have been a quest of months rather than years he was in a position to put pen to paper. His work survives in Volume I of Sommer's gigantic 'Vulgate Cycle', written c. AD1230. My own quest has taken some eighteen years to reach its goal, or perhaps even a lifetime.

Claiming Merlin as a direct ancestor (see App. 12) whose arms (or imputed arms) I proudly bear, I set out to find him in historical and genealogical sources contemporary or near contemporary, and I claim to have found him, *as* and *with* 'King Arthur' and his fabled entourage. It is only proper that I should present my findings as history; and of this you shall be the jury. However, Professor David Dumville of Cambridge University, a respected British scholar with a far from negligible following, wrote of Arthur in *History*, 62 (205): 173–92, 'I think we can dispose of him [Arthur] quite briefly. He owes his place in the history books to a "no smoke without fire" school of thought… The fact of the matter is that there is no historical evidence about Arthur; we must reject him from our histories and, above all from the titles of our books'. (Earlier the same author was less dismissive; see p. 338 of *Proceedings of the Royal Irish Academy*, 73, Sec. C.) Candour requires me to display this formidable 'health warning'. However, my book attempts to show that there were ten historical 'Arthurs', but only one historical 'Merlin'.

My approach is strictly classical, archaeological and epigraphical. I have worked only from my sources, after rigorously appraising them; I have used the prosopological method (in a nutshell, the 'what's in a name?' approach), moderated by genealogical discipline. I have found astonishing congruence between all my sources, particularly as to chronology. And I have encountered a technical problem to which you may not like my solution.

The problem is names. As my historical characters emerged blinking from their disguises I found that they had too many names, familiar and unfamiliar. Thanks to scribal and oral corruption the Romance, Teutonic, and Celtic names were the most fecund, and I therefore at first intended, since I was writing of real-life Romans, to use the Roman system of nomenclature as my primary system.

Alas, I found this was not so easy. Well–born Romans had a whole armoury of names: legal names, family names, filiatives, surnames (*cognomina*) and, above all, nicknames (*agnomina*). We know them nowadays by the name they went by when they were earning themselves that reputation which has survived. But no one called the Emperor Caius 'Caligula' to his face; only behind his back. No one called the author Macrobius (a minor character in this book) 'Macrobius' ('long-lived') until he was in his autumn years; and, tiresomely, I shall give you his other names as he used them. The situation is still worse when we come to my principal characters, not excluding Old Merlin himself. They went by all too many Roman names.

My solution, therefore, has been to impose my own system of primary nomenclature – daring, like Adam, to 'name the animals' – and ***to invite you to adopt my names as the benchmarks for this book***. Believe it or not, it really does make it simpler. For example, Merlin's brother is the usurping Emperor Constantine III, but is also Pelagius the heresiarch, Bendigeid Vrân of Welsh myth, Sigurd the Volsung and many others whom I must mention. ***I invite you to remember him throughout as 'JJ'***. So for all my principal characters I give a 'Dramatis Personae' (see page xxix). (Minor 'walk-on' Romans bear only that name by which they appear in classical sources. I provide ample family trees in Apps. 1–9, so that you may remind yourself who's who if you get lost; but I have tried to make the variations emerge naturally, chronologically, and in context.

This book is in its way a 'novel' sort of doctoral thesis, the demonstration following the model of a Renaissance *Orrery*. An Orrery displayed the celestial bodies in three dimensions and in motion, so as to allow their many interlocking speeds and orbits to coincide with one another at the very points where astronomers predicted that they would conjoin. A moving marvel of mechanical ingenuity and precision, the Orrery not only entertained and instructed; it demonstrated patently that there was a solar *system* underlying the apparently random movements of unconnected bodies in their discrete orbits.

This is what I have attempted to demonstrate in this, my historical Orrery, or model. In one orbit I have placed those 'bodies' securely identified in classical sources; in others, those found in myths and legends of every variety and tongue;

in another the shadowy bones of the Saints from their *Vitae*; in another, the precious detritus of legend so remarkably preserved by dramatists and operatic librettists; in another the pabula of fair story and nursery rhyme. All, importantly, carry their appropriate prosopological penumbra, so that a sort of 'identikit' portrait emerges.

When I had assembled all these 'bodies' onto my Orrery and found that their orbits were correct and that the 'conjunctions' coincided *exactly* with the best historical chronology of the period so far agreed, I concluded that there was an underlying 'solar system' of historical truth behind the non–classical sources, and I have cautiously made historical use of the latter sources. The 'proof of the pudding is in the eating'. Does my Orrery *work*? I claim it works almost uncannily well; that's why I claim to be writing *history*. Indeed I have needed to invent no incidents, no locations and no characters, save the team at the Nubian gold mine – whom you will meet in Book IV and that mine is real.

I chose Merlin himself as my principal narrator because thanks to his reputation as prophet, time-walker, seer, mage and polymath, this purely technical device enabled me to expatiate without editorial intrusion, and to indulge in as many anachronisms as would help to make Merlin's mind understandable to modern minds. 'Morgan the letter-writer' is another device; real enough herself, I have felt able to use her as a mouthpiece for family and world news.

For the same reason I have felt at liberty to use the vernacular of the time in which I write, instead of imposing on myself the bogus 'vernacular styles' of some historical novelists. We all like to think that 'Ivanhoe' and the Crusader knights actually talked as Sir Walter Scott has them talk, and Regency Rakes spoke in the style of Miss Georgette Heyer; but we really do not know how they talked to one another. Still less so the Romans, where Classical literary sources give us little clue. We should not take too closely as models the re-created speeches with which such great historians as Polybius, Sallust, Livy, Tacitus, and above all Thucydides have seen fit to adorn and lighten their narrations. I have thus followed distinguished masters by, like them, utilising *oratio recta*, but have preferred the vernacular of the present time. 'Honi soit qui mal y pense'. I have, however, invented my own norm for addressing and referring to the Augusti: 'Your Serenity' or 'His Serenity' ring quite convincingly to the ears. Better, I think, than 'Your Dominacy' or even 'Your Divinity', as other authors have essayed.

Because my historical conclusions differ so dramatically from so much currently-received scholarly wisdom, I have given full 'chapter and verse' for each of my assertions in a 'Commentary for the Curious' (see page 257) which should be considered with the Appendices. Such allusions are marked in the text with an asterisk: *, and are thus traceable via the Commentary to the Bibliography, and bear full page – and where necessary even line – references. The Commentary is cross-referenced internally and to the text by page and key phrases, so that the curious may glance through it easily, and scholars may follow up their particular interests comprehensively. A comprehensive index is also provided on page 362.

Like Gibbon, I have written this book with the inestimable Tillemont always on the table before me. Luckier than Gibbon, I have had Clinton's *Fasti* also open, with their refined chronology and copious source quotations. The family trees, too, are rooted in Clinton (supplemented by Hodgkin and Bartrum). Farrar has proved a convenient short cut to relevant patristic writings. The Loomis (1959) compendium *Arthurian Literature in the Middle Ages* is a cardinal gateway, leading where necessary to original Romance sources, although the heroic Bruce is valuable in his own right, together with Löseth and Paton. Lewis Spence's *Dictionary of Mediaeval Romance and Romance Writers* (1913) is also on the table. Finally, P.C. Bartrum has enabled this whole enquiry, with his selfless *Early Welsh Genealogical Tracts* (1966) accounting for virtually every Welsh name and context utilised in this book.

I set out in quest of 'King Arthur' and his Knights. To my surprise I have found myself writing of Saints and their companions, and have been forced to treat them as human beings like ourselves. It is a well-attested characteristic of Saints that they are the very first to insist on their sinfulness. I have depicted them realistically and, I hope, truthfully. I have shown them at times in less than flattering situations, but they will know that I intend disrespect neither to them nor to those who throughout the centuries have rightly venerated and still do venerate them. Indeed, like Pope Damasus on page 56, I count myself of that company. Nevertheless I have been pricked in my own conscience to discover just how vividly my characters practised, and agonised over, their faith. Maybe I had overlooked that it is the *Holy* Grail which has provoked this book. May this Queste provoke you too.

I would like, in this century, to remember affectionately the Rev. Lionel Lewis who started so many Glastonbury hares; also my own kinswoman Lady Flavia Anderson whose *The Ancient Secret* (1953), just reissued in a revised edition, broke much relevant ground; finally, Geoffrey Ashe who has tramped ahead of me up so many slopes in the last thirty-two years only to disappear in the mist down some side spur. Again and again I have feared he would beat me to the summit. His *From Caesar to Arthur* (1960) still reads uncommonly well, and in the footnote to page 95 Ashe throws out a challenge:

> *May I take up a suggestion of Professor Collingwood's, and recommend Pelagius to the attention of historical novelists? Constantine III and the British revolution would supply plenty of violent action; while for the essential female interest we have ... Gerontius' wife Nonnichia who died tragically through her husband's political intrigues, and Honorius' amazing sister Placidia,* whom it is unluckily impracticable to work into a history of Britain.*

These authors threw down the gauntlet; I have gathered it up and entered the lists. I am *not* an historical novelist, and this is *not* an historical novel. Let me, in my turn, throw down the gauntlet: *This book is history; history from, and only from the sources.*

'History' is from Greek Ιστορια, meaning 'the telling of a story'. The 'historian' has a duty to his readers to appraise and evaluate *all* available sources, to reconcile them if he can, and if he must reject any, to reject only with declared reason. He has a further duty to his readers however, namely *to come off the fence!* Today's 'scientific' historians may seem in some danger of shirking the latter duty.

Other 'Arthurian' books, good, bad, and occasionally downright boring, continue to pour from the world's presses. I hope this one won't bore you. The few page footnotes, which purport to be by Old Merlin himself, are of too much importance for the general reader to be relegated to the Commentary. (I have offered no commentary on Merlin's 'Proem', since it is so dense with allusion that, in a sense, the whole book is a commentary on it.)

Unlike Merlin, the general reader may have 'little Latin and less Greek'; maybe none at all. This doesn't matter. All that needs to be translated I have translated or explained. You can readily guess the rest.

I have surveyed all the 'Saint's Lives' which seemed to me remotely relevant, but have nevertheless used them very sparingly. I have traversed the vast range of Welsh and Irish legend, of Saga, and of the Romance sources. As you will see I claim to have succeeded in identifying almost all the characters in Myth and Romance, but space prevents me from giving more than a few signposts (and a 'skeleton key' of identifications in App. 10]. However, these should allow you to act as your own Hercule Poirot.

The 'Commentary for the Curious' is as terse as I can make it, using my short bibliography of 'gateway' books to lead scholars back to my original source reference. From such scholars, appropriate competence in Greek, Latin, Norman–French, Middle English, Old German and Old Welsh is thereafter assumed. I have funked Old Irish, Flemish, Spanish and Italian, Norse and Anglo–Saxon as supererogatory, and relied (in this peripheral area) on translations. Scholars are invited to judge for themselves whether I have used my sources responsibly and in context. They may note how little use I have made of 'Gildas' or 'Nennius', although I do give them more than a passing nod – indeed I give them the whole of my important and provocative App. 11.

This is not to say that the Commentary will be of no interest to the general reader. Indeed, if they have any special interest in individual Arthurian fields they may pick up a lot of the allusions and have some good fun. I say *fun* because, despite the high and occasionally tragic theme, this book, if it is to be true to Merlin's character in all the traditions, *must be fun.*

It has proved perilous fun to my distinguished forerunners. Sir Thomas Malory and John Jones of Gelli Lydi (the seventeenth-century Welsh genealogist), both ended up in gaol; poor Leland in a lunatic asylum. We know, nowadays, of Tennyson's foible, which he shared with T.H. White; more recently, E.A. Bruce and John Morris both died of apoplexy – still questing.

Plainly, this Queste is fraught with goblins and foul fiends. What else would you expect?

Theologians will note my diagnosis that it is the loss of literacy in Greek which has caused so many religious schisms and controversies.

Scientists are invited to appreciate and admire the luckless but dogged experimentation and the transcendent speculations of their forerunners, the alchemists. Amateurs of 'Black Magic' and the occult will surely be disappointed to find that they have such pure, overt, and indeed innocent progenitors.

Scholars and the general reader alike will note my preoccupation with Shakespeare and Wagner. That they should, unknowing, have known so much surely tells us something significant. Nursery rhyme makes the same point. Were similar 'heroic' resonances audible to Homer? Did he write the '*Gesta Graecorum*', the '*Matière de Grèce*'? If so, can history yet be retrieved from Homer's works?

Maybe only little Merlin knows the answer.

Christopher Davson

# *PROEM*

*One day my laugh'll be the death of me. Split my sides, like old Calchas the seer. I can see it coming. Funny way to go. I'd have been made a Saint long ago but for my laugh. Son of a martyr, adopted son of a patriarch (St Ambrose – now there was a man). Cousin of a theologian (St Augustine – make up your own minds about him). And I've got all the right personal qualifications: great passions, great crimes, great repentance, great forgiveness. But I can't see them letting me into the Sacred Canon with my daimonic sense of humour.*

*So I suppose I'll have to settle for what I am, Old Merlin the seer, who's seen it all, done it all, even prophesied his own death. I've written my epitaph with a touch of the old poetic deftness,* 'rex quondam, rexque futurus', ***the once and future King****. I'll have them put it in my tomb, wherever, like the one I put in Caratacus' and Boudicca's graves when I adorned their tombs in the cemetery over yonder and embellished them with pyramids.*

*Meanwhile I sit contentedly in the drowsy autumn sun in the cloister of my own abbey. In the great garth grows quite an orchard of apples and pears, and around them root little porkers eagerly fattening up for their baptism in apple sauce. The long grass gleams with rotten windfalls and growls with wasps, too fuddled by the fermenting juices to take wing, or sting, or do their will in anything. That stirs memories.*

*Above the roofs to the East I can almost see my old observatory tower upon the Tor. Many a barbecue we had up there in the old days as I peered through my telescope at the mysteries of the Zodiac – the real revolving one.*

*From the basilica I hear the muffled sounds of the continuous Office, the* 'laus perennis' *which I caught from Basil and Benedict, yes, and Martin, so long ago, and fleshed out with hymns from Ambrose's circle, to make a twenty-four-hour garland of worship. Hope the Almighty doesn't get bored with it all. If so, I'm in trouble.*

*Myself, I find it a soothing background to my thoughts as they flit to and fro, now in the past, now and again into the future. For they rightly call me a prophet.*

*I have this rare and rather useless ability to move about in the past and future as if they were today. Isaiah could do this, and Nostradamus will. Some of the better Sybils, and Pytheas of the Delphic oracle. Even old Calchas the seer. Nobody can understand my prophecies at the time, not even me. Else I could subvert the future. Only God can both see and foresee that, as my kinsman Boethius will one day explain to you.*

*So, dipping my toes in the future, I foretell that I shall not finish these memoirs with which I occupy my evening, but that my dear son Gawain will do that for me, yes, and bury me too. Dear good Gawain, beautiful and best;* 'oed Gwēn goreu onadu' *as my Cambro Britons will have me say. I wonder which Guinevere he will choose as my bed companion for the long sleep? They were all worth the candle, every one. I dedicate this, my last literary effort, to my old loves. May we meet again where there is no marrying and giving in marriage, and suchlike fret.*

*Meanwhile I have two splendid young scribes to whom I dictate, the Librarian plies me with such books as I need refer to, and the monks and novices laugh respectfully at my jokes when I limp over to the refectory.*

*One day this book will be done, and I* **will** *that it be buried here in the crypt, on top of my other works, until the years have cleansed the passions and made the secrets innocuous. Thence a certain Dunstan will exhume them, and after him a certain Walter.*

*Finally, so many years ahead that I can scarce reckon it, one of my own descendants will find the scattered sheets and reunite them; and I will make him understand, so that he may tell again, to a world which has by no means forgotten me, the true story of King Arthur and his valiant Knights, of Merlin the Mage and his Tables Round, and of how we found and lost the Holy Grail.*

*I, Lucius Claudius Ambrosius* **Merlinus**
*have written thus far in my own hand,*
*in this my eighty-sixth year,*
*in the Nones of October,*
*Symmachus Junior and my nephew Aëtius being*
*Consuls, the latter (deservedly) for the third time.*

*Glasdunum: Britannia Secunda*

# *DRAMATIS PERSONAE*

***Merlin***, myself as Lucius Claudius Ambrosius etc; twin younger son of ***Glorious Dad*** (Honorius Sr, St Alban), and ***Little Mother***, daughter of ***Grandad Max*** (Magnus Maximus) by his first wife.

***JJ***, James Julius Saturninus etc; my boozy twin.

***Elissa***, the Great Bear; our step-cousin once-removed, and joint love; Maximus' thrilling athletic daughter by ***Justina the Ambitious***, his third wife.

***Ginger*** and ***Serena***, our nice-ish younger half-sisters.

***Morgan***, our benevolent stepmother.

***Doxy***, our 'nympho' stepsister by Morgan and Genobaudes.

***Uncle Icarus***, son of ***Gt Grandad Theodores*** and ***Eucheria the Pious Maccabee***.

***Uncle Heliodorus***, Glorious Dad's scholarly younger brother.

***Uncle Ted*** (the Emperor Theodosius the Great), Glorious Dad's tough youngest brother and tragic murderer.

***Cousin Vic***, Maximus' son by ***Melania the Holy Terror***, his second wife.

***St Ambrose***, my revered adoptive father.

***Cousin Augustine***, St Augustine of Hippo, son of Count Marcellinus.

***Arbogast the Prussian***, Little Mother's second husband.

***Genobaudes I***: brother of ***Merobaudes I, the Ruthless Fleming*** and Morgan's second husband; father of the pestilent Doxy.

***Aunt Helena***, *the damsel of Caernarfon* and Maximus' last wife.

***John-George***, JJ's son by Elissa; my nephew and foster-son.

***Ursula***, the Little Bear; my daughter by Elissa.

***Aëtius*** (Etzie), JJ's heroic son by Doxy; also my nephew.

***My Gawain***, my admirable son by Doxy.

***Arcadius*** and ***Honorius***, Uncle Ted's two boring son/Emperors.

***Galla*** (Galla Placidia/Cordelia), Uncle Ted's august and adorable only daughter.

***Stan the Inexorable*** (Constantius III, General, then Augustus), besotted lover and eventual husband of Galla in a loveless marriage; father of ***Valentinian III***, and of ***Honoria the Whore***, alias St Geneviève of Paris.

***St Germanus***, my adoptive first cousin once-removed.

++++ and a sizable supporting cast. ++++

Merlin's Labyrinth from the *Liber Gradalis*, or *Book of the Holy Grail*.
It symbolises a *quest*

# BOOK I

## *Children of the Sphinx (AD361–370)*

[NB: * indicates a reference in the Commentary]

I was born* on the very Kalends of the month of Mars in the consulate of Taurus and Florentius in married quarters in Babylon-on-Nile* (Old Cairo), where my twin brother had preceded me, as it were, by a short head.* We were *castrenses*, soldiers' sons, and my little mother Gratiana* was a 'soldier's wife'. By this I mean that, as with so many of us expatriate Romans, my Mum and Dad were only married '*mensam et thoram*', i.e. at common military law. In the case of the other ranks their marriages would be legitimated, along with their children, on final discharge after twenty-five years. The officers did not generally stay so long, moving instead to senior civilian positions; so it was for them to remedy this defect at a later date or, in my case, to fail to do so. Dad and his brother Ted were *castrenses* too, and for the same reason, for their father Count Theodosius Sr spent his whole life in uniform. In this respect we were all of us in the same boat as my great-great uncle, Constantine the Great, whose mother, St Helena, was never married at civil law to his father Constantius I Chlorus, Emperor and Dynast.

My father was a Tribune of the *Legio IInd Trajani*, the famous Theban Legion, at the time (appropriately, as you will see later), so no one dared to call us 'little bastards' around the camp. More sinister, even though unfounded, were the whispers around the bazaars of the cantonment. Twins always excited special interest, and since the days of Castor and Pollux old wives have gossiped that dissimilar twins have different fathers. Now my brother *Julius* and I were just as unlike as could be. He was a big choleric sort of baby, with hair the carrot side of auburn. I, *Claudius* – for that is my prenomen – was, (am) a little runt. I had a thatch of bright yellow hair (*gilvus** we Romans call it) which was by no means confined to my head. I must have looked like a golden hamster. Little remains now, but I still have a tussock of once-golden hair* from spine to nape, *as will my progeny the Merovingians*. That's why they called me *Carpilio*,* hairy.

The first thing I remember is our home, and my nursery, in a comfortable married quarter in Hermopolis Parva, East of Alexandria on the Canopus Canal, where lay the Legionary Depot. Blue-brown ponds with fish going flip-flop in the muddy shallows and ducks like clouds winging in at sunset.

Flamingos, too, in the reeds. And silly rough-and-tumble games with my brother, and spicy smells. And one perplexing day a sudden silence and sadness falling like a curtain on the house, and our wet-nurse and the slaves all looking the other way and no meals on time and no 'Little Mother' anywhere to be seen. Julius and I were too stunned and frightened to cry or sleep.

A few nights later, in the still moonlight, I toddled along to my parents room and it was void. Mother's bed was empty and undisturbed. Father's bed was often empty, as he was away soldiering. Not for long this time. The very next morning, I think, there was a clatter of hooves and chariot wheels up the drive and the sentries saluting, and there was Dad, '*Glorious Dad*', with his straight fair hair, blue eyes, strong white teeth, and a strange woman; tall, fair, fluffy-haired, soft rich clothes, jewels like a peacock, and a very different smell to 'Little Mother'. She kissed us little boys and told us to call her '*Mater*'. That night she was in my mother's bed and Dad was there too. We were not yet two years old and one takes things as they come at that age, glad only that meals were back on time and Nanny and the slaves smiling again. Even to please Dad, though, we couldn't bring ourselves to call her *Mater*. When we were older we used to call her *Morgan*. Why is quite a story.*

'Morgan' and I were to become good pals; it is she who has told me all I know about my origins and my amazing family, and difficult names like *Hermopolis Parva*, and who 'Little Mother' really was, and why she went away, and with whom, and what happened. And Morgan was very rich (always such a help), and very kind and extremely learned. She made me long to be learned like her, and I think maybe I have surpassed her; so it is with hindsight and her help that I fill in these early years of mine. I told you in my *Proem* that I was a seer, and this does make me a bit vague as to whether I am in the past or the future; nevertheless I will try to tell the rest of this tale as far as possible in order, as I recall it happening, and to keep foresight and hindsight in their place.

Let me explain first that I am a Roman, from a senatorial, indeed a patrician, family. My father's full name (most of it anyway) was Titus Flavius Ulpius Marcianus *Honorius* Constantinianus, later, as you will read, to be surnamed *Albanicus*. The Marcians were an ancient branch (famulus,* sept, what you will) of the Ulpian Gens* whose greatest ornament was the Emperor Trajan. I have no hesitation in hailing *him* as '*Imperator*, Emperor', or 'Commander-in-Chief', since he led Rome's armies in battle as none has since. But '*Augustus*' is the true title of the ruler of Rome, and in these days, when poltroons like young Honorius the poultry breeder sit on the throne of Caesar, I prefer to reserve '*Imperator*', Emperor, for the triumphant generals to whom it still correctly belongs.

The '*Flavius*' is a bit of a cheat. My great-great grandfather Flavius *Constantius I Chlorus* Caesar Augustus (of honoured memory) only bore it because his yellow-haired (*flavus*) father Valerius Eutropius Dardanus hoped he might be taken to descend from the famous Emperor *Flavius Vespasian* Augustus or his son *Titus* (that's where Dad got his 'Titus' from). Eutropius married a true-blue of the Julia/Claudia gens (more 'good' names for Dad), and that's why I'm called Claudius and my brother Julius. Romans are crashing snobs.

**Figure 1**

Constantius I, the Dynast, father of Theodore and of Constantine the Great; husband of St Helena



The 'Ulpius-Marcianus' bit, and the money and estates in Sicily, only came in when my great grandfather Flavius Octavius Constantinianus *Theodorus* married as his first wife Gratiana II Flavia-Ulpia-Marciana. But the rich and/or well-born will keep marrying one another so we have incorporated many Caesars and Augusti into our family tree, and lots more money.

Names don't matter too much to me as a bastard, but it's good to have a large stock of them to draw on when you need an alias, as I so often have. A friend of mine has thirty-six proper names: I must have myriads, not all 'proper'; perhaps that's why they will call me 'Myrddin'. I shall challenge my scribes to draw up some family trees* for you, and these should make all clear. One tip on names may help you. If you find a name like 'Constantinianus' it means someone, usually a son, whose father *could* call himself Constantine; 'Justinian' would be the son of Justinus, himself son of Justus; Julian, a son of Julius; Claudian, a son of 'Claudius' – and all these names will prove very relevant to you and to me. I said '*could*' call himself, whether or not he normally used them; if '***Glorious Dad***' owned all these names, I can help myself to them at will by way of filiative, besides earning my own *cognomina* and *agnomina* as I tread my path. 'What's in a name?' you ask. The whole substructure of this book, that's what.

I must say a few more words about the Marcians. The family have lived for centuries in Sicily (town-house and catacombs* in Syracuse, estates all around Ibleia) although their historic deeds till now were done in Thrace. We left several Augusti, near-Augusti and Caesars there, and even had a town Marcianopolis* named after us. Latterly, in the West, we can claim a Vicar of Britain,* a Count of the Saxon Shore, and an unsuccessful pretender to the throne (Nepotianus).

Thanks to Dad and Morgan I was to spend much of my youth in Sicily so that when I say I am a Roman of Old Rome, I am one of those funny and useful Romans who have been bilingual almost from birth. *Magister utriusque linguae*, both Greek and Latin. (Would that our theologians were. That'd be the end of half the schisms.) We Hellenophone Roman Sicilians and Apulians have the whole Imperial Services of Old and of New Rome as our oyster, whether as soldiers or civilians, since Greek is the language in use throughout the Eastern Empire – the Praetorian Prefectures, that is, of Illyricum and the East including Egypt, Cyrenaica, and Eastern Libya.

Italy (from about Capua southwards) and Sicily also speak Greek from the time when they were part of Magna Graecia: Latin is, of course, the official language, but our country folk still know some Oscan, mainly from performances of the Atellan Fables (precursors of the Commedia dell'arte, of which more anon). In and North of Rome, only scholars and churchmen know Greek, and the latter are fast forgetting it with church services now in the vernacular – Latin.

That's how Dad came to be soldiering in Egypt and later in Arctic Britain, and I to follow him to both countries. Ambitious 'patricians' like us do our bit in the army, or navy, and pass up the soft civilian option introduced by Hadrian (another ancestor!). Civilians can only aim for the top of the Civil Service, competing all the way with eunuchs – ugh! If you hope to become Augustus you need an Imperator's baton (sceptre if you will) in your knapsack. So we do our National Service almost to a man, even if we then move on to being lawyers, governors, poets, professors or bishops. So much for the Marcians.

In the year of my birth my older cousin Julian* became Augustus: Julian the Apostate. And considering the state of the Church at that time who shall blame him? Read what my godfather Basil* of Caesarea (St Basil they will call him), says of it: 'In matters of opinion some were the merest traditionalists ... while others with equal bigotry were fierce against sound doctrine. Heretics, ignorant and rash, flung themselves like swine upon the pearls of truth. Others rejoiced in a feeble eclecticism. Simoniacal bishops ordained presbyters for money or from nepotism and, of these presbyters, many sought ordination only that they might escape the burdens of military service'. In other words, the Church was in the *excrementum.**

Not only do I not blame Julian, I am to follow his example. But, for a start, I was baptised a Christian; I know this from Dad. Baptism on the name day (ninth from birth for a boy, eighth for girls) has been the Roman custom since the days of Numa (*Ab Urbe Condita* 38 – thirty-eight years, that is, from the legendary date of the foundation of Rome). On this *dies lustricus*, or baptismal naming day,* the pagan *flamen* (priest) would come to the house and sprinkle the baby's head with holy water from the temple stoups, with invocations to Jupiter and Liber, or Juno and Tellus, according to sex. He then named the child from one of the very limited number of *Prenomina* on offer. In Egypt, where we were, any number of priests of Isis, or Jewish rabbis, would have been more than willing to do something similar; maybe even circumcise me. Wish they had. It comes painful in adult life. Even as I write there are still Roman parents, Christian in more than name but pagan by long habit, who keep up the old *dies lustricus* for 'luck' whilst waiting sometimes to their deathbed for Christian baptism.

Dad himself, like all the 'Constantinians' – even Julian – was a 'cradle Christian'. That's why he felt so much at home in the Theban Legion with its own Christian Padre.* He chose to follow the tactful African compromise, adopted over one hundred years ago in Carthage in the days of Cyprian (in the teeth of Tertullian's almost unanswerable objections), whereby a Christian Presbyter took the place of the *flamen*. Cyprian was no great shakes as a theologian* until he became a martyr, since when it would be thought impious to challenge him; indeed my cousin Augustine of Hippo builds one of his 'proofs' of original sin on Cyprian's practice. I leave it for you to judge whether being a 'cradle Christian' did me any good. All I can say is that I have explored most other paths since, yet I shall die an orthodox catholic Christian.

**Figure 2**
Julian, the mad Boy Scout
© Trustees of the British Museum

Basil was a good chum (and cousin*) of my mother, and I'm told he was present at my baptism and bestowed Christian names on us also. I was 'christened' *Lucius Luke*, and my brother *Jacobus* James, and we use these names in the family. I was to come to love and respect Basil, and even to copy many of his ideas, like how to run a monastery – who'd have thought I'd ever do that? But Julian was the suitably tragic hero of my teens. Was he Plato's ideal philosopher-king, wise, brave, earnest, chaste? Or was he just a bewildered Boy Scout? When Julian headed East, on his last doomed contest with destiny and the Persians, he took *his* uncle (my great grandfather) Theodore* with him. Together they had imbibed the eclectic neo-Platonism of Libanius, the magical labyrinth-searchings of Chrysanthius; together they had held clammy hands at the flesh-creeping séances of that intolerable old charlatan Maximus,* to whom I shall frequently re-advert. All this intoxicating broth was eventually to wash over me, and am I yet clean?

I was but a baby, and Sallust consul, when Julian and Theodore stood on the ruins of the Holy of Holies in Jerusalem and vowed to rebuild Solomon's temple. There, too, on an earlier occasion in Jerusalem Theodore wooed and wed ***Eucheria,* the pious Maccabee***. Morgan has often thrilled us boys with the tale of how one Alypius descended into the cellar safe-deposits which were all that Hadrian had left of Herod's work, only to be driven back like Heliodorus on an earlier occasion by a supernatural wall of flame charging at him like a fiery horseman. We used to act this as a charade, pretending it was my own Uncle Heliodorus, of whom more anon. I now realise that the 'wall of flame' was no more than the inflammable *πνευμα* or gas of the large stocks of naphtha stored there, ever since the days of the High Priests, for purificatory rites; but to me as a boy this was splendid hair-raising magic. I longed to go there, and I have.

On Julian's death the Imperial private estates descended by his will, which in accordance with ancient custom had been lodged with the senior Vestal Virgin. With typical kindness he left the *Casa Sicelis** (in Sicily as the name implies) to *his* uncle (my great grandfather) Theodore. This Palace* took its name from an old farm amid the forests some nine miles from Morgantina.* When Diocletian decided that the two Augusti should abdicate in favour of their chosen successors, one of them being my great-great grandfather Constantius I Chlorus *Χλορος*, Constantius *Galba* 'the Sallow', patriarch of the whole House of Constantine and of Theodosius, and hence of this book – which they did in 1058 – he at once set about building his own retirement home in Salona in Dalmatia. A veritable Palace, it was soon called by that name (*Palatium* – now Split), and I see it still standing seventeen centuries later.

Diocletian's co-Augustus *Maximianus* 'Herculius' chose to build himself a very different retirement home, also built to last. He was in every way an Outward Bounder, and he rebuilt the old Villa Morgantina on a lavish yet informal plan, renaming it the *Casa Sicelis,* or 'Casa Sic' as we always used to call it. Never was there to be such a hunting lodge. The best architects laid it out. The best artists were hired to decorate the floors with lavish hunting mosaics and mythological scenes, and by the due date had completed the North wing containing the apartments of the future ex-Augustus.

Maximianus never lived there. Public life, he felt, was not ready to spare him. Resuming the purple he plunged hectically back into the all too muddy waters, and unlike Diocletian, died, some say by his own hand, contending ungratefully against his son-in-law and rival Constantine the Great. Constantine had him buried in the cemetery of St Victor at Milan, which would have infuriated him as a pagan, and erected an Imperial mausoleum there.

For sixty years the Casa Sic passed, half finished, from one member of the house of Constantius to another. Now suddenly it belonged to my ***Gt Grandad Theodore*** and his new wife Eucheria, whose interests in the Holy Land were even more 'spiritual' than her husband's – positively 'pious', she was. They were both in their sixties and their future activities still lay in the East, so their sons Theodosius Sr, my grandfather (whom future generations will remember for all time as 'Count Theodosius'), and Eucherius,* whom they called '*Icarus*' when his political wings fell off, but who is to rise again as we shall see, moved into the Casa Sic with their growing families, including Theodosius Jr (Theodosius I, the Great, my ***Uncle Ted***), and of course Ted's elder brother ***Glorious Dad***, with his new wife ***Morgan*** and his two little babies, *Julius*-James and me.

The Casa Sic was to become Morgan's home, and sometimes mine, for the rest of her life, though she also used the Marcian town house in Syracuse-Neapolis and the old castle with the exciting sub-marine cellar on the tip of Ortygia known as the *Castellum Balaena* – Whale Castle, from *φαλαινα*, a sea monster. As Morgan moved in, with all the youngsters, so did the artists, and room by room, nursery by nursery, the decorations continued, with stylistic changes as the work went on.

We moved from Egypt to Sicily in AD363 and Morgan commissioned a picture* (among more hunting scenes) of Dad and Uncle Ted. To decorate the rooms south-westward of Maximian's wing* she was able to obtain the services of Justina's top mosaicist, who had done such impressive work in the Imperial Palace at Milan* a few years before. Doesn't Dad look (Plate 5) a fine young man: serious, soldierly, blond, inseparable from his Tribune's military *tunica angusticlava*? For Dad was a narrow-striper (a fighting soldier, not a mere *laticlavus* or staff officer), and I was glad to give him all of a boy's worship. Although a Christian, he is giving the usual preparatory huntsman's sacrifice to Diana, for luck. (It is for keeping up this same pagan custom that my cousin St Eustace *Germanus* will get into such trouble with St Amator, Bishop of Rouen in almost thirty years' time.)

Uncle Ted, (Plate 5) Dad's junior by five years, has reddish hair, true auburn really, which is the *Ælian* blood coming out and, I'm afraid, even at the age of eighteen, a sign of the 'Aelian' temper. A randy and unruly fellow at times, but generally good fun.

Sixteen years later (AD379) Morgan had a picture done of me and Julius-James with her on the way to the bath. The artist rather flatters my height. We were in our late teens then, and I was insistent on flaunting my long fair locks hoping to start a new Roman fashion; or rather, to revive one, for I had learnt at school to venerate 'long-haired Apollo', and rather fancied myself as Apollonius.* You'll hear much more of the latter impersonation. The golden hamster now looks more like a hare; later on, when as a soldier I grew a full set of whiskers, I looked quite like Mars Aper – the wild boar.

The Casa Sic was a real family home, and quite a family album.* There are pictures of later members of the family there including my remarkable daughters 'working out' in their bikinis (Plate 10); but I shall come back to them later. If the mosaics survive, as I'm sure they will, you will be able to see what we all looked like, as if in a frozen Camera Obscura. The latter will be one of my cleverest inventions, (worked up from Hippolytus*), even though Roger Bacon will later claim the credit.

The years AD363 to 370, by which time *JJ* – as I call my brother – and I were into our tenth year, passed happily and uneventfully for us at the Casa Sic, but in the great world great events were taking place. Julian had been succeeded, briefly and dishonourably, by Jovian. Then Valentinian and Valens became co-Augusti (both Marcians on the mother's side* I'm glad to say). Valentinian got the job on soldierly merit; Valens (who took New Rome and the East), through mistaken brotherly loyalty.

I must now introduce ***Justina the Ambitious*** (see App. 3), whom I called great-aunt although the relationship was more complex. Peering with my prophetic eye into the future, I foresee that a certain 'Walt Disney' will portray her unforgettably, and not too unfairly, as the 'Wicked Queen' in his visual rendering of the tale of 'Snow White'. She had a penchant for marrying Augusti.

Her first husband was Magnentius, the handsome Frank, who failed to make good his claim to the purple and fell in the crash of AD354 when so many Marcians were 'topped'. Undaunted, in 365 she married (as his third wife) Flavius Magnus *Maximus* Maximianus*, sourly nicknamed 'Clement' by his victims, and the name stuck. He is the 'Macsen Wledig' of Welsh fable and genealogy. Maximus was trying for Caesar – if only of Britain – on the death of Julian, on the strength of his former marriage to Valentinian's sister Grata; on the strength also of his earlier military service in Britain and Gaul as equerry and cupbearer to Count Theodosius Sr and to Julian as an unsuccessful Master of Horse. Valentinian roundly snubbed him, and he and Justina were lucky to be fobbed off with provincial governorships of Corsica and Sardinia and later of Tuscany. His second wife, divorced in favour of Justina, was the famous Melania Sr (***Melania the Holy Terror***), the Maecenas of the Church. More of her and her tribe later.

**Figure 3**

Handsome Frank



Justina hitched her aspirations to Maximus' star and stuck with him until the pogroms of AD370. That same year, Valentinian's second wife having left the scene, Justina rightly divorced Maximus for cruelty and married *Valentinian Sr*, Augustus of the West – the third marriage for them both. On Valentinian's death in 375, the Senate confirmed Justina as Augusta, as Empress-Mum and Regent for her son Valentinian II. In religion she was a confirmed Arian and had awful tussles with Ambrose, as we shall see later. Anyway, she was not a bad old thing (ambition excepted) and we had to be nice to her on her rare trips to Sicily. She really was awfully grand and powerful. Her daughter by Maximus, ***Elissa***-Guinevere will play a compulsive part in my later life.

Meanwhile, what of Dad? He had been promoted to command a mixed cohort in Further Gaul, under the command of the Count/Admiral of the Saxon Shores. The Armorican and Nervican Tracts – the land of the Morini – were his field of operations; his enemy, the now piratical Saxons. Morgan was happily house decorating in Sicily. Tomorrow I'll tell you what happened to Little Mother. Just now it's vespers for me and my sweating scribes, Basil (Blaise) and Anthony* (after Anthony of the Desert). I christened them myself as you may infer. Sorry if my readers are sweating too. There's been a lot of background to fill in before we can really get underway.

Heigh ho.

# BOOK II

## *Giants and Leprechauns (AD370)*

When Octavianus Caesar (Augustus the Great) established the *Pax Romana* in which some of us still, in some sort, live, he set the northern frontiers of the Empire at the great rivers *Hister* (the Danube) and *Rhenus* (the Rhine). True, he tried to push yet further NE to *Albis* (the Elbe), as who should know better than me, but the frontier stabilised for four centuries at the Rhine and the Danube. Beyond these streams lay forests of immeasurable depth, and in those depths, as all children know, dwelt *giants*. From time to time they crossed the frontier and threatened us, and the Legions would wheel into action and, with a massive show of force, drive them back into the forests.

Now giants love fighting, so since Caesar's day it had been Rome's practice to enlist into her armies those who had no political axe to grind, but simply enjoyed the crunch of steel on bone. At first they were only recruited as Auxiliaries (native troops under Roman officers) with the lure that on retirement they and their families would become Roman citizens. We adopted a similar policy with prisoners of war, merely ensuring that they served, initially, far from their homelands. So true-born Romans now formed only a small minority of the Roman armies, the cavalry being wholly barbarian and the infantry increasingly so. It was only a matter of time before the pressure to admit barbarians to the highest military commands, for which they were qualified both by natural aptitude and by loyal service, became irresistible.

Such was the tendency within our ranks, but a parallel tendency was at work among the friendlier nations beyond. Such were the Batavians, Frisian inhabitants of the Rhine Delta. Tamed by Vespasian and made independent Federates, we called them *Franci* ('free' in their tongue) because they paid no tribute. Not only did they guard and defend the mouths of the Rhine with total loyalty, but for centuries they provided recruits to the legions and even to the Imperial Bodyguard.

In AD358, just before this story started, Julian had admitted the Batavians to the low-lying woodlands and heaths of Broceliande – the country around what will one day be called Brussels, though few will know why – through which the Rhine, *Mosa* (Meuse) and *Scaldis* (Scheldt) debouch into the Northern

Ocean. Ten miles East lies *Dispargum** (Duisburg) my future capital. The true 'fountains of Barenton' lie only one hundred and ten miles to the SW; eat your hearts out, you Breton *conteurs* and *jongleurs*: you're in the wrong Province.

In Celtic (i.e. Doric Greek*) this Wasteland was called Τοξανδρια, because the trees were good for bows (and bowmen). As their southern frontier, Julian fixed the great Roman road from *Colonia Agrippina* to *Bagacum* (Köln to Bavay).

Another such Romanised but independent nation was tamed by Aurelian one hundred years ago and settled in the valley of the lower *Moenus* (Main). They too were made federates by Julian. We called the northern nation 'Salian' Franks, and the southerners 'Riparian' Franks. I foresee that I shall reign over the Northern Franks as King Clodion I, and my brother over the Southern Franks as King Pharamond. Worse, I foresee that we are destined eventually to fight. Apart from these 'tame' Barbarian kingdoms, there are many other peoples among the Rhine forests (Burgunds, Alamans, Swabes, to name a few you will hear of later), and pressing behind them are the Vandals, who are not Teutons but Slavs.

At times, during the years after 365, one or other of their rulers fought for Rome under the dual title* of Teutonic King and honorary Roman *Dux* (duke). So, on the one hand Barbarian professional Roman soldiers were demanding equal rights of promotion to the top Roman commands, and, on the other, allied Kings were, albeit temporarily, holding them.

One of the first Barbarian Giants to succeed in jumping the gulf was called *Arbogast* ('The stranger from the Elbe'*), and in AD363 'Little Mother' married him.* He was about Dad's age and a Troop Commander in the Cavalry. You know what it says in the Good Book (Ezekiel 23:6–12) about cavalry officers; all the glittering gear, and leathery smells, and thighs. Most aphrodisiac. I say nothing of Ezekiel v.20, nor do I really know how it all happened nor who ran off with whom; but I never saw 'Little Mother' again, although we shall hear more of ***Arbogast the Prussian.***

**Figure 4**

Stern Valentinian

©Trustees of the British Museum

Well, Valentinian did a good job of pacifying the Rhinelands and taming, yet again, the Alamani; but there was another frontier to watch – Hadrian's Wall. Without the Picts and the Scots, Britain should have been one of our wealthiest and most pacific provinces, as well as the essential granary of our Rhine armies. But while Julian's old fleet of six hundred unarmed merchantmen were plying the North Sea with grain, the Saxons of the Elbe took it into their heads to take to the water as pirates, and very good seamen they proved to be. Privateering was not enough – they soon took to raiding the British coasts, and in AD367 the Channel Fleet, *Classis Britannica*, under the command of the Count of the Saxon Shores,* was defeated and its Admiral, Count Nectaridus, killed. There may have been some collusion, as there certainly would be in the future, for it was at this time that the Picts, Scots and Atecotti crossed Hadrian's Wall in force.

Yet another British rescue was called for, and Valentinian found the right man for the moment in Theodore's son, Count Theodosius Sr., co-owner of the Casa Sic and my beloved grandfather. In 367 Count Theo mounted his campaigns in Britain with the near-imperial rank of *Patricius*,* taking with him, as up-and-coming young officers, my Dad and Uncle Ted. ***Grandad Theo*** was one of Rome's strategists and statesmen. Given the chance he would have made a fine Augustus. That's what killed him.

Theo saw at once that a mere show of force at such long range would be a waste of Rome's money. Like so many of us, he had read Tacitus' *Agricola* at school and saw he must play the role of a second Agricola – indeed, he will soon earn himself that *agnomen*, and it will stick in the family. Not only must he recover and subdue Albany of the Southern Picts from Strathmore to the Mounth* (*Mons Graupius*), but he must complete the programme Agricola I had put forward* unsuccessfully to Titus. Agricola I had said that 'it would be easier to hold Britain if it were completely surrounded by Roman armies, so that liberty was banished from its sight'. He added that 'Ireland could be reduced and held by a single legion with a fair-sized force of auxiliaries'.

Count Theo had just this; moreover he had the full resources of the *Classis Britannica*, whose ships and morale he had just restored. But first of all he had to settle accounts with a pretender to the purple, a cousin* of Valentinian's called Valentinus, who had set up as Caesar in Britain taking the name of Carausius II,* and even minting a few coins as such. This done, Theodosius moved north to the lands of the Votadini (Albany) where he ordered Dad to reoccupy Agricola's old fortress of *Pinnata Castra*, which will even take its modern name of 'Inchtuthill' (the water meadow of Tudwal) from Glorious Dad. Here Dad 'won his spurs' to such effect that he was promptly surnamed Duke '*Albanicus*' by his legionaries (appropriately enough the good old XXth Valeria Victrix, whose ancestors had conquered Caledonia under the first Agricola). The 'XX VV' was very much the family regiment, and I treasure, and often used to wear, Dad's officer's belt or *cingulum* with its gilded boar, so apt for me.

The winter of 367 was spent in winter quarters along the old Scottish Wall of Antoninus, while the fleet, which had already subdued Shetland and Orkney, was prepared for the conquest of Ireland. A new port was built on the Clyde and named *Portus Theodosius* (Old Kilpatrick); Agricola's old port at *Rerigonium* (Stranraer) was refurbished; and landing barges were constructed. Thus would Mars conquer the 'Gardens of the Hesperides'.

The campaign of spring 368 was, as predicted, a pushover. The Scots (or Ul-aid of Uls-ter, *Julius-terra*) never knew what hit them. 'Yomping' and leapfrogging down the Eastern coast of Ireland by land and sea, mostly the latter, they toppled the chieftains of the tribes of Munster and Leinster one by one, until eventually the fleet found its way to *Segontium* (Caernarfon) and the ring was closed. As his command and supply base for this brilliant amphibious operation Theo used the island of *Monarina-Eubonia* or *Manavia*, (later to be called the Isle of Man), where 'Patrick's Isle'* still commemorates him like Kilpatrick on the Clyde. Detachments fanned out ruthlessly into the somewhat desolate wastes of Middle and Western Hibernia.* No wonder Irish folk memory cannot forget the advent of the 'Milesians', Roman soldiers of the XXth *Legion*; nor of the 'three Collas' (Agricola II, Dad and Uncle Ted). In due course they would have equal need to remember me, and my progeny and kin.

At this point I break off to explain a vitally important point for posterity. The truth is that we Romans had no useful word for 'North'. We knew, like the Greeks, that the seven stars of the Great Bear (called *Αρκτος–Καλλιστω*) ever wheel around the Seven Stars of the hardly discernible Little Bear, the brightest of them, *Polaris*, being the true North Pole star. The Great Bear looks more like a plough, and we Romans preferred to call its stars the 'Seven Ploughing Oxen' of the Bear. If you look up 'North' in any good *Gradus* (dictionary) you will find the correct word for North is therefore *Septentrionalis*. Phew, what a word! Six clumsy syllables. It's a bore to say, a bore to write, and quite impossible to work into any line of decent poetry. All Romans, therefore, like the Greeks – be they poets or geographers* – normally called the North the *Arctois*, pronounced 'Artois'. Do you begin to see what I'm getting at? The Pole Star is 'Stella Artois'.

But we learnt yet more from the Greeks, for the Greeks were great astronomers, as well as poets and mythmakers. There is a very bright star to the left of the Great Bear's tail, and this the Greeks called *Αρκτουρος*, the guardian *ʼουρος* of the Bear 'Arktos'. We Romans call this star *Arcturus*, pronounced 'Arturus', the Guardian, Warden, Protector of the 'Bear', Protector of the 'North'. Indeed, the reliable Ammianus uses it in this very sense. Do you realise the implications* of what I am telling you? If not you soon will.

You should not now be surprised that Count Theo, in addition to his full names of Flavius Valerius Ulpius-Marcianus Severus Constantinianus ('of the race of Constantius', in Welsh *Cunedag* or Cunedda,* in Irish, Conn-acht), was from this time hailed by his panegyrist as *Arthur* (*Arcturus*). That Panegyric* (of this second Agricola) was written by his own son, 'Glorious Dad', thereby winning himself the nickname of the 'second Tacitus'. But, as you will learn, it never got to be read aloud on the Capitol. Public plaudits apart, as conqueror of Britain's offshore isles, Theo also won the epithet of '*Pelagius*',* making all his progeny henceforth *Pelagiani*. You do well to prick up your ears, but lay them back for now – my story must go at its own pace.

Agricola I had made his first task in the pacification of Britain the 'Romanisation' of the civilian population, and it is as schoolmaster no less than as general that his fame stands. Similarly with Theo. Britain was now, as promised, 'ringed by Roman steel', and major strategic reorganisation followed. The whole of Western Britannia became the new Irish Sea provinces of Valentia I and II, the latter governed initially from the Clyde (later from Carlyle), the former from Segontium. Grafted onto Senatorial *Britannia Secunda*, Valentia I was governed by a *Praeses*,* whilst Valentia II, as part of the military zone, was under a *Rector Consularis*.

Agricola I had taught 'Romanitas' to the Britons by sumptuous civic buildings. Ireland offered little scope for such shows of opulence. All I can really offer you is the 'Great Hall' of Tara,* or what may remain of it. Deeply primitive, the Irish were strangers alike to money and to stone buildings. The army detachments which spattered the country lived, for the most part, in turf huts, although they left a legacy, still visible, of *sudatoria* (saunas*). Justice was organised on a 'dual mandate' system with a Roman 'Resident' (*vir judicundum*) sitting in on the native rulers. Romanisation of Ireland would have to start at grass roots, in the schools.

This is how Theo came to found Ocean College, eight miles South of *Bomium** (Bridgend) in Valentia and conveniently accessible by the Antonine Roman road XIV,* or by sea. It will be known to the Welsh as 'Coleg Theodosius* by Caer Vortigern', and the sons of Irish chieftains were to be sent here to receive the very best in Roman education.

Some tame Roman pupils were needed to set the courses rolling, and in the Autumn Term of 370 Julius-James and I (aged nine), four of our cousins and a squad of surprised Spanish and Gallo-Roman boys, found ourselves settling into our damp windswept Welsh dormitories, together with some indescribably smelly and incomprehensible young princelings of Eireann. We were under the distinguished leadership of my Uncle Marcianus Heliodorus* (whom I mentioned in Book I) who was the college's first Headmaster. Here, JJ and I were to spend the 'happiest years of our lives', which were cut short by the most 'Dolorous Stroke'* (*colpus dolorosus*) that ever fell on Britain.

During these years, as I have said, Theo was sorting out Britain, and Valentinian I was containing the Germans, not with total success, from his palace at Trier. Valentinian's opponent, I'm sorry to say, was a drop-out Marcian who was seeking among the barbarians to avenge on Rome the death of his father Martinus, formerly Vicar of Britain and a casualty of the Magnentius crash. Am I fated to follow this path too? Meanwhile my other and unbeloved grandfather, 'Little Mother''s father Maximus (see App. 5), had been rescued from his rustic governorship at Fiesole by Justina's wiles and 'pull', to take up the onerous and not very prestigious post of *Praefectus Annonae* (effectively, deputy secretary for social security) at Rome. Quite soon Justina got him promoted to *Vicar* of Rome (Deputy Prefect). Diocletian had erected the *Quadriga* of *four* great Praetorian Prefects to rule the Roman world, but he had retained two of the old Prefectures, Praetorian by location, but of lesser prestige: those of Old and New Rome.

The Prefect of Rome had a number of ceremonial tasks (including the Speakership of the Senate). He heard legal appeals in Rome, especially in inheritance cases, and was often Consul (*ordinarius* or *suffectus*). Thus, he needed deputies to do the real work. Maximus became director of public prosecutions, and my beloved Uncle Manlius Theodorus (see App. 6), not to be confused with ***Gt Grandad Theodore***, used to have to appear before him as an advocate, so what I now write is *not* mere gossip.

**Figure 5**
Grandad Max – the 'clement'


It was in this job that Maximus earned himself the stinging nickname of 'Clement' – 'Maximus the Merciful'! The case was a talking point in Rome for years – its subject, *magic*. Now here's a kettle of fish. All my family have been 'into' magic for generations, and I shall do my part in advancing the frontiers of knowledge in this direction. Gt Grandad Theodore (not Uncle Theodore, although he was well immersed in it too) was to lose his life through it; also, in some sort, Theo, though political jealousy lay behind his murder.

Magic, the lore of the Magi, represented the far-Eastern tradition of natural philosophy, the science of nature, the study of the Creator through his Creation; this was the science of the Parthians, the Medes, the Armenians. But a parallel line of research had developed in the age-old civilisation of Egypt, the land of 'Khem', and this was known as 'Chemistry'. The Greek philosophers had shoved their own brilliantly speculative oar in, and all these streams converged on the great public library at Canopus (near my birthplace), called the 'Serapeion' after the Temple of Serapis, the Bull God, nearby. (To suit Greek taste and art, Apis the Bull God of Memphis had been anthropomorphised as Serapis, and assimilated to Pluto.) Peering into the future, I see one of my popularisers, Wolfram von Eschenbach, writing nearly correctly of me that I 'worshipped a calf'. If he had written 'bull' he would have been quite right; much as I am to get tangled up with the 'Golden Calf', I swear I never worshipped it.

Now why should this interesting and, one might think, essential part of any intelligent man's birthright have become an occult forbidden science proscribed by the Roman State? One reason was practical. The 'Chemists' were absorbed by the mysteries of chemical change. One day they hoped to 'make' gold and silver out of less precious metals. But gold and silver (and their mines) have always been a State monopoly and the store of State power. A wit once said 'Rome will fight to the last *solidus*, not the last soldier'. Hence, magicians and chemists might – if their claims were true – become a threat to the economic stability of the State; veritable traitors, in fact. So Diocletian saw them, when in AD296 he proscribed 'magic books' relating to the noble metals.

But there was another, darker reason, tinged with fear. We Romans are credulous, pagans particularly so, since the ancient religion of gods and goddesses has some very murky fringes: thaumaturgy, conjuring, divination, auguries, spells, necromancy even – once you leave the respectable high-road trod by Virgil you are soon in deep water. People with occult powers might threaten the Augustus himself. Valens (Valentinian's co-Augustus in New Rome) was as credulous as they come. His brother, despite a fair veneer of Christianity, was hardly better. Julian had flirted enthusiastically with magic, and the Valentinian brothers resolved to stamp it out.

In AD370* a nest of top senators in Rome were caught in a séance or conversazione by the *Agentes in Rebus* (Secret Police) with scientific books in their possession. Maximus pressed for and obtained the death penalty for them for High Treason. Two top Anicii (the most prestigious gens of the time), Camenus and Tarracius Bassus, the latter a former Prefect of Rome, fell to the sword, together with several other senators. One Lollius, son of Lampadius, another Prefect of Rome, had the cheek to appeal for clemency over Maximus' head to the Prefect, on the grounds of his youth. He was executed just the same, and the Senate hated Maximus ever after.

What Morgan only learnt later from Justina was that, before he was caught, Lollius had secretly copied one of the scientific books, and that copy has in fact ended up in the cupboard beside me as I dictate this tale. By the time my book is read, I foresee that it will be safe to bring the *'great secrets' of the Holy Graal* into the public domain, and I intend to do just this; but in the intervening centuries it would have cost one's head and one's place in the next world. Shall 'The Holy Grail' be a chapter in its own right, or relegated prudently to an Appendix? Or shall I 'leak' it piecemeal? I think I shall do best to reveal it piecemeal, just as I myself learned it.

Magic was therefore a forbidden field of knowledge (although still seething away in secret enclaves at Rome and Constantinople), for reasons which did not seem valid or binding to my Uncle Heliodorus – himself, if I may be excused yet another pun, a 'name to be conjured with' in this field of knowledge, especially in the distant valleys of hither Valentia. As a result, 'Science' was put firmly on the curriculum at Ocean College, for older boys doing the *Quadrivium* of Geometry, Arithmetic, Music, and Astronomy. 'Geometry' was really mostly surveying and chorography (maps, and the like), and was to become one of my specialities; indeed, some fourteen years later, I invented, or at least perfected, the Odometer* or distance-measurer. 'Science' was grafted naturally into 'Music' which, Pythagoras had taught us, was so much more than a mere congeries of notes. Astronomy* was also to become one of my better subjects.

For the present, however, JJ and I were doing our best to be a good advertisement for Magna Graecia and Old Rome in our cold wet Celtic Gymnasium. The first hurdle cleared, unexpectedly, was the language barrier. It was our Gaulish *copains* who first spotted that what our Irish and Scottish schoolmates were talking was, in fact, a very debased form of Greek. Their quantities were all wrong, their pronunciation bizarre, but the language was unmistakably the language of Hercules,* as I suppose we should have expected. So JJ and I, and our four cousins, Heliodorus' sons, became the bridge between the two groups.

Let me tell you more about my four cousins. These were two more twins (identical this time) called Verrenianus and Didymus,* Lagodius, later to be called Chrysanthus for reasons we shall see, and Theodosiolus (little Theodosius), who was the youngest. That's the full Marcian squad. Funny how twins run in our family.

So we set about civilising our wild and woolly neighbours and they set about toughening us up. One thing we had in common from the start was that we all arrived wearing knitted woollen stockings in Caledonian style – there are lots of mosaics of us wearing these at the Casa Sic (Plate 5) – and these saved our shins somewhat when we were introduced to hockey, or 'shinty' as it was appropriately called. We for our part introduced them to draughts and dicing, for we Romans have always been obsessed by the gaming board (*tabula*) where luck and skill contend in mock war. In freestyle wrestling we were on common ground, literally. By the time of the Saturnalia we had all shaken down, and I was hardly homesick.

*Mens sana in corpore sano. Floreat Oceania et haec nostra domus esto perpetua.*

Heigh ho.

The general historical interpretation in this Book derives from Professor Sheppard Frere's *Britannia* (1974). See Bibliography.

# BOOK III

## *The Little Victims Play (AD371–376)*

AD 371 saw us ten-year-olds hard at work on the *Trivium* (Grammar, Logic and Rhetoric), a two-year course. The traditional idea was to build education on a foundation of language: Grammar to teach exactly what words mean and how they can be strung together to communicate ideas; Logic to teach how ideas work and how to use them constructively; and Rhetoric, the art of communicating ideas to others. We worked simultaneously on all three subjects in Latin and also, in the peculiar situation of Ocean College, in Greek. Uncle Heliodorus was keen on making us write poetry and prose and we churned out lame hexameters, and also free prose compositions which he called *Novellae* (stories, essays, what you will). Naturally we modelled these closely on Heliodorus' own *Æthiopica*, a thrilling and fabulous tale, in the classical Greek manner but set largely in wildest Æthiopia and affording a startling instance of anti-white racial prjeudice; affording, also, the source for the pathetic tale of Tancred and Clorinda. A copy is with my old school books in the cupboard beside me, together with my own 'prentice imitations'* duly marked 'Commended', or sometimes 'Highly Imaginative'. When our Irish friends unleashed *their* imaginations we all found ourselves a bit out of our depth.

Summer vacation and the sailing season coincided with Dad's furlough as Military Governor of Valentia II. Commercial sailings ceased at the Autumn Equinox, to resume in late Spring. During the winter months only the Imperial Mailboats plied tentatively between the gales – also pirates and the like. We went first to visit him in Scotland and he showed us his headquarters at Inchtuthill and took us on a tour of all the battlefields, which was very thrilling. We then crossed to the Western Island (Ireland), where he took us to see the 'Tomb of Hercules' (New Grange) – for it can hardly be that of a lesser hero – a few miles up the *Buinda* (Boyne) River. The great white barrow like a giant wedding cake, (Dad called it a θολος*), stands nearly four times as tall as a man, and two hundred and fifty paces round as we ran it. There is a little blocked doorway with a huge richly-carved sill and an Egyptian-style lightshaft above, but our guide said it would be 'bad *geis*' for me to penetrate that – we had got all too near as it was.

To appease the god we did what other visitors were doing, and offered 'an obol to Charon'. Spinning round three times with our eyes closed we each threw a coin over our shoulder. Dad had furnished us with some old coins, of Magnentius (Fig. 3) (Justina's first husband), for this purpose, and said the Irish would let them lie as they don't use coins anyway. I wonder if they're still there?*

**Figure 6**
Glorious Dad, the Cavalry Tribune
©Edizioni Poligraf

Dad seemed immensely popular with his men, and was particularly proud to have recruited a bodyguard of two troops of cavalry from his Irish, Scots, and Atecotti – these latter were Southern Picts* from Albany who at an earlier period had fought and settled their way into the land of *Novantae* (Galloway), and who were known to the Romans as **'Alban's Horse'**,* although they were in the Army List as *Honoriani** from Dad's principal cognomen. The Irish called them the *Fianna*, because **blond** Dad was 'Finn' (*Fiachna*) in their tongue. Dad had some Slav troops* too, who had been in the country for nearly a hundred years. They called him **Beo-Wulf** (Beowulf Sr, **not** the dragon-slayer), ie. 'Ulpius the Fair' in Teutonic. Dad's scheme was that the officers should in due course be drawn from the alumni of Ocean College.

We could not help noticing a change in Dad. He had always been religious, *pius* we Romans call it, and had found no difficulty in following the Marcian (and Constantinian) path of Christianity. On his furlough of AD359, *en route* to taking up his posting in Egypt, where we were born, he had looked up his uncle Martin – his great-uncle in fact, but there was little more than a generation between them. Sulpicius Severus' *Life of St Martin* has been a best-seller since it came out some fifty years ago, so I don't need to rehearse to you the story of Martin and his cloak, nor how he came to be thrown out of the army by Julian in 355 as a conscientious objector, a veritable pacifist. At this time (359) he was 'dropping out' in a shed just inside the Western Gate of Milan, where there are market gardens.* He was forty-three, disgraced, disowned by his parents, and harried by the Arianising Bishop Auxentius; all in all he really did seem down on his luck.

I do not know whether it was as a cousinly or as a Christian act that Dad went to see him, but they kept in touch by letter over the next ten years while

Martin was hermiting around Gaul – Caprera, Ligugé, Marmoutier – and I think the ferment of Martin's zeal and example must have been working on Dad's mind. Although he was still carrying out his military and civil duties in exemplary style the signs of what was to come were discernible. Anyway, 371 brought the surprising news that Martin had become Bishop of Tours, accepted by the 'Establishment' of Church and State, even if his behaviour and garb raised many eyebrows. Naturally Dad went to visit him at Tours,* leaving us 'pups' at *Lutetia* (Paris) with Morgan. I foresee that my future readers will refer affectionately to their offspring as 'kids'. But we Romans, Greeks and Celts always called them 'pups': *catelli,** *κυναρια*, *ceneu*,* respectively. I don't know why goats should have displaced dogs like this.

We loved Paris and I would that I had been able to spend more of my life there. My son will do so, and will make my memory forever green there; but that story cannot be told yet. We returned to Ocean College for the Autumn semester in good heart and loaded with Gallic toys, while Dad returned to his 'Septentrionalian' duties (see what I mean about this tongue-twisting epithet; much easier to call them 'Arctic' duties), with a bit of Christian evangelisation on the side. Back to the *Trivium*, and our last year in the Lower School.

One last event of AD371 I record. While we were in Paris, Morgan heard that her cousin Ambrosius had been made Proconsular Governor of Aemilia and Liguria (i.e. virtually the whole of Italy North-West of *Bononia* – Bologna), at the instance of the celebrated Sextus *Anicius* Petronius Probus, who was Ambrose's patron and Consul of the Year besides. Despite being easily the richest man in the Empire, Probus was a good Christian; alas, he did not survive to become my father-in-law.

Ambrose's job was a more prestigious appointment than it sounds, since it included the Imperial Capital of Milan, quite overshadowing Old Rome in power, although lacking its ancient prestige. *St Ambrose's Life* by Paulinus is on my shelves, and perhaps on yours, but at this time his sanctity was far from evident, at least to Hieronymus (St Jerome of Aquileia) who published a particularly vicious lampoon on him that same year, calling him a 'hanging judge'. Ambrose quite rightly kicked him out of the province, whereupon he was lucky to be able to join Uncle Heliodorus, ***Melania the Holy Terror*** (see App. 6) and some other friends on a sightseeing tour of the Middle East (AD372). This chapter will end with Ambrose adopting me, and the more I have grown to love Ambrose, the greater my contempt for waspish little Jerome.

During the summer vacation of 372 Uncle Heliodorus and Aunt Verrena went on leave to Aquileia with their four kids, never to return. There he met the celebrated Greek Sophist **Eunapius*** of Sardis (true Greeks, as opposed to little Roman 'Greeks' like me, only bear a single name, just like slaves!) and persuaded him to take his place as *Magister Informator* (Headmaster) of Ocean

College. This was a real coup, and was to win international prestige for Ocean College. It was also to have a permanent effect on me, since Eunapius was not only a brilliant Classicist and Rhetor, but he had studied 'Philosophy' with Chrysanthius, Julian's old tutor and colleague in magical research of great grandfather Theodore; colleague, too, of that unspeakable ruffian Maximus (the Cynic Philosopher). Maximus liked to be known as **'Heron'** (by which name I shall refer to him in future to avoid confusion with ***Grandad Max***), because it aroused echoes of *Hermes Trismegistos* and of *Thoth*, both of them excellent names to conjure with.

Thus when JJ and I arrived in the Upper School to imbibe the heady potions of the *Quadrivium* we found that our science teacher was in every sense a real wizard. Bearing in mind Valentinian's and still more Valens' antipathy to 'magic', I think Eunapius had found it quite convenient to cross the water, and he brought his manuscripts and laboratory equipment* with him in a wooden chest which he jokingly called the 'Ark of the *Coven*-ant'.

Meanwhile, Magnus Maximus had survived the scandal of the 'magic' executions in Rome (and the hatred of the Senate), and had persuaded Valentinian to make him Praetorian Prefect* of Gaul. You can imagine that great-aunt Justina, his ex-wife and now Valentinian's wife, was not best pleased by this, but Valentinian could be very stern in what he thought to be his duty, and Maximus not only deserved so high a post on merit, but was to earn the rare honour of a second term. Such were the opportunities of enrichment that Praetorian Prefects were normally only allowed one bite at the cherry; whatever else, Maximus was not corrupt.

Thus rehabilitated, Maximus managed to woo and marry, as his fourth wife, Helena Eucheriana (see App. 5), my second cousin once removed. It is from her distinguished father Eucherius (who, as I told you in Book I, was known to his cronies as 'Icarus'), that I obtain one of my many *agnomina* – to wit, 'Eucherius', well remembered by my Cambrians as *Llaw Gyffes*, 'of the cunning hand', of which it is indeed an exact translation. I have a nephew Eucherius who became bishop of *Lugdunum* (Lyons) itself, whose surrounding territories of *Gallia Lugdunensis* (I to IV) were to be the scene of many of my adventures and of my kin's. They were indeed the '*lost lands of Lyonesse*', lost to the sea of advancing Barbarians in the fifth century. Another disappointment, I'm afraid, for the Breton conteurs, even though they did live in part of *Lugdunensis* III.

I cannot say whether or not Maximus actually wooed Icarus' daughter, the fair Helen, in Segontium as Welsh tradition* will insist. But it is far from impossible, as Icarus was Vicar of Britain* at the time. Maximus cannot have realised that we were under the corrupting influence of Eunapius, or we would never have been allowed to remain there.

In the summer of 373 Dad went on furlough again, on the completion of his second tour. He went alone, and to Gaul, and once again to Martin. Morgan went separately to Sicily, and we stayed in Britain with friends. When Dad returned to Valentia late in the Autumn he had been ordained by Martin not only as priest but as a 'Bishop Peregrinus',* a bishop without a diocese. This was a typically Martinian act, of the sort which was always getting him into hot water. For the next two years Dad was Bishop and Apostle of Britain-beyond-the-walls. He will long be remembered there as St Ninian I, or Stinian, or even Trinian, in various corrupt spellings; the nearest the natives could get to saying 'Constantinianus'. As a bishop, he was required to put away his wife Morgan; she would never had made it as a nun, so they divorced by consent, leaving Morgan free to look elsewhere.

**Figure 7**
Randy Ted, the future Duke
© Edizioni Poligraf

In 374 Uncle Ted, whose tour as Military Governor of Valentia (I) had expired with Dad's, was promoted to Duke of Moesia,* the heartland of the Marcians on the Lower Danube frontier, thus earning his epithet 'Meriadoc'.* This was a real fighting post, just right for a twenty-eight-year-old, as the Quadi and Sarmatian Barbarians were out of hand again. Uncle Ted really distinguished himself under the very eyes of the Augustus and was crowned on the field for valour, besides getting the usual *phalarae* – medals, or 'gongs' as they were aptly but vulgarly called.

At this time came terrible news from New Rome. ***Gt Grandad Theodore***, inspired by his ouija board to shrug off his years, had been persuaded to take the purple in Asia in opposition to Valens. Valens overpowered him within four months and had him executed. Was his whole house to prove a nest of subversion?

Meanwhile friends in the Senate – where we had so many friends and connections – wanting to honour Count Theodosius, the hero of Valentia and Orkney, but knowing he could not attend in person to accept the honour whilst still on active service in Africa, had blandly proposed his sons Glorious Dad and Uncle Ted as the Consuls* for 375 in his stead. They did not know, of course, that Dad was now a bishop, of sorts, and presumably ineligible to stand (though there had, as yet, been no precedent on this). This was a recommendation which would normally have received the glad approval of the Augustus, but the surge of 'Theodosianism' faced Valentinian with more than a political dilemma. Not only did he have a son, Gratian, whom he had made Augustus at the tender age of eight (who was now thirteen, and for whom he hoped to leave the succession open); he also had an infant son, Valentinian II (aged three), by Justina the Ambitious who would fight like a tigress to win *her* son a throne. For these two to have a chance if Valentinian I were to die – and his blood pressure was already causing concern – a strong, loyal and successful General would be needed as Regent. Justina had just the man to hand, a blond hairy Frankish 'Giant' called Flavius ***Merobaudes***. To make matters more complicated, this very year, Morgan who, was by no means enamoured of Christian celibacy – chose to marry Genobaudes, Merobaudes' brother, with extraordinary consequences later for me and JJ. But that story must wait.

Valentinian's choice was clear. The interests of the State required him to support the admirable sons of Theodosius for Consul. He signed the scripts. Justina and Merobaudes fought back. They thought the 'House of Theodosius' a real threat. Just as the diptychs had been prepared and had been dispatched round the Provinces with the names of the Consuls from whom AD375 would take its date, Valentinian's resolve was broken. Too late to elect new Consuls, he revoked his script, and there was nothing for it but to let the existing Consuls (Gratian for the third time and Equitius) run on another year in what we call a Post-Consulate. Always a sign to the Provinces of dissension in high places, it was much remarked and long remembered in Britain.*

Also in AD374, Helena bore Maximus a daughter, who by marrying Faltonius Probus will become mother of Petronius Maximus, belated Augustus of AD455, and assassin of Valentinian III; and Valentinian I, Gratian and Merobaudes brought the German War against Macrianus to an honourable peace. Meanwhile JJ and I continued our education at the hands of Eunapius. We were by now rather lonely and forlorn, with no family apparently concerned for us save Morgan, whose monthly letters cheered us up, and 'Uncle' Icarus who visited us occasionally.

375 passed in the same numb but busy way, with the normal baffling intimations of the onset of puberty. Just as well we were away at boarding school. ***Uncle Theo*** (see App. 6) went East to take up the Proconsular Governorship of Macedonia and Pella. Maximus and Helena were on their second tour in the Praetorian Palace at Trier, and Valentinian I was off campaigning on the Danube. He had dropped off Justina and Valentinian Jr at *Vindobona Murocincta* (Vienna)* on the way, and left Gratian (in effect Merobaudes) in command of the West. In April Gratian and Merobaudes suddenly sacked and exiled Maximus on the belatedly renewed charge of cruelty.* Like other exiles, Maximus chose to cross the water to Britain, and made initially for Segontium – scene, maybe, of his earlier courtship. Merobaudes then joined Valentinian on the Danube.

Morgan's gossip letters told us that previously, on the 7 December, Ambrose had been suddenly catapulted into being Bishop of Milan. He rose instantly to the combined challenges of piety and belated celibacy, and had little difficulty with the job. He had been ruling Milan for years in one capacity; by sheer integrity and force of personality he continued to do so for another twenty-two years as Bishop. Meanwhile, church authorities in Britain and even in Rome were hearing with admiration, mixed with some unease, of Dad's missionary exploits in Britain-beyond-the-Walls. He was valuable, he was beloved, he was a gentleman; he must be contained. When a vacancy arose for the bishopric of the ancient *municipium* and *civitas* capital of *Verulamium* they had little difficulty in persuading him that it was his duty to accept it. We Romans are gluttons for 'duty', so T. Flavius Ulpius-Marcianus Constantinianus Severianus (after his Dad) **Honorius Albanicus** became Bishop of Verulamium* (soon to be called St Albans after him), and rejoined the Establishment, with permission to continue to wear his tattered Martinian half-cape or ἀμφιβαλος* on a personal basis.

This did not mean that we boys saw anything of him, much as we longed to. Our hero seemed to have moved into another dimension. We continued with our work, and with our play. One aspect of this at which I excelled was wrestling. While JJ was starting to shoot up alarmingly, and people said he was outgrowing his strength, I hardly seemed to grow at all. However, I was filling out, and was surprisingly well-muscled for my age. 'Pocket Hercules' the boys called me; also 'Samson' and 'Apollonius' because of my long hair.* All my Merovingian descendants* will make a great thing of their long fair hair, and my Cambrians will remember me as Gwri Gwallt Euryn,* 'the little chap with the golden thatch', or **'Goldilocks'**. I would not have got away with this in any other school, but with all the hairy Scots and Irish around no one could say me nay.

Where others preferred running and beagling, you could not keep me away from the mats of the *Palaestra*.That's why they called called me **Milo**, after Milon* of Crotona, the great wrestler. By the same token I got to be called **'Nitonius'** (glistening) by the ushers because I never seemed to find time to wash off the oil we used in the ring. A greasy little boar (*aprunculus*), I was.

I can't help thinking, though, of Phaedimus and Tantalus in Ovid,* gleaming with wrestling oil as they were mown down. They were two of the 'twelve stricken children of Niobe'; will they be called Nibelungs* one day? It's worth a thought.

My fellow Silurians call me 'Gloyw'* (glowing), while the Gauls call me *Vasso.** By and by I am to meet a mate who deserves the name for another and prettier reason. 'Nitonia',* she is: **Snow White**, for that's what *nitonia* means.

On 18 November Valentinian I died of a well-earned stroke at *Bregetio* (Szöny), on the Danube. Merobaudes rushed to collect Justina and little Valentinian and bring them from Vienna to Trier, where on 23 December Gratian ordained Valentinian as Augustus by the customary acclamatory exposition and imposition of hands,* and invested the poor little infant with a purple smock.*

The death of Valentinian left the Empire in real instability. Valens was now Senior Augustus and in his thirteenth year as such. Crafty, credulous and frightened, he yet ruled the East securely. The West was in the hands of two boys, one seventeen, one four years old; and of a jealous scheming woman. At this moment of need, Count Theodosius completed the pacification and restoration of Africa. He was already *Patricius*, the near equal of the Augustus; on his return to Italy, the Roman populace would greet the restorer of their vital corn supply with joy and acclamation. Could *Grandad Theo* be denied promotion to co-Augustus or at least Caesar?

To anyone but Valens this would indeed have seemed a wise solution to the weakness of the West, but Valens was still obsessed by the famous séance of Antioch five years before where the *tabula ronda* or ouija board had spelt out TH. E. O., betokening that the future ruler of the world would not be of the Valentinian house. (This was the first of my three Round Tables, which I later rashly exhumed from Gt Grandad Theodore's grave. Made of silver, it had a Medusa head* in the middle for luck, and the letters of the alphabet round the outside. It rotated cunningly on a centre spindle and could be made to spell out answers* to questions. In the circumstances it was a dangerous toy, and I was later glad to get rid of it.) Valens had topped Gt Grandad Theodore, who had threatened him in the East; now Theodore's son was striding onto the Western stage in triumph. It was not for Valens to intervene directly in the domain of his co-Augustus, but a secret letter to Gratian would do no harm.

In the West, Merobaudes was jealous of Theodosius and Justina feared him as the ultimate block to the succession of her infant son. Gratian was a pliable young man. So the scheme was hatched.* It was put about Rome that Theodosius was plotting to resume the grain embargo of the rebel Firmus. Then, when he had the Romans by the jugular, he would descend on Rome, topple the lawful progeny of Valentinian from the throne, and seize unchallenged power for himself. The grain threat frightened the Senate into acquiescence, and Theodosius was proclaimed an 'Enemy of the State'. Orders were sent to the Governor of Africa for his execution as a traitor. On Maundy Thursday AD376 in Carthage, his baptismal chrism* still gleaming on his brow, Grandad Theodosius, Count and Patricius, mounted the scaffold to confirm his innocence by his meekness. Whether he aspired to what he so evidently merited and was accused of seeking we shall never know; he will be numbered among the victims rather than the martyrs.

This tragic news was brought to Britain by Uncle Ted himself. He rode, and a Duke's bodyguard rode with him. The Aelian hair flamed on his head, the

Aelian blood thundered at his temples. To Verulam he spurred, his one thought: retribution! Enough local troops had joined him *en route* to convince him that once again a British army could proclaim a British Augustus. **Dad should be that man**, and Ted would be proud to be his Caesar.* For a while the sword of justice must replace the crozier. Together they would wreak vengeance on the cruel boy, the wicked stepmother, and the treacherous barbarian of Trier, and purge the West of its filth.

The brothers met, embraced, talked. But there was no meeting of minds. 'Didn't Christ himself wield a whip in the temple? Didn't he encourage his disciples to buy two swords in preparation for Gethsemane? Is it never right to use force in the cause of right?' Ted had chosen the wrong listener. 'Honorius' might have yielded. With his Martinian cape on his very shoulders, 'Alban' could not.

'Brother, you are tired from your journey. Come share my modest table and we will talk again tomorrow.' Couches were rolled into place, and food and wine brought. Alas for the wine. The talk resumed, bosom to bosom, and as Dad became ever quieter and firmer so Ted became the more flushed and furious. Suddenly Ted lost control.

'This is just talk of peace and mildness,' he said. 'I'd like to see you imitate your precious Jesus and turn the other cheek if I really hit you.'

'Try me, brother,' was Dad's response. The first blow raised an angry red mark on my father's left cheek-bone and jolted him, but all he said was, 'Lay on brother if you choose, here is my other cheek.' Then Ted saw red, and half rising to free his left arm, he smote my father with all his force with his left fist above the right ear, and Dad, who had also half risen, went over backwards on his left shoulder and his head cracked on the hard floor like an egg. So died the white hope* of Britain. Later I had this story, as I tell it, from Ted's own confessor the ever-blessed Ambrose. He absolved him then, and was to do so thereafter. But for now, the 'dolorous stroke' was to lie heavy on Britain. Like to the bonny Earl of Moray who might have been a King, like enough to the Tragical Tale of Balin and Balaan.* Alas, all too like.

So, at the age of fifteen, from bastards JJ and I became orphans. We had already too many mothers and no mother. Now we were soon to learn we had no father either. Ted's remorse was always as terrible as his rage,* and his sense of duty truly Roman. He sent a freedman for us boys bidding us to pack our things, make our farewells to school, and join him post-haste at *Rutupiae* (Richborough) where a mailship lay ready. He said nothing to us throughout the journey and we knew nothing. All the way to Milan we pursued this strange silent eerie journey, from posting inn to posting inn past the great lake (Geneva) and through the Alps, until late one evening we arrived at the bishop's house in Milan.

'Most blessed father,' said Ted, who had gone white as a sheet, 'I present to you two sons, to the care of Him who forsaketh not the fatherless children and widow. God have mercy on me a sinner.' Then he fell to the ground and wept as if his heart would jump out of his throat. JJ and I stood absolutely unmade, unable to take in what Uncle Ted had said. All I could feel was deep embarrassment; never before had I seen a man weep. Ambrose passed us frightened boys to servants with instructions to give us soup and a little wine and put us to bed, and though we were too tired and strung up to sleep yet merciful Morpheus found us. So we came of age and found a new and true father, and a good and kind family, and new names, and made a fresh start.

**Yet had Cain peace who slew his brother?**

# BOOK IV

## *King Solomon's Mines (AD376–379)*

The next morning we woke to the novel sound of church bells ringing from the Basilica, and the servants told us that Uncle Ted and Ambrose had gone over there, and we were to rest and amuse ourselves. We were tired. Meals came and were eaten. Street sounds were all around, but we were cocooned inside the gate and walls of the clergy house. Towards evening Ambrose returned to us, tall and grave in his *tunica alba* (alb). His face was full of kindness and his eyes near to tears as he told us of the dark deed of Verulam. 'Young men,' he said, 'God has forgiven your uncle, as Jesus forgave those who crucified Him. Now it is for you to do the same. Your father is with the blessed Saints and Martyrs. My brother and I will adopt you formally – that you may no longer be bastards – and you shall join the *Gens Aurelia*. Henceforward our names are your names, our family is your family, and our houses are your home. As a clergy house is poor entertainment for teenagers, I have arranged for my dear brother Satyrus, who took in my own children* when I became Bishop, to welcome you into his house. He is waiting in the next room to meet you and take you home. I shall call on you there in a few days to discuss what is to become of you. You can find me and see me here any time for the rest of my life.' At this he embraced us and we both wept a little and knelt and kissed his hand, for he was very majestic in his simple white robe. Almost frightening was Ambrose.

We did not see Uncle Ted again. We heard that he had left that very night for Rome and Sicily. Later we heard that he had collected my sisters and taken them with him to *Italica, Baetica*. Later still, we learnt that he had adopted them, having married his cousin Aelia Flaccilla, and was bringing them up as his own.* It's typical of the thoughtlessness of youth that I never told you I had two sisters – half-sisters in fact, Dad's children by Morgan. They too were now orphans; moreover, Morgan having run off with Genobaudes, they too lacked a mother and a home. The eldest, Marcella Thermantia (θερμαντια, 'Fiery-haired' in Greek) whom everyone called *Ginger*, had the Aelian auburn hair whilst her younger sister Aurelia ***Serena*** was blonde as could be. They were younger than us, and girls at that, and we had been at boarding school; so one way with another we hardly knew them. But, as 'Regan and Goneril',* they were to play a big part in our lives and in history.

'Uncle Satyrus', as I must now call him, was the jolliest man imaginable. He was of medium height, lean and active, a young-looking forty-five I would say, with hazel hair and short beard, and twinkling eyes, and his mouth crinkling the whole time into a smile as though he was bursting with some secret joke. His real name was Uranus, but he did look like a friendly satyr. He turned out to be a merchant and extremely rich. It was back to the creature comforts of the old Casa Sic for us. We went back with him that night.

When we got to his house we found another boy of our own age already there, whom Satyrus introduced to us as our cousin Antonius Victricius. Victricius was Maximus' son by Melania,* his second wife. When Maximus divorced Melania to marry Justina, baby Vic was left with his mother, who was frightfully rich so all should have been well. Eight years later, when he was twelve, Melania, who had been moving in very pious evangelical (almost Martinian) Christian circles, decided to 'go sell all that she had' (or at least enough to notice) 'and give to the poor, and follow after her Saviour'. Which she did, abruptly making little Vic a Ward of Court* and taking off towards the Orient to 'do good'. She was a '*Holy Terror*', Melania was. Ambrose, being at that time Governor of Milan, automatically became Vic's guardian and trustee and, although he did not formally adopt him, he was bringing him up as a son. On becoming bishop he had turned him over to the care of Satyrus. So there we were, the three of us, all in pretty much the same boat – like Noah's Ark.

Ambrose called over to see us each evening, and had long talks with his brother. One night they called both of us in. 'Well my boys,' said Ambrose, 'we've been discussing what's to be done with you, and we've come up with a couple of proposals. Satyrus is ready to pay for one of you to go on to higher education, which in practice means law school in Rome, for three years. He can board with my sister-in-law on the Aventine. And I've been having a word with a former military colleague, and he's prepared to take one of you as a cadet into the service. Let me know tomorrow who wants to do what.'

'No need to wait until then, Father,' said I. 'Bags I the army. I'm fed up with school. I like the outdoor life, and maybe there'll be boxing and wrestling and riding too.' That's how Ambrose came to adopt little me. That's how JJ came to train as a lawyer, and Satyrus to adopt him; it was to be many years before I overtook JJ in the world of books. Action Man, that's how I saw myself.

So it was arranged that we should both go to Rome until our sixteenth birthdays in the Spring, and then our ways would part. I'll never forget my first sight of Rome, *The City*. We came in, of course, by the *Porta Flaminia* (Piazza del Popolo) and there all round us were the 'Seven Hills', gleaming with temples and marble. We made straight through the crowded streets towards the Aventine, the original Rock of the Sabines,* the last resting place

**Figure 8**
Merlin as Apollonius the hairy hero
©Edizioni Poligraf

**Figure 9**
Merlin's brother 'JJ' in philosophical mood
©Edizioni Poligraf

of King Tatius* and the stricken Remus, standing, as it will ever stand, in cool seclusion above the Circus Maximus. Here, three hundred years ago, St Paul wrote and taught; here JJ and I were to reside. Our carriage drew up at the gate of what seemed to me a veritable palace – I was later to find that there were many such on the Aventine – and there was Satyrus' wife, now my aunt, to welcome us. Satyrus had houses all over the Empire, and was always skipping from one to another in the course of his business. Auntie Satyra preferred to stay put in Rome, where she had so many friends.

The next few months passed in a round of excitements, and I will spare you and my panting scribes an account of what every visitor to Rome will know as well as I – but two episodes I must tell. The first occurred on New Year's Day, AD377. Auntie had got us good seats for the Consuls' Inauguration at the Capitol. From a perch beside the Temple of Juno we could see all that went on. Procession after procession of soldiers wound down the Via Sacra to the foot of the Capitol, ending with the white-robed priests of all the Pagan Colleges – for although Rome was nominally Christian, the city liked to keep up the old traditional ceremonies. Then the *lictors* marching with their *fasces*, and finally two four-wheeled chariots drawn by four snow-white horses. The first chariot seemed to me to be made entirely of ivory, although I now know it to be plated. In it stood two men each wearing the *tunica palmata* glittering with gold thread. One of them was a slim young man of eighteen with dark brown curly hair bound with the imperial diadem; this was Gratian, the Augustus. Beside him, almost crushing him with his 'height and bulk, was a blond giant wearing a simple *corona civica* of oak leaves; this was Merobaudes. There, smilingly acknowledging the applause of the crowd, stood the man who had murdered my grandfather. The chariot behind them, of dark wood with silver ornament, held two women both of whom I knew. One was great-aunt Justina Augusta. The other – how did she get there? – was Morgan.

Suddenly the sun seemed to have gone in, and Rome to have turned to ashes. We both claimed to be feeling ill – as indeed we were – and had to be taken home, missing the Consular Games and Show in the Colosseum. What had 'Father' said about forgiveness? We were trying to forgive Uncle Ted; but surely Father didn't expect us to forgive Justina and Merobaudes too, did he? (I called Ambrose 'Father' because to me there could only be one 'Dad'). However, we managed to get over this emotional squall quickly enough. Rome was too absorbing, and there were clothes and lawbooks to be bought for Julius – the Army would clothe me. But we both had to attend the tailors to be fitted with our *Togae Viriles* and Satyrus was coming to Rome to sponsor us through the traditional ceremony at the Capitol on our birthday.

On our own great day, the Kalends of March AD377, Satyrus led us boys once again up the Capitol to the chapel of Juno where we each cast the traditional coin – not this time to Charon, as we had in Ireland, but to Juventus, the God of Youth whom we were about to forsake. We went on to the *Tabularium* – the greatest registry office in the world and what kept Rome ticking whoever ruled – to matriculate our new names, in the manner befitting members of the Senatorial class.

JJ cut a fine figure in his toga; I looked quite a clown in mine as I only come up to his shoulders. **There is room for a whole extra head on top of mine** (keep this sentence in your mind for now; we shall hear more of it in Book XV) but I'm no dwarf, and if anyone calls me one I'll sort him out on the mats. It's just that when JJ and I are together I do look a bit small. He's going to be a real bull* when he grows up, I thought. It was funny to think we might never wear our togas again until our funerals.

Not long after this I enlisted into the army, took my *sacramentum*, or sacred oath, to the Imperator and the State, and received my token denarii. For the next eighteen months I was to be a tyro (Latin *tiro**), a recruit-in-training attached, thanks to Ambrose's influence, to the Palatine troops, so I was now a 'paladin'. The 'Household Troops', *Auxilia Palatina*, were organised by 'schools' (like whales and porpoises!) – hence our nickname, *scolani* – and since these were a *corps d'élite* the training was as gruelling as elsewhere, only more so. I won't describe it all, as many of you who read this will have been there too; army training never changes. Suffice it to say that by the Saturnalia of 378 I was a full *singularis*, every inch of me a soldier, and no mere Private. I was a Guardsman, a *scolanus*; if chosen for duty, I might even become one of the *Protectores* (Imperial Lifeguards). I had comrades, I had pride, I was tough, and I was a noted swordsman, as my new nickname, 'Strong arm'* still bears witness. 'Once a Guardsman always a Guardsman'.

During the last summer of my training, on 9 August to be precise, Valens was killed in the disastrous battle of Adrianople which he had 'attended', posing as an 'imperator'. The much-abused Vizi-Goths,* who had fled the Huns to our side of the Danube hoping to become peaceful federates of Rome, had wreaked an appalling vengeance for Rome's perfidy and cruelty to them under their 'king' Fritigern.

*I can hardly overstress the importance of what I am about to write, which I foresee will unlock so many genealogical doors.** *Frit* is Teutonic for 'peace'. ***'Tigernus'* is how the Greek *τυραννοζ* emerges from the Teuton larynx;** and 'Peace Ruler' was what Fritigern had sought to be, had Valens given him the chance. More than thirty years of bloody strife were to follow before I was destined to lead the Goths at last to peace and to win a similar name from them: Gott-fried, Godfrey, Geoffrey or Jaufré, as it has variously been written.

Meanwhile, Valens had left no son living, nor accepted successor. The whole Imperium of both Romes rested in the hands of the nineteen-year-old Augustus, Gratian, and of Justina and Merobaudes – with, I'm happy to say, ***Uncle Theo*** as their Chief of Staff (*Magister epistolae*).

Rome had lost two thirds of her army at Adrianople. New Rome quivered in apprehension. Happily the Goths were hardly less appalled, and at a loss as to what to do. Into this political hiatus fell the calming advice of Ambrose, Gratian's godfather. Gratian had at once moved with an army to the aid of Valens, but too late. Retiring to Gaul he then met Ambrose in Milan. 'Father,' he said, 'what am I to do? The weight of the two eagles is too heavy for me to bear alone, and I distrust my closest advisers.' (The **double-headed eagle** was the badge of the Empire of East and West, as divided by Constantius I, 'Chlorus' and Galerius.* **One head spoke Greek, the other Latin.**)

**Figure 10**
Uncle Ted c AD380, as new Augustus of New Rome
© Trustees of the British Museum

'There is one man,' said the astonishing Ambrose, 'a man who has already shown his skill in war, who has learnt the ways of statecraft from his noble father, a man whose heart calls him to blot out the sins of Valens. This man has been exiled, Sir, not by you but by me. I know his place of refuge and I alone can recall him. The man is Theodosius.' Yes, dear reader, it was Uncle Ted, soon to be ordained Augustus,* and later to earn himself the title 'Theodosius the Great'.

So Gratian and his crew bestrode the West, and Uncle Ted the East; where would there be a future for little me? Ambrose was a match for this one also. Before my eighteenth birthday, on 1 March 379, my posting came through to report to Ambrose's friend General Celerinus* in Alexandria. Back to Canopus and the IInd Legion, the '*Trajani*'. In due course I took ship with a mixed draft from Brindisi and, skirting Crete, we slipped into 'Alex' past the famous *Φαρος* – that 'Wonder of the World' which has given its name to all subsequent lighthouses – and I was back in the land of my birth.

My luck was in, and I was soon to see action. Celerinus was ordered to lead a force from Egypt to the relief of Carrhae* (Haran in Mesopotamia, once the home of Abraham). The Pers-Armenian border had been in a state of semi-war for the eight closing years of Sapor III's long reign as King of Persia. The Persians were the only Empire we Romans never truly beat. Indeed it was at Carrhae that nearly four hundred and thirty years ago Crassus the Triumvir threw away the flower of Rome's and Pompey's legions in dire defeat. The most we could do with that long frontier from the Arabian desert to the Black Sea was to fight as best we could, sometimes winning, sometimes losing, and then see how long the diplomats could make some sort of peace stick. This was one of the times to fight.

The summer was alarmingly hot for fighting, but we marched North (*ad Septentrionem*) by the ancient 'Way of the Sea'; through Palestine, past Jerusalem, past Tyre and Sidon and the Dog-River, picking up the Xth Legion 'Fretensis' *en route*. That legion had been based at Caesarea since Augustus the Great, and what they didn't know about those peculiar people the Jews was nobody's business. They had actually crucified Jesus, and claimed his seamless robe among their regimental treasures; some of them, by now, were Jews themselves, especially since Julian's day.

We marched on by dawn and dusk, resting up in the heat of the day and eventually came out into the dusty desert. Messages reached us that Carrhae was still holding out and we pressed on across the Euphrates and up into the hills to Edessa where we paused to regroup and prepare for the attack. The Persians had come in from the West via Nisibis. Celerinus' plan was to outflank them from the North, keeping always in the hills and to descend on them at a rush from the North-West hoping to surprise them and make them fear for their lines of communication. So speed, stealth and silence were the orders of the day.

Celerinus was a good tactician, we were well-trained troops (even me) and it all went as planned. We could see the Persian campfires from our hiding place where we rested for the night, and well before dawn we descended on them. I learnt one thing about war that morning: that once battle commences chaos reigns. Total bloody chaos. Nobody has any idea what is going on. You get in there and run and crawl and shout, and if you see anyone not wearing the right uniform you have a go at him and he at you. And arrows zing past you and stones, and you listen for the bugle calls, and try to watch the signalling standards, so that if lost at least you're all lost together. And you don't throw your lance until ordered to – you keep it in your hand to poke people's eyes out. I learnt, too, that it is a good idea to enlist the animals on your side. A few terrified horses or camels charging about out of control among the enemy lines do their morale a lot of damage.

Well, I got away with a few cuts and a bruised cheekbone where a stone hit me. And I lost a lot of sweat, and I don't *know* that I killed a single Persian. But the day belongs to Celerinus. His plan was faultless, and as he foresaw, the Persians were taken completely by surprise with us coming in from the wrong direction, and in the darkness they could not know by how much they outnumbered us. We set their tents on fire and freed all the animals we could, and about midday we heard their trumpets going for retreat. The siege was lifted, even if the Persians had few casualties. That night Carrhae went mad with joy, we were the heroes of the town, and I lost my virginity – with what result I care not.

Next day the troops thronged about Celerinus. They knew of the death of Valens. They did not know as yet that Uncle Ted had succeeded him. In their enthusiasm they surged around Celerinus cheering, shouting 'Celerinus Imperator', 'Celerinus Augustus'. Celerinus listened with a smile, then after a while he raised his hand and held it still until they too grew still. 'Children,' he said, 'you know not who you are, nor what you are. You and I have won a victory; but not a war. The Persians flee; but in good order. They will return in time. We are an incident in history and no more; and New Rome has a new Augustus, Theodosius, whom I am proud to serve. So long as we have Persians to kill we need no civil war. I am your general. Follow me home. I thank you for your love. Now give me your obedience.' He gave them a salute and they cheered him some more. Then they quieted down and a week later we started home.

This time we followed the desert track, the 'Kings Way' (the old caravan route) trans-Jordan from Damascus past the Greek towns and Petra to the great Arabian gulf; Saracen country all the way. The Xth Fretensis of course were on their own way back to Caesarea and their interminable guard duties in Palestine, and about half our Legion and their auxiliaries went with them. But Celerinus marched with us and soon I found out why. One evening I was summoned to his tent and found him alone. 'Well, my boy,' he said. 'I've been watching you, as your father asked, and I quite like the look of what I see. By all accounts you went berserk in that last little scrap. That won't do, you know. You'll get killed too soon that way, and be a bad investment of Rome's time and effort. We're on our way now to another scrap, this time among the fuzzy-wuzzies.' He stopped at my surprised look. 'Didn't they tell you about them at school, my boy?' he said. I blushed deeply; I'd forgotten Eunapius and the Æthiopica so soon. 'Rome is ringed with barbarians,' he said. 'Fair and dark, tall and short, all equally smelly. I'm off to do the same job down South that I did at Carrhae. Teach them yet another lesson. But first of all I'm going to teach you a lesson. You're not coming with me.'

At this I looked so downcast that he laughed. 'Promotion is what you need young man. A little responsibility, independent at that, will make you grow up fast. Do you know why Rome is in Egypt?'

'For the corn supply, Sir,' I stammered.

'True,' he said, 'but there's more than that. Have you not heard of King Solomon's Mines?'

I had to confess that I had not, so he went on to explain. The only mines in Palestine were the copper mines at Timna, past which we would soon march, and tradition was that they had been worked since the days of the wise Jewish King. But King Solomon's gold mines were not in Palestine at all, but in Egypt and Nubia; and Rome still worked them – or at least the Nubian ones, since those of the Mons Claudianus in the Arabian Mountains were now quite worked out. 'The gold,' Celerinus said, 'belongs to the Augustus and his Treasurer.' (The *Comes Sacrae Largitionem*, or Count of the Sacred Largesses – a job many of my family were to hold.) 'Hardly any public monies still flow to the Senate's Quaestor, as of old,' Celerinus continued. 'The Augustus has appropriated all the rest, together with control of the currency. The mines are worked by slaves, and the product is taken covertly by caravans across the desert to ports on the Nile or on the Red Sea, thence by boat, until it reaches official hands. Many robbers pursue these caravans. They go under armed guard. You, my boy, will be that guard. We go by boat to "Berenice the Golden"* and across the desert to Philae by Assuan on the Nile, where the Legion has a permanent camp. You will stop off at the mines of "Um Garaiat" where you will be attached to the Mine Manager's special police for a three-year tour. Next time I hear of you I want to hear that you're in command of them, but that's up to you. The work is dangerous, lonely, boring and undermanned. Don't let any of the gold stick to your fingers or I'll cut them off personally. Now be off.'

My ears and cheeks burned with fury as I saluted and left the tent. Here was I, a boy-veteran, still lightly scarred or at least scratched from battle, turned aside to become a ruddy transport policeman. I was young; how would you feel in my place? But I looked with more than idle curiosity at the copper mines when we passed them, and got the supervisor who showed us round to tell me something about the process. And I was just the right size to go into the shafts or *adits* as we call them. 'Maybe that's why old Celerinus picked me for the job,' I thought sulkily. As I went to sleep that night, bits of what Eunapius had taught me in 'stinks' class at Ocean College started to come back to me; and bits of Aristotle and Pliny.

And gold is something special isn't it? Worth giving your life for? Already I was starting to get interested. Goldilocks, that's me. In due course I shall find my Three Bears. Maybe one or more of them will be sleeping in my bed – not, I hasten to add, at the same time!

Heigh ho.

# BOOK V

## *Snow White and the Little Dwarf* (AD *380–382)*

So we piled aboard ships at *Aila* (Eilat) and the Etesian winds bore us South in eight days to Berenice the Golden. Hot days and orange coloured cliffs first to port, later to starboard. I could see why it is called the Red Sea. Even the sky seemed red with heat.

Berenice is a neat little Greek trading town, perched above an excellent south-facing harbour and protected by a headland. Funny to think the Queen of Sheba probably put in here. There are emerald mines nearby, but these were not our goal. We paused only to gather up stores of food and water, and camels to carry it. Also guides, because you can't afford to miss the trail in this land. Then it was foot slogging again, three hunded miles in a fortnight. The first two days we marched inland, then we branched South on the old caravan trail for Nubia for five more days, climbing slowly all the while. Most days at least one caravan passed us heading seawards, the camels deeply burdened with hides, carpets, baskets of dates, pots and who knows what else hidden within. They were accompanied by white-robed camel boys, each wearing a burnous against the sun, and Celerinus allowed us to buy ourselves burnous from them. They stared sullenly at us soldiers but brightened up at the sight of our money. At intervals down the road were wells with a few palm trees round, but I soon saw why Celerinus had made us carry our own water as the northbound caravans had often drunk the *hydreumae* dry before we got to them and we could hardly wait around for them to refill. There were wretched little trading posts, too, at these wells, where scanty offerings of dates and chickpeas were on sale.

At the end of the week we turned off the caravan trail onto a military track which followed dried-up wadis, uphill at first, then slowly downhill towards the Nile, one hundred and fifty miles away as the crow flies. No more caravans here, and the guides really came into their own, especially in finding us water. For, amazingly, there is water in the desert if you know where to find it. At certain low-spots in the wadis the guides would signal us to dig, and using our entrenching tools we would excavate a hole up to six feet deep. Lo and behold, in the morning there would be a few inches of water. Sometimes more. These wadis are really old rivers.

Twice in the next week we passed a military convoy heading North. At least I assumed they were military – gold probably – although no soldiers marched with them. Presumably the convincing-looking Arab or Nubian camel boys were in fact soldiers in disguise. Certainly they all wore villainous hooked native swords at their belts. Am I to be one of these?

At the end of the second week we reached another fork, and when we stopped Celerinus sent for me and ten of my mates. 'This is the parting of the ways, my boy,' he said. 'Once upon a time, Rameses the Great extended Egypt one hundred miles into Nubia, where the old Gods of Abu Simbel keep watch over his old frontier; but it is at Paphnutis that there stands the sacred Sycamine tree which forms the present frontier of Egypt and Nubia under us Romans, even as under the Ptolemys. We continue on to the Nile at Paphnutis.* You will lead this small detachment to the mines, two days march to the North, and report there to the mine manager. Here's your commission and a letter to show to him. I leave you two guides. You're on your own, brother. Hail and farewell!' I almost choked with pride as I saluted and turned away. My general, my hero, had called me, a common soldier, 'brother'. Such is the way of the service; the bond is strong.

We watched rather anxiously as the column moved away next day, until we could only see the column of dust where our comrades plodded on. Suddenly I thought to open my commission. It read:

> '*Decurion** and *Beneficiarius* Claudius Eucherius is hereby appointed to lead this draft to assume duty as mine guards, with unpaid acting rank of *Optio*.*
>
> **Celerinus**, *Magister Militum**

I think I should explain to you here that a '*decurion*' was in charge of a section of ten, be they infantrymen or cavalry troopers. In civilian life, a decurion was a councillor in charge of ten districts of a *municipium*. (These men had an awful time as they were personally liable for the tax rates levied in their district.) In the forces this rank was equivalent to Corporal. *Beneficiarius* simply means 'excused fatigues' or 'privileged'; in this case, 'Cadet'.

'Well,' I thought, 'you're in command and you've jumped two ranks. You'd better get on with it, Lucius my lad.' So I stood in front of my men and shouted at them, and to my surprise they obeyed me and fell in. Maybe my voice did it. I've really got a huge voice* for my size. I have a bit of a stammer* in normal speech, but this goes when I let fly. The Roman war cry or *barritus* is famous, whence modern 'baritone'.

So we moved off up another wadi, and soon we were on our own in the red hills which were climbing gradually, becoming cliffs on either side. The guides led us steadily on and towards evening of the second day, as the walls of the wadi drew ever closer in, we rounded a bend and saw smoke. Blessed sight: our fellow men. Where they could live, so could we. The wadi Khowanib ended in three short valleys walled by cliffs which barred all further progress. In the walls of the cliffs we could see dark holes like doorways, and tracks and ramps leading to them. In the centre of the valleys stood a small well-walled township and I could see by the trees that there must be wells. Within the town stood the usual fort, and soon I was marching my men in by the principal gate and up to the verandah of the *Principium*.

What a relief to see a sentry again, to whom I gave the password, and to feel back in a way of life I knew. But it was a funny unmilitary sort of place. White-robed civilians everywhere, and near-naked Nubians, and donkeys. Scruffy, I thought. I marched into the Commandant's office, to find no standards in the chapel, no orderly room clerks. Behind a table a tall grey-haired Greek in a white tunic rose in surprise to greet me with a 'Who the hell are you?'

'We speak Latin in my unit,' I replied rather stuffily in Greek. 'Here's my commission and a letter from my general to the Mine Manager, whoever he may be.'

'Obviously you don't think it's me, young man,' he said, still in Greek. 'But you've got a lot to learn.' While he said this he was opening the letter and as he read it his face changed. 'So the General has remembered us after all,' he said. 'I thought we were quite forgotten. Let me introduce myself. I'm Onesimus, the Manager's freedman and chief clerk. I'll show your letter to the Manager when he "comes round". You won't see much of him, though, as he spends most of his time "sleeping it off" and dreaming of leave. Out of sight out of mind. I run the show, in his name. Very glad to see you.' With this he held out his hand and gripped mine in a way that seemed strange. 'So you haven't been "raised" yet,' he said. 'I'd have thought an *optio* like you, an officer cadet according to this letter, would have "seen the light that shineth in darkness" by now. Still you've come to the right place. We've got a nice little working lodge here. What a lot you've got to learn.'

'The first thing I want to learn is where the quarters are for my men, and food, and stabling for my animals,' I said, trying to look a bit haughty but not succeeding.

'All right, keep your hair on young man,' said Onesimus laughing, 'you're tired and you're right. We'll try to do you pukka.' He rang a bell and a kilted Nubian orderly came in, a necklace of beads on his bare chest. 'When you and Kiffi,' for that was the orderly's name, 'have got your men settled down and you've had a clean up – we've even got a swimming bath – come over to the mess and we can get better acquainted.' So started my two and a half years as a gold miner, years which were to lead me inexorably towards the Holy Grail, though I could not know it then.

Meanwhile, as I later learnt, quite a lot had been going on in the outside world while I was playing the hero at Carrhae.* Ambrose had been trundling Gratian along the path of statesmanship and magnanimity. Not only had he persuaded him to make Uncle Ted Augustus in the East, he had also got him to confirm little Valentinian (now aged eight) as co-Augustus of the West (with Justina the Ambitious – to her huge satisfaction – as Regent). Ambrose had even rehabilitated Magnus Maximus by appointing him as Vicar of Britain.* Maximus thus replaced Uncle Icarus, who had gone East to become joint Governor of the Orient (and Consul in AD381). Justina was of course less than pleased by Maximus' promotion but could not withstand Ambrose. Grandad Max had this extraordinary career, like 'snakes and ladders'. But he kept on climbing right to the end.

The other event, while I was in Egypt, was JJ's engagement. He had completed his legal training in Rome and in the Spring of 382 he was to marry Elizabeth Avitia, Justina's daughter by Maximus. As you can see from her name, Elizabeth was a 'cradle Christian', for Maximus was a strongly orthodox Catholic; ***Justina***, alas, was Arian to a fault).[1] Elizabeth or **Elissa*** as everyone called her, was three years younger than JJ but was really his half-aunt, or first cousin once removed, if you prefer. Some may say in the future that they were brother and sister – we Romans had no word for the true relationship. Surely no whiff of **incest*** there? Not for the time being anyway.

---

[1] This is no place for a theological discourse, but I must say a few words on the heresy which for two hundred years racked and weakened the Empire. On a fine, and readily misunderstood, point of semantics, and under stress of dialectic controversy, an Alexandrian Deacon called Arius allowed himself a definition of Jesus' status which quite downgraded Him from the Trinity. The Council of Nicea reinstated Him, with short-lived success. Thanks to Athanasius' long and heroic battles He was eventually accepted theologically as a full member of the Trinity. While the theologians were slanging one another, many bishops and several Emperors tried to find a middle way; they called themselves Semi-Arians, but their Orthodox enemies, with the honourable exceptions of Hilary of Poitiers (and Athanasius himself) denounced them all as Arians. Constantine the Great closed his days with Arian (Semi-Arian) baptism. His last surviving son Constans imposed a Semi-Arian consensus in AD361 on East and West.
The Goths and other barbarians were converted during this period and thus became in all good faith Christian 'Arians'. It was centuries before they were finally to be won over to 'Athanasianism'. Ambrose's predecessor at Milan, Bishop Auxentius, was a Semi-Arian. Families were split. The two rival denominations acquired tribal and political identities. Theology was quite forgotten. It will all seem very strange in the future, but it was real enough for those who had to live with it.
In the future, a certain Hilaire Belloc would write: 'Oh let us never never doubt, what nobody is sure about'. In this spirit I have been Orthodox among the Orthodox and Arian among the Arians, and married by both rites. I try to be a Christian, when I'm not flirting with Isis, Mithras, neo-Platonism and other buzz-religions. At least I know what I don't know, which is more than some theologians. The 'Catholic' and the 'Arian' denominations treated each other (at least until the time of Gaisarix* in the mid-fifth century) with adequate charity. The main quarrels were about church buildings and endowments. Mammon, as it were.

Meanwhile, in King Solomon's Mines, little 'Goldilocks' was plying his hammer and learning all about metallurgy. I found that my military duties did not take up much of my time. Three or four times a year there was a gold convoy to organise and escort. The gold could be shipped either via Berenice or via the Nile, and we planned the convoys at irregular intervals and with plenty of fake convoys in either direction. I learnt many tricks of disguise* which were to serve me well later. 'Cops and robbers' was the name of the game; spies and counter-spies. Two of the convoys I took right down to Alexandria, which gave me a chance to enjoy the fleshpots and the stews, and to visit my childhood home at Canopus. There I also had the chance to delve in the great technical library and museum of the Serapeion,* and I used to disappear in there for days at a time, reading everything I could find about metals – gold in particular – but also silver and copper. There, one day, I saw a most curious exhibit: in a glazed cupboard was a miniature iron chariot with four horses. A lever raised the floor of the cupboard about a foot, so that the chariot was close to the ceiling. Suddenly, with no one touching it, the chariot jumped into the air and remained stuck to the ceiling as if glued. Here was magic. However, could the trick be done? I consulted one of the priest-curators, who told me that this was only 'magic' in a scientific sense, and that above the cupboard's false ceiling was a powerful lodestone. This sort of scientific 'magic' will haunt me to the end my days; indeed I'll write a poem one day about the lodestone, and Book XX will see me inventing the navigational compass.*

When my comrades asked where I spent the days I used to say I was worshipping Serapis. And on my journeys back up the Nile I would stop at Memphis where the priests of Ptah ran a college of metallurgy going back to the times of the Pharaohs. Onesimus had trained there as well as at Laurium (the famous silver mines of *Λαυριον*, near Sounion, were the source of Athens' power; the techniques of deep mining, as opposed to open cast, were pioneered there) and learnt enough of the old Egyptian language to get along. It was he who introduced me to the *Arcana* of Zosimus of Panoplis* of which I now have his copy, and who taught me how easily a secret can be hidden in full view of the undiscerning by means of camouflage.*

Onesimus often used to take me up into the hills around, and show me how and where to search for gossan and gangue and all the signs of underlying minerals, using a geologist's hammer, like a little mattock. *Marculinus** we Romans call it (vulgarly **Merlinus**), and I was to have one at my hip for many years.

All my readers will know how gold is washed and panned from rivers. But how did we win it in the almost waterless desert? That is a great Imperial industrial secret, which I hardly dare to reveal. I will go a little further than Aristotle, however, and name sulphur and mercury* as his two primary reagents: sulphur which interpenetrates yet is burnt away, mercury which dissolves yet remains. Sulphur, the Dragon; mercury, his sister and mate. If you're a working alchemist like me, you'll know what I'm talking about.

In these ways my time passed surprisingly quickly in Nubia. After our rough start Onesimus and I became great friends – I was always looking for a 'father figure' – and he confused my young mind with much curious knowledge. Not a Christian, he was a free-thinker, and although he could not interest me in the old Egyptian Gods, I fell into his syncretic attitudes when it came to Isis. After all, I'd read Apuleius' *Golden Ass* at school, and who can be unmoved by the Ass' appeal to Isis in Book XI, apostrophising Her as 'the quintessence of all the heavenly Mothers, by whatever name worshipped'. All male and female gods are in some sense a glimpse of one God. That makes sense to me; it fitted in well, too, with my progress in the Lodge of Mithras (thirty-six years later in Athens, after much study, I attempted a synthesis* of all theology within a Christian matrix, and though I say it myself, it was pretty good).

Onesimus had arranged my initiation to the First Degree in my first month. The Lodge was held in an old mine shaft which made an admirable cave, and old Paeonius, the Mine Manager was sobered up sufficiently to preside as *Pater*, and to admit me. Onesimus was, very properly, Mithras-Heliodromos the 'sun-runner'; the others (about a dozen in all) made up the lower degrees of Persian, Lion, Raven, and Soldier. I found it quite alarming becoming a 'Crypheus'* and being blindfolded, lowered into a real grave and a slab put over me. After what seemed an age the slab was raised and the cave was ablaze with lights, in symbolic resurrection. I was to 'see the light' again at Eleusis many years later; for are not all initiations akin? But for now I was to greet the brethren, learn the words and signs, and to watch from the lowliest seat the enactment of that stirring rite of the triumph of light over darkness. Oh Ambrose, were you ever an initiate of Mithras? I bet you were. I was a lion, **Leo**,* by the time I left the mines, and I kept up my membership and rose steadily through the degrees as long as I remained in the army. In fact 'Leo the lion' was to become one of my nicknames among the Cambrians. Confusing for a former hamster and wild boar!

In the first week of January 382 a letter arrived in the mines bearing the official seal of the *Magister Militum*. In it, 'Optio C. Eucherius' was instructed to proceed on three months leave, at the end of which I was to report to Headquarters in Milan for posting to commissioned duty in the West. Obviously Onesimus had been writing good confidential reports on me for old Paeonius to sign, and Celerinus had not ceased to keep an eye on me, nor forgotten to keep Ambrose in touch with his adopted son's progress. I was overjoyed at the prospect of keeping my twenty-first birthday with Ambrose at Milan, and of being reunited with my brother in Rome. I decided to make my way first of all to the old Casa Sic where Morgan, I knew, was still living. Whether her new husband Genobaudes would be there or not, I'd have to leave to chance.

So in mid-January 382 I said farewell, for the time being, to the Pyramids and the Nile, and bustling clammy Alexandria teeming with merchants and monks and priests and Rabbis, and found a ship bound for Syracuse and home. I spent my first weeks at Syracuse (Naples) with Uncle Theo (Manlius) in his home in the upper town (Νεαπολις *Neapolis* 'Naples'); and I was not the only one to call him the 'second Virgil' of Naples* at this time, for he was employing a long vacation from Gratian's court in Paris by translating many of the Greek philosophers into Latin. He said that the biggest problem was that Latin didn't have enough words to convey the nuances of Greek thought. The Greeks always 'had a word for it'. He had to fudge and paraphrase, or even to coin new words and hope they might be understood.

Uncle Theo really was a fascinating man. His latest hobby was astronomy, and he had devised a machine with two curved mirrors where, by looking through a hole in the middle of the nearer one, you could see the stars and planets many times larger than they were in the sky. He called it a 'telescope', and said he had the idea from reading the works of Archimedes, Syracuse's famous applied scientist. He hoped to rig this machine up in Hadrian's tower* high up on the *Mons Clarus* (the conspicuous mount, Montesclaire or Etna) where the air was thin and he hoped to see some of the smallest stars. In due course I set up several such observatories of my own, including one on Glastonbury Tor. My own particular contributions to the development of the telescope would be the introduction of rock-crystal refracting lenses, and a movable platform* on wheels so that the apparatus could be turned to follow the object observed.

Uncle Theo said Gratian was still going to seed in Paris, neglecting state affairs in favour of hunting in the forests around, in all too intimate company with his bodyguard of Alans. I hoped we hadn't got another pervert Augustus on our hands. Alas for poor Rome, and for poor Ambrose.

Morgan was at her town house, and often dined with us. Goneryl and Regan were at New Rome with Uncle Ted. Genobaudes was away soldiering on the Rhine frontier, but Morgan had had a pretty little daughter by him, now rising eight, whom I had not met. Her name was Chelidonia, 'little swallow' which Morgan said Genobaudes, in his Teutonic way, pronounced something like 'Gerlinte'. (Oodles of classical reverberations here; think of Philomel and Procne.*) She was a dear little thing, and I was quite taken by her. I predicted that many men would one day sing her praises as **Eudoxia**, the 'well-praised'.

Some evenings I dined with Morgan at her castle at the tip of Ortygia, and she showed me her underground aquarium, with a porthole below the waves (cunningly contrived from Indian mica) so that one could watch the fish swimming as freely as if they were in the room. By night the fish were a-sparkle with phosphorescence. It was all magic to me. Who wants to go to University like JJ, when there are so many thrilling things to be learnt from one's own family? Morgan told me that Grandad Max was having a tough time as Vicar of Britain, lucky as he was to get the job. It was the Picts and the Scots as usual. I think the departure, then death, of Dad, must have unsettled them, not least the burgeoning recruits to 'Alban's Horse'. Romanitas had not had time to bite deep into Further Valentia; but Rome would, and indeed must, triumph.

In mid-February I said goodbye to Morgan and Uncle Theo, and took ship for Rome. But arriving at *Portus* (Ostia) I found a message that JJ was already in Milan with Uncle Satyrus, preparing for his wedding; so I quickly took a coaster* to Genoa and pushed on to Milan. I was dying to see Satyrus and Ambrose again, and above all JJ and his betrothed. Poor Elissa, she had nothing to do with Grandad Theo's murder, and Maximus had always been 'clement' enough to us boys. I tried not to think of her as one of the 'enemy camp' and wondered what she was like?

So I reached Milan, and there was JJ and Satyrus and Auntie. Satyrus was twinkling as ever. He had just pulled off a big coup in the spice trade* and made a lot more money. They had arranged a party for my twenty-first birthday where I would meet Elissa for the first time. It would be a modest affair as the Lenten fast was still on, so the real whoopee would have to wait until JJ's wedding on Easter Monday. Cousin Vic was back with us too. It transpired that Ambrose had wangled him, like me, into the Army, but he 'did a Martin' on them. Didn't cut up his cloak, but handed back his *cingulum* and went all pacifist. He was lucky to get away with an ignominious discharge. Ambrose had taken him back with love and respect, and he was destined for Holy Orders. I was sure he would do well. How difficult was this business of Christianity and Pacifism. It was like Dad and Uncle Ted all over again. I knew which side I was on. 'The sword of the Lord and of Gideon', that was me. Or that's me now anyway.

**Figure 11**

'Sweet Catullus' all-but-island, "olive-silvery Sirmio"'

Comfortably off as he was, Satyrus was very pious and kept the fast as strictly as Ambrose, who was very busy with his catechumens classes over at the Basilica Theclana in preparation for the orgy of baptisms on Easter Sunday. This was the original Basilica of *Mediolanum* from which Justina would attempt to oust Ambrose. The large and impressive Baptistery where Ambrose dipped so many catechumens, including St Augustine, adjoined to the West. Near by, Ambrose would add the Basilica Nova to the complex. Yet later, during the struggle with Justina, Ambrose built his very own basilica of SS Gervasius and Protasius, later to be called San Ambrogio after him.

Ambrose introduced anthems into the services, on the Eastern model, and had been very busy translating them into Latin, choosing musical settings, and training the choirs. He came to my party and I knelt and kissed his ring, but he pulled me up and hugged me. No side about Ambrose – as a man, that is. 'Welcome home, my little Christian soldier,' he said. 'At least I hope that's what you are. Celerinus has been keeping me in touch with your progress.'

'Well frankly I'm not too sure if I'm a Christian, Father,' I said. 'I mean, I'm a "Leo" now, a Mithraist; I really think Mithras has the answers at this moment – for a soldier anyway.'

'I won't let that come between us now,' said Ambrose. 'Maybe you'll be a Christian Lion in God's good time.' And he moved on to the other guests.

And now to what I'd been waiting for, the fabulous ***Elissa***. How can I find words for her? First of all, if JJ was a giant, she was a match for him. She really was a *large* girl, with long fair plaited hair piled thrillingly on her noble head, broad high cheekbones, blue eyes, skin like white silk-velvet, and the frame of a pugilist. No, that sounds ugly and she was beautiful. More like a goddess. Yes, that's it. A statue come to life, like Pygmalian's.* Ye Gods, what a torso! Soft and all woman, but you could sense the underlying muscle. The Teutons will remember her as **Brünnhilde** (*prünk-hilde*, a 'splendid heroine' in Teutonic). You will do better to remember her as the first Guinevere, Arthur's wife, and wait to see which Arthur I mean; for 'Arthur', *Arcturus*, was the Guardian and protector of the Great Bear,* and Elissa was that self-same Bear. Lucky old JJ, thought I as I gave her a brotherly embrace which landed titchy me face first among her warm bosoms and flashing necklaces. Intoxicating, it was. Lucky, lucky JJ.

Easter was quite a riot. Ambrose's anthems sounded splendid, especially his new Song of Praise called the 'Te Deum', which he had purloined from Paulinus of Nola.* Paulinus was a distant relative, a close friend of Ambrose, and an adequate poet. He would become a saint, and my spiritual director. It was while Ambrose was visiting him at Nola that he met Nicetas, Bishop of Remesiana* in Eastern (Greek speaking) Illyricum, and, admiring his anthem, resolved to translate and adopt it. I foresaw that it would still be sung in Church fifteen hundred years on. The Easter baptisms, too, were touching and impressive, and I really longed to be part of them myself and felt quite out of things as a lapsed cradle Christian. When with Father I felt very much a Christian. Would it last? I was in such a muddle.

The next day was JJ's wedding which took place at Satyrus' house, in proper senatorial fashion by *confarratio*: the ceremonial eating of pieces of wedding cake, the exchange of rings, and some of the less obscene pagan customs. Ambrose gave the bride and groom a solemn blessing, and I ventured to sing a little *epithalamium* which I had composed in my best Ocean College vein, and which I blush to think of now. Indeed I blushed at the time. Little boars do.

Next day JJ and Elissa, duly consummate, went off on honeymoon to Lake *Benacus** (Garda), where Justina had made available to them her Imperial Villa at *Sirmio* (Sirmione). So the festivities subsided, and my leave ebbed away.

One morning Satyrus called me in. 'Luke,' he said, 'I haven't forgotten, even if you have, that you've got a date at the Praetorium. And I happen to know that James is invited along too.'

'James too?' I burst out in surprise, to be met by one of Satyrus' knowing winks, from which I guessed that Ambrose had been up to something.

So off we trooped, the very next day, down to the *Castra Vetera** near the Palace (thank goodness Justina was up in Rome), and past the usual stamping sentries and orderly-rooms into the office of the Count of the Domestics (*Comes domesticorum et stabuli praesentalis*), the General commanding Milan and North Italy. A large grey-haired man in a simple dun fatigue tunic rose to greet us and beckoned us to sit. Soldiers only wore 'battle dress' (cuirass and armoured kilt) on the parade ground, or on active service; at other times 'fatigue dress' was the order of the day. Ever wondered what a legionary wore under his kilt? Same as a Senator under his toga: a *subligaculum*, or jockstrap.

'Let's deal with the professional soldier first,' said the General, looking at me. 'It's planned career development for you, young **Eucherius**. You speak Latin, Greek and Celtic. Paeonius writes that you have learnt a lot about mining. You know Britain and the Britons know you. Your lamented grandfather (Grandad Theo) has returned the Valentias to the strait and narrow way. We want to see Britannia pulling her weight again among the Provinces. So, young as you are, we're going to take a chance on your being the man for the job. I have here your commission for three years as Procurator (Manager) of Mines for the two Valentias: responsible, so far as minerals and bullion are concerned, direct to the Vicar your grandfather (Grandad Max), and so far as military matters are concerned, to his local Duke. For these are military provinces,* still under military government. With effect from today you are hereby seconded to the XXth legion at Chester in the Britains, retaining your substantive commission in the *Auxilia Palatinae* in which you first enlisted and trained. While Procurator, you will draw army pay as a Captain and Adjutant. Any questions?'

I blushed with excitement. Wish I didn't do this. Another two ranks up, *and* in Dad's old regiment, *and* only twenty-two. 'I shall be proud to serve Rome and the Empire in Britain,' I stammered rather pompously, but already the General had turned to my brother.

'As for you, **Agricola**,'* he said (for that was my brother's principal surname at that time), 'you're not going to get a wet shirt; it's the staff for you. Maximus has found a berth for you at his Headquarters. Garrison towns and fleshpots for you, and lots of paperwork; but you lawyers know all about that. Rank will be that of Tribune, but only *laticlavus* of course, and a temporary commission at that. You can take your wife, which is more than your brother can; but then he probably knows how to look after himself around camp by now.' I did.

Well, JJ looked stunned and quite pleased all at the same time; a Major already, but only a Staff Major. The 'broad stripers' always came in for a lot of derision from the other ranks, with their education and breeding and manicured hands. So I wasn't too jealous of him, even if he had rather stolen my thunder.

In fact I was quite pleased that we were all three going to be in it together in Britain, especially all **three** of us. Little did I foresee just how close the third of us was going to become.

Heigh ho! or maybe rather, Hi ho!

# BOOK VI

## *'Twanky Dillo' (AD382)*

*Here's a health to the jolly blacksmith, the best of all fellows*
*who works at his anvil, while the boy blows the bellows;*
*which makes my old hammer to rise and to fall.*
*Here's to Old Cole and to Young Cole, and to Old Cole of All**
*Twanky dillo, twanky dillo, twanky dillo dillo dillo dillo...*
*a roaring pair of bagpipes made of the green willow.*
(Old Welsh Song)

Strange how folk memory will persist. 'Old Cole' is Count Theodosius (Grandad Theo) – 'Coel' 'Godebog', Agricola the hawk of the forests. 'Young Cole' is of course my brother JJ. 'Old Cole of All' is Cnaeus Julius Agricola, first conqueror of *Albania*. And I, Merlin, am Wayland Smith, Wilkin (the little yellow chap: Guillaume), with my big smith's hammer *Marcus*, and my little prospector's pick *Marculinus* or 'Merlin'. 'Twanky Dillo' (in Welsh, *Twncyn deilo*) means 'heap of charcoal'* – a prerequisite of forgework – and provides me with a future misnomer as 'St Teilo'. The 'bagpipes' are bellows. Metallurgy is the name of the game.

A few weeks after our meeting with the general, JJ, Elissa and I took leave of Ambrose, Satyrus, Vic and all our friends in Milan, and headed for the Arctic. We travelled, by warrant, on the Post Coaches retracing our sorrowful route with Uncle Ted, this time in joyful expectation. JJ's had not been the only Easter wedding. Regan and Goneryl too were wed, as we had learned from Morgan. Uncle Ted had been frightfully ill two years back, and was even baptised *in extremis*. Recovering, he had defeated Fritigern's Vizi-Goths, and cowed the Ostro-Goths and allied barbarians from across the Danube. Peace should be underpinned by diplomatic marriages. Ginger was spliced to a tame Vizi-Goth cavalry tribune called Alaric; Goneryl to an up-and-coming young Slav general called Στιλιχω, 'Stilicho', from his prematurely-grey hair; he was of Vandal stock, but heavily Romanised. So all Dad's children were now married save little me.

We had a good Channel crossing on the mailboat from *Bononia** (Boulogne) to *Rutupiae* (Richborough) and on to *Augusta* (London) where we learnt that the Vicar was at *Eboracum* (York), the headquarters of Northern Command. 'Vicar' is short for Vice-Prefect; the whole of the Britains were his Diocese, with Provincial Governors, Presidents or Consular Legates under him.

Time does not allow me to describe London to you, save to say that it has quite a grand appearance on its two hills above the river adorned with public buildings, triumphal arches, amphitheatres, and the like; hardly gleaming with marble, though, like Rome. Another week's travelling brought us to York, a worthy rival to London, where we duly presented ourselves to Maximus and Helena, who received us kindly and put us up for the first few days – longer would have caused jealousy among my future brother officers. Helena helped Elissa to move herself into a little married quarter, a three-roomed flat with servants' quarters. I found myself a billet among the *auxilia Palatinae* where, as anywhere in the Empire, my fellow *scolani* would be sure to welcome me, and busied myself taking over from my predecessor, getting the insignia of my new posting, and acquiring a soldier servant. I had brought with me Dad's *cingulum* of the XXth Legion, the good old *Valeria Victrix*, with the rampant boar* on its buckle; so all I needed was the *cornicularius*' badge to hang round my neck.

This turned out to be an ornamented disc of gilded bronze about the size of a battle 'gong' (i.e. four fingers across) with a single projecting horn in the middle made of silver. Makes one think of the fabled unicorn, with echoes from Ovid of and Ἀμαλθεα; Ἀchelöos,* in Ovid's version, had one horn ripped off by Hercules his fellow-suitor for Deianara, but the naiads transformed it into the Cornucopea, the Horn of Plenty, leaving poor unicorned Achelöos to pour his flowing waters for ever into the mouth of the Gulf of Corinth. Which brings me to the Cornucopia, for the Corn*ucopia* gave its name to Lyons (Colonia *Copia* Lugdunum), and appears on its coinage; I shall 'come up with it' again there in many senses. Again, my little *cornicula* gives me, perhaps, a touch of Priapus, the Greek god of fertility; exuberantly phallic, his emblem a cornucopia. The Arcadians worshipped Priapus as 'Pan the goat,'* and we Romans as 'Faunus', and I shall be remembered in all these guises. All in all I thought my adjutant's badge was rather a rude little object. Did it suit me?

I had only the one brief session with Maximus. He seemed in tetchy mood. 'Well my boy,' he said. 'Don't forget why you're here. Rome needs money. And yet more money. The annual returns show a steepening decline in mineral production, in mineral royalties, and in recovered gold and silver. Tin seems to have petered out altogether. I just don't believe it!' He gave the table a terrifying bang. 'Rome's being cheated.* That's what's happening. Seen it elsewhere. Slackness, sloppiness, fraud. Those *publicani* are cooking the books like Jews; the army mines are probably just as bad, and a disgrace to discipline as well.'

*Publicani* were Jesus' 'publicans and sinners'. We Romans often 'farmed' the state monopolies to corporations of entrepreneurs for a capital sum plus rent or royalties; you will one day say we 'privatised' them. Governmental financing and entrepreneurial morals do not change. I mean no slur on the Jews, whose experiences under the Tobiads (the Hellenistic *publicani*) were likewise remembered with disgust, but Maximus held all orientals in contempt.

'Get round them all, d'ye hear me?' Maximus went on. 'Take 'em by surprise like a good auditor. You have the powers of a Magistrate to interrogate, if need be under torture. Press them hard; imprison the ruffians if you need. But get production up; get the recoveries and the royalties up. Get the search for new lodes going again, and start with the tin mines. Rome needs all the silver she can win, for her currency. Let the Britons eat off pewter again – but for that we must have tin. Send to me if you need more troops to do the job. You have exactly twelve months to transform the scene, and my favour if you succeed. If you fail? Well, I'm not called Clement for nothing.' This rather alarming monologue closed with a handshake and the ghost of a wink. Nevertheless I was glad to salute and get out of his office. Only a year to make my mark. Plainly I had a busy time ahead.

Meanwhile, to my amusement, JJ was kitting himself out for active service. '*Primicereus*' was the job he'd walked into: staff officer to Andragath the *Comes Britanniarum* on campaign against the Picts and the Scots. *Primicereus* means Military Secretary.

Before JJ went off to war, sword at hip and a crate of pens and wax tablets under his arm, Helena gave a farewell dinner for him to which I was invited. Aunt Helena, as I call her, was a real charmer, small, dark and vivacious. She told us that her dad, my Uncle Icarus, had been Consul in 381 and was now governor of Palestine. With typical generosity Uncle Ted had paid for her widowed grandmother, poor old ***Eucheria* the pious Maccabee***, to visit the Holy Places and stay with him. She was tremendously proud of being both a Jew and a Christian, and her diary* would probably make good reading. Elissa, now confirmed as pregnant, would stay behind with Helena. Maximus made it clear to me that the sooner I was away to Cornwall the better. Maybe if he drank a bit more he would show more of the social graces. By way of contrast JJ got well and truly plastered, and we sang 'for he's a jolly good fellow' and cracked dirty jokes at his expense. So ended a mixed evening.

Next day I started to make tracks. Apart from my batman *optio* (who I paid myself), I had a mixed detachment of twenty men with me. Men from the Legion, tradesmen that is, chosen for their metallurgical experience; a clerk and an accountant; surveyors (*gromatici*); four military policemen; a groom and a pony for me. No more coach warrants. Footslogging again, cross-country where necessary. I liked it. More like the good old days in Nubia, save for the weather. Until you saw our belt badges you wouldn't know if we were soldiers or civilians.

I skim over the next few months, as these are my memoirs not a travel book; if you want descriptions of that sort why not trace my steps, and see it all for yourself. Suffice it that we reached Exeter where I got a briefing at the local tax offices. Maximus was right; the tin industry seemed to have petered out. What the stannary *Publicani* needed to do was discover the placer deposits, and to search for the lodes. I could see Onesimus' training was going to come in really useful to me in this job.

We set off into the wet windy peninsula and covered the whole of it, working clockwise. All too true, southern Cornwall was just about worked out at surface level. I called meetings of the dispirited stannary companies as we went round, and tried to enthuse them with the prospect of a valuable new market in pewter – home and export – and of rising incomes. I led parties of them up into the hills and actually found some lodes of tinstone for them with my little pick. I passed on my knowledge of up-to-date crushing and ore technology. After that it was up to them. They would work better from greed than fear. Who doesn't?

My next call, in July 382 and glorious weather, was on the old Mendip lead areas. These had been worked by *Publicani* since the conquest, hence their name 'Mendip' (deep mines), and were still going strong. The problem here was fraud. Rome's interest was not in the lead but in the silver extracted from it. The royalty demanded used to be one tenth of the silver, but we had gradually increased our demands to *all* the silver, leaving the *Publicani* only the lead to market for themselves. Curiously we seemed to be getting no more silver at 100 per cent than we got at 10 per cent. This seemed more of an economic and a psychological problem than a technical one, and I decided to settle in at Charterhouse for a month or two, keep a low profile, and wait for them to give themselves away. 'Hail fellow, well met' I was to all and sundry.

I even organised a series of camp concerts* in the little amphitheatre, which had not been used in living memory. I taught my men the basics of the Atellan Fables or pantomimes and they soon picked up the necessary Oscan vocabulary.* The Atellan Fables were the ancient charades of Southern Italy and Sicily. With constant accretions from noted players of the parts, they would become the Commedia dell'arte. Simple slapstick humour, traditional situations, no set texts but all ad lib. My chief part, of course, was Maccus the Clown, but I turned my hand to most parts: Casnar* the old miser; Miles Gloriosus* the braggart captain; Gratian the learned Doctor – my very own name, or one of them, and a role for which Ocean College had prepared me – all these were among my repertoire. The men all took their parts well and we had our audience in stitches. Morgan must really get the credit for this: we used to do the Oscan charades at Casa Sic as kids every Saturnalia, a family tradition which we claimed went back to our supposed ancestor Hadrian.*

The trick worked well. No one in the Mendips took me seriously, and after a time they talked indiscreetly in front of me. Fraud it was, as I knew it must be. False returns, false books, cupellation rigged to give minimal yields, with the slag reworked in secret furnaces to get the real silver for the 'black market'. I couldn't hope to put all this right in a month but I hoped my report to the provincial governor, copied to Maximus, might win me a few 'brownie points' with that hard man.

The fame of our concerts had spread and on our last night I was surprised to see two Roman ladies in the audience. The elder proved to be a cousin of Melania the Holy Terror (Morgan's sister). The younger, to my astonishment, was Elissa. I couldn't wait to get off stage, and still in my actor's togs I rushed to kiss her. 'Elissa, what in Jupiter's name are you doing here?' I asked (very pagan I was that month).

'And why shouldn't I be?' she replied. 'Anyway I could ask the same of you. I thought you were playing the solemn magistrate and now I find—'

'—a clown, a buffoon, a Harlequin,* a trickster,' I broke in. 'How do you like me?'

'I like you very much indeed,' she said after a tiny pause, the while fixing me full in the eye in a way that made all sorts of things start to happen to me; blushing was the least of my problems. Elissa was intoxicating, as I had found earlier. Was I to be my brother's keeper?* So we wound down the show and the ladies took me off to their chariot for a picnic supper. 'May I introduce my brother-in-law Luke,' said Elissa. 'Luke, this is my hostess Anicia Faltonia Proba. I am staying at her Villa at Wells,* fifteen miles away. She owns half of Britain.'

'And probably half the Empire too,' I said as I gallantly kissed the elder lady's hand. So there were explanations, and we parted with plans for me to visit them at Wells the next day.

I was in a bit of a turmoil that night. Elissa and JJ see-sawed in my dreams. When I awoke my mind was made up. JJ was a good brother to me; I would be a good brother to him. Elissa was my sister-in-law. Just that. The boy has nice instincts. Ambrose, are you proud of me?

The next day was one of the happiest of my life. The sun blazed down on the green marshes dotted with isolated knolls as I pricked my way down to Wells. Faltonia's three sons* were at home to receive me, and insisted that we join them in a tour of the farms. They did indeed own most of the country from the Mendips to the Estuary* (Bristol Channel) and very well they farmed those lands. Their names were Olybrius Hermogenianus, Anicius Probinus and Faltonius Petronius; the eldest two about my age, Faltonius a little younger.* My first commission as a poet, in 395, would be to write the Consular eulogy for the first two. St Faltonius Benedict, who we shall come up with in Book VIII, was their maternal uncle.

Over a picnic lunch – we Romans love picnics – Faltonia was able to fill me in on the latest events in the wider world. First, Maximus and JJ were having a successful campaign through the Great Glen (Strathmore), and hoped to teach the Picts their place. On their return they planned to sweep across Galloway. Rumour had it that they wouldn't stop there with the Atecotti* but would carry on and do a 'show of force' among the Scots of the Western Island.

Rome was all abuzz. Gratian, on an infrequent visit there, had removed the famous Statue of Victory from the Senate House as a pagan idol. Symmachus, representing the pagan conservatives in the Senate, had pleaded for its return and had locked horns with Ambrose, who needless to say had won the argument. But the Senate was still smouldering, and Gratian was glad to get back to his Fontainebleau shoot.

What about Justina the Ambitious? Well, she'd kept her head down while Gratian was there. No good playing rival Augusta to the Senior Augustus with Ambrose breathing down both their necks. But Milan was uneasy about Justina; she had enrolled a bodyguard for herself and young Valentinian, made up exclusively of tame Vizi-Goths. If you're not a Goth and an Arian you're nobody. The Senate didn't like Goths, regarding them as barbarians; Ambrose didn't like Goths because they were Arians; and behind the scenes Merobaudes the ruthless Fleming towered over the whole of the West as *Magister Utriusque Militum in Praesentalis Occidentalis* (Celerinus' opposite number). That was the real threat. The overmighty subject.

After our picnic we wended our way home along the foot of the hills and paused to quench our thirst at a beautiful fountain which gushed out at the foot of a single isolated knoll (the highest around) of a haunting and enigmatic shape. This was Glastonbury Tor. There was a cemetery nearby for the whole area, with a considerable Christian cultus, and consequently some resident clergy. The area was ringed with villas and the road ran through on a causeway. One day I'll rebuild its bridge.

I must say a word here about cemeteries. Since Constantine the Great we Romans have returned to burial – the Christians at least – as against cremation. Now, the then Bishop of Rome, Damasus, after wading breast-high through corpses to win St Peter's chair, had turned out to be a relatively unassuming and pious prelate. Too sensible, to try to pull rank on the 'Pope' of Trans-Padine Italy and Cis-Alpine Gaul (Ambrose), he had occupied himself with opening up and clearing up the catacombs, embellishing them with rather touching poems of his own composition.

A hundred years earlier, Pope Felix had decreed that regular Masses should be said over the bones of the martyrs, and this had been gradually turned arsy-versy to mean that martyrs' bones were essential to a proper Mass. Peering into the future, I descry the catacombs of London with therein the solemn warning 'Dogs *must* be carried on the escalator'. What if you have no dog, no martyr? Damasus was a match for this. A cornucopia of officially warranted relics poured from the catacombs of Rome and elsewhere to put the altars of the Western Empire on a proper footing – all Christian, some even genuine.

Cemeteries were therefore venerable, guarded, regularly served with the sacred rites by regular clergy (what the Celts will call a *clas*). This was just such a cemetery.* We shall come up with some others in due course.

On our amble home in the setting sunshine Elissa made me a proposition; or maybe she announced a decision. I had told her that my tour of inspection of my mining fief would lead me northwards, always through the hill country, to Caledonia where I might well meet up with Maximus, or at least JJ. Elissa said she would come with me. Things move so fast. I tried some gentle demurs about 'a girl in her condition' but it was no good; she was all too plainly in excellent shape and intended to remain so. She said she loved the outdoor life and 'roughing it', having been brought up by Justina at the Casa Belgica* in the forests of the Ardennes. So that was that. You didn't argue the toss with Elissa, as others are to discover.

In the 'Forest of Arden' you will expect to find Robin Hood, Will Scarlet, Friar Tuck and Little John; also most of the characters in *As You Like It*; and you will not be disappointed. Just follow along with me to Brünnhilde's rock and see who turns up!

So started my chaste partnership around the mining camps of the West. Wales was our first port of call, for I knew that Maximus would be keen on Britain's only gold mine, Dolaucothi* near Llandovery – since named after me. There was ample water here for ore-washing, but there were drainage problems too. Deep mining. The gangue was very hard to separate, and I could see I would have to teach them a few Nubian tricks. If I could only introduce the amalgamation process here, we should at least double the yield; but where to find the cinnabar? Then northwards through Wales, my prospector's eye seeing new lodes everywhere I looked in the mountains. I was going to be as rich as Croesus, after giving Rome her proper share of course, richer even than Lydian Gygēs who won the 'Ring'.*

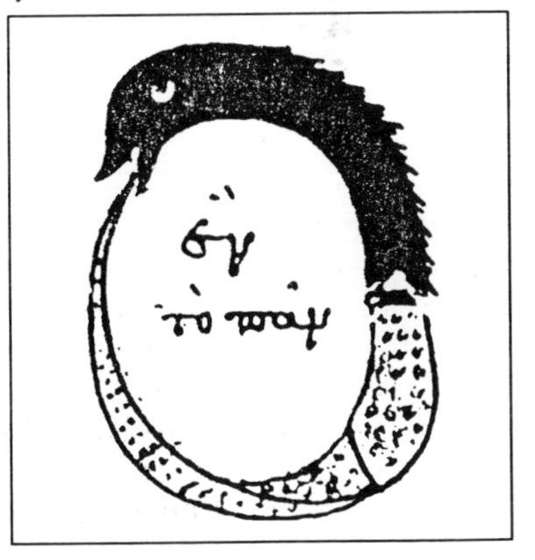

**Figure 12**

Ouroboros, the Nibelung Ring, from the author's facsimile copy of the *Liber Gradalis*

Maybe I was going to be 'Ædonius Pluto', King of the Underworld. In future times his true name, Ædonius, will be exchanged for his epithet '*Ploutos*', 'rich', not so in my day. This name really stuck to me, and would long survive in 'Scotland' (i.e. Ireland) and North Britain as 'Aidan' (variously spelt), even shortened, via AEd to Ed (as in Ed-ward). Ædonius the rich,* that's me. The next Book sees me cutting this, my very own name, in Ogham.

Slogging up to North Wales across the mountains (*trans montes*, i.e. 'Trawsfynydd'), we spent a few nights at Tomen-y-Mur where the XXth Legion had a mountain-warfare training school. Elissa and I were the toast of the camp with our performance as Punch and Judy in the camp theatre, and she quickly picked up the Oscan style of slapstick. What a trooper that girl was.

As we passed the Snowdon massif I could tell we were now in copper country, and not only by the name. Snowdon, the *Mons Eryri*, has been assumed to take its name from the Welsh *Eryr*, an eagle – all too common in the mountains. But *Eru* has meant 'copper' ever since the Tower of Babel (specifically in Kassite* – however did they get here?).

At Segontium we got baths again, and I sent off another interim report, and thought of lovelorn Maximus asking Uncle Icarus (Eudaf Hen*) for Helena's hand. On to Anglesey, thence by boat to the Isle of Man where there were some good mines, including the Cadmian earth (zinc) which is always in short supply for making brass. On by boat to Cumbrian Lowther. (Lowther takes its name from Lead in all the Teutonic languages. A caution here; Lothian district on the Firth of Forth got its name from Maximus, (as Amlawdd the First, 'guletic',* and not from lead.) Here I insisted that Elissa and I should part ways. Winter was coming into sight, and I was heading for the military zone where law and order would be uncertain. Not the right scene for a woman in late pregnancy. I dispatched her firmly, with a couple of policemen as escort, to join Helena at York. As it turned out Helena had followed Maximus to Caledonia, so, Elissa being Elissa, she naturally followed her. For my part, I crossed Hadrian's Wall and the Solway and was soon back in my element in the lead mines of Nithsdale and the Strathclyde Lowthers. It was said that gold had been panned in the Upper Clyde, and I wondered if I could trace the fault North and South from Dolaucothi. That *would* make me rich.

Army uniform for this country and arms at the ready. The tribesmen seemed sulky, even hostile. The mines had a few forgotten military units but did not seem to be being worked at all. The *Procuratores Montium** (as *Procurator Metallorum* I was their boss) grumbled that they couldn't get labour to work the pits, and couldn't have paid them if they had them. Oh for some slaves! What we needed were some prisoners-of-war. Maybe JJ would come up with some Picts to help me out. In due course, by now much less encouraged by my task, I found my way to Kil*patrick* and the Antonine Wall. Here I sought some news of Maximus and JJ and what I was to hear put me in good spirits. Andragath and JJ had had a hugely successful campaign in Albany. They had pushed right up to the Moray Firth* in the steps of Agricola I and Severus, with only one pitched battle. The latter, like that of the Mons Graupius, had led the Northern Picts or *Taifali* to make an enthusiastic treaty of peace; the news that the terrible boar of the XXth was on their tails again, having twice before proved irresistible, had demoralised them. So Maximus had gained what I needed: slaves and prisoners of war.

The army was in winter quarters up and down Albany – some back at the Antonine Wall – and Maximus himself was ensconced at Stirling (*Medionemeton**) where Theodosius had once had a camp (Cambuskenneth, Campus 'Cunedda'*).

At Stirling I rejoined Maximus, and found JJ there too. He was thrilled to see me. He had filled out yet more, 'stuffed with Scots porridge' as Jerome would write of him thirty years on, and his naturally pink complexion had been distinctly reddened by the rigours of camp life, or maybe by too much 'Caledonian wine' or Pictish beer – the best and strongest in the Empire. Whiskey would come soon, as we shall see; but not yet. On mess nights the regimental silver was filled with filthy imported wine. North of the Border, 'Beer is Best'. I was a little anxious about how to broach to JJ the notion that for the last six months I had been sharing a tent with his wife, but he had already heard all my news from Elissa herself and knew I was a dependable brother. She had come up to Stirling, but was now back with Helena in Bernicia, South of the Antonine Wall, supposedly on her way back to York. JJ had been promised paternity leave when the time came, but just now he seemed to have become Vicar's secretary, Maximus' left-hand man. His sword had cut no flesh, but his styli had cut an awful lot of wax.

Maximus was in genial mood until I gave my report. 'Let's see,' he said, frowning. 'Sounds as if the most you're going to be able to offer me, even with the Strathclyde mines worked up again, is a 25% increase in revenue. And I need more. Much more. 50% minimum. 100% if I am to fulfil my plans and achieve my destiny.'

'What's that, Sir?' I stammered, sensing that he was in the mood to talk.

'You wouldn't have heard this yet, boy, where you've been. But destiny calls me nearer to the heart of the Empire. It really won't do, a Barbarian like Merobaudes ruling the West. Gratian divides his time between hunting and sodomy; Ambrose can't pull his strings any more. Justina flaunts her Vizi-Goths and her Arianism in Milan. The Senate is worried stiff. Look at this letter I've had from Symmachus.' He pulled a tablet out of his reading desk. It read: '*Dilectissimus Maximianus frater*', on the next Kalends of January Field Marshal Count Merobaudes mounts the steps of the Capitol for the second time. The third time he will mount as King of the Romans unless... Remember March, the Ides of March* remember. The Senate back you; and, I think, Theodosius. Ever, your loving Brutus.' 'There lies my destiny, boy, and Rome's. And Symmachus is an honourable man, though I know neither he nor the Senate love me. Effete cackling pagans most of them. But I *am*

Great Constantine's grandson* – you didn't know that, did you? – reared in secret and obscurity perhaps to this great end. Twice Praetorian of Gaul, the common people once loved me there. Merobaudes shall die. Gratian shall die. Justina shall flee. *In hoc signo vinco.*' Here to my embarrassment he pulled a crucifix from under his tunic and kissed it savagely. Here we go again, I thought: 'the sword of the Lord and of Gideon'. Where did I stand this time? Time to distance myself, I thought, before I got drawn too far into conspiracy – maybe JJ's there already. But Maximus had not quite finished with me.

'So now you know why I need silver and why I need gold. I was impressed by your reports. Rome's future rests with you perhaps not less than me. Go, win me gold, boy. What about the Western Island? Did not Hercules find the golden apples there? It's all your province, you know. See, I will give you extra powers so that in the Western Isle you can command, and in Britain requisition men and supplies. I appoint you Vice-Cor*rector* Consularis of the Valentias; young Agricola shall write you the scrip today. Now be off. Do not dare fail me, and tell no one what I have told you today if you value your life.'

I didn't blush this time, as I saluted and left the room; JJ said I was white as a sheet. 'Had a nice chat with the Boss?' he said.

'Yes, thanks, I think I'll just go for a stroll.' I mean, it's all very well playing Ædonius the rich, Goldilocks with the Midas touch, if it's just a game. But this was the biggest game I'd ever played in. And I could tell no one.

Heigh ho, and again Heigh ho.

# BOOK VII

## *Potiphar's Wife (AD382–388)*

When I got back to the Mess JJ was waiting for me with a big flagon of beer and two goblets. 'Cheers,' he said, 'I think we both need a drink.' We drank for a while in glum silence. JJ was the first to speak. 'So now you know too,' he said. I nodded. There wasn't anything more to say. 'Oh well, I'd better go and write your Letter of Appointment. Congratulations.'

'Thanks a lot.'

Back to work. Snakes and ladders. I needed to get a confidential letter about sources of cinnabar off to Uncle Theo in Rome. At this time he was *Comes Sacrarum Largitionum* (Chancellor of the Exchequer). As officer in charge of the currency, all the 'noble metals' pertained to him. Mercury (from cinnabar) was his special care not only for its uses in gold extraction but also as an essential ingredient of the production of the silvered-bronze coinage by the wet-washing process.

We remained at Stirling for the Saturnalia, recently renamed Christmas (as a 'Leo', 25 December was already very special to me as the birthday of Mithras). So we feasted and exchanged gifts. Helena and Elissa were at *Camelon* (Falkirk). In the New Year Maximus returned to London with JJ, while Helena and Elissa were to move on to York until the baby was born. Andragath led a last show of strength across Galloway and into Ulster, and I followed in his train and would remain on the Western Island for at least a year.

Elissa talked Helena into making a leisurely round southwards while the hunting season was still on, as she was insistent she could still shoot from a chariot if the game was driven. A crackshot with bow and arrow was Elissa, a veritable Diana or Pentheselea.* That's how Elissa came to have her nasty accident at 'Dun Peredur' (Traprain Law) when her chariot went over a cliff and she took a frightening spill. She was taken by litter and boat across the Firth to Culross where one of Dad's Whithorn monks, Servanus* of Loch Leven, ran a mission hospital. There on 13 January AD382 Helena helped him to deliver my little nephew (Owain) *Eugenius Pompeius*. He was promptly christened John, in case he did not live; moreover, in true Pictish style, Servanus insisted on tattooing* a cross on his shoulder, just like that which I foresee the Anglo-Danish trouvères will discover on the right shoulder of their hero Havelock the Dane: and this memory will be exact, as you will see in Book VIII.

In due course mother and son were moved to the army hospital at *Trimontium* (Melrose*), and Helena left her there on the clear understanding that she would follow her back to London in the Spring. I got wind of all this, via the mail, while I was still in Galloway and hastened to visit her in hospital. I found a very fit couple. Elissa had got her figure back, and the baby was absolutely his father's son. Hair a bit more foxy* than JJ's and with his pink complexion, but already showing incipient freckles. A real Aelian. He looked as if he was going to be a big boy. Maybe he'd even be an Augustus one day.*

Elissa was in a dangerous mood. She knew that JJ faced more campaigning (though she didn't know where, as I did). She knew, too, that she was to be left behind. Endless backgammon and gossiping among the memsahibs. She listened with panting attention as I described my new command and prospects. She knew me better than she knew JJ, and up to a point I knew her. JJ should be at her side if he hoped to hold on to her. Did we part under a misapprehension? Something in her farewell kiss told me no. It was all too like Joseph and Potiphar in the Bible.

I duly crossed over to Hibernia Julia, or Ulster as it would be called, where Northern headquarters had been established by the 'three Collas'* at Emain (Armagh) in Oriel (itself a corruption from Agricola). The island showed marked signs of Romanisation since I was there with Dad twelve years before. The camp had a proper *Principium* with the standards in the chapel – notably, the Red Hand* of the 1st Maniple of the good old XXth *Valeria Victrix*; Dad had left them here as the nucleus of Rome in Ireland. *Numeri* of other units had been added and withdrawn from time to time, and now the XXth themselves were to go with Andragath, leaving control of the country to me and the *Honoriani*, plus some enlisted N. Pictish prisoners of war (*Taifali*),* whom I hoped to knock into shape.

Rome had not been idle in Hibernia. First had come the surveyors to do a triangulation, the base line being from Mount Leinster in the South, westwards to Carrantuohill* (named, like Inchtuthill, after Dad) in the South-West, the highest peak of Macgillycuddy's Reeks; then northwards to the *Boreum* Promontory,* Malin Head (the tip of Inish*owen*) – the latter a splendid line. Then an initial network of military roads had been commenced, but progress was slow with mainly local labour no keener to work, even under the lash, than Galgacus' men under the first Agricola. ('Galgacus' sounds a good Pictish name to me – with Kassite* overtones?). Trees had to be felled by thousands to make corduroy (Irish *Ceis*, 'a wattled causeway') because of the wet hillside and innumerable bogs. One of our roads ran NNE from Kesh (note the name) on Lough Erne to Grianan Ailech; I may give you clues to some of the others if time permits. At all events, by now one could get about quite fast to the main centres of population.* (Claudius Ptolemaeus, the second century AD geographer is your best guide to these; oddly, he leaves out – perhaps as too well known – Limerick, the place of the *Limen* or Royal Harbour.)

Grandad Theo 'Cunedda' had found Ireland basically divided into a Northern and a Southern kingdom* with a No Man's Land in the middle called Meath. Each had its capital of sorts. Dad had charge of the Northern Kingdom (Conn's half), and Uncle Ted oversaw the Southern Kingdom (Muig's half*). They had set up a central garrison on the hill of the '*Uisneagh*' (Theodosiani) in Meath. The surveyors told me that the potentially ore-bearing mountains were all on the perimeter of the island. So, as in Cornwall, I planned to make a quick tour clockwise, starting with the gold areas of the Wicklow Mountains. Andragath's army marched ahead of me to the South (*Decumanus Pars*, whence the *Deisi**) and returned to Britain from *Menapia* (Wexford) carrying with them yet another harvest of slaves. I haven't called them prisoners of war because they proved quite unsuitable for recruitment into the army and Andragath ended up dumping them disconsolately in *Menevia* (Pembroke) where they remained and settled. They will be my subjects again when I finish my present task.

In April 383 Andragath and his army returned to Maximus in London, leaving me panning the Avoca River as though my life depended on it. The 'seeds of gold' (*χρισανθι*) were what I was after winning, and 'Chrysanthus' (Klingsor) was the name my fellow prospectors soon gave me.

The first news I had from Britain came in June by very special messenger. You've guessed of course. It was Elissa, plus baby John. Maximus had duly raised the flag of rebellion in May and taken almost all Britain's armies with him to the Rhine, where he hoped to win over the XXXth Legion at Xanten. He'd taken the XXth Legion with him, never to return. Only one Legion remained in Britain, the IInd Augusta, and Maximus had moved them from Caerleon to Richborough in case he needed them. JJ was with him; if Merobaudes was the man I thought he was, I would never see either of them again.

But Elissa – 'Ye Gods, what a torso!' – was with me. Was this an abduction, or a seduction? The *Vita Gildae* (*Life of Gildas* – that's me) will put the blame firmly on Maelwas* (Vasso the Great – that's me again), and say I carried her off to Glastonbury. So I did, and others in their turn would carry her off to various destinations. All I knew at the time was that she was with me and I was glad of it. It seemed that fate pulls both ways. By her own choice – and you didn't argue with Elissa's choice – Elissa was mine now, *my* very own Polar Bear, *my* Guinevere, *my* Snow White, *my* love. And baby John would not want for care or love from me; he was *my* little 'kid', *my* 'pup', *my* 'Cu'-Chulain (Scolan's 'hound').*

Proprieties apart, work goes on: Emperors come and go but the machine still turns. Maximus would by now have appointed his Vicar-successor, and if he lost his gamble, Gratian the true Augustus would appoint another. I still had a boss and a task. Maybe I would leave my new name Ædonius, writ in Ogham, on an island in a Northern lough?* It remained to be seen what Dido (Elissa) and Ædonius could make of Ireland.

The sad answer, after ten months panning, hiking and prospecting, was: 'very little'. It was April 384 and together we had climbed every hill in Ireland, tapped at every possible vein, waded and panned every stream, and were back in the North at what would be called Grianan Ailech,* the great hill-fort west of Londonderry. Elissa was again heavily pregnant – all my own work – and happy as a lioness.

**Figure 13**

Magnus Maximus as Augustus

© Trustees of the British Museum

We had got back to civilisation to find all my fears for JJ and Maximus belied. Official despatches confirmed that Maximus was the new Western Augustus, stationed at Trier and recognised by Uncle Ted. Army and civilians alike had flocked to welcome their former Prefect. Merobaudes had fled. Gratian was dead (not a pretty tale*). Justina and young Valentinian were keeping a very low profile in Milan. And I had a new Vicar, Constantianus* – a kinsman, needless to say. Constantianus survived the impending Maximus crash to become Praetorian Prefect of Gaul in 389; his son Constantius III is to play a baleful part in my future life and lovelife (but all this is yet to come). I felt I should make my report to the Vicar on my Irish constituency promptly. In economic terms it would make sad reading. **'Not worth conquering; not worth retaining.** Domitian was right.'* The military argument remained as Agricola I had put it: 'the *Pax Britannica* should be ringed with Roman steel'.

Well, now it was, and the army had found new recruiting grounds. At the very least, Hibernia would give the world mercenaries. But not only mercenaries, glorious as their exploits would be; I foresaw Saints streaming out of Ireland to evangelise the barbarians all over Europe, and maybe I would have a part in promoting this.

Since my role as Chrysanthus seemed to have run into the sand, I settled down to do justice for the remainder of my tour to my role as governor (vice-rector). Findracht, the Hibernians now call me 'the blond Rector'. Yes, I would be St Ind*racht*,* and I would indeed be buried initially at Glastonbury. I would also be confused with Finn Mac Cool.*

Day by day there was much recruiting and training of the Atecotti, Scotti and Taifali to be carried on, all now answerable to me. In Dad's day 'Alban's Horse', his Irish auxiliaries, had consisted of three troops, the *Honoriani Primani,* who would be called the 'pascentii' from their white tabards, signifying their bodyguard duties; the *Theodosiani Secundani*, Uncle Ted's mob, who had green pennants; and the *Marciani*, who had red pennants.* (The Romancers will tell of knights fighting in 'tournaments' thrice changing the colour of their armour, in a confused recollection of their hero charging with each troop in turn under its variously coloured pennant.)

Instead of infantry standards, Cavalry had these spendid Dragon pennants, vividly described by Vegetius. They were tubular with open jaws, and on the move they inflated, writhed, and even made quite a fearful roaring noise in a charge. The names of two of these troops of '*Fenians*' will be long remembered in Ireland as the Clan 'Baskin' (from the 'Pascentii') and the clan 'Morna'(from the *Marciani*). Now, with our new recruits, we could split them into *Seniores* and *Juniores*, largely under the command of Ocean College alumni. In vulgar parlance *any* cavalry commander was called **the pendragon**, or 'Chief Dragoon'.

All the resulting exercises and training marches gave good backing to my attempts to establish a Romanised civil government. The South, which we had previously neglected, was my prime interest, and I moved the old tribal capital of Rathmore* in Kerry to Cashel, where I commenced holding Petty Sessions. Meanwhile Elissa had given birth to our little daughter '*Nitonia*' (from her '*snow white*' mother) Marcella Julia Gratiana (Gudrun). She would always be best known by her pet name ***Ursula***, though she would acquire many others.* She was a dear little baby; her auburn hair was proof that I too have Aelian blood. Quite soon Elissa was following me around in a chariot together with her two cubs; 'The great Queen', the Irishmen called her (the Mor-rigan*). In the future she will be hopelessly confused with dear old Morgan.

It was Elissa, however, who was intended as the Romance 'Morgan la Fée', and I pause to explain why. 'La Fée' is Latin '*Fata*', Greek 'Μοιρα'. The Greek 'Moirae' (Fates or Norns) had sister-messengers called 'Κηρης' to communicate their decisions. These will be remembered by the Teutons as Wal-keres, 'fate informers', or 'Walküre'.

Elissa/Brünnhilde was the archetypal Valkyrie. Was Tacitus right when he said the Teutons knew Greek? And was Elissa as ineluctable as Fate herself? We shall see. There is plenty of Irish myth about Elissa as Queen (Mavis), Médbh or Máb.* Whereas I, of course, am *Erek* the pocket Hercules', the Romancers' 'little King'.*

So passed 384 and in the Spring of 385 the reliable military machine brought me a Leave Warrant and Notice of Posting. Maximus can't have been too thrilled by my performance as a temporary acting unpaid Rector. It was back to planned career development for this regular soldier, and a fighting Tribunate in the East. Hurrah. But what was I to do with Elissa? She didn't want to face JJ any more than I did, but plainly she couldn't accompany me on this one. Besides, two infants deserve a mother's care. Maybe I could park her with Faltonia, the kind hostess of the Mendips; after all, what had happened was partly her fault. So that's where we spent our leave, and in June 385 I left Glastonbury for Constantinople to report for my new duties. Maybe I would meet up with Goneryl and Regan again.

I decided to give Trier a wide berth – I still had a conscience – and made my way by the Western crossing to the Unellian Chersonese* (Cherbourg/Cotentin), Paris and Lyons, *en route* for Milan where I badly needed to see Ambrose. Thereafter I could travel by the Flaminia, Appia, and across the Adriatic for the Via Egnatia to New Rome, which would give me an idea of the country I might have to fight in.

By early August I was in sweltering Milan. Uncle Satyrus was away, so I claimed my right to put up at the clergy house and, at least over frugal meals, Ambrose found time to talk to me. A few affectionate family enquiries brought the whole tale tumbling out.

'But are you sorry, Luke?' he asked, looking balefully at me. 'After all you were best man at JJ's wedding, as I well remember.'

'No, Father,' I stammered, 'I can't honestly say I'm sorry. I'm not particularly proud either. Like Joseph with Potiphar's wife I could blame it all on Elissa, but I should be even less proud of that.'

'Well, if you're not sorry, I can't let you off the hook,' said Ambrose. 'You admit you've broken the Tenth Commandment, if you know what that is. All I can say is "go your way and sin no more". You're still very young, only twenty-four, and have much to learn. At least you're honest. That'll help.'

So Ambrose, bless him, did not directly condemn me; and we had a happy week together. He had much news to give me. He had excommunicated Grandad Max for Gratian's murder ('wholly unnecessary and unjustifiable'), for his refusal to let Justina have her stepson's body for burial ('petty'), and for executing Priscillian and four other Spanish clergy for heresy ('shall the Church turn persecutor and drag the misguided to Christ with the sword? Never, and again never'). The mischief, as so often, had started with that awful old charlatan Heron* who had fooled even Ambrose four years previously. In fairness, Priscillian's enemies had really got under Maximus' guard by charging the Priscillians with *magical* practices. You'll remember Maximus and the 'magic' persecutions in Book II. Talk about red rags to a bull. Nevertheless Ambrose had rebuked Maximus sternly, and so had dear old Martin who had toiled from Tours to Trier to make his – alas futile – protest.*

What else? Well, Uncle Icarus had been promoted again, to become Praetorian of the Orient. Uncle Heliodorus had taken one of Jerome's nastier suggestions* all too literally and had castrated himself, before becoming Novatian (Puritan) Bishop of New Rome. Damasus was dead, and his successor had relieved Rome of Jerome's presence by shunting him and the faithful Paula off to Bethlehem to do the first-ever translation of the Old Testament direct from Hebrew, as opposed to the Septuagint.* But, the main excitement was Ambrose's tussle with Justina which had provoked riots that very Easter. Justina had actually ringed the Basilica Thecla* with soldiers (Goths of course) while the services were on, imprisoning the congregation for more than twenty-four hours. Ambrose had opposed swords with psalms, keeping up the spirits of his beleaguered flock with community singing. The Goths, who are good-hearted fellows, had ended by joining in too, and Justina had to admit temporary defeat. But she was still plotting and smouldering down in her Palace, and we hadn't heard the last of her.

I learned that I had a new cousin currently in Milan, one Augustine (*Augustinus*) (see App. 6), a young lawyer from Africa. He did the Consular Panegyric for Genobaudes (Morgan's second husband, the rather nicer younger brother of Merobaudes) that year. Quite a man with his pen, Augustine, by all accounts. Not yet a Christian, he had an exceptionally pious mother, an illegitimate son by an earlier concubine, a fiancée, and yet another concubine, all in tow, and was groping not unnaturally for spiritual guidance and light. Ambrose would be good for him; he had steadied me down quite a bit that week. Maybe I'd be a Christian soldier yet?

So we parted, and I ploughed my way East to Constantinople where I arrived at the end of August. My first visit to New Rome. Beautiful but sinister. Eunuchs were everywhere, like toadstools. Serena (I'll drop the Goneryl bit for the time being) received me joyfully. Her husband Stilicho was on a prestigious diplomatic mission to Persia. I was instructed to inscribe my name in the Palace visitors' book, but Serena warned me that that was about as near as I was likely to get to seeing Uncle Ted. Flaccilla had a new son, Honorius II (after 'Glorious Dad'), who would be Augustus one day. Serena had two girls, and had just had a baby boy, like me called Eucherius after Uncle Icarus, so her hands were full. Stilicho's ambitions to win his Eucherius the purple would almost cost him his life, but for a deft *clericatus.** He ended up as Bishop of Lyons (but we shall come to that in Book XIV.) Ginger (Regan) was in Constantinople too, and I would meet her in due course, and would probably meet her husband Alaric when I began campaigning.

One thing Serena insisted I do as soon as possible was to matriculate myself at the Eastern Tabularium as a member by birth of the senatorial class. In the West I was a '*Vir Clarissimus*', often, loosely, a '*consularis*', although strictly the latter meant only those Senators who had received a 'Writ of Summons'

– whence the *Patres 'Conscripti'*. Now I could, and would, call myself a '*Gerontius*' too (slang Greek for Senator). 'Always keep your options open,' said Serena. 'We Graeco-Romans never know which of the Eagle's heads we may need to serve – I mean, look at me. And now you're going soldiering in Thrace. It's still one Empire for the likes of us.'

I had made my number with the local *Auxiliae Palatinae*, received my new Tribune's commission at the Praetorium, and was soon off to take command of my Mixed Cohort – very mixed as it turned out – in furthest Thrace, right on the Danube at Tomi,* whence Ovid wrote so plaintively. There was always fighting going on there. Promotus was the General commanding, to whom I would report.

So, prickly and unsure of myself, I took personal command of near a thousand cavalry and infantry who did not know me, and we plunged straight into war with the Greuthungi under their King Odotheus. We defeated them soundly, made them lay down their arms and retreat across the Danube. I had intended to be very dashing and show Promotus what he could expect of me, but in the heat of battle it was *my* men who ran. Ye Gods, they turned and fled. Finding myself all alone out in front I had no option but to turn back after them. Oh the shame of it! With hindsight I blame myself entirely. I gave confused orders. They did not know me. We had not trained and marched together. Me playing the hero – showing off, if you like – up front was not leadership. A bad general blames his men. God help me, I did. When we got back to our lines the rest of the Roman army were celebrating the victory. I was bawling out my men in half-forgotten Greek, threatening every kind of punishment: forfeiture of pay, privileges. I pitched particularly heavily into my Gothic cavalry. I really lost my head. My officers were shame-faced and embarrassed, the NCOs near to mutiny. I was young and inexperienced; over-promoted in fact. Word quickly got back to Promotus and the next day I was arrested, suspended from my command, and sent to Theodosius under escort to face court martial.

So the hero of Carrhae, the terror of Hibernia, cooled his heels in a cell in Constantinople, and learnt the oriental cruelty of Byzantine intrigue. Delay was the principal torture. My case never seemed to come up. Even if it was only to give me the biggest roasting of my life I thought Theodosius would at least *see* his nephew. He never did. I wasn't that important. One of Promotus' sons had been assigned to me as defending officer – to his great embarrassment – and he was my only contact with the outside world. He brought me glum news. 'You've really put your foot in it with His Serenity. Just when he's trying his damnedest to make friends of the Goths you go slanging them all ways in the name of Rome, calling them faithless self-seeking cowards and degenerate barbarians. Pray God he doesn't try this case himself.' But he never did. Rumours reached me that he never would; that I should rot out the rest of my life in a Byzantine gaol, untried, unsentenced, unheard. Bitter bitter months.

* * *

Serena was my saviour, though the story is not to my credit. She had heard of my plight, tried even to intercede for me with Theodosius as only she could,* but to no avail. One day a letter from her was smuggled in to me: 'There is no justice in Byzantium, to be awaited or even to be hoped for. Money rules in New Rome, and money has made you free. I have raided Stilicho's coffers, I have sold jewellery, and I have bribed your gaolers. Go at once, your cell is not locked and they will look the other way. Go in the disguise you will find outside the door. Get out of the Eastern Empire. Do not come back to it while Theodosius lives. Destroy this letter. Repay me if you live. Your loving Sister'. And so it was. And so I did, though the debt hung over me for years.

I grew up in that cell in Constantinople. A cocky little bastard I was when I went there. A humbler wiser man slunk through the back streets of Constantinople that night to make his way by his wits back to Elissa – I really didn't know where else to go. How I traversed the Empire as a travelling clown, juggler, conjuror, fire-eater, and in the last resort beggar, would make a book in itself. I was not a criminal, not even an outlaw; but I had no friends, no reputation, and above all *no money*.

I learnt to live as the poor live, and to find them fellow mortals like this once-proud 'Senator'. I worked and played among the Barbarians I had so despised, and all the time I plodded my way steadily Westwards. Sometimes I worked my passage on boats, and learnt the ways of the sea, and it was as a paid crew member that I crossed over to Britain, sailing on a Bordeaux wine trader up the Severn estuary.

By then I was a Christian as I had never been before, for on my journey North through Gaul I had met Paulinus,* a distant relative, in Angers and he had taken me in for a month and befriended me. His story is on record, and you will read it in any good book of the lives of the saints.* Not yet baptised, he had turned his back on his promising career in the Civil Service (he was Governor of Campania) following a personal tragedy, and he and his wife Therasia* were following in the steps of Jesus – and it seemed to me he wasn't far behind his Master. How can you describe conversion? How explain it? It doesn't come from books – I've read them. For me, I caught it from another human being. True, He caught me at a very low ebb – but then He often does. Paulinus showed me, and He won me. It was like a blinding glimpse of the obvious. Now I *knew*, that I would fail and falter and sin and repent again and again, and stumble hopefully ever forward. I was born again, one of the *Columbani*, from the baptismal dove (*colomba*) of John I.32. (The concept of being 'born again ... of the spirit' is in John III.5. There must thus be thousands, millions even, of Christians entitled to be called 'Columba[nus]' – Donegal alone acknowledges ninety-six saints of this name. The name didn't stick too well on me, but would really adhere to my nephew, baby John.)

Paulinus was still four years away from the priesthood, but priest or no, I reckon he absolved me then, yes, and gave me a fresh start. He gave me a little keepsake when we parted, which I have to this day; just a little gold coin, an old Angevin stater.* It was in this new and penitent guise that I returned to Elissa, like Odysseus to Penelope. Elissa, once she had recognised me, took me back as if I had never been away, and the babes chortled at the strange man. She comforted me as only a woman, and a wife, can. Women are great realists. 'Stop whingeing', she said, 'about your failures. I don't love you for your brains or your muscles, nor your hair nor the inches you haven't got, nor your glorious career. I think you're really nicer as you are. Now what about getting a job? Your blessed Jesus says "my Father works and I work". Time you did the same.' That's how in the Spring term of 387 I became first an assistant master, and a year later Headmaster of Ocean College.

It was good to be back in respectable society again, and the Headmaster's house, since burnt by pirates, was most comfortable. My fellow ushers were from Bordeaux University, which is as good as they come, and all the time I was learning as much as I was teaching. The pupils were still the mix I remembered: Roman-Brits, Gauls, Spaniards, Atecotti, Scots, Hibernians. Still '*Mens sana in corpore sano*' – it was good to get back into wrestling again. Elissa was on the way to being a mother once more, and I felt really worthwhile. In class I proudly wore Uncle Heliodorus' robe,* richly embroidered with the Muses of the *Quadrivium* in gold thread, which had been handed down from Headmaster to Headmaster. In all the circumstances I thought it best to take new names for my academic role. To the boys I was *Magister Donatus* (Theodorus in Latin); to the staff I was Aelius Theodorus. One day I'll be remembered as **St Illtyd.***

I was back on Morgan's mailing list, and it was to her I owed such knowledge as I had of what was going on beyond the walls of Academe, for there we spent the next three years, with vacations close at hand in South Wales and Cornwall. There too Elissa bore me twin sons, Aurelianus Maximus and Valerius Genesius (more twins in the family), and a daughter, Constantia Tullia. You will see in time what happened to them. Suffice it for now that Constantia was to become the mother of the famous St. Patrick* – he of the *Epistle to Coroticus* and the *Confession.*

Young John was about of age to start school with us. Long, bony, freckled, with his mop of reddish hair, he looked quite like a 'Molossian',* the famous classical hunting dogs. Ursula was small but tough and vivacious. Elissa was a natural mother and ran the home easily.

News from abroad was not good. First politics. Merobaudes had surfaced again, summoned to Justina's side. Maximus went after him in 387, invading Italy like his grandfather before him. Justina fled to Uncle Ted (recently widowed) at Salonica, bearing with her young Valentinian and his sister Justa Grata Galla, just as nubile and as pretty as Salome. Theodosius greeted Justina with about as much enthusiasm as a rattlesnake; but little Galla was another story. Twenty-five years her senior, haggard and choleric from intemperance, like another Herod Antipas Uncle Ted fell – and fell into bed – and, as a widower and a good Christian Emperor, promptly married the lass.

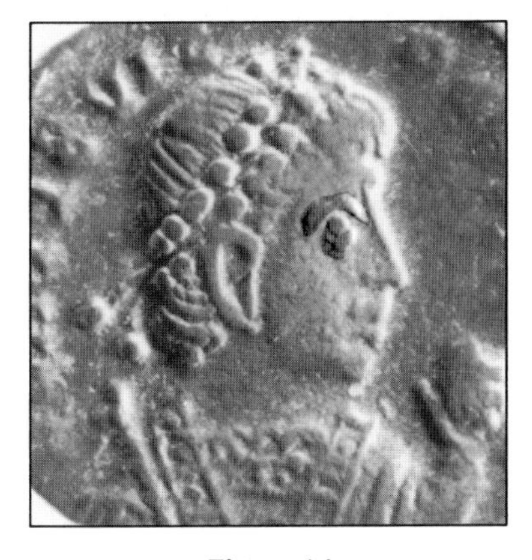

**Figure 14**
Worried Ted eyes Fate, AD388
© Trustees of the British Museum

The price? 'Justina-Herodias' had primed her daughter with the answer: 'Maximus Clement's head on a charger.' So, reluctantly and wearily, the prematurely-aged Despot of the East mobilised his armies to destroy his brother Despot of the West –

Catholic against Catholic,

Augustus against Augustus.

Maximus might well have withstood this ponderous assault, but for Genobaudes (as Morgan told me), for Maximus had managed to catch up with and kill Merobaudes on his way through the Alps. Determined to avenge his brother, Genobaudes had then joined the *maquisards*. Crossing the Rhine to his fellow Franks (Riparian), he had set up an unholy alliance with the Alemans under Marcomer and Sunno – bad precedent this – to attack Maximus' soldier son Victor, whom he had left at Trier as Caesar (admirably propped with generals) to hold Gaul. So when Maximus, after making a benign entry into Rome and receiving a fulsome (and you may think well-earned) eulogy from 'Brutus' Symmachus and the Senate, turned North to Aquileia to defy Theodosius, his heart was torn with fear for his heartland, Gaul, and his heart's joys Helena, his latest wife, and Victor, his eldest son – for Maximus had a heart, whatever they say!

**Figure 15**
Flavius Victor, Max's doomed son
© Trustees of the British Museum

Fooled by successful disinformation from Constantinople, Maximus had sent Andragath with the Adriatic Fleet, based at Classe (the future Ravenna) to await Theodosius' Armada. Not the man to lead his armies in the field in person, he had sent them on patrol under the temporary command of his brother-in-law, Marcellinus 'the born loser',* into Illyricum – the disputed territory. The *political* praefecture stretched from Istria in the Northern Adriatic to the very gates of New Rome. Diocletian, as Eastern Emperor and a Dalmatian by birth, had placed it, together with Pannonia and Noricum, under the Eastern Empire, but Old Rome found this strategically, politically and emotionally unacceptable. On Uncle Ted's death, war became inevitable, as you will see.

To Maximus' dismay Theodosius came overland, and Marcellinus lost yet again. Uncle Ted followed close behind his generals, Promotus and Arbogast the Prussian (my stepfather; see App. 5). Young Stilicho and Alaric were there too, in subordinate commands. Quite a gathering of the clan. Even yet Maximus might have won the day had his morale, and consequently that of his men, been high. He had a strong, well-supplied fortress, and Theodosius' lines of communication were at full stretch; but with Genobaudes' fangs in his back he was a beaten man. His men knew it and deserted. Uncle Ted was in mind to spare the blubbering wretch, but Arbogast knew Justina's mind better, and Maximus was beheaded. Salome had danced too well. Andragath drowned himself from chagrin, on hearing the news, while in Salonica Justina died, all unknowing, in her hour of triumph. It made me think of one of those ghastly family reunions from old Greek Tragedy. Thank God I was not part of it, as I might well have been. Maybe He was looking after me.

Turning to the 'Home' Front, if I can force myself to a wan pun at this sad time, that's how Elissa came to inherit the Casa Belgica (under Justina's will). Valentinian got Sirmione; while lucky Morgan got the '*Villa Simbruina*' at Subiaco and a palace of her own on the Quirinale. She was delighted. I was saddened and shocked. Poor old Maximus. He *was* Elissa's father, and my grandfather. He was to have been the saviour of Old Rome.

Whose turn will it be next, to stand out against the Barbarian ascendancy? Who is there? What happened to JJ? Did he get clear of doomed Aquileia? The next book will tell, when my scribes have had a breather.

Heigh ho.

# BOOK VIII

## *Joseph of Arimathea (AD388–393)*

Did JJ escape from Aquileia? It was nearly two years before a letter from Morgan told me the whole story, and hot-foot on her letter came JJ himself. In view of his truculent mood it was as well that I was prepared – but that must wait its turn. However, I will answer the first question without more ado.

JJ did not have to flee Aquileia because he never went. Crossing over with Maximus to the Rhine in April 383 with the XXth Legion *Valeria Victrix*, they had paused at Xanten to recruit the XXXth Legion *Ulpia Trajana* to their cause, and had then made for Maximus' home ground of Trier, where his old Prefectorial Palace was soon at his disposal. There was a three-month pause, during which he established himself and minted some *solidi.* Then it was on to encounter Gratian at Paris where, in Mèrobaudes' absence in Italy, they won a resounding victory, and Gratian fled to his death. Maximus now moved South on Lyons and over into Spain returning, in the glow of a bloodless victory, via Arles and Lyons to Trier. Maximus was now sitting pretty, with every hope of a purple robe as soon as Uncle Ted at New Rome could be persuaded to bestow it on him.

At this point the Armoricans of Lyonesse II showed their independent spirit, not for the first or last time, with an outbreak of general 'bacaudism'.* Maximus had returned the XXXth Legion to its duties as guardians of the Rhine; it remained for him to send the XXth to semi-permanent posting in what would, partly in their memory, be called 'Brittany'. These thoroughly British legionaries were of course *limitani,* standing Frontier Garrisons, accustomed to have their wives and families with them, to farm smallholdings, and to breed up sons to follow them in the legion. They feared for their families' safety if left to the tender mercies of the Picts and the Scots. Perish the thought that the good old XXth should ever mutiny; nevertheless they were not happy, and Maximus agreed that the Legionary Depot and all the families should be permanently relocated from Britain to Gaul. It was to JJ that Maximus delegated this massive and somewhat tedious administrative task, for which he will be remembered by Welsh legend as 'Conan Meriadoc',* Constantine of the legions.

For the next two years JJ was busy with his task, returning to Trier in late 385 to resume his duties as Maximus' left-hand man and to win that hard man's solid gratitude. Soon he was Count and *Magister Epistolae*.*

In 387 came the news that Barbarians were pressing on the Pannonian frontier (Hungary), and that Merobaudes, who had been all this time with Justina and young Valentinian in Milan, had taken what troops he could muster off to the fight with him. Here was the chance Maximus had been awaiting: 'the Ides of March remember'; '*in hoc signo vinces*'. Maximus marched on Milan, whence Justina had hurriedly fled, and on to Rome to be received rapturously by the Senate; JJ went with him, wax tablets ever at the ready.

But JJ did not accompany Maximus to Aquileia and death the following year: instead, Maximus had left him behind in Rome on a well-earned leave. Five years of life at the top, of daily attendance on an Augustus, had narrowed his character and coarsened his frame. Ambition, excitement, success and power had driven softer thoughts, for a time, from his mind. I don't think he even missed Elissa,* any more than Aeneas, 'Man of Bronze', missed Dido. He and Maximus were going to save the Western Empire. True, his encounters with Ambrose and with Martin on their fruitless embassies had stirred JJ's conscience for a while, but affairs of state loomed larger. Maximus, (his father-in-law and his grandfather), was the keeper of JJ's soul.

And suddenly Maximus was dead, and Uncle Ted, like an avenging Fury, was with Ambrose in Milan. The time had come for a major rethink. At this time JJ was lucky to fall in with cousin Augustine, also in Rome, baptised the previous Easter by Ambrose, and still grieving for his mother Monica. Many nights they spent together in the taverns of Trastevere where the Jews resort, probing the mysteries of the Universe between them over a flagon or more of wine – but it was JJ who drank the deeper. Augustine soon recognised that JJ had a drink problem – had not his mother Monica anxiously counselled him on this from her own experience? He pressed on JJ the idea of a temporary retreat from the world, a brief monasticism* such as he himself had found so rewarding, and commended him to Faltonius Benedictus* – Saint Benedict as he would be known (brother of Faltonia Proba of Book VI, and thus kin to the whole rich Anician gens) – and the little community of hermits who had gathered around his grotto above Subiaco on the Anio in the 25 years since he fled there as a disturbed teenager from his posh home in Trastevere.

'Get out of Rome,' urged Augustine: 'Theodosius will soon be here, and you *were* on the wrong side. Moreover, you're a complete mess, a failure as a Christian, as a husband, as a citizen. Go and look for Jesus among the rocks of Subiaco, and maybe He'll show you what He wants of you. He's told me to go back to Africa and dedicate my intellect, my pen, and my life to His service, and that's what I'm going to do.' So Augustine went off to Hippo, leaving JJ some little pamphlets he had already written that year as a precocious Christian (two on morals and sexuality, and one on Free Will* which was to have far-reaching consequences). In his turn JJ detached himself from the fleshpots of Auntie's palace on the Aventine and headed forty miles up the Tiber and the Anio* to try his vocation as a monk, or at least to 'dry out'.

Of their life around the Sagro Speco (the Sacred Cave) you will be able to read in the life of St Benedict written by his own descendant, St Gregory the Great, also of the Anician gens. Among the novices there, JJ found a young cousin, just sixteen, called Aurelius Placidus, later, for his staunch orthodoxy, to be dubbed *Ευσταθιος* (St Eustace).

'Little Benedict' was a great and holy darling, and he soon recognised JJ's notable administrative powers by making him Abbot-coadjutor. The monks called JJ 'Big Benedict' (Benedictus Majorus), or just 'Maurus', to distinguish the two men (and the 'Benedict' bit was to stick with him as Brân Bendigaid* in the memories of my fellow Cambrians). The name 'Brân' results from an antiquarian (and incorrect) restoration of 'Vrian', and in Roman epigraphy V and U are so often the same. The name you therefore seek is **Urion**, to be mis-remembered by the Welsh bards as 'Urien Reget', who was in fact JJ's son John. The ancient Greeks knew 'Urion' as 'Orion the Giant', and Ovid tells a messy onomastic tale of Orion's conception from the 'urine' of three separate gods. The Irish would come to call him 'Brian(*t*)'. I called him JJ. Orion's final kingdom was *Rhegium* of **Apulia** (and Messina*). That's why the Welsh bards would call JJ '**Pwyll**'. So much for the 'Celtic' kingdom of 'Reget' in Cumberland. Never was!

Thus passed JJ's first year of 'work and prayer' under St Benedict's wise and homely rule. Chastity, mental as well as physical, was very much a part of this, and here Morgan really upset the applecart. I said at the end of the last Book that she had inherited Justina's *Domus* on the Quirinale, with the Villa Simbruina as a summer residence. In sweltering July 390 she came with a large house party* to try it out. As I have said, Romans love picnics, and also al-fresco saunas* and swimming after. Thus the monks were invited to accustom themselves to happy screams and splashing from the lake and glimpses, which they could hardly bear to look at, of naked bodies of both sexes sporting innocently enough on the green meadow opposite. There's nothing like celibacy – for all but a few – to stimulate the sexual imagination. Little Benedict saw nothing for it but to remove the Community, or as many as would still go with him, to Cassino.* JJ didn't go with him: Benedict didn't really think he was cut out for the monastic life, but his Christian zeal was impressive and his drink problem seemed to be a thing of the past. JJ now wanted to do something active for Jesus in the outside world, so Benedict sent him as a missionary to the pagan alpine rustics of the Tarentaise.* He'll be remembered there as Saint James every 16 January; will he also be remembered as St **Maurice** (Maurus, Moritz even?). I'll leave him there for the moment so as to return to Wales.

* * *

Back at Ocean College another 'born again' Christian was also trying to serve his Lord, with all that enthusiasm which is so hard to retain. Schoolmastering has its own rhythm, but I was keen to give it a Christian slant. It seemed to me, first, that Christianity was for real, second, that it was indubitably the religion of Rome and her Emperors, and third, that *most* of my provincials were still in complete spiritual darkness, regarding Christianity as little more than a passing Imperial fad. What better place to start to put this right than in the schools? Who knows, the kids may even convert their parents. So I started to make some gentle changes in routine. We started our morning Assembly with prayers, in fully Christian terms, for the Augusti and the Imperial family. We said together the Lord's Prayer and sang Ambrose's Te Deum. Community singing always goes down well, and the Te Deum* would teach them most of the Creed in an easy form. I even wrote for them a little poem about Jesus* in good classical hexameters, in an attempt to improve on Damasus.

The curriculum offered little scope for change. I managed to squeeze a bit of Bible study and Religious Knowledge in under 'Music', and into the Lower School I introduced *Novellae** on Christian lines to vary the tired old essays on the amours of classical gods and heroes on which I had had to cut my own literary teeth. Our new heroes were, of course, the Saints and Martyrs and we had some genuine – and deeply moving – accounts on which to base our efforts. Plenty of scope for imagination, writing Saints' Lives and Passions; Ambrose was already showing the way with his *Life* of Saints Gervasius and Protasius, perfectly genuine but unknown martyrs whose relics he had pressed into service in the fight against Justina. Damasus' relic-trade was so rapidly endowing every altar that Uncle Ted had had to pass a law prohibiting tomb robbing for the purpose of the relic trade. If the faithful were to venerate relics they would naturally want to know something about the martyrs concerned. We set about filling this gap in knowledge, neither the first nor the last, nor the only scholars at the time to engage in this huge literary industry.*

I have already said that Science was a subject in which (thanks to Uncle Heliodorus and Eunapius) Ocean College really led the scholastic field. My 'born again' eyes turned inquisitively to this field of knowledge. Was it possible to exclude Jesus from any area of human effort? Surely not. Here Elissa's enthusiasm encouraged, maybe even seduced me. I would hesitate to call her 'born again', although she went along gamely enough with my religious practices, but I was fast discovering that her brain matched her body – and that's saying something. Maybe girls ought to be allowed to go to school, indeed I foresaw that one day they would. But for the moment Elissa was my star pupil. She helped me to prepare for science class, she attended and helped me with the experiments, and afterwards she asked endless searching questions. My textbooks, of course, were old Eunapius' books and files: Aristotle, Democritus, Parmenides, Pliny, and his own arcana, to which I had added a few I got from Onesimus.*

It was Elissa who first drew my attention to the fact that all these complicated experiments were seeking to answer questions about God. From 'How' to 'Who'. 'The more we can understand the mysteries of Nature the better we shall understand the Creator,' she said. Good Neo-Platonist stuff. But while the Neo-Platonists just speculated endlessly, we have the means to try it out. Elissa had her head well forward, the bit between her splendid teeth. 'Doesn't your own St Peter* say "be ready at all times to give a rational explanation of your faith"? Well let's get on with it. Maybe *we* can answer those tiresome questions the educated pagans* put to us like "How was Jesus actually conceived by the Holy Spirit and born of a Virgin? How did He turn the water into wine and how does He turn His body into bread and wine or is it vice versa? How could His risen body pass through walls and doors? Where is He now? Can He turn anything into anything? What is God?"* If we could answer some of those, we'd really put the theologians out of business, if they aren't already. The reasoning pagans will flock to join us.'

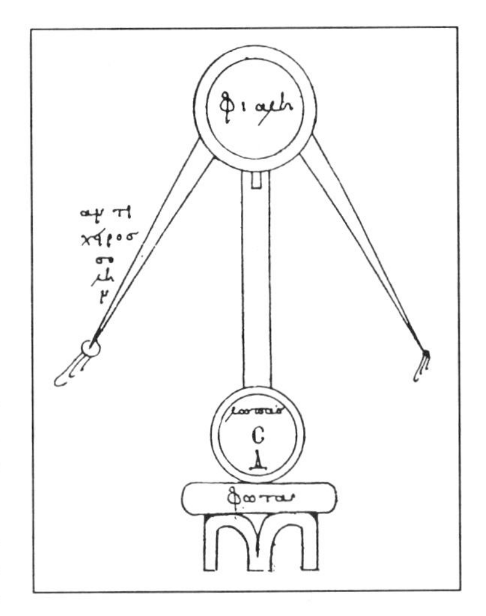

**Figure 16**
Merlin and Elissa's chemical apparatus

'Steady on Elissa,' I put in anxiously. 'I'm not Aristotle, nor John the beloved disciple.'

'Of course not,' said Elissa. 'But you are my own wisest Luke, my *Λουκας ἀριμαθος*.*

'Together we're going to find out some answers. If only we had more and better books; half of what we want seems to be missing. You'll have to scour the world's libraries.' And so I would. The Quest had begun. It would be idle to pretend that I was able all at once to drop everything and set out in full-time search of the 'missing chapters', as I will call them, of the *Book of the Holy Graal* (or *Liber Gradalis**) and although in the course of the next fifty years I would make some headway, I knew that I should die with my task incomplete. My grandson, Galahad II, will get nearer than most to success; and then it will all be forgotten for a long while.

Meanwhile life, as ever, went on. Thus in 389 my old boss of mining days, Constantianus, went off to become Praetorian of Gaul. His place as Vicar was taken by Ambrosius Theodosius,* Ambrose's son, whose own son Placidus* had entered Subiaco as a novice.

I had a letter from Ambrose telling me of the sad early death of Uncle Satyrus, which had deeply grieved him. I would miss his puckish grin and kindly ways too. On 13 June (Morgan wrote) Uncle Ted entered Rome in triumph, and received a Panegyric from Pacatus which naturally blackened Maximus from top to toe. Morgan said that most of the pagan senators, with the honourable exception of Symmachus, had rushed to get themselves baptised before His Serenity confronted them. They were queuing outside the Lateran Baptistry like the Public Baths on a busy night! Cousin Vic (Ambrose's letter again) who had been made Bishop of Amiens at the tender age of twenty-five had been promoted to be Archbishop (still very young at thirty) of Rouen.

So, between Christianity, Science, running the school and bringing up the five kids (including John), 389 and most of 390 passed quickly.

Shortly before Christmas 390 we had a surprise visitor. No less than JJ himself, and in a towering rage. He had carried out his evangelistic mission in the Tarentaise with some success, but under the influence of good food, healthy exercise and pure mountain air his thoughts kept turning to Elissa and told him he wanted her. Naturally he turned to Ambrose for guidance, and over dinner at Milan Ambrose gave it him straight between the eyes. 'So Benedict didn't think you were really cut out for celibacy?' he said. 'In that case God has left you one option. You are, as I remember, a married man, "one flesh". In the words I myself pronounced over you, "whom God hath joined let no man put asunder". Luke has told me the whole story over this very table. Are you a man or a mouse? Go after her and reclaim her. **Isn't it your turn to be "Arthur"?'**

JJ had tracked us down without much difficulty at Probus' villa* near Glastonbury where we were spending the Christmas vacation. To us entered, like the giant Orion himself, JJ purple with self-righteous fury, behind which I thought I detected a measure of uneasy self-justification.

He did not come with armies, as later myths* would suggest. His own anger, and his inherent rights in the matter were enough. I could see Elissa eyeing him with some relish – women love to be fought over, and she had never seen JJ like this before. My first instinct was to fight. I was very strong and fit from training in the ring. I knew just where to place the blow. I reckoned I could easily lay him out, maybe almost kill him. Almost... Oh Jesus, here we go again, I thought. Uncle Ted and Glorious Dad rose before my eyes. Cain and Abel. I can't. I couldn't do it. 'Blessed are the meek.' I never thought I could be that, but when your back's against the wall you can do surprising things. So I backed down, and I could feel Elissa's scorn for what she took as my weakness. She recognised perhaps for the first time that she had a husband, and for the moment she admired him. I fled the house with my thoughts, Probus whispering to me that I could find a bed at one of his farms nearby.

The next day I started my journey back to Ocean College to close up the house and pack in the job. My number two would be well able to take over as Headmaster. I wanted out of Britain. In trouble, one tends to run to family, that's what family is all about. My nearest relative at that time was dear old Great Aunt Eucheria, the Pious Maccabee, in Lyons, and it was thither that I therefore made my way. Meanwhile, as I later learnt, JJ had carted Elissa and the 'quiverful' off to Casa Sic for a holiday and a bit of bridge-building. 'To each cow its calf';* the kids went with Elissa. I had done my best to love and bring up little John. Now it was for JJ to do the same for my brood. In time, it would be Morgan to the rescue.

Through Paris, up the Seine and down the Saone, I made my way, still slightly shell-shocked, conscious only that I needed to earn some money again. A bit better off this time, but still 'Poor Henry', like in Book VII. Maybe Eucheria could help me find a job, something better than working the Funfairs, though I could still do that if need be.

Lyons was a great city by any standards. Sensationally situated at the confluence of the Saone and the Rhone, the old Gaulish city of Sarras lay up the cliff on the West bank (Fourvière, *Forum Vetera*), positively crusted with marble temples and public buildings. No wonder it would one day be called the 'Holy City of Sarras'.*

The ancient Praetorium* where the Emperor Claudius was born was now offices. Indeed most of the palaces which once ennobled the hilltop had been deserted since the aqueducts which brought their life blood were so irreparably vandalised eighty years before. The aristocracy had now joined the rich merchants in the busy town below, leaving the palaces to squatters who lived a frugal life catching rainwater in cisterns. Most of them were priests, of the many bizarre heathen temples, Cybele, Isis, Juno Moneta (the Imperial Mint). Actors too, for the great theatres of Augustus and Hadrian still drew full houses. Finally there were the Christians, serving the Basilica of 'St Irenaeus and the Holy Martyrs' (of AD177). None of this motley crew had much use for water. Cleanliness and Godliness did not march together in the Holy City of Sarras. It was in such a crumbling palace in what would be called after her the Via Maccabii that Eucheria had established herself, and there I duly presented myself to this very great, very saintly, rather rich, rather dirty little old lady, and received the warmest possible welcome.

In my youth I thought Morgan was a liberal education in herself. Eucheria was to be better yet. For a start, she wholly approved of what I had done in letting JJ have the better of me. 'But what else could you do?' she said. 'Now move on. Jesus has a purpose for you I'm sure. As to work, I'll speak to my friend the Bishop.' Bishops and priests, yes and monks and nuns were always in and out of the house which she ran like a caravanserai. In her eighties, tiny, active, indomitable, with a throbbing guttural voice which rose to a squeak whenever she got worked up, and deep-sunk intense brown eyes beneath her white eyebrows, I could still see why Gt Grandad Theodore had fallen in love with her. '*I'm* the light to lighten the Gentiles *and* the glory of my people Israel, my dear,' she would chirp as she dragged me off to yet another Mass. Everyone adored her.

Quite soon she found me a job: a locum Readership at Lyons University. 'Only literature and history, I'm afraid,' she said, 'but then you're not very well qualified. You'll have to follow up your scientific and philosophical enquiries on the side. And do, do, be sure to tell me *all* about them.'

The University was way below, in the triangle between the Saone and the Rhone, near Augustus' amphitheatre of the 'Three Gauls' and the *Νεμετον* (druid grove) where he built the great Altar of *Caesar et Augustus*, later to be corrupted to 'Croix Rousse', to teach the Gauls who was boss. This was the spiritual capital of Gaul. The seventeenth-century 'Rosicrucians', sniffing around Lyons without my book to guide them, would select the wrong quarter of Lyons for their 'stemma' – Sarras should be their real goal. In twenty years time, fear of the Barbarians would move the political capital to Arles.

So nearly two years passed in happy work by day and in even better talk by night. I really learned my religion – as opposed to my faith – around Eucheria's dinner table and, of course, she was only too ready to tell of her recent trip to the Holy Land. She encouraged me, too, to learn all I could about the pagan religions around me. 'Know your enemy,' she said. 'Let's discover what they have. Only then can we try to offer them something better.' She even persuaded me to take up my Mithraism* again. 'Your faith is quite safe while it's in my hands, and I really think you can serve Jesus rather well as a polymath. Think of the effect upon your heterodox young students if you can really stand in their sandals.' I think she was taking quite a risk, and the Bishop would have been horrified if he knew I was becoming an expert in comparative religion. But Eucheria was right about one thing. I was indeed safe in her hands.

To suit my status as an academic I had grown my beard as long as it would grow and looked the very image of a grave, if pint-sized, philosopher. I did my lectures and tutorials without much remark. And I kept fit trotting daily down the hill from Sarras, citadel of the Cornucopia, and up again. There did seem to be some sort of funny pattern in my life, and not only mine. For Eucheria told me that this very palace, then called the 'Maccabee Palace', was in fact the old Avitian palace* where Justina was brought up by her stepfather Justus Avitus (see App. 3); indeed Justus had become almost a brother to Eucheria. Fleeing the world's wickedness, like so many aristocrats of the day, he had become one of the sainted band of Desert Fathers. Justus had died the previous year in the Egyptian Desert, and now Eucheria had a plan for me. 'At the end of your contract, Luke dear, I want you to do a job for me – at my expense of course.'

'I'd do anything for you, Gran, you know that.'

'I want you to go to the Thebaid in Egypt, to track down dear Justus' remains, and to arrange for them to be reverently exhumed, coffined, and shipped home to me here. I can't have very much time left myself, and my will is – he left me trustee of the property when he went to the desert – my will is that he and I should lie together in the great basilican hall of this palace, which shall be given to the Church as a "titular" mausoleum and place of worship.'*

'Of course, Gran. It'll be a privilege.'

But Eucheria had not finished with me. 'Your reward, dear boy, will be a free holiday in the Holy Land at my expense. Not only will the thrill of the sites give a solid foundation to your faith – see, I am turning it back to your own keeping – but there is a library there at Caesarea which I think will be useful to your researches, especially since His Serenity (Uncle Ted) has just carted off all the best books from your old haunt the Serapeum to augment his library at Constantinople, and given orders to destroy the rest. You may even find the counterpart to this.' Here she rummaged in a chest and after a dusty struggle presented me with an ancient papyrus* scroll in faded Greek letters. 'Study it at your leisure. Then we'll talk about it. Meanwhile I've one more charge for you. Take this pilgrim locket' – here she delved in her bosom – 'and place it in the tomb of my dear husband Theodore in Askalon. It contains, so I verily believe, a splinter of the True Cross. Remove from his grave, if it is there, the *Tabula Ronda* or ouija board* which was the cause of his death, and do with it as you wish. My locket will make a better pillow for him.'

So in the second week of January AD393 I parted sadly from Eucheria, knowing I should hardly see her again, and set off East to do all she had asked. But before I left we had talked about the curious and wonderful papyrus she had given me and which I had by now deciphered.

**Figure 17**
Cleopatra's Dragon

'Any help?' she asked.

'Wonder upon wonder,' I said. 'My mind reels. It looks like the very clue to the *labyrinth** which Elissa and I have ventured into and got so lost. The diagrams, of course, are spot on for me as "Chrysanthus the Goldmaker", though I don't yet fully understand them. The "*dialogue*" is more of a sublime rhapsody on "our theme".* Who on earth was Cleopatra? And how did you get hold of it?'

'Oh, just family papers which have come down to me,' said Eucheria. 'Don't forget **I'm a Maccabee*** with all that that implies. And if I tell you Cleopatra's Jewish name was Mari-amne, you can work the rest out for yourself at Caesarea.'

That was all I could get out of her. To understand the full depth of her meaning at this stage you will need, like me, to quarry in Josephus' *Antiquities*; the rest of this book, however, may spare you the journey – or if not this one, then maybe, its successor.

I made my way briskly down the Rhone, passing Vienne where one day little John will be in danger of his life, and passing Orange, which the Romancers would erroneously connect with me, confusing the Roman name for Orange (*Arausio*) with *Carausius (III)*, a name which I bore briefly in the latter part of AD406. The Romancers would bungle this as 'William of Orange'.

In due course I reached Marseille where I soon picked up a ship for Alexandria, my old stamping ground. Alexandria is the principal mart of the Mediterranean, for gossip as well as merchandise, and I soon picked up some surprising news. My informant was Tertius Synesius,* son of my old General Celerinus (now retired), who was on a cultural and shopping expedition from their country estates in Cyrenaica. He told me that Promotus, my recent general whom I had failed so abysmally at Tomi, had been murdered – rumours said for Rufinus, Uncle Ted's Secretary of State in the East. Genobaudes had suffered the same fate (so Morgan was again a widow). Uncle Ted, uneasy, had returned hastily to the East, bearing with him a newly promoted Master of Horse known, from his rollicking manner and habits, as Gaudentius* 'the Jovial' who, it transpired, was none other than my own beloved and 'born again' brother.

Would JJ prove to be the original of the Teutonic god 'Wotan'? Would he, like Odin and Orion, lose an eye? Would he put Brünnhilde to sleep on a fire-girt rock? Not long to wait. In the same vein, maybe he'd be remembered as *θαλιαρχος* Thaliarchus,* the 'ruler of the feast', for JJ was to win an ill-starred fame for his prowess in the arts of the table,* solid and, regrettably, liquid.

'I hastened to congratulate him by writing him a truly irreverent '*limerick*',* which I prayed would be taken in good part. I cannot resist the temptation to quote it in full here.

*To James, Master of Horse:*

By the ashes of St Paul and the shrine of holy Peter,
do not 'rubbish' my verses, Duke James.
So may St Thomas prove a buckler to protect your breast
and St Bartholomew bear you company to the wars;
so may the blessed saints suffice to prevent the barbarians from crossing
the Alps
and St Suzanna endow you with her strength;
So, should any savage foe seek to swim across the Danube,
let him be drowned therein like the swift chariots of Pharoah;
even so may an avenging javelin strike the Getic hordes
and the favour of Thecla[1] guide the armies of Rome;
so may your guests, **dying in their efforts to out-drink you,**
assure your board its triumph of hospitality
and the broached casks overcome your thirst;
so **may your hand never be red with an enemy's blood!**
– do not, I say, 'rubbish' my little verses.

The thought of 'broadstriper', quondam Benedictine co-Abbot, JJ as Master of Horse did make me wonder, for Rome's sake, whether to laugh or cry. I hoped I hadn't hit too hard with my crack about his drinking.

As for me, my ways were to lead me among monks and undertakers until I could see Justus' body safely stowed aboard ship for Marseille; and my own for Palestine.

Eucheria had given me letters of introduction to the Patriarchs: Theophilus of Alexandria, a real *thug* but at least he cleared my path through the maze of bureaucracy, and John of Jerusalem. So after completing my task in Upper Egypt, and shedding a scholar's tear over the debris of the Serapeion* I took ship for Askalon, one of the better ports of poorly furnished Palestine. I had business there, and grisly business* at that. The cemetery there lies in a dense grove, and having no opportunity to obtain the patriarch's faculty for what was, since Uncle Ted's last edict, an illegal enterprise, I saw fit to carry out my sepulchral intervention all alone and by starlight only.

I reconnoitred the grave by day, and armed myself furtively with one of the sexton's spades. I would have been glad of my little pick as well, but managed to do the deed without. The grave was a simple slab with the name 'Theodorus' on it, topping a raised tomb of hard mud-bricks. I carefully removed one side of these. Then it was down to groping about inside in the dark with my bare hands. I soon managed to work out 'what was what', and to make the grisly substitution. Theodore now sleeps with the True Cross, and the accursed Ouija Board is in my travelling pouch. I replaced the bricks carefully, and hid the spade by a remote tomb where the sexton would find it. Then I headed

[1] By 'Thecla' I was alluding to Ambrose at Milan, where the old basilica was called after St Paul's girlfriend Thecla. Did you know St Paul had a girlfriend?

back to the inn, heart pounding. 'Had a nice walk by the sea?' asked the innkeeper as he wished me goodnight, and I said I had indeed but it had left me chilled.

The next morning I set out early for Jerusalem. Poor philosophers like me walk – no problem for an infantryman – and on the evening of the second day I was entering the Holy City. I decided not to make my number with 'Melania the Holy Terror' and Rufinus on the Mount of Olives; low profile for the moment. Instead I headed for the Patriarchate high up in the Holy City itself. On presentation of Eucheria's letter John at once sent word for me to join his table and put up with him, and here I spent some very happy days as guest and pilgrim. He spoke with the greatest love and affection of Eucheria, and when I left him on my way to Caesarea it was as the bearer of yet another Round Table, which he entrusted to me to take back to Eucheria.

'Take greater care of that than of your own life,' he said. 'You are holding in your hands the very plate on which He once took bread and, having blessed it, gave it to His disciples saying "Take, eat..."'

Well, maybe. John believed so, and Eucheria would too, I was sure. If you believe, it is so. I must confess that to me it looked like an oldish silver salver or paten richly adorned round the rim with beads of blue-green lapis lazuli.* (It will be remembered as 'St David's magic altar', but I'm not 'St David' yet: also as the 'Emerald Table' of the Vizi-Goths, but I haven't joined them yet either.) I promised to take good care of it, and for as long as I was able I did. But by the time I revisited Gaul, Eucheria, bless her, was long dead, and I thought she'd like me to have it.

Eventually, on one of my many staged 'deaths' the Vizi-Goths would get it. I had to part company rather abruptly with the Vizi-Goths in AD415, and I expect the table was eventually melted down; but I foresee that monkish legends will persist* in the future, about my magic 'sapphire' altar, and that I was actually ordained bishop of St David's by John the Patriarch. Wish it were true.

My visit at Caesarea drew something of a blank. The librarian of Pamphilus' great library was charming, but I found no partner for 'Cleopatra'. Or did I? We shall see. He said the place for me was the Theodosian Library in Constantinople. 'You'll find what you're looking for there,' he said, as he wrote me yet another letter of introduction.

The Quest continues.

Heigh ho.

# BOOK IX

## *The Good Ship* Venus *(AD393)*

The usual cautious and unpredictable winter voyaging – Sinbad the Sailor, that's me: Guinbaut, Baudwin, the fair bastard – brought me to the Bosphorus and New Rome at the end of March. I must admit I felt a bit uneasy; but who would connect the cocky young Tribune of eight years ago with this bearded sage in his long brown philosopher's robe? I had to see Serena somehow, though. I had some money to repay her, from my very own earnings.

So I made my way to Stilicho's Palace, and after a lot of parleying with the servants managed to gain her presence. She wasn't fooled for a moment. 'Luke, you clown,' she said as she hugged and kissed me, 'whatever are you doing in that fancy dress?'

'Have a care, Madam, how you address Ælius Theodorus, quondam Headmaster of Ocean College, quondam Reader in history at Lyons University.'

'You really are an absolute scream,' said Serena. 'You must stay to dinner and tell me all about it. Just one thing. That beard comes off, or at least gets a reasonable trim, before you sit at my table.'

'Quite frankly, I thought I might need a bit of disguise, still, in this town.'

'Bless your heart,' said Serena. 'That all blew over long ago. I picked my time carefully, and squared Dad.' Serena had the knack of this, as I have written. 'He thought it very funny – you know he doesn't harbour grudges. "Serve the young cub right," he said. "Teach him a lesson. How much did you have to shell out? I'll see you right".'

So off I went to the barbers. Dinner that night was a matter of earnest catching-up; but in the following nights there were parties, and at one of these who should I find myself next to but Promotianus, my ex-defending officer. As the wine circulated – a treat for a frugal academic like me – we plotted deeds of revenge on Rufinus. We were both a bit tipsy. 'Come back to my place Claudius,' (already we were on *prenomen* terms if not on Christian names) 'and I'll show you some sport. We've got a really cosy set-up!'

Little did I know what I was in for. Serena should have warned me. The house of the sons of Promotus* was *the* high-class bordello (heterosexual, I'm happy to say) of Constantinople. '*Tout le beau monde*' went there. So did we. Low lights, sweet scents, and a band of guitarists to get you in the mood. And lots more wine. I didn't know who my girl was at the time. But I *am* rather an unusual size and shape, and maybe she recognised my (by now rather slurred) voice because she let me sleep on. I surfaced painfully the next morning to find that I had just laid my step-sister Eudoxia/Sieglinde, Morgan's daughter. ***Poxy Doxy*** I now call her, because she gave me a dose of you-know-what which would give me a lot of trouble in the future. You'll be able to read more about it all in Wolfram's *Parzifal*, where I'm Am-fortas (Ambrosius the Strong), besides some other characters.

***Doxy*** was to give me a son, too, in due course; my own dear dear Gawain. (I foresee much confusion between the two Eugenius'. 'Little John' (Owein, Ivain) you have already met: he's only my nephew and foster-son. This little bastard is my very own. He will have no name* save 'Gawain' for many years, but will find his own eventually as Flavius Merobaudes II Meropius II.[1]

Over an anxious breakfast of the 'hair of the dog' Doxy told me her sad tale. She had been travelling through Pannonia with her father Genobaudes when a band of Hun auxiliaries (in the pay, she gathers, of Rufinus) broke into his tent by night, killed him, and dragged her away captive. The chief of them – she thought his name was something like Hulding – decided to take her unceremoniously to wife, or rather slave. Had she been fully nubile she would doubtless have had to bear him some little Huns. 'Smelly little yellow creatures,' she said. 'Too disgusting.'

Around the forests they roamed in the usual Hun nomadic way, burning their old huts,* building new ones. They claimed that Rufinus had made them honorary Roman soldiers. In March 392 they were encamped, somewhat idyllically, on the southern shores of Lake Balaton,* and Eudoxia was sulkily doing her hutwork when a 'conquering hero' (**Siegmund**: that's what it means) burst in. Huge, florid, red-cloaked, in glittering uniform with gilded belt and scabbard. Plainly a Roman officer of high rank. 'Can you tell me where I can get a horse?' he asked. 'Mine has bolted and thrown me, and my men have gone ahead.'

Recognition came slower than it had with me, but it was no ordinary 'mare' he rode that afternoon. ***Doxy*** does have this knack of leading men on. Twelve years later, when she was an Empress, her Consul would find a word for it

[1] *Meropius* means 'courteous, well-spoken'. JJ earned it and, perhaps most of all, so did my spiritual director and mentor, Paulinus of Nola. The epithet will rightly stick to 'my Gawain', not least in its corrupt form **'Merovech', eponymous founder of the Merovingian dynasty, Kings of the Franks.**

which would become standard Greek: *Λαικας*,* a whore. Meaning that, as Gibbon writes, towards the *laity* (male) her 'charity was boundless'.

With recognition of who they were, where they were, and what they had just done, the need for flight was obvious, and Uldin's horses were readily available. So JJ, for it was none other, regained his men complete with concubine – they were much impressed – and she stayed with him as he pursued his military duties under Timasius, the general whom Uncle Ted had appointed to replace Promotus. It was at *Durosternum* (Silistria) in Lower Moesia – deep in the Marcian country – that on 4 January 393 Aëtius 'Son of the Eagles' was born. He will be remembered as long as history is read, and Romance. He will be Siegfried, and Lancelot, and Tristan, and Galahault le Haut Prince, the 'best knight in the world'. JJ thought it best to move the young mother to Constantinople – to Serena, of course (so she knew all about it). But Eudoxia had learnt to value other joys than motherhood and, leaving Serena to arrange a wet-nurse for baby Aëtius, she had offered herself as a 'paying guest' to the sons of Promotus.

Jesus, what had I let myself in for? I felt horror, compassion, shame, revulsion. I didn't know as yet that I'd given her a baby. Offering her some money (part of my ransom money actually) which she took in a very matter of fact way, I mumbled some excuses, gathered up my pack with its precious cargo of relics, and made my escape. Phew. Ambrose, how would you have handled that one? I decided I should go to confession. Then I'd have something to say to Serena.

Confession was no problem. I found an old priest up at the Basilica of the Holy Apostles who took me off into an alcove. He didn't seem much concerned and absolved me readily. 'Intention is what counts,' he said. 'If you meant to do it, I should be concerned. Next time put some more water in your wine. As penance, you can pray for your benighted step-sister. Now, go in peace and don't do it again.' Alas, in years to come I was to do much worse. And to intend it.

It was a sunny April afternoon when I found my way back down the *Μεση*, through Uncle Ted's new Forum, where his newly-completed column and statue celebrated his victory over Maximus. 'At least Trajan conquered barbarians rather than his own kin,' I thought sadly as I passed. I received Serena's embrace coldly, and it wasn't just the hangover. 'You're a rotten sister to play a trick like that on me,' I said.

'Oh, grow up, Lukie,' she replied playfully, 'you're thirty-two and this is New Rome. What would you say if I told you I rather fancy you myself? Anything goes here, so long as you go to church to please "Dad".' (I'll drop the inverted commas after this. Just wanted to remind you that Ted was only Serena's and Thermantia's *adopted* father. Their real father, like mine, was Honorius I, **Albanus**, 'Glorious Dad'.) 'Of course, it's too awful about poor Eudoxia,'

Serena went on, 'but I suppose she can't help being a nympho. I'm trying to pick up the by-blows aren't I? You should see baby Aëtius,* he's quite a poppet. And now you and JJ have something else in common. You've neither of you been exactly faithful to Elissa, have you? Better make it up.'

'Yes, Serena, but that squalid place...'

'Be careful what you say about my landlord's enterprises,' Serena replied. 'He'll put up my rent again if he hears. Besides, no one could call the Casa Promotus squalid. It's the most luxurious establishment in Town.'

'Who is this landlord of yours, then?' I asked.

'It's old Eutropius the Giant Pander,' said Serena. 'The richest man in Constantinople after Rufinus. Real estate's his game. Ghastly creep, eunuch too. He's got Dad's ear currently. In fact he's on a secret mission to John the Dwarf for Dad at the moment. John's one of the Desert Fathers with a great reputation for prophecy. Dad wants to know if he should take up arms again to exterminate Arbogast and avenge young Valentinian. Says he can't move without an oracle from God. I'm really worried about Dad. I think he's beginning to lose his marbles.'

I forgot to tell you that while I was piously communing with Eucheria in Lyons the worst had, yet again and predictably, happened. I mentioned at the end of Book VII that Arbogast the Prussian, the hero of Aquileia, had surfaced as Uncle Ted's new white hope. Uncle Ted had left him as Commander-in-Chief of the Gauls and guardian of young Valentinian. The stage was set for a replay of the Merobaudes saga; the problem of the overmighty subject. Did Valentinian commit suicide in his impotent young frustration, or did Arbogast strangle him at Vienne? Doesn't much matter. What does matter is that the Roman Senate – and here I think we can see the hand of the Symmachi (the faithful and by now rather desperate pagans) – supported Arbogast. In unholy alliance with a hated Barbarian, the Senate appointed their own Augustus, a respectable civil servant called Eugenius.* Eugenius means 'well-born' in Greek (a fairly common indication at the time of the 'bar sinister', or the 'wrong side of an aristocratic blanket', just like 'my Gawain', above). He claimed, and his name gave good grounds for the claim, to be a by-blow of Valentinian the First (see App. 2) by a concubine. As such, if true, he probably had quite a claim to the throne. Uncle Ted had been sitting uneasily on the problem of whether or not to recognise the usurper for nearly six months – hence Eutropius' mission to the dwarf soothsayer. 'Salome' was egging him on to show his majesty again as he had with Maximus. All in all Uncle Ted had problems that year. So did Rome. So did Ambrose.

* * *

'Talking of marbles,' said Serena, 'they're completely "old hat" nowadays, and draughts, and backgammon. Just look at this.' She produced a wonderful ivory set of players and a board. 'It's called "chess", the Persian War game.' (By and by, Little John would introduce the game to Britain, together with falconry.)* 'Stilicho brought it back from his mission to Persia. New Rome's going mad over it,' Serena continued.

**Figure 18**
John the falconer

'Not today, I think, Serena. I've got too much on my mind.'

'Well here's something else to put on it,' she said. 'You're invited to dinner by His Serenity. Just a little party to celebrate Dad's forty-seventh birthday. The two Prefects will be there; otherwise only family. I've put you by me on the seating plan, in case you're nervous, and you can glower across at JJ as much as you like. Stilicho thinks the world of him. So what you've got to do is get down to the tailors. If Dad's received you back into the sacred family you dress accordingly, d'you hear? Tunic and chlamys.* I'll lend you a brooch. Pity none of Stilicho's gear will fit you.'

'*All* the family, Serena?' I asked.

'Indeed yes. Full house. Dad and Galla. Arcadius – he's sixteen, and been Augustus for ten years, poor lad – Uncle Heliodorus, me and Ginger – the only women – plus our husbands, you and JJ. Honorius is only nine, and baby Galla Placidia only five. They'll dine separately, and come in to wish Dad happy birthday. Have you got a present for him?'

I thought of my two relics, one sacred, one profane, and decided against it. I could always write him a birthday ode.

'I think I'll turn in early, Serena, it's been quite a day.'

The next few days passed with visits to the tailors, as instructed, and in following up my letter of introduction to the Librarian. They were in complete chaos at the library with all the new accessions from Alexandria to process. God knows how I'm to find a partner for 'Cleopatra' in that haystack. Still, I had nothing better to do, and I liked books. I was glad to have my own room in the town, too. Palaces were not my scene. I was, and am, a poor shop-soiled Christian philosopher. That's me.

Be this as it may, the evening of 4 May (the Ides) saw me, dressed up to the nines, my beard trimmed and lightly oiled, marching up to the sentries of the Δαφνη Palace, just South of the Hippodrome, even winning instant salutes due to my confident bearing. Through flowery courtyards with fountains, and corridors ablaze with mosaics, I was led by an equerry – a *scolanus* like myself – until we reached the ante-room, the archway into which was flanked by two of the famous *Silentarii*, the personal sentries of the Augustus. At this time they were Armenians, imported by Stilicho, and specially chosen for their height and physique. Black-haired, moustached, with curved swords hanging on their all-white uniforms, they made an intimidating sight. Their duty was to stand, motionless, silent (hence the name), hardly even moving their eyes, around the rooms occupied by the Sacred Presence. Because of the strain, they were relieved every hour. I knew it was good form to pretend not to notice them. Anyway my eyes were already on the group of splendidly arrayed men and women within. I made straight for Serena, who after introducing me casually to Stilicho said 'Come on and meet your uncle and auntie. Best get it over.'

And there he was, the master of the world, slight, raddled, in simple purple robe and slippers, with a wreath of roses on his head. His mop of auburn hair, now thin and receding, was sprinkled with grey, and his eyes were hollow beneath his bushy eyebrows. His face was deeply lined, and he seemed to have shrunk since I last saw him, eighteen years ago. JJ towered over him; Stilicho too. I hardly recognised him, nor he me. But when Serena presented me, and I made my bow, he held his hand out to me almost diffidently. To shake or to kiss? I played it safe and kissed his ring. Did I feel a tremor in his hand? Was he perhaps embarrassed to greet the son of the man he had killed? The moment passed.

'So, it's Luke I behold,' said Theodosius. 'Serena has told me all your tale, as Celerinus and Promotus before her. The rolling stone is welcome to New Rome. Your uncle greets you. Galla, my dear, greet a nephew.'

Another bow and scrape. So this was 'Salome' herself, Justina's daughter too, but not like her half-sister Elissa. Just approaching twenty-one she was at the peak of her charms, but her hazel hair was so smothered in pearls and her robe so bejewelled that one could only guess at her underlying beauty. Her nose was prominent like Justina's, above a rather thin, almost cruel, mouth. She acknowledged my salutation without much interest and turned her rather anxious black eyes back to watching her lord and master, which seemed to be her full-time occupation.

In the background a band of flutes and guitars were playing popular music of the politer sort as I circulated under Serena's protection, round the other guests. 'Prefect, may I introduce my brother Luke,' said Serena.

'How do you do sir.'

'That's Aurelian, this year's Lord Mayor. Arbogast killed his brother last year. He's some sort of a cousin of ours,' Serena whispered.

'Praetorian, may I introduce my brother Luke.' A deep bow, I thought, for him.

'That's Rufinus, last year's Consul. Dad dotes on him. I don't trust him a yard,' Serena said as we moved on. 'Ginger's over there with Alaric. Come on.'

Well, Ginger was the same as ever anyway. Handsome, mischievous looking, her auburn* hair beautifully coiffed as usual.

'Duke, this is Thermantia's and my half-brother Luke,' said Serena to our next encounter. I looked with keen interest on the young Goth. Tallish, with fair straight hair brushed down from the crown of his head onto his forehead, then curled under in the Gothic fashion.* He had very blue eyes that looked as keenly back at me. 'I hear you don't think much of Goths,' he said with a twinkle.

'I know how to change my mind,' I said. And I had. I liked the look of him. He and I could do business. I wouldn't mind serving with him. Maybe I shall.

Next it was young Arcadius, a swart rather puny lad, looking justifiably self-conscious in his purple robe. I made to kiss his ring in proper fashion and he squeaked out 'Don't do that, cousin!' in a high, rather silly voice. A bit of a wet, I thought him. Still I wouldn't be in his shoes for anything; nor, I thought, would he.

It could be evaded no longer. No hiding behind pillars. There was JJ.

'Is it peace or war, brother?' I stammered, rather shyly. His answer, bless him, was to seize me in both arms and hug me.

'Luke, me old chum,' he said, 'good to see you. You've got to "know" Eudoxia too, I hear. Women are hell aren't they? Mustn't ever let them come between us. Now come and meet our old Headmaster.' And there he was. Somehow I'd forgotten about Uncle Heliodorus, save that he was a bishop somewhere out East.

Uncle Heliodorus beamed all over his long face and embraced us both. 'Sorry to hear you never took your finals,' he said. 'I always thought you two would go far.' Clothes-wise, Uncle Heliodorus really was the odd man out. The rest of us were in palace gear; uncle was in sackcloth. You know, the stuff they make sacks out of. The very best sacks, and bleached almost white, but still sackcloth. A bleached cord was around his waist, and *bare feet.* He had no hair at all (not that he ever had much). He wasn't bald, though; I could see the stubble. Funny sort of Bishop. (Prelates at this time dressed like prefects; not so the Novatians, who were ascetic to a fault.) Uncle wanted to know what I was up to in New Rome, and when I told him of the chaos at the Library he said, 'Maybe I had a hand in bringing that about. Strictly between us, I've got the pick of it down at my Convent. Sounds like the stuff you might be looking for. Don't worry,' for he had seen my anxious glance towards Uncle Ted, 'Ted knows what I'm up to. Indeed he's very interested himself now that, under Galla's and my influence, he's shaken off the stern hand of Ambrose. *I'm* his confessor now. Tell you what. I could give you a cell down at the Convent, and you can have the run of our library, and our laboratories. Mum's the word for now. Come and see me if you're interested.'

'That I am, uncle,' I said, and just then the band struck up for dinner.

Uncle Ted and Galla led the way into the most beautiful dining-room* I had ever been in. There wasn't much room. It was a belvedere, looking towards the Bosphorus, the Senate House and Acropolis to the North, and over Marmara to the hills of Pontus.The couches were arranged in a horseshoe with Uncle Ted and Galla at the head, with Arcadius inevitably on Ted's right and somewhat marooned. Ginger, Stilicho, JJ and Aurelian completed his right hand side. On his left hand side, weird-looking Uncle Heliodorus was in the second place of honour. Then Alaric, Serena, me, and Rufinus. Across the middle, where the slaves circulated with the food and wine, was a small couch ('For the infants when they're brought in,' whispered Serena). At the four corners of the room stood four impassive sentries. The music of the band could still be heard, now far off.

Uncle Heliodorus led off with a fervent grace, as we stood with bowed heads. Then down we got. I had heard that Uncle Ted kept a good table,* and was not disappointed. The first course was spicy cheese in pastry. Then there was a dish of sturgeon stewed with herbs. Then Anatolian roast venison with onion sauce. Nothing too much. This was a choice family dinner, not a banquet. Servants kept our glasses filled with delicious amber wine. Uncle Heliodorus drank water only, and engaged himself in drawing out Uncle Ted and Galla, neither of whom seemed in top birthday form. I went rather easy on the wine, after my experience with young Promotianus, and the priest's advice. Stilicho and Alaric seemed to be glowering a bit at one another. I left them to Serena to sort out and addressed myself to the other end of the table. Rufinus was my task. A surly rather shifty fellow I thought, though obviously capable. Aurelian, across the table, looked quite a good egg. But he was too far off to help me. So I talked to the Viceroy of the East about my impressions of New Rome, and how thrilled I had been coming in by Uncle Ted's Golden Gate, which had not been there on my first visit.

This struck warm, and Rufinus went off on a long diatribe against Old Rome. 'Old Has-been' he called it. 'This is the one true capital of the world. We must outdo Rome with gold and marble, and we are.'

'I never thought to hear a Gallo-Roman say that,' I said, knowing he came from Gascony.

'Go where the money is, my boy. Already we can buy out Old Rome. Hardly need to bother to fight that old gas-bag Eugenius.' So we talked politics and strategy. Rufinus said Romans wouldn't fight any more; it was just a question of who could hire and train the best mercenaries. 'So Eugenius can hire himself some Franks and Alemans,' said Rufinus. 'So what? We can hire as many Goths as we like, and then trump the suit with limitless Huns. No one can fight against *them*.' He said all this in a low voice in case Stilicho and Alaric were listening. 'Mark my words, boy, money will win the day.'

Ugh! I hated him. Me a pure Roman, a *scolanus*, a Palatine trooper, to have to listen to this subversive stuff. I turned for a while to chat to Serena, and as I did so, glanced at the head of the table. Uncle Ted seemed to be only picking at his food, but his goblet was doing full duty. I could see Uncle Heliodorus was trying to soothe him. 'Eutropius will be back soon. John the Dwarf will speak Heaven's blessings to you, whichever way God in His wisdom may direct.' But Uncle Ted had fallen to whimpering, his head bowed over his plate. A sort of silence was falling on the company. Suddenly Uncle Ted raised his head and half rose, Galla tugging at him. 'I want my children,' he said. 'I want to see my little ones.' Hastily an equerry went out. 'God loves me no more. Fortune has deserted me, like the Altar of Victory. *Look* at me, ***look*** at me. 'I'm **old!**' (This in a sort of trailing yell.) Truth to tell we didn't know where to look. Fortunately this brainstorm was interrupted by the entrance of young Honorius, and little Placidia with her nurse. They took their places at the centre couch and bowed deferentially to Uncle Ted before tucking into the stuffed dates. At the sight of Placidia's pretty little curls and blue eyes Uncle Ted seemed to cheer up. Then he looked at Honorius and frowned again. With his foxy hair, sticky-out ears, and protruding lower lip the boy hardly looked prepossessing.* 'Look, *look!*' cried Ted. '*This* is all I have. This is the trick my God has played on me. I am the sole Augustus, and I know I have not long to live. I need **sons**! Mature men, strong men, *Romans*! And I get these ... *puppets*!'

We dared not look at Arcadius and Honorius. The silence was ghastly. Uncle Ted restored himself with a goblet of wine, instantly refilled, and looked wildly round on us, though I think he could not see us. 'I will not wait upon a dwarf soothsayer. Ha, I am an Emperor. Perhaps the pagans are right and I am myself a God. Hear then, what this God will do. I will abdicate here and now. If I have no sons worth the name, at least I have daughters more than worthy, and they have strong husbands to support them. Thermantia, Serena, to you I resign the Empire, for I know you love me both, as though I were your true father. And I have one little darling of my own breeding. Bring me my Placidia, bring me my little girl.'

At a nod from Galla the nurse brought the little child up to the head of the horseshoe facing her father, who picked her up and kissed her tenderly, then put her down in front of him. 'Come my pet,' he said. 'You've come to wish Dad "Happy Birthday". Let's all hear you say you love Daddy more than anyone – more than all your "sisters". I have the whole Empire to bestow; one day maybe it shall be yours. How much do you love your very own Daddy?'

Poor little Cordelia. Her face crumpled. Her arms twitched. She looked desperately around the room, then burst into tears. Not a word could she say. It was late, and frightening, and she was only five. At Galla's signal the nurse hurried her away. We all stared at Ted. 'So, that is *my* daughter. My only true daughter. A mere child. Oh brother of mine, I have paid dearly for that fatal blow, that "dolorous stroke" eighteen years ago at *Verulamium*. Now I settle the debt. *Your* daughters shall share the Empire, and I ... to save my soul ... if there be mercy left.' His voice died away and he fell to weeping, at first silently.

'Come on everyone,' hissed Serena. 'Time for bed. Father is not well. Let us go quickly, and keep silence for Rome's sake.'

The party started to slip away, the officials first. I hung around Serena, who was slow to go; Galla was trying to comfort Ted but he was pushing her almost violently away. Suddenly he raised his head and started to sing, an old soldier's song that I knew well. The words are not suitable for print. I would not sing them before my own mother. But suddenly Ted was shouting at us as if on a long forced march. 'Come on my men. Just a few more miles to go. Sing soldiers, sing you bastards! Where's the band, dammit? Old Theodosius'll get you all home safe'.

Stilicho and Alaric joined in the well-remembered songs like old hands and so did I. I don't think JJ knew the words. 'Broad-stripers' didn't.

'Servants, more wine,' cried Ted. 'We'll beat the bastards yet!'

Uncle Heliodorus materialised at my elbow. 'Luke,' he whispered, 'go grab a guitar from the band. I know you can play. Taught you myself. If we've got to sit up all night singing dirty songs, at least let's sing them in tune. I've seen Ted through these turns before. If we "play soldiers" well, we may win back an Emperor. Can't spare him yet.'

So, that is how little **David*** came to play the 'harp' to Saul when the evil demon came on him that memorable night above the Bosphorus – and on many nights in the next few months when the bad fit came on him. Although I moved out into Uncle Heliodorus' Convent in dockland the very next day, I remained on call, and on a message from Galla I would be up at the Palace with my *κιθαρα* (guitar), to soothe the savage breast. The *κιθαρα* comprehended quite a variety of stringed plucked instruments, lute, harp, mandolin, and over the next few months I wrote an essay* on them (linked rather uneasily with chemistry) to interest Uncle Ted. After all, at Ocean College, science was part of the 'Music' syllabus.

Sometimes I think it was little David, armed only with his guitar and Eskimo Nell, that held the Empire together during this strange lull in history. Ambrose, I think, would have been on my side. I hoped Jesus would forgive me if I was at fault. My intentions were good. I was in such a muddle. How could a clown* like me ever hope to find the Holy Grail?

Heigh ho.

# BOOK X

## *Orion Agonistes (AD393–395)*

Uncle Ted was to be off work for a whole year after that dreadful night. A complete nervous breakdown, the doctor said. Rest would do the trick. Marvellously, history seemed to stop too. No laws. No wars. Is there a lesson in this? I had taken up Uncle Heliodorus' invitation, resumed my brown philosopher's robe, and moved into the Convent of the Resurrection* up in the VIIth or 'Cycnus' region, brooding over the busy dockland which is the Golden Horn. Κυκνος means 'swan'. This was effectively 'Constantinople Polytechnic', its nucleus the old church of the Novatians or Puritans.

Strictly, the Novatians were a schismatic sect and should have been banished, like the Arians, outside the Constantinian walls (the 'Theodosian' walls were only completed for Theodosius II by Anthemius in AD413), but with Uncle Heliodorus as Bishop, and tutor of the royal princes,* the Patriarch, Nectarius, saw no reason to make a fuss. Like Damasus (and, in future times, Bishop Samuel Wilberforce*), Nectarius would receive less than his meed from Church historians. In fact his was an inspired appointment by Uncle Ted. Under his eighteen years of bland churchmanship Arianism withered away. To him you owe the Nicene Creed which will still be being said as you read this. Is concensus politics so blameworthy? Must we condemn him as unspiritual because he ate in the houses of publicans and sinners? The Novatians were perfectly orthodox, too, and had attended the Council of Nicaea. Sort of latter-day Essenes, or proto-Puritans.

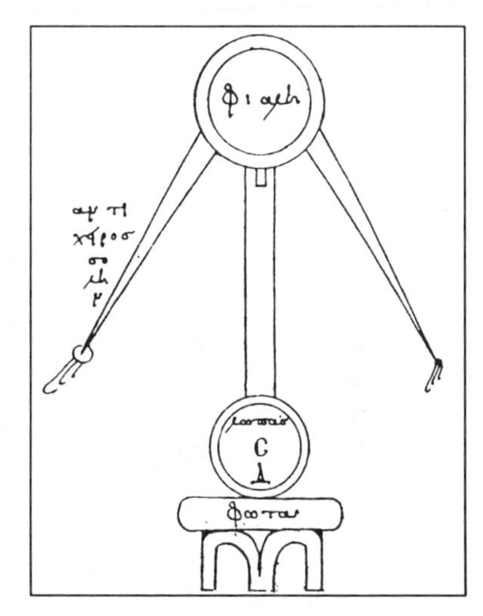

**Figure 19**
From Eucheria's Papyrus

All was white there. White sackcloth, whitewashed walls; an oasis of calm, piety and scholarship. They were coenobites – that is, they ate formally together in a common refectory – but, services apart, everyone did their own thing. I was given a simple cell, with water ewer, palleasse, quite a decent desk and stool, and a curtained alcove for my things. Who needs more? After lunch, Uncle called me to him. 'Let's have a talk about your enquiries, Luke, and see how we can best help you.' I told him a little about Elissa's and my quest, and my bootless trip to the Library in Caesarea. Then, fetching my pack, I produced Eucheria's papyrus.* Heliodorus read it, frowning, then looked at me with amazement. 'We'll have to be moving your cell; bring your pack with you.'

Without more ado Heliodorus led me through a rabbit warren of passages and outhouses to a door which he unlocked with a big key that he produced from under his robe, carefully locking it again behind us. 'You know I'm a real bishop,' he said, 'so I've got twin Cathedrals* just like the Patriarch up the hill. One for the Catechumens, one for the Initiates. Baptistery of course, in the middle like Jordan river. I wasn't sure which you would best fit into.'

'But the locked door, uncle, isn't that a bit unusual?'

'I wouldn't like you to think we have anything to hide here,' said Heliodorus. 'That is, Ted – I mean, His Serenity – knows just exactly *what* we have in this convent here; but it's easier for him not to know *who* we have. Come Luke, let me introduce you to the Director of our "think-tank" and his team.'

A double knock, and we entered a fair room with several men of various ages sitting round a long table on which were strange objects. At the end sat the strangest object of them all, a venerable old man with a shaven head like a skull and deep-sunk eyes. He looked like the Abbé Liszt gone Hare Krishna, if I may thus 'time-walk' to help you envisage. This apparition rose and greeted me in an unctuous quavering bass voice and seemed reluctant to release my hand. 'Dear dear boy,' he intoned, 'I am ravished to see you. You may not believe this but I have been long expecting you to arrive on this very day; indeed, your Gt Grandad Theodore and I predicted this together, some twenty years ago.'

'Luke,' said Heliodorus, 'may I present you to our most famous philosopher, Heron the Great himself, quondam Patriarch* of this very city. Greet, too, Pappus and Theon, leading lights of of the former Serapeion Library and Museum, and Olympiodorus their young assistant. The fifth, I think you already know.'

Great Scott, it was Eunapius. 'Looks quite like an Ocean College Old Boys Reunion, Uncle,' said I, determined not to be overawed.

So I joined the Coven of the Resurrection and when they saw my papyrus it was apparent that they accepted me as one of them. I said before that there seemed to be a funny pattern in my life. Who could have predicted this? Yet one man had. I understood the locked door now. Valens had banished Heron;

Maximus would have had him executed as a magician; Ambrose had excommunicated him as an impostor. Now Heron was to be my teacher. Still, Eucheria was with me in spirit, her precious salver in my pack. (Alas, the ouija board was there too!) It was too late to back out now. With Uncle Ted and Uncle Heliodorus to vouch for it, surely this place was all right and above board?

I was to spend a fruitful year in that asylum, – like the 'Cave of Adullam', where David the harpist used to rest up when Saul was in one of his rages. I was called out from time to time to the Palace, thirty minutes walk away, to play the harp to Uncle Ted. Not often bawdy songs now; the man really appreciated good music, and I played him all my repertoire. By and by we would fall to talking about affairs of state, about family, even warily about the think-tank. I thought we were becoming very close. But for now, Little Merlin was settling down to complete his education amid – Heron himself excepted – delightful company. I felt like a newly elected Fellow of All Souls.

There I was to read and re-read Aristotle and all the classic philosophers, and much more. For there, brought from Alexandria ('clever wheeze of mine, getting Ted to let us pillage *that* library, eh?' muttered Uncle) were the whole arcana of Bolos of Mende* (Pseudo-Democritus) and of Zosimus of Panpolis* (Godfather Basil's brother-in-law). Here surely there was a bridegroom for 'Cleopatra' – chasms of meaning here for initiates, for those 'in the know'; my own exegesis must go at its own pace. There, in Cycnus College Faculty of Science, my colleagues were actually writing the *Book of the Holy Grail*, the *Liber Gradalis*, the 'Book of Steps'. And I was invited to put in my own two denarii worth, and so indeed I would.

My new cell was just like the former one, and most of us, save the 'refugees', ate at High Table in the main refectory. Some of us used to join Uncle Heliodorus and his co-adjutor Sisinnius at the services which punctuated the day. Marvellous singing and a real feeling of holiness. 'Do I have to castrate myself and have my golden locks shorn off, Uncle, to really join your lot?' I asked him one day. (Not all Novatians, of course, went the whole Origenite hog, as Uncle had. I was not just being flippant however, as I had real trouble in this quarter at the time.)

'Forget it,' said Uncle. 'I can see your vocation doesn't lie at all that way.'

The second morning, Olympiodorus had been deputed to show me round. I thought at first I'd stepped into the smelliest kitchens ever. Fires and smoke and steam, and the stench of rotten eggs. In other rooms were furnaces where some sort of metallurgy seemed to be going on. Labourers toiled up ramps with barrows of charcoal and ores for these.

Still descending the wooded spur of **Monsalvatsche**, *mons silvaticus* (the bluff now occupied by the Botanical Gardens is still wooded, and bordered by steep cliffs) towards the Golden Horn we came to the Glass House. Here sweating men were blowing red blobs of glass on iron spontils into weird shapes. 'Old Doc Heron's making absolutely impossible demands of them,' said Olympiodorus. 'Every day he designs a more outrageous piece of laboratory equipment for them to attempt. Says the whole success of the 'Great Work' depends on them.'

'The Great Work?' I enquired.

'Shsh,' said Olympiodorus. 'He's undertaken to demonstrate the Incarnation before our very eyes.'

'Oh Jesus,' was all I could say. But Heron never made it. Maybe the glass-blowers let him down. He died the following year still questing, and Eunapius left for Athens to write his biography. (Eunapius then continued for the next twenty years writing his own great history on which, with my own published works, future historians must rely for the years to AD404).

The trouble, as I soon found out when I was set to read them, was that Heron's *Arcana*, or operational instructions, are as clear as mud. Huge exhilarating general statements are closely followed by instructions for chemical experiments supposed to demonstrate these truths in practical terms. The instructions were simply inadequate. Under Doc Heron a team of some fifty acolytes, among whom I was soon enrolled, were at work trying them out. The operations went on day and night, often for months. Shift-work: the *ἀκοιμετης*,* 'sleepless ones', they called us. Similar to Basil's, Martin's, and my own '*laus perennis*' where the monks chant the offices throughout the twenty-four hours. By the end of my year I had not seen one recipe succeed.

But we had our successes, and it was for these that we received, I was to learn, a Treasury subsidy. One day the Chancellor of the Exchequer, Hadrian Synesius, came in to inspect us. (Apart from his younger brother Tertius, later Bishop Synesius, to whom I have referred, Hadrian had a beautiful sister for whose sake I would eat some memorable humble pie* only ten years hence). My old General Celerinus' eldest son, Hadrian made straight for me and asked me to show him round.

'My brother told me he'd seen you in Alexandria earlier this year,' he said, 'and I thought you might end up on my payroll. Old Heron's promised His Serenity to manufacture gold for him, which would help the Exchequer no end if it came off. In the meantime we are getting a big spin-off in technological advances not only in metallurgy, gilding, furnace design, but also in chemicals for the dyeing trades. Heron's actually hoping to invent a magic bleaching powder,* to replace the old time-consuming bleaching by sunlight. He's distilling salt in vitriol and has managed to impregnate some limestone with the "whitening pneuma", but I fear the process is proving unacceptably dangerous. At heart Heron's more of a theoretical scientist, but I'm more interested in applied science. New Rome demands value for money.'

My laboratory was experimenting with distillation. Back in Nubia, old Onesimus only knew the vinegar process for making mercury from cinnabar. Now we distilled it in iron stills, and we distilled anything else that would melt or sublime. Heron's artificers had made us glass retorts in which we distilled eggs (in the hope that we might recover the elixir of life – what a hope!). We distilled herbs in water. No joy. Then we tried distilling them in wine, and thus discovered liqueurs. (Now *they* were more like the elixir of life. Made the sick feel good, and the well feel even better. The monasteries are to make a speciality* of them for centuries to come.)

Old Heron used to come and rhapsodise behind us distillers. He was convinced that he was an avatar of Hermes Trismegistos. Maybe he was. Alcohol, of course, made him think of Cana in Galilee, and he had a very pregnant quotation* from the *Liber Gradalis* to buoy him up in this – once again, let initiates prick up their ears, as I leak 'les grands secrets' piecemeal into the public domain. 'See how the highest descends to the lowest and how the lowest rises to the highest,' Heron would croon, quoting in fact from Eucheria's papyrus. 'Boys, you are now looking at Jacob's ladder.' He looked as if he could actually see the angels. I could only see some vapour, and not much of that.

So passed May and June. Early in July Uncle Ted was well enough for Galla to move him out to the summer palace* of 'Ε*βδομον* or Bakarköy, a few miles West of Constantinople on the cliffs. The doctors said the sea breezes would do him good, and Galla hoped the bugle calls from his very own 'Theodosiani' in the nearby barracks would arouse him. Ted was in one of his religious moods, and Ambrose had sent him some fresh relics he had just dug up. Not knowing the names of the rightful owners, he had rather cheekily called them after JJ and me, as Sts Agricola and Vitalis* – the latter, one of my many epithets in youth and beyond, would be long remembered by my fellow Cambrians.* With the relics came a stern warning: 'Eugenius is not acceptable to Mother Church as Augustus. Rome waits on you'. On the distaff side, Galla was demanding vengeance for her strangled brother Valentinian II (see App. 3). Finally Eutropius the Pimp (Serena's and Doxy's landlord) had returned with a prophecy from John the Dwarf in the Desert: 'Uncle Ted will conquer Eugenius, and soon after die, leaving the Western Empire to a ten-year-old boy'. So ran the rather bitter oracle. To 'sweeten' it Eutropius had brought home from Chalcedon* nothing less than the Head of St John the Baptist – the only one available at that time. Maybe Eutropius was making a coded political comment against Salome/Galla, since Ted was already bitterly regretting having topped Grandad Max, who had ruled the West so well. I think Eutropius thought this double message might cause Ted to remain in Constantinople, but Rufinus, Eutropius' arch-rival for Ted's ear, cleverly turned poor John Baptist's head to his own use, volunteering to build a memorial chapel specially for it (St John in Trullo*) at his own expense. Meantime the Head watched over Ted's convalescence and maybe hastened it. I was no longer needed.

During the hot months JJ took to dropping in on me at the Convent. With no wars in progress, but maybe one in the offing, General Timasius has given him the most boring job imaginable: nothing less than to update the Army List, the *Notitia Dignitatum*. Months of dreary work on official returns – who'd be a broad-striper?

Besides the Great Officers of State and their establishments, the *Notitia* gave details of every military formation directly under Roman command and on Rome's payroll. Because of the policy that provincial troops, especially those recently recruited, should serve as far as possible from their homelands, the War Offices of Old and New Rome continued to cooperate by posting troops to serve under one another's commands on a reciprocal basis, for more than a hundred years after the 'splitting of the eagles'. Officers were also cross-posted, as part of planned career development; the system survived civil wars in a quite amazing way. I foresee that the principal surviving MS will end up in the Bodleian Library.

JJ soon attached himself to the 'Gilding' laboratory where, he claimed, the Quartermaster's Department had a 'vested' interest. 'With all these new Barbarians to kit out, a process for mass-plating their insignia could save a lot of money,' he said. In the event he was to contribute a bonny little tract on gilding to the 'Sanct Graal' under the '*nom de plume*' 'Pelagius* Pelagianus' (to which he was, as I so often remind you, entitled like all Theo's descendants). He learnt, with all of us, how to 'kill the dragon', but also took quite an interest in my 'cooking', and was particularly attracted by our 'liqueurs'.

Come September, the news came that Galla was pregnant again, so Uncle Ted was plainly on the mend. I continued my 'cooking' and reading, especially of Josephus. I had made my own contribution to the team's output by suggesting a solution to the problem Heron was having with the glass retorts breaking when fire was put to them. This didn't happen with alcohol, which only needed a low heat; but Heron was now on to trying to distil strange and obstinate chemicals. I suppose it was Uncle Theodore's experimental telescope* that gave me the idea. 'Doctor,' I said, 'light passes through glass without heating it. If we could collect sunlight with an Archimedes mirror, and then focus it critically with a lens onto the chemical in the retort, the problem might be solved.'

'Capital, my boy,' said Doc.

'I'll get in some lens grinders and design an apparatus.* You've given me another idea too. Maybe with mercury we could make a glass mirror,* which would be more efficient than Archimedes'.'

It took some months to get this done, but it worked! 'Light from Light! Very God from very God! The Egyptians were right!'* crooned Heron. He really did go on.

One of Heron's projects was to distil the elixir of fire. Naturally we chose sulphur for this, since natural sulphur goes on fire of itself, so plainly contains the spirit of fire. But it would not distil for us. However after much experiment we managed to distil vitriol (sulphuric acid) out of ferrous sulphate and alum. Here was an exciting and dangerous fluid,* which did interesting things to metals, including dissolving some. Were we on the right track?

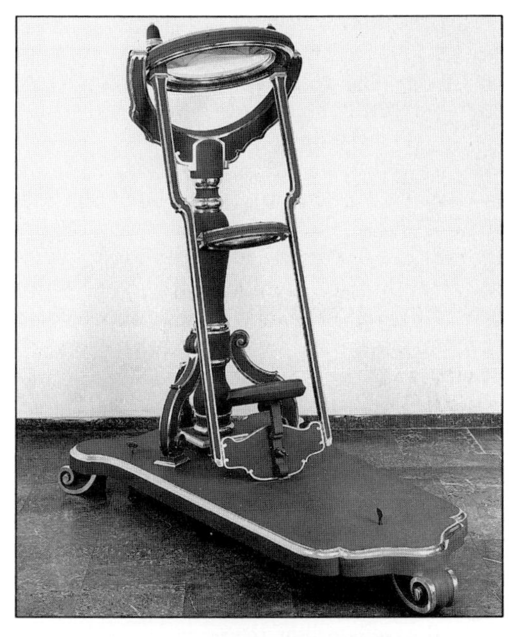

**Figure 20**
Von Tschirnhaus imitates Doc Heron
© Staatliche Kunstsammlung Dresden

Heron was insatiable now. 'If we could find the elixir that dissolves *all* metals, we should be close to the all-powerful Creative Spirit itself. Go on distilling, boys. Use the vitriol to dissolve other chemicals in turn, then redistil the mixture.'

By Christmas we had discovered Aqua Fortis (Nitric Acid) by distilling nitre and alum in vitriol. 'On, boys, on!' cried Heron. 'You shall soon see the Holy Spirit himself.'

Oh Ambrose, were we all going mad? The excitement in the laboratory had become overwhelming. JJ was round nearly every day, to watch and wait and lend a hand. And that was how, on a sunny day in late February, JJ had his terrible accident. He was peering from below at the retort, which seemed reluctant to boil in the weak winter sun, and I was adjusting the lens trying to improve the focus. I must have got the hot spot a little too near the edge of the contents, because suddenly the glass shattered and a gout of nitric acid went into JJ's left eye. He fell to the ground screaming and we rushed to pour clean water into his eye. By and by we changed this for milk which seemed to give him some relief, for he was in terrible pain. Then we tried olive oil, but to no avail. In this way **'Odin the Giant' surrendered his eye to Mime the dwarf, by reason of the serpent's venom.*** Uncle Heliodorus was sent for, and had JJ taken to his own quarters where for some days I nursed him and played the harp to him. Serena suggested that the place for him was the Casa

Sic: 'There's nothing Morgan doesn't know about herbal remedies and salves. If we can't save his left eye, and maybe Morgan can even do that, at least she can make sure he keeps his other one.' For, perhaps in sympathy, JJ claimed to be blind in his right eye too, though it looked all right to us.

So, for a time, ended JJ's military career, and also mine as a research chemist. Serena booked JJ a passage on a merchantman bound for Syracuse, and I of course accompanied him.

'You're well out of New Rome again, Luke,' said Serena. 'You don't seem to have made a friend of Galla – did she make a pass at you those nights up at the Palace? She's quite turned Dad against you. No chance of a command for you in the coming war, although Stilicho was willing to give you another try. Even though Dad's made Stilicho Commander-in-Chief this time, he hasn't been allowed to give Alaric a decent command either. Ginger's absolutely hopping mad – she says Dad, at that frightful birthday party, put us two girls in charge, of whom she's the senior sister, so her husband should be senior general. Dad says he remembers nothing of it.'

'Looks like I'm well out of it, Serena,' said I. 'Where's Elissa?'

'At Casa Sic with the "quiverful" of course, you silly,' Serena replied. 'She only went North last summer in order to take possession of her newly inherited Casa Belgica. Doesn't she write to either of you?'

Now this was going to be really awkward. I loved JJ – all the more now. I loved Elissa. I loved my kids. I loved old Morgan. Could we achieve a *ménage à trois*?

As we coasted westward I could not help thinking hopefully of blind Orion's trip to Lemnos and Crete in search of his sight. We stopped a few days in Crete awaiting fair winds, and I went to visit the site of the famous *labyrinth*. There was nothing to be seen by that time,* but I bought an old coin of Augustus as a keepsake which shows it well. I had done the same in Askalon;* I'm a real tourist at heart. Another week's sailing brought us to Syracuse and home. By good luck Uncle Theo was there, having an extended sabbatical after his years as Chancellor of the Exchequer in Rome, and glad to be back at his books and studies. He was dreadfully concerned at JJ's plight and undertook to see us on our way to the

**Figure 21**

Knossos heads for Tintagel, and Hollywood

Casa Sic as soon as possible. 'If anyone can cure him, Morgan can,' he said. 'She's a real healer.'

He and I talked half the night through, for I had much to tell him of the 'Coven of the Resurrection', and of events in New Rome. The next day he put JJ in a horse-litter, and we rode beside him out to the Casa Sic. 'I'll go in first and tell Elissa,' said Uncle Theo, while I waited anxiously. I need not have worried, Elissa was a real trooper. She was straightway at her husband's side, kissing and comforting him. Romans know their duty. A perfunctory embrace for me with a 'the kids'll be glad to see their "uncle" again.' I felt this was a bit tough, for John was away at Ocean College and all the quiverful present were mine. Nevertheless, 'Fate' had spoken, and that's how it was going to be. Well, I knew my place, and at least I *had* a place.

**Figure 22**
'Morgan' the Matriarch: wife and healer
© Edizioni Poligraf

JJ and I were to spend six months *en famille* at the Casa Sic. Under Morgan's treatment, and Elissa's kisses, JJ's right eye soon returned to normal. The left eye healed up after a fashion, with much scarring round, but the cornea was wrecked and all he could see through it was a faint and painful blur. To shade the eye he wore a broad-brimmed hat (a peasant *πετασος*), with the brim turned low on the left side. In bright sun he wore a patch. Gradually his spirits and confidence returned, and he and I and Elissa talked Christianity, and science and astronomy when we weren't playing with the kids or picnicking in the woods. Morgan was great on astronomy. In the evenings I amused myself with my pen by writing a long poem on the Rape of Proserpine, which, of course, had taken place only ten miles to the North at the *Lacus Pergus*.* We often swam and picnicked at the lake, where I used to recount the old myth to the kids; and it was a fellow house-guest, one Florentinus (an old Ocean College chum and currently Quaestor of Rome), who encouraged me to put it, as best I could, into verse.

It was a good, if strange, summer. We were out of the war, out of time almost.

Morgan's intelligence system was excellent, however; reports from the stewards of her Rome properties, and letters from her friends there, told us the news that Uncle Ted was on the move. He had left New Rome in late May, to hear in Adrianople in June that Galla was dead, in childbed. Now the need to avenge her brother was a sacred charge. Heavy at heart and racked in body, the ageing Augustus headed North by the same road as six years earlier, with the same general, to make inevitably the same mistake. Timasius and Stilicho rode with him. Three *ala* (wings) of tame Gothic cavalry rode with them, under their individual commanders, Gainas, Saulus, and Pacurius. Honorius and Serena waited anxiously for the signal to join him.

Meanwhile, Alaric and Ginger had departed in the opposite direction in the highest dudgeon. Alaric* and his wing rode furiously back into Thrace, where there was a large population of Vizi-Goths, the remnants of Fritigern's and Athanaric's followers, whom Uncle Ted had given a home there. Their fighting men had gone West with Ted. You could call it mutiny, but the remaining and undefended Goths did not wait long to call Alaric 'King'.

'Hell hath no fury like a woman scorned', 'tis said, and Old Rome was to pay the ultimate penalty for this slight to the Emperor's eldest daughter. **Götterdämmerung**, no less.

Of Lear's terrible night on the blasted heath, of the painfully won victory of the River Frigidus, of the taking and deaths of Eugenius and Arbogast I do not need to write. The history books are full of it. Suffice it that Uncle Ted reached Milan in a total state of despair and collapse. Only constant draughts of wine enabled him to keep going. Ambrose visited him and tried to praise and reassure him, but the black dog was fast on his shoulder. Hastily, messengers went to fetch Honorius and Serena, and by the end of September they were all with him in Justina's palace in Milan. In Constantinople laws were being published by Rufinus in the name of Arcadius. From the palace at Milan came no laws, no messages. Old Rome sat aghast and waited for the end, as indeed did the whole Empire of the West.

When we heard, in Sicily, that Eugenius and Arbogast were dead, Morgan decided to return to Rome, and we all went with her. JJ was by now very fit again, and talking of going back to his old law practice. I went because they were all going – believe it or not, Elissa had never been to Rome – and the kids were thrilled at the prospect.

'You could always find work teaching again,' said Elissa to me in her usual offhand way. I felt very out of things with them all; not really wanted, if you know what I mean. So they all settled in on the Quirinale; but something told me Uncle Ted could do with his little harpist again, and I pushed on to Milan, where Ambrose received me with his usual affection. The man really combined Roman *gravitas* with Christian serenity. He directed me straight to the Palace.

'You'll be useful there, and you'll be welcome,' he said. 'I call in often, and take your Uncle the sacrament. A much flawed man, alas; nonetheless he has served the Church and Empire well. Give him what comfort you can.'

At the Palace I got another surprise. Honorius was there, of course, and Serena, and Stilicho. I had not quite expected all the babies. 'Couldn't leave the little innocents to Ginger and Rufinus' mercies now Galla's dead,' said Serena. 'And besides, something tells me I shall never see New Rome again, so I've brought my three, and Placidia, and two of Doxy's. Come and meet *your* son; not knowing your wishes, we've called him Quintus* (number five) for the time being.'

'What on earth do you mean, Serena?'

'Well, you gave poor Doxy something, as well as vice versa. He's got your golden hair too, and I hope that's the end of the resemblance. He's eight months old. Dear little fellow. I seem to be running some kind of crèche.'

True enough, in the royal nursery was little Galla Placidia, the pet – a primrose-haired toddler; young Aëtius, Son of the Eagles; and finally the little golden boy without a name. My boy. He who was to be the apple of my eye – yes, and bury me. And the only name I had to give him was 'Eugenius'. Poor little bastard.

'Dad has his ups and downs,' said Serena. 'Mostly downs. He's made Uncle Theodore Praetorian of the Gauls, so at least they're in safe hands. I don't know if he'll recognise you, as he's really wandering in the mind. Better grab yourself a guitar. He'll know you from that.'

So we watched and waited by the sick bed, and I harped and sang to him; in fact I sang him my recent 'Rape of Proserpine'. For me, it was the belated birthday ode I'd promised him. 'You're really quite a poet,' said Serena. 'Maybe you could do it professionally.'

That's how, in my off-duty hours at the Palace, I came to write my first paid official commission. It was Serena's idea and she organised it. My old Mendip friends Olybrius and Probinus, Faltonia's sons, were Consuls-elect for 395. They readily agreed that I should write and recite their Consular Panegyric at the Capitol. Hastily gathering to myself specimens of all the previous Panegyrics I could get hold of – for the form and style were rigidly conventional – I set to work. If cousin Augustine could do it, so could I. 'Floreat Ocean College' and all that. For this new career, as it was to become, I took like many before me and still more after, a pen-name. **Claudius Claudianus** I called myself; good names, and *my* names. Was not my *praenomen* Claudius? And did I not bear it because it was a family name?* I found composing the

Panegyric gruelling hard work, but I like to think Uncle Heliodorus and Eunapius would have been proud of their pupil. Uncle Ted really liked the bits I read him, and readily gave me leave of absence to go to Rome to read it on the first of January. Little did I know that I should repeat this performance five times in the coming years.

Ted's chief preoccupation seemed to be that Honorius should finish off the great Basilica of Saint Paul ('*fuori le mura*') in Rome which he had left incomplete in 391. Honorius and Stilicho made repeated promises to this effect – which they kept. At long last Ted remembered the Empire. 'Puppet or no, I have nothing else to give. Have Honorius' purple robe and sandals made, and have them prepare the official bust.' (The first task of an aspiring Augustus was to sit for his portrait in wax; bronze copies of this were sent to the two Senate Houses for display – if accepted – and thereafter scores of copies were sent to the Provinces. This was a useful safeguard against counterfeit coinage, and indeed counterfeit Augusti.

So on 14 January 395 – having just managed to grace the Christmas Games, briefly, with his presence – Uncle Ted was carried to a chair in the Colonnade before the Palace, and there, before a small crowd of Milanese, surrounded by the Palatine guards, supported by the Prefect and the Bishop, he laid hands on young Honorius, placed the diadem on his head, and raised him up as 'Imperator Augustus' to the repeated 'three cheers for the young Emperor, Hip-Hip-Hurray' from the well-drilled soldiers. Turning to Serena and Stilicho as they helped him back into the Palace he said, 'The future of the Empire rests now on your shoulders. I can do no more.' Tough on Ginger, wasn't it? Three days later Uncle Ted was dead. The end of an era. The end of the Empire in the West, did we but know it.

In his last weeks Ted had talked a lot about where he should be buried. 'I won't be buried here, in Justina's mausoleum,' he said. 'Harpy and heretic she was. No peace there. And Rome's too pagan. Look how they all apostatised under Eugenius. If only I'd finished my new Basilica of St Paul's that might have done. But too late now. New Rome's my city, with my arch, my forum, my column, my palace, my family graves.' That's where I *will* to be buried, and I *will* that my brother Heliodorus be the man to inter me. He knows all about the sacraments; he shall take care of my resurrection.[1] And young Luke here shall pronounce my funeral oration in Latin and Greek. He's the only one left who can.' God help me, I thought.

---

[1] Like all pious but educated Christians of his day, and maybe since, Uncle Ted was honestly curious to understand what Jesus actually meant when He said 'this is my body ... this is my blood'. How could this be? Was He merely talking allegorically? If not, what change took place in the bread and wine? Aristotle had taught that matter was *solid* through and through (although its outward appearance or 'accidents' might be varied). Hence, inevitably, if Jesus were to be taken literally, the doctrine of **Transubstantiation,*** in which the natural bread changes to 'Flesh' which still looks like bread.

Well, it didn't happen quite like that. Ambrose conducted the funeral and gave the address, and read a Panegyric by my beloved Paulinus of Nola. The body was embalmed, and it was agreed that I should accompany it by sea to Constantinople. What would happen there, we should have to see. Throughout Lent the body lay in state in the Great Basilica in Milan, for all to pay their respects. Masses were said and dirges sung. After Easter, I and a small cortège of officials and clergy embarked at Ravenna for the voyage to New Rome. Serena, scared of Ginger, decided not to come. Stilicho had work to do. It would be for Arcadius and Rufinus to decide how much of a solemnity to make at their end. As it happened they had other things on their minds.

My doleful shipload arrived at the end of April in Julian's new harbour to find New Rome *en fête*. Three days previously Arcadius had taken himself a bride, or been landed with one, and the fountains were still running with wine. Uncle Ted had left Rufinus as Arcadius' prime minister, and he was Ginger's friend. He had a daughter, whom he destined for Arcadius; as father-in-law of the Augustus his position would surely be more or less impregnable. But Eutropius (in some sort Serena's friend) was no less ambitious. As a eunuch, he naturally had no daughter. But he had a plan so daring that if it had not come off, and if it were not solid history, you'd never believe it.

Rufinus had just returned from a hurried mission to Antioch (in the matter of Uncle Icarus and the Southern Huns as it happened), and was all dressed up for the wedding of his daughter to Arcadius on 27 April 395. On the great day the bridegroom's procession left the Daphne Palace to fetch the bride for the ceremony but, sweeping by Rufinus' house without check, made straight for the Casa Promotus. There, chastely – if that is the word – concealed behind her bridal veil* stood none other than Doxy, arrayed as 'Persē' incarnate. Now in Greek legend Persē is 'the fair daughter of *Ocean*' (for whom Genobaudes the Fleming would stand in admirably). She had two sons, Aētes (Aëtius) and Persēs (Gawain), 'sons of Persē', '*Persei filii*'. *Both* can be, and are to be, conflated as Parzival, Perceval, and many variants. They must *not* be confused with 'Peredur', whom I'll explain later.

Minutes later Doxy was in the imperial chariot, and that night she was in the Augustus' bed as his lawful wedded wife, not that even her skills would be able to coax children out of him. A surrogate would be needed for that – one Count John.

Now, Count John, as my friend and tutor Eunapius will tell you, was an

---

Uncle Heliodorus and his researchers (especially Doc Heron) had come up with a more up-to-date view of matter, as being far from 'solid' in the sense that Aristotle (following Democritus), had thought. In their view there was thus ample room for Jesus, by the Holy Spirit, wholly to impregnate the bread, which thus became '*Bread*', without doing violence to the laws of nature. This doctrine of **Consubstantiation*** had greatly reassured Uncle Ted, and would also satisfy Luther.

intimate of Arcadius and the supposed father of his children. He was later taken hostage by Gainas the Goth,* and his neck spared in a scene so closely akin to the future folk tales of Sir Gawain and the Grene Knight and of Cu-Chulain in Bricriu's Feast that they must surely be based on it. (Later Romancers will, pardonably, confuse the two Johns.) My John, 'Little' John (later to be called John-George) is meant for 'Sir Gawayne'. To avoid confusion with 'my Gawain', I'll call John 'pseudo-Gawain', or else Gawain I.

With Eutropius' star now in the ascendant, Rufinus had no option but to attend the wedding, raging inwardly but outwardly obsequious – vexing for him, that trip to Antioch. It was into this astounding scene that I brought Uncle Ted's coffin. No one was much interested. Uncle Heliodorus turned out to have died a few weeks previously. Nectarius, the Patriarch – thank God there was someone decent still around and doing his job – received Ted's body with appropriate dignity and laid him up *pro tem* in the temporary Cathedral of (St Irene).

Heigh ho! I thought, as I repaired rather anxiously to Ginger, to find out the lie of the land.

# BOOK XI

## *'Ephialtēs'** *(AD395–399)*

I was to spend the next six months *chez* Ginger, unwilling to leave New Rome until I had put Uncle Ted 'safely to bed'. I spent much of my days down at the Swan Convent, as an outpatient. I mentioned earlier the genito-urinary problems for which I have Doxy to thank. Ginger's medic told me that they were developing a new treatment, based on arsenic, down at the Anastasis, where I was put in the hands of young Olympiodorus. I found the Convent less hectic, since the death of old Doc Heron, and Bishop Sisinnius, who has succeeded Uncle Heliodorus, did not command the same prestige as had the brother of the late Augustus. Nevertheless, church and laboratories remained busy. Already they had succeeded in distilling Aether, the first local (later general) anaesthetic, which was to be serviceable to me in future years. The government subsidy still continued. I found, too, that there was no one quite so dead as a dead Augustus. With no more legions to command or favours to bestow, Ted was quite forgotten. The construction of his porphyry sarcophagus went forward at a snail's pace; all craftsmen were kept busy on Arcadius' new Forum with *his* statue. Still, Nectarius kept on prodding.

Ginger had stationed herself in Town, because she felt that, on the strength of that dreadful birthday party vow, she was Guardian and in some sort Regent for Arcadius. (She grudgingly accepted that Serena had the same role for Honorius.) Up to three days before, that had meant her keeping as close as possible to Rufinus. Doxy's sudden arrival at the Palace, and Eutropius' ascendancy, called for a tactical rethink. We had many intimate talks, mostly about politics, in our evenings together. With no husband at hand, I might have found the brother/sister relationship hard to maintain in this situation, but in my present state of health it was no problem.

Alaric was gallivanting around the Marcian country with his Goths, and a subvention from Rufinus had been sent to keep them quiet. It won't succeed. From the East, the tidal wave of Huns flows like locusts towards us. I mentioned earlier that a branch of the Huns had taken the South side of the Black Sea and were ravaging Syria, and that Rufinus had bought them off on his untimely recent trip to Antioch. But it was the huge Northern branch who were now pressing ever harder on the Danube. That meant hordes of refugees: Alans,

Sarmatians, Dacians, Massagetes, Geloni, all pressing into Scythia and Moēsia on top of Alaric's Vizi-Goths. Money wouldn't make them stay there; very soon the Goths would be on the move. Alaric couldn't, maybe didn't even want to, hold them. Could Ginger find a role for them? Had she perhaps already done so?

Thus Rufinus had his problems. The biggest was that Uncle Ted took with him, to beat Eugenius, the entire fighting strength of the Eastern Empire, which was now quite defenceless. The armies of the East were currently lolling around the cities of the Po, eating the citizens out of house and home. A great man, in his way, Rufinus had hatched an audacious plan to save New Rome, at the cost of losing some land permanently to the Huns, and yet more to the Goths. Was it statesmanship to gamble on this huge scale? Had he any real alternative? Despite what I have already written,* and Eunapius too, about the history of that year, I foresaw that future historians would remain baffled. So I will use the benefit of hindsight in what I now write. For, as a participant myself, I too was hoodwinked at the time, and later, when I realised the full extent of the double-cross and how much of the blame for it would rest on me, I was to be deeply angry. So let me set out the course of events as I now know it, and you shall judge me and Ginger, and Rufinus for yourselves.

In May AD395, acting via Ginger, Rufinus secretly invited Alaric to turn his Goths southwards, on the understanding that he would find them a new and safer home. By June the Goths were storming at the gates of New Rome, and convincingly pitiful messages could be sent to Milan. However the appearance of Rufinus outside the gates, crying '*Ich bin selbst ein Gothiker*' seemed to calm them 'strangely', and onwards they swept. A bloody skirmish with local forces at the River Hebrus and they were through westwards into Macedonia. Stilicho heard all this and naturally decided to intervene. Were not he and Serena the true guardians of the whole Empire, by Ted's dying charge? All he had to do was to crush Alaric and Ginger, and then march into New Rome as its saviour.

The best validation of this presumptuous and illegal action would have been Uncle Ted's Will. Serena went to the Senior Vestal to collect this, and had a terrible row with the poor old lady – the last of the Vestals as it proved. They had quite a tussle over the scroll, ending with Serena grabbing it, and at the same time ripping off a sacramental necklace, which she kept. The Vestal put a swingeing curse on Serena, all too like Harmonia in Greek myth, and it seemed unwise for Serena to keep the necklace. Draw what conclusion you like from the fact that Ted's Will was nevertheless not published. I can tell you, however, that he left the Villa Sirmione in trust for young Placidia, which as 'Joyeuse Garde',* would prove to be very joyous for her, for me, and for others I shall name.

In July Stilicho, 'man of steel', with the combined armies of East and West, headed eastwards up the Egnatia into the Balkans just as Rufinus meant him to. Hearing that Stilicho's troops were making for him, Alaric pulled his Goths back from Epirus and set off southwards instead, skirting Olympus, for the plains of Thessaly where they laagered around Larissa. Rufinus' timing was impeccable. By early August Stilicho's armies were at Salonica where, hearing that Alaric had gone south, they turned south in pursuit. That same night a fast messenger (*agens in rebus*, 'MI5 man') was galloping to Rufinus. The trap was set, and I was to be the cheese in it.

At the time I was to blame Ginger, but now I blame myself for yielding to her blandishments, her cunning flattery. She really 'conned' me, but in the heady excitement of the moment I allowed it. So, the last week of August saw me back in official service in the dual capacity of secret agent (of Rufinus) and love-messenger (of Thermantia), bearer of her 'pathetic farewell message' to Alaric. For the latter task it was put to me that for my own safety I had best go disguised, and it was with the black robes* of a monk over my tunic, my unshaven locks concealed by its cowl,* that I boarded a fast mail galley for Bolos (Volos).

Under my robe I had concealed two dyptychs – hinged tablets. The erasable message was on the two waxed surfaces inside, and the whole packet was security-sealed. (Tryptychs were used for longer messages. Permanent documents were scratched in copper or, at leisure, written with quill and ink. Consuls often commemorated their year by sending beautifully carved ivory dyptychs to their friends as souvenirs, and many of these informative and often beautiful relics survive.) One of my two dyptychs was for Alaric from Ginger, the other from Arcadius for the Proconsul of Achaia, one Antiochus.

I reached Alaric early in September and delivered Ginger's missive. He received me distractedly, and thankfully did not recognise me, nor did I intend he and his entourage should. They did not seem in a pro-Roman mood. Hurrying back to Bolos I shed my monk's disguise and resumed my journey to Corinth to deliver my Imperial Dyptych to the Proconsul. I assumed it contained instructions to call out the Citizens Levy, declaring a State of Emergency for the purpose, and to lead all the resulting troops to block Alaric at Thermopylae. To my horror I found that it did the exact opposite. Thermopylae was to be left unblocked, the Isthmus of Corinth undefended, and Alaric's Goths were to be ushered, if they would be so kind, through the Isthmus into their proposed new homeland, the Peleponnese, or Morea. As a good civil servant, Antiochus had no option but to obey.

I arrived back, fuming, at New Rome at the end of September, determined to unmask the traitor behind this debacle. I did not, of course, know that shortly after I embarked for my outward voyage to Greece an official delegation from Rufinus had left by the Egnatia to catch up with Stilicho, bearing openly, indeed proudly, another sealed Imperial Dyptych: they need fear no molestation from their fellow-Roman 'liberators'. They came up with Stilicho just as he was approaching Larissa, whence Alaric had moved only days before, on getting Ginger's message that the road South lay open to him. Stilicho tore open the seals. It read:

> His Serenity the Lord Arcadius Caesar Augustus to Flavius Stilicho *Magister Utriusque Militum Occidens*. Greetings. We thank you and our brother Augustus for returning to our sovereign command the armies of the Orient which our blessed father the Augustus Theodosius took with him last year for the liberation of the West, together with their pay-chest. With our own forces, now dutifully restored to us, New Rome is well able to defend her own frontiers. We therefore command and require you to withdraw those troops which rightfully belong to *your* command to their own territory, where they can be more usefully employed. Farewell.

Rufinus' trap had been sprung.

In setting this trap Rufinus had shown himself not only a master of timing but also of psychology. Put more directly, he knew his Stilicho. Such a plan would not have worked with Arbogast; but Slavs are simpler and more emotional than Prussians. Loyalty means a lot to them, and in Stilicho's case it was loyalty to the Roman Army and to Rome's dead Emperor whose son-in-law he was, which had made him. Could he disobey the new Augustus whom he had vowed to sustain and support? Any man would have found this choice difficult. Around him his Teutonic troops chanted 'Heil Stilicho! Sieg Heil! Stilicho, "Stalin", man of steel, lead us on to Byzantium.' But Rufinus had judged him right. Sadly, Stilicho said farewell to his Eastern troops and turned back for Italy. Nevertheless, with the Eastern cavalry rode a commander who knew Stilicho's true mind: Gainas the Goth.

Of how, on 27 November, Rufinus met his most terrible death you can read at length in my own words,* written almost at the time; I cannot better that account. But ere this happened I was already on a boat for Italy, my task in Constantinople completed, for on 7 November, in the presence of Arcadius and Doxy, of Rufinus and Eutropius, of Ginger and me, Nectarius presided over the translation of Uncle Ted to his simple and noble new sarcophagus in the narthex of the Basilica of St Irene. The sole decoration, as Ted himself had wished, was his Regimental Badge, the standard of the Theban Legion in which he had started his service. It consisted of the Egyptian *ankh* or looped cross, christianised by Constantine by inserting the Chi-Rho in the loop. There was a modest public attendance. No one called on me for a Panegyric; indeed I was the victim of ugly rumours. 'Ephialtēs', I heard voices in the crowd cry, 'Ephialtēs, traitor of Thermopylae. 'And one of those voices I knew.

Now it was Ephialtēs who in former times disclosed to Xerxes and the Persians a secret mountain path bypassing Thermopylae, thus rendering Leonidas and his Spartans' heroic last stand no more than a futile gesture. 'Ephialtēs' had been a by-name for traitor in Greece ever since. Antiochus the Proconsul came in for the same obloquy as me; he too was called 'Ephialtēs'. In time we came to be confused, and I got the nickname 'Antiochus' to add to all my others. (Remember this the next time you read the romance of Apollonius of Tyre, to which I so constantly refer you* – it is very far from irrelevant.)

But there was yet more to this horridly relevant epithet: in Greek myth Ephialtēs and Otus, two brothers, fought for the giant Titans against Zeus and the Gods on Mount Olympus, piling Mount Pelion on Mount Ossa to form a siege tower – all this just East of Larissa, where the present action was taking place. I myself refer briefly to them in my 'Gigantomachia',* but it is the author to be named in the next paragraph who would use 'Ephialtēs and Otus'* pejoratively against me and JJ, in our efforts against the 'Olympus' of Old Rome herself in only ten years hence. JJ he called 'Otus', and me he derided as 'Ephialtēs'/*Otulus* 'Otello' ('little Otus'). Who was the Moor? I'll tell you in App. 11.

I said there was a voice in the crowd I knew. It was that of Taurus Jr, Claudius Rutilius Aurelianus Namatianus Taurus II,* to give him his full name, my future rival as a poet, and lifelong political opponent. His really rather nice father, Count Aurelian,* was at Ted's fateful birthday party as Prefect of New Rome, and was to succeed Eutropius and do much to clear up the mess he and Rufinus had left; he didn't manage to clear my reputation, though. Rufinus might well want me assassinated before I told the truth. Now, young Taurus had turned the crowd against me. It was time to get out quick. Maybe Taurus was part of Rufinus' plot. Scapegoat, I was. The Gods will not be mocked, though; ere long I'll have my revenge on Rufinus and the whole rotten lot of them.

Meanwhile the Huns had Scythia, and Alaric, not yet 'ushered into the Peloponnese' was running amok around the Gulf of Corinth. 'Athens cringes, Corinth burns'. In actual fact the Athenians invited him in, and were much relieved to find that Flavius Alaricus* was no rough Goth but a very civilised adopted Roman. He enjoyed their baths and banquets, and declared Athens an 'open city'. At this same strange time Poxy Doxy, the butter still unmelted in her mouth, ascended to the commanding heights of power with pious, exemplary, dignified steps. Soon she would be Augusta: maybe the Gods were being mocked after all.

I took ship hurriedly for Old Rome where I put up with Aunt Satyra once again, while I found out the lie of the land. I learnt that JJ and Elissa were at Morgan's *domus* on the Quirinale where I hurried to call on them. JJ was amiable, and a lot thinner. He had resumed legal practice, but spent most of his evenings at Aunt Marcella's Bible classes* at her Palace/Convent on the

Aventine. (I call her 'Aunt' for convenience. She is in fact my adoptive step first cousin, see App. 6.) JJ was developing into quite a theologian, and was currently working on a Commentary on the Epistles of St Paul. Phew! I hadn't even read them.

It was at Morgan's house that I ran into my friend Florentinus, the guest at Casa Sic who had encouraged me to take up my poetry. He was currently Prefect of Rome (Lord Mayor) and he told me that the Senate was desperately seeking someone to do the forthcoming Panegyric for Honorius' Third Consulate. 'You made a good job of this year's Consuls. Do you think you could do a rush job?' he asked.

'Well, I'd need some money, and somewhere quiet to work,' I said. I was broke as usual.

'Not supposed to be any money in this,' said Florentinus. 'The glory of praising the Augustus is supposed to be enough. But I think I could wangle you a sinecure in the Tabularium which would give you some money and a room.'

'Thanks,' I said, 'tell the powers that be that I'm their man.'

I can't remember anything of the remainder of that year. Just the wet towels round my head. I still had six months to go, too, of my course of arsenic which I found rather lowering though it seemed to be working. Suffice it that I made my deadline, although the opus was a bit shorter than is usual on these occasions, and on 3 January 396 I ascended the podium in front of young Honorius, of Serena and Stilicho, of the assembled Senate and their wives and of the Chief Officers of State, to 'bore for Rome' in the traditional manner. Though I say it myself, it was well received. I think they liked its brevity! I saw Serena and Stilicho nodding eagerly at lines 153–154 where I said that Uncle Ted had made them guardians of his *two* sons and of the *whole* Empire. Well, I too had heard him say it, or words to that effect, three days before he died. Stilicho called me up afterwards to congratulate me. I did myself some good there.

I have said little of Stilicho, so far, as a man, because up to now I'd really seen very little of him. Let me just say that, if Rome had to bow to Barbarian Giants, he was the man. Well over six foot tall,* he looked younger than his thirty-six years despite his prematurely-grey hair. He was oval-faced, clean-shaven and more Roman than the Romans in his manner and speech, but with an attractive slavonic tone to his rather deep bass voice. He presented a courteous and reassuring image to the rather anxious Roman aristocracy. Here, one felt, was 'Mr Clean'. And so, maybe, he was? The man had charisma, that was it. Rome hadn't seen him before, and already they were eating out of his hand. So would I. And how.

Still using hindsight I can tell you that on hearing of Rufinus' successful assassination, while I was still at work on my recent Panegyric, Stilicho had hurried North to Trier in search of troops. Arcadius' script at Larissa had forced him to part with the Army of the East, but he still had Eastern aspirations and for them he needed men; many more men. Uncle Theodore was still Praetorian of Gaul, and together they pored over Army Lists, and arrangements were made to denude the 'Arctic' defences yet again. The Franks and Alemanni must be bribed once more; better still, they might furnish federate troops.

Back in Rome, Stilicho sent for JJ. 'Agricola,' he said, 'you know more about the Army List than anyone alive. Rome needs *you*.' (How we Romans ever respond to that pointing finger.) 'I hereby appoint you as *Primicerius Notariorum Co-adjutor*,[1] reporting to your Uncle Theodore, to complete in the Britains the task that he and I have just been doing for the Gauls. You will retain the rank of Count* which you held in Thrace under Timasius before your accident, although you are no longer on the active list.' (Poor old JJ, never really a front-line soldier, would be ever remembered, not unkindly, by my Irish as 'Ailill, Edge-of-Battle', and by my Welsh as 'Cad-wallon'* the 'battle-avoider' – and who could blame him, with only one eye?) 'You can take your family with you,' concluded Stilicho. 'Look after yourself. What about getting me some more Picts and Scots, yes and some of those new Irish?'

**Figure 23**
Army haircut for this Irish squaddie

So JJ put aside Jesus, or at least St Paul, for the time being, gathered up Elissa and the quiverful, and set off for York. I said polite farewells to Elissa: 'to each cow its calf'; I reckoned I'd lost the quiverful. The

[1] Assistant 'Chief Secretary'. This deceptively modest title conceals the twin masters of Old and New Rome. The 'Sir Humphreys' as it were of *Yes, Augustus*. Chief Establishment Officers of the whole Public Service, Civil and Military, they prepared the lists of the 'great and good', and were responsible for career planning, personal appointments and unit cross-postings, between the provinces and indeed between the Empires. Of high, but cunningly not the highest, rank they contrived to remain, so far as the 'Media' were concerned, completely anonymous. Thanks to them the State could and did take good and bad Emperors in its stride, while they continued with the 'orderly management of decline'. Do any bells ring?

best men don't always win. So a rather cynical middle-aged Poet Laureate settled back to his clerk's duties in the Tabularium and sharpened his pen. I decided to work off my spleen on Rufinus and had written two Philippics against him by the end of July.

'You ought to publish them,' said Serena. 'I'll put up the money for the copyists.' Within six weeks they were on the bookstalls of Rome. I felt the better for it too. 'Traitor of Thermopylae' indeed. I reckoned I'd settled that score.

The same month Stilicho launched his second bid for world supremacy. A little less grandiose this time; all he wanted was *all* Illyricum for the West. But that meant war on Alaric and his Goths who had finally taken up their 'invitation' and were enjoying themselves around the Peloponnese. Posing as liberator of Achaia, Stilicho took an armada to Corinth. He and Alaric then played peek-a-boo around the Peloponnese until he finally had the Goths penned up on the killing grounds of Pholois in Arcadia (a plain between the Rivers Alph and Pineos, some twenty-five miles North of Olympia). The night before the battle a black-gowned and cowled monk, with a small escort under a flag of truce, left the Gothic lines and penetrated eventually into Stilicho's tent. In low tones the monk demanded to speak to Stilicho alone and, the guards dismissed, she threw back her cowl. It was Ginger! What should Stilicho say to his dear sister-in-law? Hospitality was inescapable. Ginger had a strong head. Stilicho was normally extremely temperate. Ginger was persuasive, tearful, flattering, appealing in more ways than one. (Plate 9) 'Let not battle commence the next day; we have so much to talk out.'

Orders were given that the troops could stand down and take off their armour for the time being. Meanwhile Ginger was fighting for hers and Alaric's life using the weapons of Venus and Bacchus. Serena would *never* believe that Ginger did not seduce him, nor ever forgive it.

The talks, if that is all they were, seemed to have gone on for about three days. When Stilicho came to his senses it was to find that the Goths had used the dark nights to steal through his lines to Patras and cross, as fast as they could be ferried, over to the mainland of Epirus. All he was left with was a monk's robes and a note which said 'Thanks for your kindness. Together we may yet rule the Empire'. With the note was yet another Imperial Dyptych from Arcadius. It read much like the previous one, only this time the tone was yet harsher. It commanded him to desist from this intrusion on a fellow Augustus' territory and to withdraw at once on pain of being posted as a Traitor and 'Enemy of the Republic'.* The author this time was Eutropius the Pimp (now Patricius of the East), in cahoots with Doxy and Ginger. Poor Stilicho. He returned meekly to Italy, but there was murder in his heart, if only he could find a way. Meanwhile Alaric, too, had received a Scrip appointing him *Magister Militum* of Illyricum.* The only question was: which part – the southern half only, or the whole Prefecture? So it was

Stilicho versus Alaric, Goneryl versus Regan, a 'Tale of Two Sisters', as it were.

Towards the end of 396 I got the news that dear reliable old Uncle Theo was coming from Gaul to be Praetorian of Italy – a move towards the newest front line. I also heard that my old paymaster at the Swan Coven, Hadrian Synesius, had left New Rome and was coming over to us as *Magister Officiorum* (Minister of War Production). I hoped that was all right and that he wasn't a Trojan Horse. Who knew what sort of plots the twin Chief Secretaries of East-West might be up to? This was one of those cross-postings which you would hardly expect during such an East-West crisis. Sometimes I wondered if the civil servants let the politicians play at 'statesmanship' and 'soldiers' just to keep them quiet. To celebrate these curious events I wrote a light-hearted lampoon which became a talking-point in Rome, and soon earned me the reputation of a heavyweight political wit.

> Manlius Theodorus sleeps night and day;
> the *sleepless* Egyptian* steals alike from gods and men.
> Peoples of Italy, be this your one prayer –
> that Manlius stay awake, and the Egyptian asleep.

I got into hot water again with my pen by writing a little too wittily about my erstwhile patron Florentinus, who saw himself too as a poet. His pen name was Alētheus, meaning 'truthful', which rather invited my retaliatory candour. Florentinus protested vigorously, but I didn't reckon his patronage was worth much any more, and thought that he was on the way out, so I published an apology to him which I hoped would make him more than sorry he had complained. I might only have been a clerk in the Tabularium but, pen in hand, I could make them all sit up and beg. Trouble was, no one begged. Commissions dried up. I wrote touting for more work to my old patrons Olybrius and Probinus. Deathly silence. I offered my services to the Consuls-elect for 397. Polite refusal. Was I the 'little wasp of the Aventine'? I felt a bit out. So I went back to Morgan for a little breast-baring.

'My dear Luke,' she said, 'if you want to have friends and influence people, do try to leave yourself at least *some* friends. You could start by thinking about your own family.'

Ouch – I thought of the quiverful.

'No not just them, come and look in the nursery wing here.' Amazed I went with Morgan, and there were little Aëtius and my own Gawain. 'Serena's got her hands full with her own three, and she needs as much time as she can make to support Stilicho in this crisis. I am their grandmother,* step-gran too, and now I'm fostering them. They love it out at Subiaco in the summer.

The '**Dame du Lac**',* that's what the kids call me. And I keep up my monthly correspondence with Elissa. Don't you care what happens there? They're all up in Caledonia at the moment. Some sort of recruiting drive. Next year they're going over to the Western Island.' (This was where JJ would drop, near Cashel, the lid of his eye ointment box,* made up for him by the best oculists in Syracuse to Morgan's prescription.) 'JJ's doing no end of evangelisation on the side,' continued Morgan. 'He's starting churches everywhere. He got the idea from your cousin Vic,* or else it's his sainted father's blood coming out in him.' (Peering ahead, I foresaw that three generations of pious 'Constantinians': Dad, JJ, and Little John would *all* get conflated as 'St Ninian' – the last two as 'St Kentigern'.) I too was 'born again' once, but it seemed to have rubbed a bit thin. Would I ever be a saint? Heigh ho!

I felt better now that I was off the arsenic, so I made a New Year's Resolution to be nicer to people in 397 for a start. There was much else good to think about. Did I tell you about young Placidus Germanus, Macrobius' son (so Ambrose's grandson), the novice whose life JJ saved at Subiaco when he was co-Abbot there? He was now eighteen, and had gone with a close chum, John Cassian, via Bethlehem, to play Desert Hermits in Egypt. So many *Consulares* there, it must be like something out of Debrett! Marcella was in touch with them. (Cassian would be the author of the famous 'Collations' of sayings of the Desert Fathers, and founder of the Monastery of St Victor, Marseille and its sister-convent. Thirty-six years hence, Germanus would dedicate a church to him in Ireland, seven miles NNW of Tara.)

Cousin Vic was back in Rouen, after his mission to Britain for Ambrose, and was busily re-evangelising the Morini of the Pas-de-Calais and French Flanders, the work which 'Glorious Dad' had started thirty years previously as Llŷr (Pelagianus) Morini.* In only a few years hence, Pope Innocent would rebuke Vic for unsupervised evangelism and he would be dubbed *Publicola* 'people-pleaser'. Vic positively relished the epithet, and the Cambrians would thus remember him as St Peblig, with his own authentic tomb at Caernarfon. Meantime, my work can't have been that bad, because I'd been promoted to work with JJ in the elite offices of the *primicerius notariarum* (comparable with the 'Cabinet Office' of the future).

There was more New Year good news. Synesius Tertius,[2] my old Alexandrian chum, and brother of Hadrian whom I had just lampooned, was in residence

[2] The history books will remember him as Bishop of Ptolemais c.410–414. Anglicans will sing his hymns in 'Ancient and Modern'. The 'Primus', 'Secunda', 'Tertius' bit indicates that he was of a distinguished and old-fashioned Roman family, the Turcii* in fact. Old families kept up the gentry tradition that sons only got their *prenomina* when they put on the *toga virilis*; daughters had to wait until they could assume their husband's *nomen* in the feminine form. Meantime they were just called 'First', 'Second', 'Third', etc.

at the Coven of the Resurrection. He was on an embassy from Cyrene – some local government matter – and Eutropius and Doxy were keeping him dangling in true Byzantine style, so he was passing the time with a bit of alchemy.* He found my name on the files, and was kind enough to write me a letter. Things really were looking up in my world.

Not so in the East/West contest. Eutropius had hatched a clever plot to keep Stilicho safely in the West. He'd stirred up Gildo, the Governor, to revolt in Africa and cut off Rome's bread supply – High Treason if it could be pinned on him. As his first task Stilicho had to organise an expeditionary force to exterminate Gildo and liberate Africa. Next, while the blockade was still on, he had to find food for Rome. His heroic answer. Britain ships all available supplies to North Gaul and the Rhineland; they in turn send their stocks to Southern Gaul; finally Southern Gaul sends its food down the Rhône to Rome – a massive feat of improvisation which left all the Provinces bruised, fretful, and short of food. The *Vectigales* (collectors of *annonae*, 'tribute in kind'), had had to use draconian powers of requisitioning which left Britain and the Gauls ripe for the 'Peasant Revolts'* (Bacaudic) which would break out in the next decade. (I had a part on both sides of the fence in these conflicts; at one moment I was Robin Hood – 'Hood' for 'Bacaud', corrupted – next moment I was on the side of law and order as Lucius Wihtigils,* *Vectigalis* father of one of the 'Hengists', and foster-father of 'Horsa'.* Geoffrey of Monmouth will call me *Lucius Hiberius.** It will *all* become clear as we go on.)

I saw all the despatches in my little office. Thank God for Britain, and for Stilicho. I thought I would have to write him a poem. Several* in fact. It would please Serena, and maybe do me a bit of good. I'd write her one too.*

So passed most of 397 and in October I got another commission, the Panegyric for Honorius' Fourth Consulship. Hurrah, I was back on the map; this had to be good, and they thought it was, when I read it on 3 January 398). The only real sadness in 397 was the death of Ambrose. He died very peacefully and suitably on Good Friday, and I went to his funeral in Milan. I returned with one keepsake of him which I would peruse at leisure: a copy of his sermons, one of which, on Lot and his daughters, would 'pierce my heart' at a later date. Ambrose's powerfully socialist *De Nabuthe* (of Naboth and his vineyard) had already powerfully affected Cousin Vic, and would inspire Little John to alarming feats of political pamphleteering in a few years time. Ambrose willed to be interred in his *own* Basilica* of Sts Gervasius and Protasius by the side of his very own martyrs, beneath the altar at which he had so often celebrated the Eucharist, and there, in 11 years time, Serena too would find her rest. I was proud to bear his name as his adopted son and he had been all that a father should be to me, though I could never be in the least like him. He had been the spiritual keel of my rather shaky little boat. And not only mine; he had been the ballast which has kept the whole Western Church upright. How should I fare without him?

398 was a good year for me. I was renting a flat in Aunty's house, and paying for it; I was doing interesting and highly confidential work; and I was very busy with my pen. Shortly after Easter came the 'marriage' of Serena and Stilicho's eldest daughter Maria to Honorius. She was a cradle Christian, as you can see from her name. Uncle Ted saw to that.

Honorius was only in his fifteenth year, Maria far from nubile: it was a political wedding, designed to buttress Stilicho's position, as indeed it did. I did them an *epithalamium* which I duly sang at the wedding breakfast and which went down well.

In July came news of victory in Africa. Mazcezel the victorious General was unfortunately murdered in his hour of victory, having violated the sanctuary of a church. (Mazcesel was Gildo's loyal and displaced brother; a clever choice by Stilicho). At all events, Rome's bread supply was restored, and an official eulogy was called for by the Senate. Stilicho commissioned me to do this, and I found the assignment tricky. Plainly all the credit must be ascribed to Stilicho, for a victory in which his only part had been to appoint the General. I was used, however, to doing Panegyrics for under-age Augusti in such a way as to give them the credit properly due to another. It was all propaganda really. Maybe I should have been called Minister of Propaganda – but I foresaw that one day one Dr Goebbels would make that name a naughty word. All I can say is that my hero, like his, really had charisma. Can't explain it. You had to be there to feel it.

In the autumn came another commission. Uncle Theo was to be next year's Consul, and he wanted me to do his Panegyric. This would be a joy to do, and it would be nice to honour a civilian for a change. I had got the form off pat now, but it was still quite a sweat. All that pagan verbiage, which Rome still clung to, quite took my mind off my own religion. Or at least it would have done but for the latest news from Morgan. This news, unfolded in a series of letters, was shattering. JJ had been cuckolded by none other than Little John, rising sixteen. There were of course unpleasant classical analogies, and Oedipus came to mind. Must John now kill his father? Yes! Elissa as Jocasta?* Yes! And she was pregnant. God, what wretched luck. She must have been behaving very unwisely, and it just got out of hand. ('Cu-Chulain rapes "Scottish" Aoife-Avitia, the Amazon!';* the Irish will never forget the tale. If they are to be believed, the incident took place on the Isle of Man.)

JJ's wrath, of course, was terrible. Elissa, and the quiverful, were sent packing to the Casa Belgica, like Brünnhilde on her rock; and it was her very own rock under Justina's will. It's time I told you where it was. It lay in the Ardennes on the River Lesse three miles before its junction with the River Meuse above Dinant. The site was not only well-nigh impregnable, and well-defended, it was also exceptionally pleasant. There were pot-holes below, in which the residents could take refuge with no chance of discovery. There were pleasant water-meadows for swimming, fishing and athletics. The best hunting* in all Gaul lay all round. The Frankish Frontier-road lay six miles North but 'Furfooz' (a name with many reverberations) lay on its own private escape road. This was the 'Safe House' to end all such. It would one day be ringed with fire, a forest fire,* but that comes later. There Elissa passed her pregnancy in seclusion; there she would be remembered as Elsa of Brabant;* there again, in widowhood, she would be Genovefa of the Ardennes).*

Meanwhile what was JJ to do with John? Cousin Vic was consulted. His two mentors were Ambrose and Martin. Ambrose was dead; so Martin was written to, and Martin's advice would have displeased neither Arnold of Rugby nor St Benedict. 'Let him work and pray,' he wrote. 'And above all, "keep on guard", Γρεγορειτε, as Jesus says (Matth. XXIV. 42). Hard work, mental and physical; austerities; cold baths to cool libido. Above all, "watch out", Gregoreite.' Cousin Vic fully agreed with this advice, and supplied JJ with his own precious Psalter which had been his godfather Ambrose's gift to him when he was ordained. (From it Ambrose had designed the doors – still extant – of Sts Gervasius and Protasius in Milan.) Vic's recommendation was that John should improve his penmanship and at the same time enhance his spirituality by copying the Psalter as a worthwhile penance. So JJ took young 'Gregory' off to his Rock for what was intended to be seven years of fasting and penance. (If I tell you that Georgios* is the more 'popular' form of Gregorios you will realise, with a bit of a shock, that 'Little John' is now none other than St George, he of the Channel, he of 'Merry England'. Church writers, and Romancers, will make a right mess of the 'Gregory' legends; suffice it now that John was 'Gregory of the Rock', and that 'Pope Gregory' came later – to my everlasting shame. All shall be made clear in due course.)

'*The Rock*'? Well they don't come a lot Rockier. This was the Isle of Aran in Galway Bay where JJ became known as St Ende* (St Benedict Maurus), and John would be remembered under so many familiar names* that they have had to go into the Commentary. I would be there too in due course in several guises, and something of our buildings will remain. The date? Autumn 398.

Having outstayed his task in the Britains for Stilicho (the results were filtering through my office), and having divested himself of his family, JJ did not feel in the mood for further evangelisation in the Arctic. Time to report back to Milan (Uncle Theo), and maybe return to law and theology. He was there at Christmas 398 having said a long and sad farewell to Elissa as he passed by the Casa Belgica ('Wotan's Abschied'; Wagner will do us proud here). No more family life for him: the 'renunciation of love'; celibacy at last. Spiritual athleticism begins at thirty-eight. He did not stay in Rome, however, for Stilicho had yet another task for him. He and Count Jovian were appointed joint military governors of Africa (JJ as non-combatant member) to restore law and order after Gildo's rebellion, and to sequestrate Gildo's vast and illegally acquired private estates for the benefit of Honorius. Or rather, since he had no need thereof, for the benefit of his laudable but impecunious* prime minister and father-in-law. (Jovian's full name was 'Jovius Jovianus', a Gallo-Roman from Clermont, and he was to play a big part in the politics of the next thirteen years. He had a brother Sebastian, and a little son Jason, both of whom we shall soon meet again.)

JJ took on this job with largely spiritual aims in view. He had not quite done with evangelism, and there was still, despite the presence of cousin Augustine, a morass of paganism in Africa to be stamped out. Early in the same year (399) Augustine was made full Bishop of Hippo by Metropolitan Megalius. Like so much of the rest of his life, even his consecration was marred by controversy,* personal and procedural, and with calumnies. It was partly to try to fend these off that for the last six years he had been 'making a clean breast' of his past life and sins and of his current piety, in his serially-published *Confessions*. They had just about done the trick.

JJ can hardly have failed to meet Augustine on this tour, and Augustine must surely have been impressed by JJ's sober fervour for the faith, and pleased to receive a copy of JJ's own *Commentary on St Paul*. For his part, JJ was to be perhaps less than happy with Augustine's *Confessions*. JJ had just adopted chastity by an act of his own will, whereas Augustine seemed to insist that *both* his own current chastity, *and* his previous libidinousness were entirely God's doing. The scene was being set for the great debate on man's free will, Augustine versus Pelagius, which would trouble men's minds in every century to come.

Back in Rome, both JJ's *Commentaries on St Paul*, and Augustine's *Confessions* were soon published and selling well. The stage was set for a public collision of ideas. At the present juncture JJ and Augustine remained 'dearest brothers',* and it was with Augustine's blessing that JJ decided to take a leaf out of Martin's book by going around methodically destroying the old pagan temples. Muscular Christianity was the name of their game.

Meanwhile, Little Merlin had paid a visit to comfort Elissa. I found that, just as JJ has 'gone off women', so Elissa has 'gone off men'. (Did I have a part to play in this, and if so which Lohengrin was I? Was I also Henry the Fowler? And did I chide Elissa for her reckless behaviour with the young men in her entourage – for her unfaithfulness as many Romances will say? Wagner will be wrong in one respect: Parsifal was not my father. Cart before horse.) I came back to Rome with my own two fourteen-year-olds Maximus and Genesius. It was time they went to school in Rome. Let the girls grow up as wild goats (*capriolae**) with Elissa if they must, but I owed the boys an education, and I'd have to pay for it somehow. Back in Milan I told Serena of my problems. As always money loomed large in these.

'I've got an idea for you Lukie-boy,' she said. 'Time you settled down with a wife, a proper one, a nice one, a rich one, someone who can be a mother to your wild oats, and maybe bear you some tame ones. I've got someone in mind for you – I'll write to Morgan and see if she can push you together. Best behaviour, mind you, and dress properly. She's a lady – dare say you knew her late husband, but I'm not telling you his name at this moment – and she's *very* rich. The rest is up to you. Don't go yet, Stilicho wants a chat with you.'

Stilicho received me in his study. He looked very grave and worried. 'Look at this,' he said. 'Despatch from Constantinople.' The despatch was an official notice that, exercising his powers of appointment, Arcadius had made 'Eutropius the Pimp' Consul. 'It's an outright declaration of war on me by Eutropius,' said Stilicho. 'How am I to carry out Theodosius' dying wishes? I've tried twice with armies and twice been humiliated without a fight. Then the viper strikes at me by suborning Africa and forcing me to use Rome's armies against her own folk. I feel like Laocöon. Will no one rid me of this pestilent pimp?'

'Maybe the pen *is* mightier than the sword, Excellency,' said I. 'Let me see what a couple of poisoned darts will do.'

So I stayed in Milan until I had written and published the first of my two books *Against Eutropius*. The second followed soon after my return to Rome. I was half proud, half ashamed of them. I doubt if anyone before or since has ever matched them for controlled sustained readable venom. Technically they were the best things I had ever written. They were truly daemonic, frightening, and, as would soon be proved, deadly. Before the end of the year Eutropius was dead, killed in Chalcedon by unknown patriots (at the instigation probably of Doxy). I didn't know words could have such power. Had I saved New Rome? Maybe I had, indeed I foresaw that – thanks in part to me – it would outlive Old Rome by a thousand years. But I felt a bit ashamed and dirty too. This was a sneaky sort of warfare. Was it my destined career?

Morgan was as good as her word, and shortly after my return to Rome I found myself at an engagement dinner for a chum of mine in the Office called Palladius to Celerina,* youngest daughter of my old General Celerinus by his second wife. I was immediately signed up to do their *epithalamium*. Goodie. Another commission. There was another distinguished-looking woman there called Secunda, dark, richly gowned and bejewelled, and, as I was soon to discover, recently widowed.* After dinner I made up to her politely to find that she was in fact Synesia, Tertius' elder sister, daughter, too, of my old General, and thus – horror of horrors – sister of that very Hadrian whom I had so egregiously insulted three years previously. 'My brother will kill me, or maybe you, if he hears we're on speaking terms,' she said, breaking into attractive giggles. I liked her best when I could make her giggle.

Soon we were making arrangements to carry on with our giggling lessons, in gardens at night and the like. 'But you must make things up with Hadrian,' she said, 'if ours is to be an on-going relationship. Show me how well you can grovel.'

'For you, Secunda, my dear, I would crawl to the ends of the Earth,' I said, drawing myself up to my full height.

'Crawl to Hadrian's office in the Campus Martius then,' she said.

And I did, for I had got the message. This might not be exactly a love match but it still looked extremely good news, and Hadrian could probably make Celerinus forbid the match if he remained indisposed to me. So I grovelled,* and Hadrian grudgingly forgave me. I really had to learn to watch my pen. For a first try, I decided to write to old Celerinus formally to seek his daughter's hand. I wondered if he remembered little 'Goldilocks', of Carrhae and King Solomon's Mines?

Celerinus wrote back graciously. He insisted that the wedding take place in Alexandria where he had a town house and where Tertius could join us as my best man. There would be a guard of honour from Dad's old Theban Legion (IInd Trajani). Very kindly, Celerinus offered us his Cyrene Villa for our honeymoon. Apart from Celerina's *epithalamium* and a Consular Panegyric – this time for Stilicho himself, which I hoped would be something of a pushover – I had no commissions on hand and Morgan, keen to see me settled, took on the two boys for the time being. As the century closed, was my ship at last coming into harbour? Time would show.

Heigh ho.

# BOOK XII

## *Calchas the Rat, and the Sinking Ship* (AD400–404)

**Figure 24**
Stilicho as Consul – should we trust a Slav?
© Fratelli Alinari

January 400 found me, once again, on the steps of the Capitol, for Stilicho's consular inauguration. Same old routine. Serena and Maria were in the second chariot, which should be gratification enough for anyone. Then came my part of the performance. I really felt a bit appalled by my glibness; I mean, I *did* admire Stilicho, and all that. But I didn't want to go on being 'His Master's Voice' for ever.

The next shock was the arrival in Old Rome of Doxy's bust. Would you believe it? She had persuaded Arcadius to proclaim her *Augusta*. Serena wouldn't hear of this, and the Senate weren't much taken with it either. I could see those busts blocking up some storeroom for years, or at least until AD421, when New Rome got her diplomatic revenge on Old Rome by rejecting the busts of Constantius III – of whom more anon.

At the end of February I handed in my resignation from the Civil Service, drew all the pay that was due, and bought my own wedding trousseau. Secunda and I spent quite a bit of time at Aunt Marcella's favourite silversmiths. Not only were there the classic gold wedding rings to be fitted and engraved, but I also bought for her, from my earnings, a gorgeous pair of pearl earrings and a travelling casket* for her toiletries. She, in turn, bought me an elegant silver dinner service,* which I would in due course turn over to my elder daughter Ursula.*

The Turcii had been a bit stuffy about our courtship. They were insistent that if 'Sneezy' and I were to travel to Alexandria on the same boat we must be properly chaperoned. Isn't that too absurd? (It was I who nicknamed Synesia 'Sneezy'; she, for her part, called me 'Arthur', not only as a son of 'Ocean' and Thule, but because I had bravely made a clean breast to her of my close, if no longer on-going, relationship with Elissa). As to chaperonage, Aunt Marcella came up with an impeccable solution, bless her. As it happened, she had stayed with her her brother-in-law Pammachius, and his redoubtable sister Eustochium. Now, 'Ευστοχιον means 'penetrating', and indeed she had a very sharp tongue (whetted, maybe, by Jerome to whom, with her mother Paula,* she ministered at Bethlehem). Eustochium had been over on one of their recurrent fund-raising drives for Paula's Bethlehem Pilgrim Hospice.* All their rich friends had, as usual, to 'ante-up'. Pammachius was to escort her and the lolly back to Palestine, and it was arranged that they would divert via Alexandria in order to take care of 'Sneezy' and me. No nonsense like staying for the wedding itself – Jerome had seen to it that they looked on matrimony with sublime disdain.

In this same year we were to hear of the sack of Trier by the Riparian Franks and assorted Teutons; indeed, as a result, the prefectural capital would shortly be removed to Arles. This was not the last time that indestructible old Trier would be sacked;* it really would earn itself its epithet '*La Gaste Cité*' (the 'Waste city'). It was at Trier, and not at 'Sinadon'* (or *Segontium* as scholars will surmise), that my Gawain, as Lohengrin II, would one day have an eerie encounter with Elissa.

In the East, Gainas had revolted against Aurelian's anti-Goth policy and come within a whisker of decapitating* Aurelian's Count John, as I mentioned in the last book. Gainas duly got his come-uppance a few months later, near the modern Bucharest, at the hands of that same Uldin, now King of the Huns, and Roman Duke, who was once Doxy's 'Lord and Master'. (In fact he was only made an under-king or *Regulus*, corrupted in Hunnish to *Ruas*. We shall encounter him again later as the wrongly-named 'Mundjuk', father of Attila.*)

One way with another, we kept tripping over Uldin, and I pause to explain why. You'll remember that Rufinus had admitted not a few Huns into the Empire. As with the Goths, their predecessors, the deal was that, in return for land and a subvention, they would undertake to become 'Tame Huns'. Even so, a few years earlier, had Uncle Ted converted Athanaric's followers into 'Tame Goths'. Gainas' Goths were 'Tame Goths', caught on the wrong side of the shifting political fence, when suddenly Uldin's 'Tame Huns' became 'flavour of the month'; that's why Gainas copped it. Throughout these manoeuvrings and double-crossings Alaric's (and Ginger's) once 'tame' now 'apostate' Goths were edging steadily up Illyricum into Dalmatia. Where and when would they halt?

'Meanwhile, in *Ultima Hibernia*, fit, pure, chastened, penitent 'John-George/ Gregory' was taking time off from his imposed task of copying out Ambrose's

1 My Ancestor Trajan, in his and my Forum

2 St Kevin's Labyrinth near Hollywood, Ireland

3 St Nectan's Labyrinth near Tintagel

4 The Labyrinth at Knossos

5 Glorious Dad and Uncle Ted at the Casa Sic Courtesy of Edizioni Poligraf

6 JJ, Morgan and Little Merlin go bathing Courtesy of Edizioni Poligraf

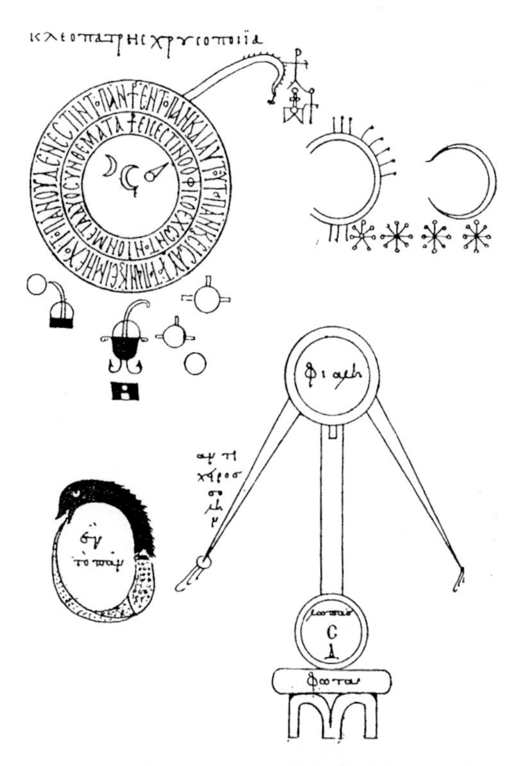

7 Great-aunt Eucheria's Papyrus

8 An alchemist at Dubrovnik

9 Ginger considers her toilette Courtesy of Edizioni Poligraf

10 Ursula, victor of the Casa Sic Triathlon Courtesy of Edizioni Poligraf

Psalter on the Isle of Aran, to spread the Faith in Connaught and Southern Hibernia as St Declan (*inter alia*).* The while, JJ was finishing up his job of Christian scavenging in Africa. John's celebrated Psalter, for which I myself later made an elaborate repoussé* book-shrine cover in gilded bronze, would long survive in Ireland as the famous 'Cathach' of St Colum-kille (short for 'Columba-Achilles') – for John-George would have many occasions both to be heroic and, like Achilles,* to skulk in his tent. In Hibernia John won for himself his Romance nickname '*Cligēs*' (Greek *Καλλιγραφης*), from his beautiful penmanship. The Irish would call him 'Scraib-*taine*' the cunning penman. His cousin, the future Emperor Theodosius II, would win the same nickname one day for the same reason, confusing the Romancers no end. Don't let it confuse you; there are two Cligēs', but John-George got there first.

None of this much concerned Sneezy and me. We were thoroughly enjoying the wedding preparations, and the nearest we got to Lenten austerities was to entrust ourselves, with Pammachius and Eustochium, to the rigours of a ship for Alexandria. I was getting to know that bit of sea. Like JJ and Elissa eighteen years before, our marriage was down for Easter Monday, but instead of Ambrose we would probably have Theophilus, the Patriarch, to bless us – he who gave me my exhumation permit for St Justus, six years before. Sneezy said I really shouldn't call him 'Thug-ophilus' even to make her giggle.

In late March, we slipped in under the Pharos with its great statue of Helios,* to be met by Sneezy's beaming brother Tertius, and his younger half-brother Euoptius.

Sneezy was duly handed over to the ladies of Celerinus' palace, and I was taken off to the brothers' bachelor quarters. Pammachius and Eustochium transhipped, ever unsmiling, for Askalon. Not long to wait now; I quite saw myself as a *respectable* married man. I hoped I still retained my prowess *sub cadurco* (beneath the duvet) after the long lay-off! Well done Serena. I would write her a thank-you letter'.*

So came Easter, and our great day. Old Celerinus made a speech. Young Euoptius did us an *epithalamium*. The Guard of Honour threw rice and pretended they remembered me. A choir of priests of Isis sang Coptic wedding hymns and waved their *sistra* (rattles) – very ecumenical place, Alexandria. Sneezy and I got fairly tiddly, but I thought I had been able to do for her that night all that the situation required. A few days later we took a coaster for Cyrene, or rather its port Apollonia. Hi Ho Sinbad, – or should I say Odysseus? – you deserve a honeymoon after all you've been through. Life begins at forty. It was as 'Odysseus' that the Irish would remember me as St Patrick Jr's maternal grandfather.* It was through my own lamentable addiction to punning that the Cambrians would also remember me as St *Oudoceus*,* instead of the correct Greek form '*Ευδοκιος* (Latin, *Vir Inlustris*), a rank I am later to hold. Oudoceus/Odysseus – get it?

Cyrene was a delightful place. A great limestone plateau rose in cliffs from the vicinity of the sea, to slope in gentle undulations ever southwards until it foundered in the Sahara. Adequate rains fell there, and, on the limestone, were either retained to give green pasture, or reappeared as springs and streamlets supplying some of the best arable in Africa – good *spelt* (Roman wheat) country. The grassy downs were adorned with great standard oaks and the like, and it all much resembled what Britons of the future would call a 'Gentleman's Park'. In those days, Cyrene itself was an ancient provincial Greek town of usual size and equipment, still suffering from the disastrous earthquake thirty-five years before, which tumbled most of the public buildings. A new Theatre* had been constructed, and the bishop had ambitions for a new Cathedral.* Old Celerinus, as chief local nob, was expected to dig deep in his pocket towards this; I foresaw a long wait for the bishop.

Celerinus' villa and farms lay close to the South of the town, and were laid out with neatness and taste, but not, of course, with the grandeur and luxury of the old Casa Sic. The whole set-up reminded me more of Faltonia Proba's Mendip farms. In this rustic comfort, Sneezy and I settled down to enjoy 'the Power and the Glory'. For the next month or so, music, gardens, poetry, dalliance, and lots and lots of giggling were the order of the day. The nights were another matter. Neither of us could blame inexperience, although unlike me Sneezy had nothing to show for hers, but with the best will in the world we didn't make out too well. Maybe Sneezy's late husband found the same problem? Yet she seemed to have loved him well. Maybe it was all the arsenic, or not enough? In some desperation Sneezy went all pagan, and volunteered to spend a ritual night in a cell of the old Nymphaeum of Artemis* in the nearby Sanctuary of Cyrene, without apparent effect.

Finally, we both thought it was time to get back to civilisation – i.e. Alexandria, and a wider range of entertainment. Sneezy was the soul of generosity, and although old Celerinus had a say in our marriage settlement – at least as far as Turcii money was concerned (never a lot of that) – she was sole mistress of her late husband Probinus' estate including the Shapwick/Glastonbury farms, and much much more, not only in Britain. So long as we both lived together, all this was as much mine as hers, so I was sitting pretty, or poncing happily, according to the way you choose to see it. Early in July, therefore, we rented a house in Alexandria, and settled down to the intellectually amusing life of a great metropolis. But Sneezy had also insisted on making a will providing handsomely for me, and if necessary the whole quiverful. She was truly loving and thoughtful, and I was all the more anxious that we should have children of our own to share in her bounty. So we kept on trying, and I intended to remain with her in Alexandria until we had a child.

It was Autumn when my brother-in-law and fellow alchemist Tertius Synesius persuaded us both to sign on for Evening Classes at the Alexandria Technical College at the Serapeum: the great 'draw' being the series of lectures on Astronomy and Mathematics by the famous Hypatia. Hypatia, daughter of

Theon,* whom I had already met at the Swan Convent, was one of the greatest brains of her age – and one of the greatest beauties. Like Novella d'Andrea in the fourteenth century at Bologna, she lectured from behind a curtain with only her head showing, to assist her male students' concentration. She invented the smaller astrolabe, or 'Catherine' Wheel, and was eventually to be martyred at, or almost at, the hands of yet another thug Patriarch (Cyril). Yes, I mean it: Hypatia was St Katherine of Alexandria. She and I and Sneezy were to become great friends.

It was Sneezy who persuaded me that we should also sign on for the 'Metalwork and Jewellery' course. She was not too interested in astronomy, but where 'philosophy' and alchemy converged tangibly as gold and silver she really came into her own and showed marked dexterity and a talent for design. Like Synesius, Hypatia and I were interested in the 'nature' of gold. Sneezy brought us back to earth. You see, pure 24 carat (i.e. 100%) gold is too soft for jewellers; it must therefore be alloyed with other metals, diluted, adulterated if you like, yet must still pass for gold. Suddenly, and for quite new motives I was back in the Swan Coven of the Resurrection, looking again at recipes like the 'Diplosis of Moses',* and thinking of JJ and his gilding* experiments.

One of the tools that Sneezy and I both had to master was the 'Lydian Stone', or jeweller's Touchstone. By rubbing a piece of gold carefully along this, a 'smear' is produced which, interpreted in the light of experience, gives a surprisingly accurate estimate of carat purity, and Sneezy became a dab hand at this procedure. Sneezy and I had many happy hours working together; indeed I too became a really skilled technician. 'That's why the Irish would remember me as 'Luch-*taine*' – 'Craft-*taine*' (from Greek *τεκτων*, a technician). The Cambrians would remember me as 'Ystader' (from Latin *Statera*) and the Romancers as 'Trebuchet' – both meaning 'a goldsmith's scales'. (In what will be called a 'Freudian' slip my scribes accidentally wrote that as 'a **god-smith**'.* Dear me, how suitable!

But still no baby came our way.

It was Tertius, in whom I had confided, who suggested I try the Rabbis. 'If circumcision helped Abraham over the menopause at his advanced age, you should stand an even better chance at forty.'

'It's easy for you to talk old chap,' said I, 'but I'm the one with something to lose. Apart from which, I'm a bit scared of those flint knives of theirs; then again, my friends in the baths may laugh at me as a Jewish proselyte.' (It's so easy to slither into anti-Semitism, following the herd; but on recalling my great love and admiration for Eucheria the Pious Maccabee, I felt I would be quite proud to be mistaken for a Jew. And of course Jesus was a Jew. Would I be remembered in the *Volsunga Saga* as King *Giuki*, the 'little Jew'?)

'Well it's just about the only religion you haven't tried,' said Synesius. 'And you're quite a laugh already, so you'd better get on with it.' And that's just what I did. It only made me keep a low profile *sub cadurco* for about a month.

So the Autumn of AD400 wore on. In December we heard bad news from the West. A confederacy of Swabes and Alemans from across the Upper Rhine, under one Rhadagaisus, had invaded Rhaëtia* on 19 November and captured Augsburg, where Rhadagaisus was to remain for the next five years. All this was in Uncle Theo's Prefecture, but there was not a lot he could do about it.

About the same time, Alaric and Ginger, who had been stealthily creeping up Dalmatia, crossed the River Fiumara at Fiume, now Rijeka, into Istria. They were now right on the border of Venetia, Uncle Theo's Easternmost frontier, and were surely heading for Aquileia, as all usurpers must. Rumour had it that Ginger bore with her an imperial relic in the shape of Valens' purple robe. This was a pretty good clue to *her* intentions. (Valens' robe passed to Uncle Ted, although he didn't wear it as it didn't fit him. And Uncle Ted was *sole* Emperor, at the time of his death.) Back to that dreadful birthday party. Was Regan's revenge on Goneryl now under way? What about the Vestal's curse on Harmonia/Serena?*

In February of 401 we heard that Alaric had bypassed Aquileia and was edging South towards Rimini – gateway to the Via Flaminia and Rome – and that Honorius, now rising seventeen, was urging Stilicho to remove the whole Court to Lyons* for safety. Honorius would be content to be Augustus of a purely Gallic Empire, leaving Italy to the tender mercies of Ginger and her apostate Goths. Courage was never Honorius' strong suit – his forte was, appropriately, poultry-breeding. 'Chicken', that was Honorius; but Serena was of sterner mettle. She, at least, was no party to any understandings Stilicho and Ginger had come to in the tent in Arcady. The Court remained, glowering, at Milan while Stilicho strove to find a plan to remedy the situation. A state of 'cold war' if you like.

To add to the complicating factors, Uldin and his Tame Huns were no longer 'flavour of the month'. In New Rome, Count Caesareus* had ousted loyal Aurelian, and resumed a pro-Goth/anti-Hun policy. Uldin had led his disenchanted Huns back into Pannonia (Hungary), near by Lake Balaton, scene of his own, and then JJ's, prowess with Sieglinde/Doxy, and was waiting there for an honourable master to serve. Believe you me, he was going to find plenty. While these storm clouds were massing in the West, my own sun rose in the East, for in April Sneezy was able to give me the joyous news that she was to become a mother at last. Eureka, or should I now say Alleluia? Our family, social, and educational life together went on tenderly and well. We, at least, now had something to giggle about.

In July I had a friendly letter from Serena. 'Don't believe all the grim rumours you may hear', she wrote, 'life here goes on much as usual, while you dally in Lotus Land. Indeed if you still think of yourself as Poet Laureate you should get yourself back to Rome quick before you're completely forgotten. There's a new Consular Panegyric coming up, Honorius' Fifth. Aren't you interested?' In truth – call it vanity if you will – I was extremely interested. Apart from the prestige, I hoped to win a little pin-money in my own right. Sneezy readily agreed that I should go to Rome to try my luck – she would be well looked after during her pregnancy by her brother and step-mother. It was agreed that I would escort her to them in Cyrene, where she could enjoy the flowers and the animals while awaiting her great day. I would continue by cargo ship to Italy.

By now it was August 401, and the baby was due in December, just when I hoped to be donning my laurel wreath in Rome. Sneezy was big about this. 'Let's settle one thing at least in advance, since you can't be there. Let's choose a name for the little mite.'

Well, you know what it's like. Each of us produced lists of names of boys and girls. None passed muster. We were still arguing on the boat from Alexandria when Sneezy had her fell idea. 'Arthur,' she said, 'haven't you still got that old Ouija Board?* Maybe it'll find us a name for wee one.'

Immortal Gods! Why did I let myself play with that awful toy? It seemed an innocent enough idea at the time, and as soon as we were on firm ground at Apollonia awaiting onward transport to the Villa Celerina, we set it up in the inn parlour. The wheel span, wavered, stopped. The pointer read 'θ'. So far so good. Another spin brought 'α'. Then 'ν' – I didn't like this – then another 'α'. When the next spin brought 'τ' I hurled the wheel to the floor. 'My God!' I cried, 'Do you see it's spelling *θανατος*? ***Thanatos***! That means "death".'*

In another moment I had pulled myself together, foreseeing the threat to Sneezy's peace of mind. 'What a stupid nasty old toy it is. An absolute "con". We're fools to waste our time on such gimmicks.' In a jiffy I had gathered the wheel back into its pouch and stowed it in my baggage. By and by I'd ditch it. For now it was bright chatter to Sneezy, and hopes that Tertius and the chariot would arrive soon, as indeed they did. I could not accompany them, as the Captain of my ship said he had a fair slant for Messina and must put to sea. So I got my farewells to Sneezy and her precious cargo over briskly, and waved her off into the distance. I felt a chill on me though. I kept thinking of Saul and the Witch of Endor. Wish Romans weren't so credulous.

Once I was on the high seas again, and we were leaving the Gulf of Greater Sirte (now Sidra), I shudderingly separated the 'Tabula Ronda Infama' from its 'Holy' companion, and **'deeper than did ever plummet sound'*** consigned it to Neptune. So ended the Romance 'Aventure of the Laide Semblance', even as it would be recorded.*

Then, with lighter heart, I enjoyed a sparkling run through Charybdis and Scylla to Portus (Ostia), and Rome. Back at Auntie's I soon heard all the family gossip. JJ was back from his profitable African mission, and had ensconced himself with Marcella. Law *and* the Prophets this time round – Jesus really had him by the throat. He had summoned Little John from Ireland, his penance satisfactorily concluded. The lad was now in his nineteenth year, and good to look at. *Pulcherius** 'Pretty Boy', some called him, though he preferred to be called George.

JJ put him to Law School, in his father's footsteps, where his insistence on still wearing his white monk's habit would cause remark. (Hence his Welsh name 'Pas-cent', meaning 'white shirt': he would be the original 'White Knight'; 'Benedictines' don't only wear black habits, you know.) The girls chaffed that he brought out the mother in them! Heigh Ho, 'twas fun to be young in my day too. One of his closest chums in Law School, a few years older than George, was a razor-witted rather oily Lebanese called Coelestius – that's Greek for Lebanese.* (I didn't take to him much when I met him, and he would lead us all into a dreadful pickle.) JJ, for that matter, although not affecting a cowled habit, flaunted a girdle of chastity around his ample waist; not only Rome's rising theological author, but also a sort of monk.*

As soon as I had settled into my old flat, I was off to the Prefect's office to find out the score about my Panegyric. My brother-in-law Hadrian was still 'Lord Mayor', so I hoped he would have looked after my interests. However, it seemed that our quarrel was not quite made up despite my famous 'grovel', for it was with rather a sardonic smile that he told me that I had missed the boat. 'Too bad,' he said, 'we thought you'd gone for good. I've given the assignment to a friend of yours from New Rome – young Taurus.' (Taurus II, that is – Claudius Rutilius Namatianus; he who had dubbed me 'Ephialtēs', and my lifelong enemy.) 'Of course you'd have done it better, but I can't let him down now.' All this in a sneering voice.

I would show him I didn't care. So we chatted, and I brought him up to date with Sneezy's and my family news. 'Well, if you're at a bit of a loose end in Rome...', said Hadrian (Ho Ho, I thought, so much for my new beginning; I'm just a 'loose end' now – sounds as if young 'poison-pen' has closed all doors against me, official and social) '...there's a bit of family business arising from my dear sister's remarkably generous Settlement which both affects you, and which you can best sort out. I'm afraid it means a visit to Britain. There are title deeds in the Land Registry there on which your interest in the Mendip property needs to be endorsed; moreover the Steward will need instructions as to remitting the rents and profits. Can't expect the Anicii to go on looking after the property now it's not theirs.'

'Just leave it all to me, Hadrian. Thanks for putting me in the picture. I'll nip over to the Island and sort it all out.'

So that was that. Before I went there would be time for some family life with Morgan and my two elder boys, who hardly knew me, and baby Gawain. It would be fun to play with him.

I saw JJ too, and John-George. He was able to tell me an absolutely marvellous story – one which had me laughing loud enough to demolish the nearest peristyle – about how he slew the dragon.* Yes, he really did, in this year of Grace AD401. '*St George kills the dragon! Read all about it!*' Damsels, specially bedecked with *flowers*, were chosen annually for the service of the 'Serpent'. Below the temple, in a grotto, stood the huge and horrid 'Dragon'. It had a moveable head, with sharp swords in its mouth by way of teeth. The lethal head was connected via pulleys to trip-wires across the stairs. Some damsels fell outright, as holy victims. The survivors of this 'Catch 22' initiation became priestesses of the old God of Healing. Into this sinister Nurses Training College entered a bold but holy monk – a protégé, posterity will be carefully told, of Stilicho, who, first disarming the machinery, was able to smash the Dragon* itself. Oodles of damsels in distress, too. In fact they had every reason to be distressed, as Pretty Boy John had just put them all out of a job. They quite fell for their deliverer, though (just like Parsifal's flower-maidens; only this wasn't 'Parsifal' but 'Peredur', remember). I'll find you some more maidens for both 'Parsifals' in due course.

All this happened in Rome on the Insula Tiberina – and you can't get much more central than that. The Anicii had a 'safe house' there, just in sight of the house of the Faltonii on the right bank. More to the point, there was still standing – until John-George came along – a double Temple of Aesculapius, in full working order and in excellent standing with the Local Health Authority.

Now, you remember how St Martin liked to destroy heathen temples in Gaul? Uncle Ted and Galla organised similar destruction in Egypt, and JJ was just back from doing his own Samson act with the pillars of temples in Africa. What call for surprise, then, if Little John turned out to be a chip off the old block? I was a bit sorry for the damsels, though. Would John turn them all into nuns? Would Melania the Holy Terror* come back from the Holy Land to support them? In fact Melania returned triumphantly from the Holy Land in December 403 and was met at Naples by her somewhat estranged son, Cousin Vic, and all her family. She was in Rome for Easter 404, and only left there for Sicily in 409. We shall see, in due course, what she did for the flower-maidens.

Before I took off for Britain, I thought I'd go and see my spiritual director,* Paulinus, at Nola. I didn't have Ambrose to turn to any more. Indeed, as I was to learn from Paulinus, I didn't have St Martin either. He died on 11 November* that year. A lot had happened to me since Paulinus last confessed me and absolved me in Angers fourteen years ago, and some of it lay a bit indigestible on my conscience. He, I was sure, still knew that I was a 'born-again' Christian, even if in the heat of the day (or the heat of the night), I kept forgetting it. There was so much religion around me in those days (bishops, patriarchs, monks, theologians) that I found it hard to remember what it was really all about.

I felt truly cleansed by my week at Nola. Paulinus and Therasia were so sweet and calm and inspiring – well did Jerome the Wasp address him in his letters as *Frater Ambrosius*; he was even more mellifluous and remedial than my own Father. I needed to have a sort of 'retreat' from the world from time to time – maybe I should make it my Lenten custom.*

So, with my resentments against Hadrian and Taurus washed away for the moment, I headed off for a quiet 'Christmas' at Glastonbury (as I will henceforth call it), Sneezy's and my future Garden of Eden. Funny to think that it was at Glastonbury that I first cast lustful glances at my brother's wife. Now, Elissa was the 'Keep-Fit' recluse of the Casa Belgica and JJ was a 'Media Monk'. And I was a landed proprietor at a loose end, and the father, or father-to-be of six children.

There was quite a lot to be taken in hand when I eventually got to Glastonbury. Stewards, seneschals, bailiffs,* all get lazy without an occasional glance from the master's eye. It was here, amid the farms I already knew so well, that in early February 402 a letter and parcel reached me from Cyrene. Tearing open the seals (Tertius'), I saw with misgiving that the tablets inside were also in Tertius' hand, not Sneezy's. They read:

> Dearest brother. Congratulations. You have a fine daughter. Condolences. You no longer have a wife. She was a bit old, perhaps, for motherhood, and had a very hard time. We did what we could for her, but she was keenest that we should save the baby. Her body has been interred, as she asked, on the Estate, and I have put up a memorial stone, with a faltering epitaph – of which I enclose a copy.* You could have done it much better.

It read: *'Hic jacet Arturi conjux tumulata Secunda; quae meruit coelos virtutem prole faecunda.'* ('Here interred lies 'Secunda', Arthur's wife, whose virtue deserved heaven's blessing of a more copious offspring'. Bad provincial Latin as you see – Greek was Tertius' mother tongue – and worse verse. Alas, all the same, and evermore, Alas!

The letter continued: 'Secunda asked me to send you her Touchstone, as a keepsake and reminder of many happy hours of partnership. 'Remember me', she told me to tell you, 'as often as you use it. And mind you teach our baby to giggle"'. I cried really rather a lot when I read this message. I had come truly to love my Sneezy. We were mates. May she sleep in peace, and awake in a land where laughter ever reigns.

I could not stay and mope at Glastonbury. My work there was done for the time being anyway. Tertius' letter had gone on to say that little Alice ('Αληθεα) as she has been named, was being wet-nursed, well looked after, and brought up as one of the Turcii. 'There is nothing *you* can do for a month-old baby. Leave her confidently to us while you sort yourself out. Your turn will come later. Sorrowfully, Tertius.'

Once I had got my 'second wind' I thought I'd head back for Rome and try to salvage my literary career. I feel a bit old and useless; a bit of a fight would buck me up. If that meant hitching my wagon again to Stilicho's star, *tant pis*.

I travelled, as usual, via Paris, where I heard rather anxious news. Stilicho had made a secret dash through the mountain passes* that November as far as Strasbourg. Here he had summoned a convention of Legionaries and Federates. He had summoned the IInd Augusta from Richborough, so Britain was now without a Legion. He had summoned the XXXth Legion from Xanten, and what's left of the XXth from Brittany, so the Lower Rhine, indeed the whole of Further Gaul, was without a legion.* Britain had been left to shift for herself against the Barbarians using the scratch odds-and-ends of troops that remained. The Batavians and Salian Franks were to defend the Lower Rhine; the Riparian Franks, joined by some questionable new Barbarian allies called Burgundians, the Upper Rhine. Would they do this task? Why should they? What promises had they been given? I hoped only money was involved. But where, in any event, would such money come from? *Mercenaries don't give extended credit.*

Taking his three legions Stilicho had then repaired to Augsburg, where with a mini-show of force, and the promise of a lot more money he had bribed Rhadagaisus to stay put and behave himself – which he would do until the money ran out at the end of three years, in AD404. His last legions trailing behind him through the Alps, Stilicho got back to Milan to prepare to settle the score with Alaric. Honorius and the Court were packed off to Ravenna, never to return. In this 'funk-hole', a galley ever ready for flight to the East, the Western Augusti were to fizzle out. The Praetorian Prefect of Gaul, Anicius Petronius (my brother-in-law as it happens), was instructed to move his Headquarters to Arles – a similar 'funk-hole'. It all seemed rather dire and reckless to me.

I reached Milan to find it *en fête*. 'Ave Stilicho, Heil Stilicho', they were all crying. The incredible man had pulled off his gamble. At the battle of Pollentia on the upper Po, fought rather provocatively on Good Friday, Stilicho brought Alaric and his Goths to battle, and if it would be coming it a bit heavy to say he actually defeated them, he certainly worsted them *in more ways than one*. Alaric, and virtually all his men escaped. But Stilicho was lucky enough, if indeed *luck* it was, to capture Alaric's rear Headquarters, containing Alaric's and Ginger's two young soldier* sons, with their wives, and best of all, *Ginger* herself.*

Now, whatever Alaric's advantage in numbers, Stilicho had him in a headlock. Only an ignominious treaty of non-aggression, of withdrawal, of good behaviour, of the giving of his own sons as hostages* to Stilicho, enabled Alaric, as *Magister Militum* of the Eastern Empire, to recover his wife from the clutches of the *Magister Militum of the West.*

It was not cricket. It was hardly even war – capturing defenceless women at their Good Friday prayers – but it had worked. Regan was humiliated, Goneryl was triumphant. Even I was grudgingly convinced.

'Right then,' said Serena to me when I met her soon after. 'Here's your chance. So you doubted my man? So did all too many Romans. He has been vindicated by events. Now I want to see him vindicated in public opinion. Take up your pen again, Lukie-boy, and give it all you've got. This could win you a Statue in Poets Corner, a pension, and fame for ever. This time I'm your patron.'

**Figure 25**
Goneril-Serena the Fair wears Harmonia's fateful necklace
© Fratelli Alinari

So for the next three months a fully indoctrinated and compliant 'Dr Goebbels' wrote his *De bello Gothico* (which you can still read, although I would not like you to take it quite as seriously as my other works). *And*, after some manoeuvring by Serena, I read it to the Senate, who welcomed Stilicho, largely on the strength of it, to a sort of mini-Triumph and the signal honour of a statue, right by the prestigious '*Lapis Niger*' in the Roman Forum. *And*, I got myself a statue, too, in my own family Forum* (the Ulpian); *and* I wrote my own inscription (see Plate 17) for it in Latin and in Greek – rather chic – which I hoped would survive for ever. I cannot resist recording for you at least my final swanky little couplet in *Greek*. (I couldn't quite have got away with this in Latin. The 'Greeks' of New Rome had no hesitation in hailing their Augusti as *Βασιλεις* (Kings); since Julius Caesar's misadventure, however, *Rex* was not a word to use in Old Rome.)

Here it is: *'Ειν, ἐνι, Βιργιλιοιο νοον, και Μουσαν 'Ομηρου: Κλαυδιανον, Ρωμη και βασιλης ἐθεσαν'*. ('Rome and her *Kings*, to One who has combined, a Homer's music with a Virgil's mind'.) How's that for a grand finale!

Would you call me a cocky little bastard? Well, at least, Little Merlin was cock of the Capitol; everybody wanted to know me again. I thought I'd go up and see Elissa and my daughters, and do a bit of bragging on the side if she'd let me.

The visit was quite a success. Elissa had built herself a villa nearby in the Forest, (Chateau de Vêves*) which was more convenient in winter, but the old 'Casa Belg' was very much the children's quarters. I spent much time up there. I enjoyed little Ursula's company *a lot.* She was nineteen and very attractive. I'd have to think of marrying her off soon, if I could find a fellow athlete. Meantime, she said *she wanted no better company than mine*, and wanted to know all about Science. Was there a whiff, here, of 'Merlin and Vivian' (Nimue)? If so, there could be worrying resonances in the years to come.

On my return to Rome, in Spring 403, after Stilicho's Battle of Verona, where he had put some salt on Alaric's tail to expedite his departure across the Alps, I found the Romans busy reinforcing and repairing Aurelian's great Walls. This seemed an odd reaction to two victories on the trot. What did the Senate know that I didn't?

I also ran into cousin Germanus (Eustace Placidus) with his chum John Cassian. Long back from the Desert, they were on a mission from the Church of New Rome, petitioning our support for the return from exile of John Chrysostom, whom Doxy had just deposed as Patriarch and exiled, because he called her Jezebel.

They said the butter was really dripping out of her mouth now. She'd erected a huge column outside St Sophia's with her own statue on top. The locals called it 'The Great Whore of New Babylon'.

**Figure 26**

Honoria the Whore as Augusta.
Read her lips?
© Trustees of the British Museum

Also in 403 I had a letter from Tertius, telling me of his engagement to a Christian girl he had met while he was hanging around the Coven of the Resurrection. (In a few years time she would win him a bishopric of Ptolemais along the coast of Cyrenaica to the West, which would nearly cost him his marriage.) I digress to tell you that on reading the 'job specification' Tertius reluctantly agreed to sell his pack of hounds, but refused point blank to give up his wife, whom he said he had taken before God in all good faith, and for life. The Patriarch reluctantly granted him a dispensation, and he went on to be a good bishop of his flock, and to write several charming hymns: just look up 'Lord Jesus Think On Me' in 'Ancient and Modern', to get the flavour of the man. The marriage would be in Alexandria at Easter 404, and Tertius wanted me to be his *Παρανυμφος* (Best Man). He sent nothing but good news of baby Alice.

In the Autumn of 403 it was inevitable that the reigning Poet Laureate should get the Imperial Consular Panegyric – Honorius' seventh, and my last (though I didn't know that at the time). For the moment I was just pleased to have seen off the opposition (Young Taurus). AD404 was to be a turning point for me in many ways. I duly did my Panegyric, this time wearing my laurel crown (henceforth I could call myself *coronatus** whenever I chose).

In February Melania the Holy Terror arrived back on the Aventine, where she put all her smart friends and relatives to shame by her austerities. Cousin Vic was briefly in Rome, and I managed to see him. He was hopping mad. He had been had up in front of Pope Innocent for suspected heresy and for breaches of ecclesiastical discipline. 'Blasted cheek,' said Vic. 'All right for him to sit in the Lateran Palace and pontificate; I could do it as well myself. But we're front-line troops, labourers in Christ's vineyard. The harvest truly is plenteous and the labourers are few. We just haven't got time for all this bureaucracy. Who does Innocent think he is anyway?'

'Maybe he thinks he's St Peter come back again,' said I cheekily. 'You could always turn your mother loose on him. She can sort him out if anyone can.'

'Let him stew in his own decretals,' said Vic. 'I'm off home.' And home to Rouen he went.

Meanwhile, in Milan, Serena was getting anxious at Maria and Honorius' failure to produce a child. Doxy had given Arcadius an heir, even if it wasn't his. This was the future Emperor Theodosius II, publisher of the famous *Theodosian Code*, and a noted penman (Kligēs II, still from Greek *καλλιγραφης*). He was firmly ruled by his very own sister, Pulcheria, as Regent, and, supported for once by well above average ministers, he would have quite a successful reign.

Without a bit of fertility soon at the Roman end, Old Rome could find herself once again under an Eastern Augustus. It was more than four years since they had arranged (and 'Claudian' praised) the official betrothal* of Serena's and Stilicho's son Eucherius to Princess Galla Placidia, better known to readers of Book IX as **'Cordelia'**. Eucherius was now a nineteen-year-old clerk in the Quaestor's Office, and now that Galla was nubile, she was fighting off increasing pressure from Serena to move out of the palace and take up married life with him.

Like Honorius and Maria's, this had never been more than a political marriage, and by all accounts Cordelia was a *far* from willing bride. Had this unease spread from her to the Senate, or was it perhaps vice versa? Serena was mad keen to see the marriage properly completed and consummated, and that 'Claudian' should do another *epithalamium*, but I pleaded off on the grounds that I had to be at Tertius' wedding, and also probably collect my little daughter.

There is no doubt that I was becoming daily more anxious about Serena, and Stilicho. Principally Serena. Stilicho was still 'Mr Clean' to me – a brave soldier, albeit a smooth operator. But since the Harmonia's necklace incident, and Stilicho's 'seduction' by Ginger in Arcadia, I had come to wonder if Serena was really on *Rome*'s side at all, or only on her own. Could it be right to leave the whole North of the Empire defenceless, just so as to dish Ginger and Alaric? I remembered with foreboding what Valentinian I said, on hearing of Procopius' revolt against his brother Valens in the East: 'Procopius is but my brother's enemy, and my own; but the *Alemanni* are the foes of the whole Roman world.'

I owed Serena so much for her love, support and encouragement over the years that it was a new and disturbing thought to think of her as a potential or even actual 'Enemy of the State'. Yet, staring unwillingly into the future – such was my uncomfortable but mercifully occasional gift – I could actually *see* her being so declared in less than four years – yes, and throttled to death. Worse still, I foresaw that Cordelia would be her prosecutor.

I shuddered at the gulf into which I saw myself slipping. It was time to distance myself. If this was when I earned myself the pejorative nickname 'Calchas the Rat', well, such was life. (Old Calchas, son of Thestor, was the wisest soothsayer of the Greeks in the Trojan War. That's how he came to abandon the Greeks rather precipitately, and some thought discreditably, at Colophon – read all about it in *Troilus and Cressida*.)

Let 'Claudian the tarnished Laureate' linger on his plinth in Trajan's Forum. Little Merlin would 'do a Calchas' and hie again to the land of his birth. There, I'd start life all over again, under a new flag with yet another set of names.

Heigh ho.

# BOOK XIII

## *The Children of Ishmael (AD404–407)*

I pass briefly over the next two months, since the ground they cover is by now as familiar to you as to me. Another ship; another wedding in Alexandria from the same house. My joy at Tertius' happiness was only clouded by sad memories of my Sneezy. Old Celerinus was getting very old. I didn't think he was long for this world, and indeed he died a few weeks after my departure.

It transpired that I was now really quite a rich man under Sneezy's will. She did not just leave me the Glastonbury farm, but also other bits of land all over Britain, and I supposed I would have to tramp them all in due course. In fact, I was 'Ædonius' for real now (rhymes with Nitonius* as we pronounced it). Sneezy must have thought this would be rather fitting for her very own 'Arthur'.

Now that I had put Old Rome behind me, I felt drawn to visit New Rome again. Aurelian (he of Books IX and XII) had been succeeded by Anthemius as Chief Minister. By all accounts Arcadius had got a real good one there; a true 'Roman' despite his Greek name. Safe hands, after the disasters of Rufinus, then Eutropius, then Aurelian and Caesarius, the squabbling brothers. The latter, whom Tertius called 'Typhos', had hoped to supplant Aurelian yet again, and to resume a pro-Goth policy, so naturally Ginger had got herself back to New Rome to press Alaric's and her interests. The while, Anthemius 'held the ring' between them all. (Anthemius was to rule the East for Arcadius and his 'son' Theodosius II for the next eight years with great distinction, and to leave a permanent memorial in the famous Walls of Constantinople. His grandson, of the same name, would be one of the last luckless Augusti of the West.)

I quite wanted to see Ginger again, and get to know my brother-in-law Alaric. When, like me, you've just done a complete political 'U-turn', it's no bad thing to look at the opposition with an open mind. Was New Rome so very wrong to declare Stilicho an Enemy of the State eight years before? After my horrible recent vision of Old Rome executing both him and Serena in four years time, I was beginning to wonder about everything.

Back in New Rome, I decided to put up, in safe austerity, with Bishop Sisinnius at the Convent of the Resurrection. I was none too keen to go near the Palace, while Doxy was at the helm. Old Nectarius, the Patriarch, had died six years before and had been succeeded by John Chrysostom.* No more good dinners to be had there – 'John Knox' was more his style. I didn't know if Germanus' and John Cassian's recent mission to the West had anything to do with it, but Doxy had recalled Chrysostom from exile and reinstated him. More likely it was the earthquake and the riots, which between them reduced St Sophia's to a heap of smoking rubble. The earthquake also toppled the statue of 'The Great Whore of New Babylon' – just fancy that – which frightened Eudoxia badly.

I found the Coven was winning itself a big reputation in the medical world. St Anastasis* *Φαρμακολυτρια* it was called now: 'St Anastasis of the Drug Therapy'. The queues of out-patients had to be seen to be believed. Funny to think I was once one of them.

I duly met up with Ginger, who seemed to be fully accepted in top circles. She was after all a *Nobilissima* as Uncle Ted's 'daughter', and so long as she kept her nose clean, that counted for a lot. So, she was biding her time warily. Alaric was with his armies in Epirus, and also biding his time.

While I was at the Convent I did lots more reading in the Library. With my new technical skills I decided to learn a bit about lens grinding, and mirrors and glass-blowing. Hypatia had got me so interested in Astronomy that I wanted to see if I couldn't make something more efficient out of Uncle Theo's invention of the telescope. A lonely widower like me needed to take up new interests, and I had had enough of high politics for a while.

So my days passed pleasantly enough. In my revived Christian guise I went fairly regularly to St Irene's Church to hear Chrysostom preach. (St Irene's had resumed its old role as cathedral until St Sophia's could be rebuilt). I must say he really deserved his nickname 'golden mouth'; not only a beautiful voice, but a lot of inspiring things to say. That's how, on Sunday 19 June, I was actually present when John denounced Doxy as 'Herodias'. 'Again Herodias raves; again she demands the Head of John,' he cried. Fighting stuff. Doxy, once 'Salome', and slimmer then (she was now heavily pregnant) – was actually present in the Royal pew wearing her purple robe and loaded with pearls. The very next day, defying God and his earthquakes, Doxy exiled John for the second time, and this time for good. Nectarius' aged brother Arsacius was persuaded to step in as Patriarch and do yet another mopping-up operation. No earthquake; God seemed content.

I was content too, for at the end of September Euoptius, my brother-in-law, arrived in New Rome with a very important companion, my little daughter Alice, now almost three, with her nursemaid. For the next sixteen years she would only be separated from me by Mars or Venus, and then not for long. As a single-parent unit I thought it best to move out of the Convent and set up

**Figure 27**
John Chrysostom denounces Doxy, from Jean-Paul Laurens
© Mairie de Toulouse

Alice's nursery, *chèz* Ginger. She was very good to both of us.

I was becoming quite taken with Ginger, as a person. I think I always misjudged her. Why should redheads be thought of as 'not quite nice'?

The six months I had allowed myself in Constantinople before making my way to Britain were drawing to a close when there occurred Doxy's horrible and fatal miscarriage.* She *was* my step-sister and the mother of my favourite son. The old priest had bidden me pray for her, and perhaps I had tried to. May she rest in peace – God alone knows where.

**Figure 28**
Ginger, Serena's red-headed sister, as Shakespeare's 'Regan'
© Edizioni Poligraf

Why did I always leave New Rome with a nasty taste in my mouth? Something wrong with the place. Maybe it was all the eunuchs! Be that as it may, my little party took the London Road ('Londra Asfalti', the Turks still call it). This was Uncle Ted's fatal road via Adrianople, Belgrade, Vienna and up the Rhine. We travelled as paying passengers on the coaches, when we could squeeze onto them, and in this way I was able to see for myself what a very inflammable situation Stilicho had left himself and Rome on our North-East Frontier. All those Teutons, on *both* sides of the Rhine. I quite liked the look of the Burgundians. I hoped they knew they were on our side.

I took the chance, as I moved North, to deviate to the Casa Belgica and show Elissa my new little one. As she was a girl I hoped we might both get a warm reception, and so we did. Warmest of all from Ursula. That girl might have been an athlete but she was not an Amazon like her mother. In fact, she so took to baby Alice, and maybe to her old Dad, that she insisted on joining me. She said Alice needed better company than just an ayah; that I couldn't cope on my own; that she had been a forest hoyden for long enough and wanted a bit of culture.

**Figure 29**

The sheer white cliffs of the 'Casa Belgica' at Furfooz
loom over the winding River Lesse
© Prof (Em) J. Mertens

Her younger sister Consentia, now in her fifteenth year, joined the argument in her own way. (Her Roman name, from birth, was Constantia, as her elder sister Ursula's was Gratiana; Elissa nicknamed her Consentia, the 'Yes-girl', because she was always most placable; quite soon I would endow her with some more punning variations.)* Consentia said what *she* needed was to meet some nice young Romans of her own class, not just foresters and gillies. Rather to my amazement, Elissa agreed that the girls should accompany me. She was happy on her rock with just little Eugenia, now an eight-year-old, for company. (Eugenia/Antigone is, as her name will remind you, the result of mother/son incest.)

Thus, towards the end of October, the five of us reached 'CCAA', *Colonia Claudia Ara Agrippinensium* – known to posterity as Cologne or Köln, but we Romans were gluttons for acronyms – whence we hoped to take ship for Britain. The town was a fine one, and one where tragic things were to happen to my family a few years hence; the martyrdom of St Ursula, no less, but mercifully I had no vision of this. Claudius had founded the Colony, or at least named it, in AD50, and Constantius II had much embellished it. When Cousin Julian let the Franks across the Rhine and Meuse in 358, CCAA became a frontier town, an independent Roman Imperial city, but with a very mixed population. This meant that it would have to live and preserve its independence by its trading prowess, or else by its sanctity,* and trade was very much in evidence when we got there, not least in glassware. CCAA had been a centre of glassblowing for centuries. Would this be of use to me?

Transhipping from barge to coaster, we duly made our way across the German Ocean to *Camulodunum* (Colchester). Camulodunum means 'furnace town' after Camulos the Celtic Hephaestos or Vulcan. There were many other towns in Britain called after him. I wondered which of them the Romancers would also make into *Camelot*? True, I as 'Arthur' would spend quite a bit of time there over the next few years, thanks to my new character as a member of the landed gentry (and more, as you will soon see), but I can't honestly say it was 'the spot I loved above all others', as the Romancers would claim.

Colchester was Claudius' original capital, and was still the capital of a province. No ordinary province, either; in terms of agricultural produce, the richest in Britain. Since Julian's day it had waxed fat on grain exports to the Rhine Army. Stilicho's sudden levies of additional 'tribute in kind' six years before, to meet the 'Gildo' famine in Rome, had left Colchester much impoverished and very angry. At the right price they would have been quite willing to sell their Grannies; but just to have their emergency reserves appropriated, without payment or thanks, so that the layabout unemployed of Rome could have their dole of bread, had left the Britons smouldering. Loyalty to the Goddess Roma, so remorselessly hymned by me in all my Panegyrics, was a thing of the past.

Loyalty to Constantine's new Christian God, however, seemed to be more in evidence, and for this we probably had Cousin Vic to thank. You'll remember he came over to Britain from Rouen in 395, at the request of the British bishops, to help lay the ghosts of the Arian heresy* to rest – the same job that Nectarius had done in the Orient, Damasus and Ambrose in Italy, and Martin in Gaul. But Cousin Vic was a spiritual child of the last two. He just *loved* relics, in their own right and as a focus of devotion. He had visited and adorned Glorious Dad's *martyrium* at St Albans, making a major shrine out of it. The cult had really caught on, with feast days, and processions. People came from miles around, and there were tales of miracles at the shrine.

I thought there was something of *nationalism* in all this; that the Britons remembered Dad not only as a Confessor for Christ – as he was – but also as the man who **should have been Augustus**, instead of Uncle Ted. They saw him as one of the 'Sons of Ishmael' (see Genesis XVI.12), elder son of Abraham, disinherited (Greek, ἀφλακος*) in favour of his younger son Isaac. In the same way Glorious Dad's sons had been displaced by Uncle Ted's. So JJ and I were 'Ishmaelites',* and thus also 'Havelocks', and I found myself, as I became known to them, an object of respect, of sympathy, maybe even of reverence. To them I was not just another landed gent, I was a symbol. I had money, I had family; and now I had a faction. Who knew where this was going to lead me?

We spent Christmas at 'Camelot'. Lots of new and hospitable friends with villas. I made various forays into *Britannia dextra*, the land of Boudicca's Iceni, to 'take seisin' of my new properties. Then in the New Year (405), I took the family to *Augusta* (London), for some plays and general culture. Here I got a surprise. Guess who was our new Vicar? None other than JJ. You remember Stilicho dragged him away from St Paul to be Count of Africa (399–400), to Stilicho's pecuniary advantage? Now the blandishments of *duty* had seduced him again into office. He always was a fine administrator, and maybe Stilicho hoped for some useful revenue collection at his tactful and experienced hands. He'd been a military Count since his days as 'Duke James', Master of Horse in Thrace, so he was combining the role of Vicar with *Comes Britanniarum*. The latter was a bit of a non-job as since Stilicho's last abstractions, Britain no longer had any Mobile Reserve, but what bits and bobs remained were under his command. Our cousin Lagodius (of Book II, and see also App. 4), was his *primicereus*, the same job JJ used to do for Maximus.

We met, of course, and embraced. With a chastity girdle over his massive tunic, in lieu of *cingulum*, JJ looked an incongruous sight, but chastity was something he was quite sure about. Another bit of news was that he'd gone 'TT'. Good idea; I hoped he could keep it up. But even more gratifying was the news of John-George's recent wedding. Chastity had proved untenable, in Rome, for this glamorous young monk. While I and my family were wending our way North up the London Road from New Rome, young John had fallen for one of his beautiful young flower-maidens called Letitia Calpurniana, daughter of an old Ocean colleague of mine (See App. 2). 'Titia', as we called her, was a 'patrician' young Romano-British girl currently at finishing school in Rome. Aunt Marcella had permitted JJ to allow the match. 'Virginity's a bit difficult for young men,'* she had said. 'I think St Paul would concede it in this case.' Their wedding took place just before JJ left for Britain. They were at present honeymooning in Campania, and JJ expected to become a grandfather in record time – legitimately, on this happier occasion.

As before, in Africa, JJ was ambitious to combine his official duties with de-paganising and evangelising rural Britain. He was therefore keenly interested in my experiences at St Albans, and in Eastern Britain. We could collaborate, at least in this. I didn't think this was the moment to tell him of how or why

I'd changed political horses, and was now in Ginger's colours; Sneezy's heir had no further need to explain his actions. JJ was going to have to be very emollient, though, if he was going to smooth the ruffled political feathers in Britain, and I didn't rate his chances of squeezing money out of them as very high.

In the Spring I took the family westward to our old stamping grounds of Mendip and Valentia. I had found some good glass sand* on one of my properties in Eastern Britain and was thinking ahead to my proposed telescope; I could always get some glassmakers and blowers from CCAA. After I had been a few weeks at Glastonbury the idea came to me that it wouldn't do young John-George's prospects any harm if he were to do a spell in Estate Management. Although legal training was about the only higher education going, it didn't mean John *had* to end up as a lawyer. Faltonia's three sons all went on to distinguished public careers in Rome from a British farming background; John could start his new life as a married man by learning to run *my* farm. JJ thoroughly approved of the idea, and wrote to Morgan asking her to pass on the proposal. Morgan's reply was brought by John-George and Titia in person.

While John-George, Titia and I were relaxing in Mendip we had a grim letter from Morgan saying that in the Spring of that year Rhadagaisus, who you'll remember was squatting at Augsburg on pension from Stilicho, had become fed up at non-payment of the agreed subvention – Rome's Exchequer must have been nearly empty. He turned his troops South by the Septimer and Splügen passes, bypassing Milan, and continued due South for Rome. Stilicho managed to trap him at Fiesole, above Florence, but could only meet him with a hastily conscripted and almost useless citizens levy, plus his 'mini-legions' and a few Tame Goths under Sarus. Fortunately for him, the ever-fortunate man, Uldin and his Huns – 10,000 of them, the fighting strength of two-and-a-bit legions – were 'on the market'. Another postdated draft on the Exchequer and the transaction was arranged. So, at Fiesole, in June 405, **the Huns saved Rome**. Just think, if I were still 'Dr Goebbels' I should have had to hymn this 'famous victory'. I'd have been pushed as usual, since although Rhadagaisus was captured and executed, most of his men got away, and we shall hear of them again very soon. Morgan wasn't at all happy about Rome's future. One day, would Britannia stand alone against the Barbarians? At least JJ and I and the bulk of my family were in the right place. Or were we?

In the Autumn we all went to stay with Titia's father, Potitus, in Hither Valentia. The Villa Calpurniana was on the road ('Sarn Helen') from Neath to Brecon, near the headwaters of the River Neath; near, too, to the Roman Fort ('Coelbren Gaer'*). If I tell you its name in our day was *Bannaventum* ('Banwen Tabernae'), 'Patrician' scholars will do well to prick up their ears. Potitus' family were real old Roman-Britons, descended from Calpurnius Agricola* (see Apps. 1 and 2 for the line of Calpurnius), who was Governor between AD162–166 and 'went native'. Thence, we all went over for the day to Ocean College. Nice for the children to see their Dad's, and John's, old school. Nicer still for Consentia who fell in love at first sight with a handsome young sixth former. Guess who? Calpurnius' own son, of course, Calpurnius Jr. What could be more suitable? Grumpy mutterings from the parents – was not Calpurnius Sr a magistrate and a deacon of his church? As a matter of form, mutterings also about calf love and gymslip sex, but I knew we would all be delighted if our two sixteen-year-olds made it. Suffice it that by Christmas they were engaged, and had talked us into allowing their formal betrothal, or provisional marriage, for the following Easter. (The marriage would only be consummated of course when they and the time were ripe; meantime I nicknamed her 'Concessa' (betrothed), but quite soon she would be 'Consortia'* (wife). The family continued to call her 'Connie'.

Thus, 406 opened with cheerful prospects. My social life, and status, advanced effortlessly. I was a big fish in a small pond, and truth to tell, I liked the pond, cool and wet as it was. There was still something old-fashioned and unspoilt about the gentry in Briton, and this reached right down to the slaves. I was under increasing pressure to enter local politics; indeed Civitas Councils in three different Provinces had asked me to stand. Maybe it was my duty. Which should it be? St Albans was the oldest and most prestigious, the first free *Municipium* in Britain. Dad's Bones would win me certain election there, and I might even become *Duumvir Judicandi* or *Eil-udd** ('twin judge' in Cambrian). Sort of local Consul.

Abroad, as I was to learn when Elissa came over, the storm clouds were darkening. Rhadagaisus' armies gathered and grew in Swabian Thuringia. They were determined to avenge him. Other ambitious anxious malcontents are joining them, notably the Siling and Asding Vandals,* but also the Quadi and some semi-detached Alans from the East. The reason for all this was that the Huns (and I don't mean Uldin's Tame Huns, but the northern tide of locusts) were pressing ever westward. Elissa was getting to feel a bit uneasy at the Casa Belgica, but still insisted on going back there after our daughter's wedding. Ursula volunteered to take baby Alice there too. Would it be called the 'Castle of Maidens'? Meanwhile, and more importantly, what would Stilicho do?

The answer to this was not long in coming. In two panicky Proclamations from Ravenna, one dated February and the second mid-April (worth reading in full in the *Codex Theodosius*,* to get their flavour), Honorius called on all young free-born citizens of the Provinces to join the army (he could hardly say to join the *legions*; there weren't any in the Northern empire, thanks to Stilicho!), and prepare to defend their homelands. Not just citizens and freedmen; even slaves should join, thereby winning immediate emancipation. As patriotism might not be enough, slaves were to get *two* gold *solidi* on joining, and citizens *ten*. Wherever from? JJ had got real problems!

I would like to say that the Britons of my day responded to this chicken-hearted call to their manhood and patriotism as wholeheartedly as I foresaw that Britons would in 1914 and 1939; but it wasn't quite like that. Everyone sat about and watched to see what their friends would do. JJ hurried off to raise the recruiting banners around Albany and Further Valentia. I would like to have unsheathed a sword again myself – I hadn't drawn blood since Carrhae – but in whose cause and under whose command? I decided it was time I was back in politics.

By way of feeling the temperature of the water, I accepted an invitation to attend the St Alban's Day celebrations on 26 June. I tried hard to look pious, mournful, and resolute all at the same time. Within a week I was on the Council. By August I was *Duumvir*, and on the rostrum.

The truth was, however, that Britain's frontier was on the Rhine. Sooner or later someone would have to lead our Dad's Army overseas. During these autumn months as I exercised and trained my new recruits, my cronies assured me that it should be me. But as what? As the loyal servant of Honorius and Stilicho and Serena? Since my vision, that road was barred to me. The ghostly voices of Clodius Albinus, of Carausius and Allectus, sang in my ears, 'a British Army can proclaim a British Emperor'.

That was how, in late November 406 at Colchester, Gauleiter '**Marcus** Flavius **Gratianus*** Severus' was all too easily persuaded to don a scarlet robe (*Padarn Peisrudd**), to bind his brow with a golden diadem and his arms with an *imperator's armillae*, to brandish a general's baton. After all, these were the names under which I had stood for election at Verulamium; 'Glorious Dad' was a *Flavian*, and so was I; 'Little Mother' was a *Gratian* (see App. 2); Grandad Theo was 'Severus'. Three good Imperial names* there, and all legitimately mine.

Catastrophe followed when I had to clamber onto a shield to be raised above my cheering soldiers as 'Carausius III'. It was Tomi all over again. First, they held the shield so badly that I almost fell off. Then, staggering, lurching, I drew myself up to my full height. That's barely five foot – no way enough. (I learned something from that fiasco: it takes quite a few inches to be an Augustus.) I tried to make a speech, acknowledging their cheers, but was soon aware that the sound I heard all around me was not cheering but laughter, helpless side-splitting laughter. So I reached the highest pinnacle of power which Rome can offer, and promptly fell off. Not all in the crowd were my friends – I could hear some ugly booing. Maybe the whole thing was rigged? Ephialtēs again? I'd been set up, that's what. Time to run yet again for my life? History will say they got me, but I wasn't 'Lucius Fortunatus* for nothing. They might write me out of the script, but I'd be back. So I ran for my life, and as once before, I ran back to Elissa. I didn't really know where else to go. So, only John-George and Titia remain in Britain.

I took ship, in disguise, for Belgium and made my way to the Ardennes, where

Elissa and the maidens didn't receive me too kindly. 'Time you grew up Luke,' said Elissa. 'Too big for your *caligulae*. You can stay here a few days, but I really think you've put yourself out of court. You can't just go back to being a British landed gent. You can't now humbly offer your services to your brother the Vicar. You don't want to offer your sword or your pen to Stilicho. Usurping Emperors who fail to make it get topped. If I was you I'd get me back to the old Casa Sic and keep a very low profile. That'll match your height!'

So, snubbed and humbled, that's what I decided to do. But, during long and anxious talks with Elissa about the military situation, I was able to persuade her to come with me. 'The Casa Belg is as good a place as you could find to ride out a storm,' I said, 'but this one looks more like Armageddon.'

Furtively Elissa and I, with young Eugenia, Ursula and baby Alice, worked our way South through Lyonesse to Marseilles, and took ship for Sicily and home. To make it even more home-like, there was Morgan. 'Great minds think alike,' said she cheerfully. 'Rome's no place to be while all this is going on. Why don't you send for your big boys too?' (Maximus and Genesius, Elissa's and my twins.) 'Rome's no place for them either. Besides, I've got a nice surprise for them. I've redecorated their quarters. Hope you won't be shocked!' So saying Morgan led us to the boys' quarters over on the right of the courtyard. 'I had a sketch made for this when Elissa and the quiverful were here on holiday in 400, but it's taken ages to get the mosaicists to finish the job,' Morgan concluded with a sly smile.

When I got there I gave way to my usual bellows of laughter, for there, stripped for action, were Elissa herself – still 'Ye Gods, what a torso!' – together with Ursula, Consentia, and several other local fillies I thought I knew, or would have liked to. (I refer, of course, to the famous 'Bikini Girls'. (Plate 10) Will posterity be open-minded enough, like me, to recognize in them 'St Ursula and her 11,000 Virgins'? Will my readers still be able to see them?)

'Well, it makes me feel younger already, Morgan,' I said, 'and I can guess the boys'll find it pretty stimulating too.' I could see that Elissa was quite tickled, if a bit self-conscious.

Thus for some months we looked on frivolously from the touchlines while JJ commenced his lonely joust with destiny.

The boys reached us in January 407 with yet more astonishing news. It had been a very cold winter – still was – and the Upper Rhine had frozen over. On New Year's Eve the Black Forest Barbarians,* to whom I referred in the last Book, had found the temptation to cross the Rhine too great. Making naturally for Trier, they had sacked the poor old 'Gaste Cité' again, and then gone rampaging North towards Britain. Their crazy itinerary took them via Rheims, Tournai,* Therouanne (Pas-de-Calais), Arras, Amiens and thence towards Paris. By and by they swung South-West for Orleans, Tours, Bordeaux and Toulouse, to be stopped only by the Pyrenees. A small contingent of Vandals actually took ship, and marched on London, getting as far as Wimbledon,* before they were driven back by the Home Guard. They ended up at Hastings, where the name will commemorate them.

On hearing this, and of the threat to Paris and indeed to Britain, JJ took action, as was his duty. First, he appointed young Lagodius to be Vicar in his stead. Lagodius (see App. 4) was Uncle Heliodorus' third son, my cousin and schoolmate. His name means 'hare' in Greek (Latin, *Leporius*). I wondered who'd become '*Leporello*'?* He would win the name 'Chrysanthus' as I did, struggling to invigorate the British gold industry as a source for *solidi* for JJ. Like me, alchemy would seduce him, in a few months, to the Coven of the Resurrection, where he would follow in his father's footsteps as a Novatian bishop* until his death in 419.

Now JJ in his turn put on the scarlet robe, and this time a 'son of Ishmael' was unhesitatingly hailed 'Imperator Augustus'.* He really looked magnificent in the part.

Spurning, after a short try, my ill-fated name of 'Carausius',* he chose to 'go for gold'. We were all, as I so often remind you, 'Constantiani', and it was as Flavius **Constantine III**, Caesar Augustus, that JJ led his cheering troops to Boulogne.

**Figure 30**

'JJ' as Constantine III, Augustus

© Trustees of the British Museum

Still 'Edge-of-Battle' despite the gear, JJ entrusted his army to the joint command of Nebiogast, a Frankish artilleryman, and to Elissa's brother Justinian, a professional cavalryman who I haven't had space to tell you about (but you can look him up in App. 5). Like me, JJ now despaired of Stilicho and of Honorius. Unlike me, he had actually done this journey before as Maximus' Secretary. He *knew* it could be done. He in his turn needed a Secretary *Primicerius*, and John-George was his choice. Not for nothing had the lad earned himself the name 'Cligẽs'.* May as well keep things in the family.

JJ's next task was made easier by the fact that the horse had already bolted. The BFBs (Black Forest Barbarians) were already approaching Paris; but hearing that retribution might be following them, they decided to spare Paris, and hurried on SW. JJ decided, rightly, not to give chase but instead to re-bolt the stable door. He made for Trier,* and the loyal Romans of Gaul, in their own Dad's Armies, flocked to join him. He was now 'Augustus' at Trier, trying to refortify the Rhine with Roman, not Barbarian troops. All this breathless news the boys brought us.

I was filled with admiration, tinged perhaps with a little envy, for my splendid brother. If only I'd had the inches, this would have been me, with my strong sword-arm ('Breich-bras'). Already I'd got a bust in Poets' Corner in *our* Forum. Even now I might have been winning myself a statue in the Forum proper. Boo Hoo! Meanwhile JJ, at Trier, was sitting for *his* busts. (It was just as well he did this. We'd soon be going to make good use of them.) Would JJ make it right through to the purple robe? Hardly, while Stilicho lived. Needless to say we were all glued to the news bulletins that seamen brought from Marseilles and Ostia. In the summer we heard that JJ with, by now, quite an army had moved unopposed from Trier to Lyons; next stop Arles, where he must defeat and expel Honorius' craven Prefect and Generals. I longed to be part of the action. Surely *both* the 'Sons of Ishmael' should have the honour of saving Rome. 'If that's how you feel,' said Elissa, 'do something about it. Get up to Lyons and offer him your sword. Be an obedient and helpful brother for a change.' Unanswerable sense. Elissa's voice was like the voice of Fate. Of course, I went.

I wasn't the only one. Stilicho, hard-pressed as he was, smelt the threat of JJ's approach. All he could spare to defend the Arles Administration and oppose JJ was a mixed corps of Tame Goths, under their General, Sarus, who had done well at Fiesole. (You'll remember there were originally three corps of Goths. One corps, under Gainas, had returned to Arcadius' obedience. Alaric's corps were doing their own thing. Sarus' corps were loyal to Honorius. Uldin's 'Fiesole' Huns, still waiting for their postdated draft to be cashed, had put themselves back on the open market again, and were thus unavailable. Cheque-book soldiering was their metier; who'd be Stilicho's Chancellor of the Exchequer?)

Sarus crossed by Montgenèvre into Gaul, intercepted and besieged JJ and John at Valence, killed Justinian in battle, and succeeded in killing Nebiogast by open treachery and breach of the customs of war. It was precisely at this juncture (November 407) that Little Merlin arrived at the walls of Valence to rescue his brother, if need be by means of single combat. I'd got such heroic ideas. If only I was taller. Romantic, that's me.

Alas, when I studied the situation I found that diplomacy, not heroics, was what was required. JJ had the resources, but neither the generals nor the will to break out. Sarus had not enough men to take Valence and was a long way both from home and his paymaster, and winter was coming on. Here I had an advantage. However unsuccessfully, I did nevertheless command Goths at Tomi in 386. Moreover if JJ and I were at one in our determination to overthrow Stilicho, I was a step ahead of him in one respect. Following my experiences in New Rome, and my stay in Ginger's palace there only three years before, I was actually *pro-Goth*; or at least pro-Alaric, which wasn't yet quite the same thing. Sarus knew, though the general public didn't, that the Battle of Fiesole was anything but a military victory for Stilicho. Maybe I could detach him from his loyalty. So, it was as JJ's concerned brother that I made my lone embassy to Sarus.

The task was easier than I had dared believe. I talked to him as man to man in a mixture of Greek and Teutonic. I congratulated him on his siegecraft. I suggested he had done quite enough to satisfy his master's objectives for the moment, and that his principal aim should be to get paid. I hinted that there was much competition the other side of the Alps for Rome's fast-shrinking stock of *solidi*, and that he would do well to be there to claim his share before the first snows of winter closed the passes. To keep his Goths in good spirits I suggested – such are the exigencies of war – that a little looting would be in order. (Sarus had a horrid time getting back through the Alps; the montagnards are natural 'bagauds' and managed to extract almost all his loot from him to obtain safe passage through the enfiladed passes.) So Little Merlin saved brother JJ by his wits, and very soon after we were reunited in Valence. My reward was all I could have wished. Affection, gratitude, and promotion. JJ made me his *Magister Militum Peditum*, which meant I was now in charge of his young inexperienced and mostly Roman infantry. Yippee. JJ found another Frank called Edobech to command the cavalry in place of Justinian. Poor Elissa; I reminded myself to write and tell her about her brother. He died bravely.

As soon as Sarus' Goths had cleared Gaul, JJ and his train resumed their stately march on the Prefectorial Capital of Arles. The Gallo-Roman provincials – like the Brits, they prided themselves on being more Roman than the Romans, and 'Constantine III' was just what they were looking for – flocked to JJ's allegiance, the while Honorius' minions, Limenius the Praetorian and Chariobaudes his General, took the ever-waiting galley for Italy. JJ was cock-a-hoop. Here at Arles he had got an actual Palace, and trappings worthy of an Emperor. He promoted John-George from *nobilissimus* to Caesar* and gave him the *nom-de-guerre* of 'Constans II' to go with it. John-George looked very fetching in his new scarlet robe; all JJ needed now was a purple robe from Ravenna and he'd be the real thing. But I was able to persuade him that there was one precaution he should take before making his bid for legitimacy. 'You need to take Spain under your protection JJ,' I said. 'Then you'll be the *de facto* ruler of the old Gallic Empire and Honorius will be in no position to refuse you. If you don't do this, Stilicho might be able to stab you in the back from Spain. If the Gallo-Romans are anything to judge by, the Spaniards should flock to you. Make some sort of treaty with the BFBs of Toulouse, and you'll be ready to settle accounts with Stilicho.' It was to be even as I suggested. But I think my scribes need a breather, so you'll have to wait for the next book to see what happens.

# BOOK XIV

## *Massacre of the Innocents? (AD408–410)*

The first task JJ gave me in 408 was to go and sort out the montagnards* of the Julian and Cottian Alps (roughly, Nice to the St Bernard), who had given Sarus such a mauling. 'I want them to know that they take their orders from *me* now,' he said. 'You'd better instal some regular garrisons.' To this end JJ gave me a corps of Burgundians, whom he had recruited to his cause on his way South from Trier, to add to my scratch team of *Honoriani*. 'You well know how to command barbarians and tyros, Luke,' he joked.

'Indeed yes, Your Serenity,' I replied, po-faced, for I had indeed commanded Goths at Tomi in 386, and tyros* at Colchester more recently, all with complete lack of success. When I talk of 'my *Honoriani*' I do *not* refer to the Scottish *cavalry*,* Alban's Horse (mostly the sons of Dad's first lot, and commanded by my old schoolmates). The latter were disciplined regulars serving outside Britain, in accordance with our usual procedures. They had been in Gaul so long that they were often called the '*Honoriaci*' after Gallic parlance,* and I shall follow this, so as to distinguish them. They were to be a valued part of JJ's and John's troops. There were another lot of '*Honoriani*' however, trainee *infantrymen*,* who had joined up under Honorius Jr's AD406 'Home Guard' laws and were still hopefully awaiting their enlistment bounty of *solidi*. It was these latter I took up into the Pennine Alps of Dauphiné, and having left quite a lot of them there on frontier duty, I was back at Arles in late March 408, my task completed.

In my absence JJ had sent Constans II Caesar (i.e. John-George as I shall continue to call him), to Spain, as I had suggested, together with his newly-appointed Praetorian, Apollinaris, and one Terence as *Magister Militum*. (Apollinaris was to become the grandfather of Apollinaris Sidonius, Bishop, author, and last of my successors as Court Panegyrist. His works will be relevant and entertaining reading for you.) Terence, like me in the Pennines, was under orders to tame the Pyrenean montagnards and to impose frontier guards of JJ's obedience. As this Book now takes us for the first time to Spain, a few words of introduction may be in order.

Spain is a mountainous country, nearly as large as Gaul, almost cut off behind the Pyrenees, for there were fewer passes through the Pyrenees than there were through the Alps. As mainland Spain had no enemies at its borders it had virtually no military establishment,* no Dukes, no Military Counts, save the Count of Tingitania. The latter (Tangier, and Morocco North of the Atlas mountains) *was* part of Spain, and here there were hostile tribesmen to be kept at bay. But Spain proper was peaceful. There was no cavalry, no need for cavalry and no fodder for cavalry; this last defect proved to be important. Such troops as there were, were engaged in police duties for the provincial governors,* and more importantly, acted as Mine and Bullion guards – my old Nubian job. For Spain was queen of Rome's treasury. There was copious silver there, as well as cinnabar for mercury and three large gold mines.

Inland were huge barely cultivable and sparsely inhabited plains ringed with high mountains. Spain, to us Romans, meant the river valleys. It was to the first of these, *Tarraconensis* of the River Ebro, that John first went. Success. The Spaniards accepted John's and Apollinaris' appointments (or reconfirmations), of magistrates cheerfully enough. Civil wars were new to them. The silver mines at Huesca were taken in hand; and the Publicani shaken up. Continuing North, *Caesaraugusta* (Saragossa) submitted, together with its little gold mine to the West.

Onwards they progressed up the Ebro, then turned West for Burgos and Leon, 'City of the Legion'. This was the key to the rich mining fields of Cantabrian *Callaecia* (Galicia). Here, surely, JJ would get his eagerly awaited *solidi*? No, I didn't make a mistake just now, when I wrote of the 'City of the Legion'; there *were* two Legions whose recruiting and training depots were in Spain, the VIIth and the XIth, always employed abroad. The other legionary depot was in *Lusitania*, later to be called Portugal.

It was while crossing the arid plains of Old Castile that John had the misfortune to run up against, and mortally offend, Verrenianus,* one of the twin sons of Heliodorus, and his first cousin once removed (see App. 4). *Latifundi* they called farms here – small kingdoms. They made my British farms look like market gardens. Here, at Palencia, Verrenianus had such a kingdom, and here John and his cavalry laagered several nights and, I'm sorry to say, grazed down most of Verrenianus' growing crops. Now the crop came early, and only once, in 'Dry Spain'; worse still, there were at the farm some refugee montagnard notables from the Basque end of the Pyrenees. These were inflamed with anger against Terence, who had just dispossessed them of their ancestral 'right' to levy and to retain tolls on traffic through the passes. *They* weren't going to be loyal to JJ as their new master. *They* thought nothing of the *Honoriani*. Looking at his ravaged fields Verrenianus thought even less of the *Honoriaci*. Verrenianus fled to his brother Didymus in Lusitania, and together they raised the flag of revolt, of loyalty, or of self-interest (however you see it). They would raise Spain against the usurper, in true official Dad's Army style. They had had no earlier cause to heed Honorius' panic Proclamations of AD406.

Apollinaris sent urgent messages back to JJ, and I was promptly sent, with my Burgundians, to help John sort things out. (These Burgundians were, of course only one corps of the Burgundian *nation*; very soon, however, that corps would call me 'Gundahar',* (Gwyn-tigernus) and would hail me as 'King'.) It was mid-May (408) before I reached John at Leon, and we then had quite a 'bonny wee campaign' (I break into Scots in honour of our Scottish cavalry) against the twins, cornering and capturing them eventually in Lusitania. John continued his, now triumphal, tour round Spain, taking his frightened captives with him, and receiving homage in *Baetica* (valley of the River Guadalquivir), and *Carthaginensis* (Cartagena). It was as Caesar that he set up his Court at Saragossa, and left me there in charge while he proceeded to Arles to get a pat on the back and to hand over our errant cousins to His Serenity's clemency. I settled down to do a bit of hard thinking.

It would be an understatement to call me worried. First among my worries was that I'd noticed at Arles that JJ was back on the bottle again. He was older now, so it seemed to hit him harder. He was still 'Thaliarcus', the ruler of the feast,* but not so often 'Gaudentius' the jolly. As the evenings wore on I often found myself thinking of Uncle Ted, but I had no harp with me this time. I didn't like the '*closing* the Alpine passes' bit either. It sounded a bit like 'Fortress Gaul'. Would JJ just be content to sit there as a Gallic Emperor? That wasn't what he had been elected for, nor what we had all followed him for. The 'Sons of Ishmael' were going to save Rome from Stilicho. We needed to *cross* the passes to do that, not just sit at table and wassail.

But that wasn't all of it. My church friends (who kept up an admirable intelligence service*), told me alarming news from Britain: cousin Lagodius 'Chrysanthus' had deserted his post as Vicar to become Novatian Bishop of Constantinople at the 'Swan Convent', and no successor had been appointed. Nor was there a Count of either Saxon Shore, and the Saxons were raiding Britain as if it were their own fief. (Soon they would turn their attentions to Armorican Gaul too, and here I remind you that to us 'Armorica' meant the whole coastal tract from Dieppe to the Loire, not just 'Brittany'.) Now I had become a big land owner in Britain, I loved the country, it seemed to have been left entirely on its own to its fate.

What had the Britons done about it? They'd read their Livy,* that's what they'd done. They'd gone back to the forms of the old '*SPQR*'. Within the leaderless Imperial Provinces were strong *Civitas* Councils each with its two 'Consuls' (I should know for I was one of them). Honorius had ordered them to take up arms and defend their homelands, and they were doing just that. He sent no *solidi* to back his words however. Very well then, they would send no tribute, no *annonae*, to Rome. UDI was the order of the day: 'Unilateral Declaration of Independence'. The Armoricans had heard what Britain had done and were hastening to follow suit.

My heart leapt at their courage and fortitude. But I cared for Rome too.

There was something greater at stake here than the mere survival of Britain. The whole concept of the *Pax Romana*, of civilisation as we had known it, trembled in the balance. Let JJ sit and quaff; I was going to do something about it. Stilicho must die, and only Alaric could bring this about.

I wrote a secret letter to Ginger; so secret that I sent it by special messenger. Who? My eldest son Maximus Aurelianus, that's who. Forgot to tell you that he insisted on coming with me from the Casa Sic as my 'squire'. I'm starting to get quite '*Romantic*' talking about 'squires' aren't I? But then, this was when it all happened. From now on you're reading the *Gesta Romanorum*: *Deeds of the Romans* – yes, and the *Matière de France* and the *Matière de Bretagne*. We would not be remembered at the hearths of Ireland, Scotland, Wales, Denmark, Iceland, Flanders, Saxony, Thuringia, Italy, France, Spain and Portugal in the sort of stale Heroic Couplets I used to churn out for a living. 'From now on, *saga* was the name of the game. Max had been with me all the way from Valence. Good lad, Max; I was proud of him. His tamer twin, Genesius Valerius, remained at the Casa Sic doing charades. (Genesius was a famous actor, and later Saint. That's how my Valerius got his nickname.) My letter to Ginger was short. 'Is Alaric still "in the lists" against Stilicho? If so, how can I best help?'

Within a month Max was back with the reply – thank God it was the sailing season with fair winds the rule. Ginger's reply, too, was short. 'Only the Senate can now unseat Stilicho; but for that we must talk to them in Rome with power. Alaric can't do it all on his own. Get you to Uldin and win him for us; tell him the Senate will see him paid; be ready to bring him with you. *Penetrabimus ad Urbem*. Farewell'. This was a deft allusion by Serena to my own *De Bello Gothico*.* (I had written there how an oracle had told Alaric that he would indeed succeed in taking Rome. I jeered then. Now I was to be part of it, loyal only in my disloyalty.) Heigh Ho.

I don't know if I would have acted solely on this invitation to treachery, had not Max brought evil news with him, which he'd picked up at Marseilles. My own brother was a murderer. JJ, a murderer. Oh my God! He'd killed the defenceless Verrenianus and Didymus in cold blood. Heliodorus' boys, our own schoolmates, our own kinsmen. There could be no political justification. That it was supposed to be done in secret only made it more contemptible. My brother was a monster; or else, he was mad. (Actually, he was drunk. Much the same; no recollection.) That clinched it for me. Early in August Max and I set off for *Pannonia* (Hungary) as soon as we could make our excuses. We said we were off to the Casa Sic to see the family, our task done. In fact it was just beginning. Disguise for this trip, and very soon a new name. 'Ataulphus'* ('Αδελφος, brother); that's what Ginger rightly called me. That's what Alaric's Goths would call Alaric's brother-in-law.

While I was thus serving JJ, sinister things were happening in Italy. In January, Maria, Stilicho and Serena's daughter and Honorius' wife, died in what was said to be a miscarriage. (Honorius' enemies said she died virgin; not so, she'd had an earlier miscarriage* – I blame the Rhesus factor.) With indecent haste Stilicho had proffered her younger sister, Ginger II, as a replacement, and Honorius, who had timorously left Ravenna for Rome to celebrate his consulship, married her there that January. Was this wise statecraft? Serena affected to be shocked by the haste; Pope Innocent was shocked by the consanguinity. More important, Honorius' new Chief Minister, Olympius, was deeply suspicious.

Soon after, Sarus limped home with the news that JJ remained enthroned, that the Passes were now 'closed', and that JJ had turned his attentions to Spain. Could have been worse. News also came from New Rome that Arcadius was ailing. Now that *was* bad news for Stilicho. Arcadius would leave as heir a seven-year-old boy, Theodosius II, who would need a strong Regent. Other things equal, that would be, had to be, Anthemius. When would Stilicho fulfil Uncle Ted's dying wish that he and Serena should rule the whole Empire?

So now it was 'sod Spain, sod Gaul, sod the whole *Arctois*, New Rome here we come' – but for that, Stilicho had first to come to terms with Ginger. Was the pact of the tent in Arcady about to be fulfilled? Before my treasonable correspondence with Ginger, Stilicho had also been secretly treating with her. As a result, Stilicho had appointed Jovius* (JJ's 'copain' in Africa in 399–400) as Praetorian of Illyricum – by implication of *all* Illyricum when the Eastern part could be 'liberated'. Simultaneously he had appointed Alaric *Magister Militum* of West Illyricum, Arcadius having long ago appointed him *Magister Militum* of his half. The price? That Alaric should reunite Illyricum under Jovius – don't forget that Jovius' Illyricum *should* have included the whole Balkans to the very gates of New Rome. Fighting would definitely be on the agenda. On Sarus' news of his failure to capture JJ, Stilicho had proposed postponing the 'Eastern' project, and sending Alaric to have his own go at 'taking out' JJ. This would have been bad news indeeed for JJ, had Olympius not vetoed it. I thought Olympius could smell a whiff of Ginger as the future Augusta of Old Rome, and even Serena had failed to win that. Having enticed Alaric into Venetia, *en route* for JJ, Stilicho had to find convincing employment for him; he decided to 'put him on ice' in *Noricum* (Carinthia), ostensibly peacekeeping among the tribes there. Olympius approved this.

We were now in April 408, and the news was that Arcadius was dying. Stilicho made a dash across to Salona* to confer with Ginger. His proposal? He would prepare a fleet at *Classe* (Ravenna) and would round up all available troops. Alaric would join him from Noricum, while Ginger tried to rent Uldin's Huns. The combined force would march on Constantinople to be 'in at the death', and would then impose Alaric and Ginger on young Theodosius as his guardians. In earnest of good faith, Stilicho would release Alaric's sons, held by him as hostages since the battle of Pollentia in AD402.

This was the plan Stilicho put to Ginger. It was not what he and Serena had in mind. That was very different. As Serena saw it, the time had come to win a throne in the East for young Eucherius and Galla Placidia (Cordelia). They should be starting breeding any minute. Together they could 'guard' young Theodosius well, and maybe end by displacing him. Even now Ginger II and Honorius might also be in the begetting game. Serena's royal grandchildren should rule the world; Ginger had got no royal grandchildren, nor looked likely to have while her sons remained hostages.

Stilicho's mission was a disaster. Ginger knew her Serena, Regan her Goneryl. 'Mr Clean', if we may still call him that, came back to Ravenna with egg on his face. None of this gossip reached me in Spain. I was to hear it from Ginger's own lips later. Ginger wrote all to Alaric, and Alaric was very angry indeed. Crossing the Brenner at a canter, he descended, with his Gothic cavalry, on Ravenna, where Honorius was not. Onwards to Rome, where Honorius was, but not yet into it. The lesson of Gildo had been well taken. He made direct for Ostia and took Rome's food supplies by the jugular.

What Alaric sought was Stilicho's head on a charger. What he got was a bribe of 4,000lbs of gold to go back to Noricum – Stilicho beggared his own reputation with the Senate to get that promise. (Yet again, who'd be Stilicho's Chancellor of Exchequer? – just for now, it was the luckless Heliocrates; soon he would be replaced by one Attalus, of whom much more anon.) But even that was not enough. Stilicho still held Alaric's sons hostage; surely Alaric deserved hostages too? He could hardly demand Stilicho's son-in-law the Augustus; he did ask for but was refused young Eucherius – now *that* would have been evens. Unfortunately the consort of the Princess Galla was not considered available as a hostage.

Stormy debates ensued in the Senate, as Alaric turned away, disappointed, to resume the blockade. Unable to get into the crowded Curia itself, an interested spectator was sitting outside on the steps of Stilicho's statue, right by the venerable *Lapis Niger*. It was Morgan. If Honorius the chicken-hearted thought Rome a safe place to be in 408, so did Morgan. With her she had brought her eldest grandson to show him a debate in Parliament, as part of his education. Through the angry interchanges of old men shouting 'Speak for yourself; are you willing to give your own son to save Rome?', there cut a piercing *tenor*. It was young Aëtius, Son of the Eagles. The Senate did not yet know him as such of course; 'Son of the Eagles' was a name to be won in the Legionary *pilus*, and that was where he would earn it. Many years later the Senate would give him, too, a statue in the courtyard of the very Curia itself; and the inscription* will recollect this very incident.

'Fear no more, Conscript Fathers,' cried this stalwart adolescent, 'I'll go for you and for Rome. I'm Alaric's nephew, and I'm sure he'll accept me.' (Like me so long ago, Morgan had got Aëtius a cadetship in the Scolani earlier that year. 'Nameless' lad as he still was – he had to go on the muster as '*spurius*' like any other bastard – his mates at once nicknamed him 'Quirinus the Posh', since his next-of-kin address was Morgan's palace on the Quirinale.*) Well, Aëtius did go for Rome as a hostage, but not without demur. With shrewd judgment Alaric also demanded – and eventually got – Jovius' son Jason* as an additional hostage. Alaric wanted these hostages principally as surety for the promised gold. He left Ostia, with Aëtius only, a few days later. 'Aëtius' was the name on the lips of the grateful Romans that night. They knew not how he could be Alaric's nephew; they knew not who his father was. Nor did he; Morgan had not yet told him it was JJ, as she was unsure how much to tell him about his horrible mother and the Casa Promotiana. However, truth will out.

Stilicho was now hardly the man of the hour. More and more voices were raised in support of Olympius' view of him as he accompanied Honorius back to Ravenna, only to hear that his worst fears had come true, and that Arcadius was dead. (He had died, three weeks back, on 1 May.) Honorius thought he knew his duty. 'As senior, indeed sole Augustus, I must attend my brother's funeral.* There, I shall make the proper dispositions for young Theodosius' guardianship. At the same time I shall probably ordain him Augustus. What a tragic business. You need not accompany me, Stilicho. There is all too much work for you here.' This was one of Honorius' few attempts to play the Augustus, and it failed. Stilicho set to work on his fears. The sea crossing was not without hazards. The Egnatia was infested with bandits. The Hun locusts were running wild around Thrace, and might abduct him. It was not in the interests of the Roman *Imperium* that the sacred person of the sole Augustus should be exposed unnecessarily to such risks.

**Figure 31**
Honorius the Inglorious
© Trustees of the British Museum

'I will gladly hazard my own person and life, as so often before, in Your Serenity's service. I will go to New Rome to represent you. There I will arrange things exactly as you would wish them to be.' Even Honorius must have started to smell a rat by now. The date was mid-July 408.

Stilicho must have been nearly mad to make his next move. Or else Serena had him tight under her thumb, and she was mad. (Maybe they were both mad; maybe it was the Vestal's curse.) Realising that there was now no hope of Eucherius inheriting the throne of *New* Rome, Serena switched her sights for him abruptly to *Old* Rome. Ginger II had told her mother that her own marriage to Honorius was still unconsummated, with scant prospect of its becoming so. Serena therefore proposed that Honorius should make Eucherius Caesar. 'Honorius will surely see the advantage of having a young diplomat as his colleague, and at the same time securing his sister's future and Rome's throne.' But Serena had made her bid too late. Honorius listened gravely, and said he would need time to think on it; meantime Stilicho should get on with the preparations for his own trip to Arcadius' funeral.

On hearing of this latest scandal Olympius acted. As it happened, Stilicho had allowed a large body of troops to congregate at *Ticinum* (Pavia). Apart from the remaining Roman *comitatenses*, the nucleus was Sarus' bedraggled Goths from the previous year's expedition against JJ. They had been intended to guard Milan from Alaric while he was sulking in Noricum, but he had eluded them. The *comitatenses* were the mobile reserve; Stilicho still had *some* Roman troops, including the IInd Augusta from Britain, and the XXXth Ulpia Trajana from Xanten (*Colonia Ulpia Trajana*, or 'CUT' as we called it with our passion for acronyms). Xanten is the gateway to the Rhine; Mediaeval scholars may claim incorrectly that Siegfried was born there. He certainly served with the Ulpian Legion, and he was an Ulpian by birth. But as I told you in Book IX, he was born at Durosternum in Marcian country.

Olympius proclaimed a seminar at Pavia for the second week of August, to discuss the reconquest of Gaul. Chief guest-speakers would be the ex-Praetorian of Gaul, Limenius, whom JJ had chased out of Arles, and Chariobaudes, his hardly more valorous *Magister Militum*. Stilicho's two Commanders-in-Chief of Italy, Vincentius Jr* and Nemorius (commanding Cavalry and Infantry respectively) would also be taking part.

To hear and confer with them, the Praetorian of Italy, Longinianus – good old Uncle Theo had retired for the moment, but he would be back again – the Chancellor of Exchequer (my brother-in-law) Petronius, and the Minister of Justice, Salvius were all instructed to attend. They were told that the Augustus would attend the closing session, and they took it for granted that Stilicho would be at his elbow.

Instead, Honorius came early, and it was Olympius at his elbow. Hardly had they arrived when the pre-planned riot took place. Acting with coordinated indiscipline Sarus' Goths ran amok, burning, looting and brawling with the other, more Roman, soldiers. Olympius dragged the terrified Honorius out of his tent in his nightshirt and paraded him through the camp 'that the sight of their Augustus might restore order'. Funny thing; it did. The next morning there were found to be just seven bodies among the smouldering wreckage. I have already named them above. All dead. More than half the Cabinet slaughtered. So the Massacre of the Innocents paved the way for execution of the guilty.

I hurry over the end of Stilicho. It's in all the history books: how he took sanctuary, like his son Eucherius, in a church; how he returned to Ravenna under safe conduct, but was nevertheless betrayed and decapitated (on 23 August by one Heraclian, who would play a perfidious part over the following six years); how his statue in the Forum was instantly demolished. He made a more comfortable end than he had procured for Rufinus, thirteen years previously. He had once been my hero. His executioner was a pagan, a creature of the old 'True Blue' Symmachi, and of those like them in the Senate who were paranoid in their detestation of the Barbarians whom Uncle Ted had enlisted and tamed to Rome's service. Soon Heraclian would be Count of Africa, and – as a pagan – would lock horns with cousin Augustine.

**Figure 32**

Barbarian Macchiavelli?
'Sir Lancelot' the tarnished
© Fratelli Alinari

Of all this I knew nothing at the time, for I was in Pannonia with Uldin's Huns, eagerly awaiting the call from Ginger to join Alaric in the march on Rome. This time I wasn't needed; the next time would be different.

I didn't know, either, that the Senate would impeach Serena, and condemn her to death by garrotting (at Sirmione, hence to be called 'Douloureuse Garde'), and with that very 'Harmonia's Necklace' which the Vestal had cursed, and which you can see her wearing in Figure 26. (Do you see the hand of the Symmachi in this?) Nor did I know that Galla would be chief witness for the prosecution.

Or did I?

I did not linger in Pannonia, for I soon received a message from Ginger with my marching orders. 'There's been a most frightful *pogrom*, following Stilicho's death. Sort of acute xenophobia, provoked by the Symmachi. The Romans have driven almost all non-Romans, however loyal, out of the armies (and even murdered their wives in another "Massacre of the Innocents"). Fortunately they've flocked to join us – nearly 30,000 trained angry men. So now we don't need you, or Uldin's Huns. We've gone on ahead to Rome. Do you get back to Spain, and restore it to proper Roman obedience.' This from Ginger! I guessed she meant obedience to *her*. It did make sense, though; I badly needed to recover my own power base. Maybe little Chrysanthus could stimulate the Spanish mines to mint some new *solidi*. Rufinus had been right: *solidi* would win the game. Meantime Sarus and his Goths were dying to have another go at JJ, and Olympius was just the man to send them, when he was ready. What ever was I to do about my demented brother?

I returned to Saragossa from my 'holiday in Sicily' to find that my 'cover' had been blown. About the time that Morgan returned to Rome, an expansive invitation had been received from 'His Serenity' in Arles for his family (all now *nobilissimae*, at least in his eyes), to join him there. Ursula, with my Alice, accepted; Elissa, with her Eugenia and my Gawain, now fourteen, elected to go with them (Genesius had opted, as expected, for theatrical management in Syracuse). Elissa said that if the coast was clear, and she was sure it would be, she would push on to see how the old Casa Belg had survived the onslaught of BFBs. Gawain would go with them to that veritable Castle of Maidens. 'It's sometimes useful to have a man about the house,' said Elissa witheringly.

Of course she had her way; that's how young 'Perceval' came to be 'brought up in the Forest'. (The Romancers will be at their wits end to guess who his real mother was. Certainly not Elissa, who was actually his half-aunt. Thanks to me, their confusions can here be resolved – it was Doxy.) Not finding me at Arles, Ursula said that when John-George paid his next trip to his Spanish fief, she'd accompany him, to restore to me my little daughter Alice. Not so little now; she was by that time all of eight.

I was able to avoid telling the true reasons for Max's and my wild-goose chase to Pannonia. Everyone was too excited to hear about the deaths of Stilicho and Serena, and the resulting pogroms. John-George and Apollinaris agreed that 'Chrysanthus' has a key role to play at that time, and that I should get active again around the mines. Ursula wanted to come with me. Funny to think that I once shared a tent with her mother around the mines of Britain. Fate is weird. Shall I say that we became very close to one another? She was a bit old to play Lolita, but nevertheless we had fun. I had reason to believe my 'sword' safe in that 'scabbard';* for I myself *am* 'Excalibur' (the 'man from Montesclair', *mons clarus*, 'Etna', hence Sicily). Lest I shock my pious scribes, I must refer you to the Commentary if you are to understand fully all that I mean here.

One thing I heard around Cantabria. The BFBs are getting restless, and Terence's frontier guards up in the Basque country were involved in constant skirmishes. Fortunately, the winter snows had quietened matters down for the time being.

It was time to return to Saragossa. Ursula and I got back in time to celebrate Christmas with little Alice. Then in the New Year came disturbing news. Apollinaris had resigned, and JJ had appointed Decimus Rusticus as Praetorian in his stead. Rusticus has sacked Terence, and replaced him with a new *Magister Militum* called Justus. I had rather hoped it might have been me. To make the message clearer, I got a job, if not the top one. I was to be Count of Tingitania – the only military Count in Spain. Not a bad job, now that Tingitania included the whole of Mauretania. 'Bash the tribesmen' and keep a weather eye for JJ on Africa proper.

Meanwhile Honorius had appointed, as my opposite number in Africa, Count Heraclian, the very man who murdered Stilicho. Who's side was he on? How was he getting on with Uncle Macrobius as Vicar?

I had been across the straits of Gibraltar about a month, when I received a letter from Ursula. 'Darling Darling Daddy', she wrote, 'I want you to be the first to know that I'm going to be a mother'. My first reaction was to laugh my head off.* My laugh's quite something, as I said in my Proem; nearly split my sides – they should have been able to hear me in Spain.

Then came saner thoughts. Oh Ambrose! what have I done? I knew we'd been a bit naughty, and Spanish wine was so strong. The words of Ambrose's own sermon on the incest of 'Lot and his daughters' rose up to accuse me. What did Martin write about John? 'Γρεγορειτε' wasn't it? 'Watch and pray'. Now I was Gregory too.* At least John couldn't point the finger at me, nor Elissa if it came to that; it was *I* who would have to live with myself. Squalid, disgusting I felt. To do it with my own daughter – even *I* knew that was a sin. 'No one must know', that was my first reaction, '*for her sake* of course'. My second was: I would never touch a drop of alcohol* again as long as I lived. To think of my so recently pointing the finger at JJ! So I wrote disingenuously to Ursula. 'Wouldn't it be a good idea if you were to go to your sister in Wales? Then you and Calpurnia can have your babies together in tranquillity, far away from these horrid old wars. You could take Alice with you. I'm sure brother John can arrange your journey, and I'll be across to see you as soon as I can.' With this glib letter I 'solved' my problem for the moment. The Spaniards, however, remembered it all, to my subsequent discomfiture.

I was sure I could count on John-George to cover up for me in this mishap, for he hadn't exactly been idle sexually during that time. Not for nothing would the Spaniards remember him as 'Don Giovanni',* the young Dominus. Oh Lord, would they remember me as Leporello?

I tried to turn to my duties, but soon I got orders from Justus in Saragossa which I didn't like the sound of. I was to review my manning levels to see if I couldn't release at least half for service elsewhere. With this came a letter from John. 'Yes, I'll fix Ursula; but have you heard about JJ?'

It transpired that, while we were Christmassing in Saragossa, JJ had had an unexpected guest at Arles. No less than Eusebius, Honorius' Great Chamberlain at Ravenna (and a eunuch to boot). Honorius was in a great fix because he could see no way to pay Alaric the promised ransom (of 408). He had surrendered young Jason as an additional hostage, and this had gained him a few months grace. Sooner or later, though, Alaric would boil over. Eusebius had been sent to ask JJ's intentions and whether there was any chance of his intervening on Honorius' side with a Gallic and Spanish army. 'Tell my brother-Augustus and cousin,' said JJ, aflame with banqueting, 'tell him, that I will come to his aid as Consul of the Year and clad with the Imperial Purple Robe as legitimate Augustus of Gaul. If I come to his aid, it will be as his equal. And tell him *not* to send any more eunuchs to *my* Court.'

Eusebius took this rough reply hurriedly back to Ravenna to find some changes in progress. Honorius, bowing to a carefully organised mutiny at Ravenna, had sacked Olympius' military commanders. So unpopular was Olympius after the 'pogroms' that Honorius deemed him now a liability. He was in debt to him, though, for ridding him of Stilicho, so Honorius had 'castled' him for Jovius. Olympius would go to New Rome to represent the West at Arcadius' funeral, returning as Prefect of Illyricum, however much of that there might still be. Jovius would take his place as Praetorian of Italy. On Eusebius' return to his new boss he had also found another visitor. This was young Theodosiolus,* brother of Verrenianus and Didymus, come to Court to plead for their safety. He did not of course know that they were dead; nor did Honorius when he decided to bow to JJ's demands. Jovius was sent with a purple robe, and sincere apologies that the Consuls Ordinary for the Year were already appointed and in office. Maybe next year would do?*

JJ pronounced himself satisfied and sent orders to John-George to join him at Arles with all the armies of Spain. The while, Rusticus was to assemble all the armies of Gaul. When John got to Arles, JJ would promote him from Caesar to Augustus.

So, one 'Son of Ishmael' went forth to war in March 409, while the other skulked in Mauretania, a moral leper. What *was* I to do? I felt quite disabled. Should I find myself a desert isle like John-George on Aran? Become a monk and do humble penance? I still had some nice instincts. In this spiritual extremity I bethought myself of Cousin Augustine, just 'down the road'. I, too, had read his *Confessions*, and knew that if any man understood sexual problems, it was he. I set out as soon as I could for Hippo. There I was received most kindly by Augustine and his bosom companion Alypius, and there I poured it all out. Yes, all – my guilt about Ursula, but also my dubious transactions with Ginger and Alaric, and my anxieties about JJ. Augustine's reactions were not at all what I had expected. As pastor, as Bishop, he was, of course, magnificent; solemnly he heard my pitiful confession and graciously he absolved me. 'But penance, cousin? Aren't you going to send me off to a rock somewhere?'

Strange how another man can see things quite differently. Augustine was much more concerned for Rome spiritually than he was about the wretched ransom. I was but a pawn in this great game, and my 'guilt' was no more than trifling egotism. He knew, too, that JJ was militarily a man of straw in his present state. In fact, he was amazingly well informed of all that went on in Italy. His chief concern was that, riding on the back of the anti-Stilicho anti-Barbarian backlash, the Symmachi might reconquer, might already *have* reconquered, the Senate; that paganism might reconquer the hearts of Rome and her Empire and might undo the whole work of Constantine the Great, of Ambrose, of Uncle Ted. It was sad, but not abominable, that Alaric and his Goths were Arians. They were, nevertheless, Christians when the chips were down. The ways of God were inscrutable. My duty, however, was clear. It was God who put me into alliance with Ginger. Who was I to question His ways?

'Your penance, Luke,' he said, with kindness but with thrilling intensity, 'your penance will be to put the furtherance of God's Kingdom, of the Heavenly City, above the pursuit of your own spiritual goals. Go back to Spain* as a Christian soldier. Watch how JJ fares with his intervention in Italy. If he faulters or fails, then you must take up his burden. You must then support Alaric, in order to save the soul of Rome. If the Romans, as I accept, have no bullion to buy off Alaric, let them buy him off with the gold and ornaments of the remaining pagan temples. Let them melt down, for him, the golden statues of Jupiter and Minerva, of the abominable Isis and Cybele. When you have crushed paganism in Rome, crushed and exterminated it, you may then think how to find a peaceful and honourable role for the Goths. For the present, Alaric is the very Hammer of God (*Marcus*) and you are his little mallet (*Marculinus*, which means 'Merlin'). Truly the ways of God are inscrutable. Blessed for ever be His Name who brought you to me here.'

Such was Augustine's clarion call to me. To say it made me see things in a different light would be an understatement. I was positively transfigured. God was working his purpose out, and I was a part, perhaps an important part, of it. My peccadillos with Ursula seemed quite trifling by contrast. Golly, what a man Augustine was. There was no withstanding him. I felt that I had found my spiritual director at last.

I returned joyfully to Tangier, gathered up a few reluctant *numeri*, or detachments – the 'Legions' by then were no more than Battle Groups, hastily flung together – to make Justus happy, and returned to Saragossa in March 409. John had already left for Arles, maybe for Italy, and his wife Titia and I waited anxiously. May brought the expected news. Old 'Edge of Battle' had duly crossed the Alps at Montgenèvre and worked his way cautiously down the Po, then eastwards as far as Verona. He encountered no troops at all, friend or foe. All busy elsewhere. Alaric was locked in negotiations with Jovius at the Council of Rimini; at Ravenna, one Allobech, brother of JJ's own general Edobech* was *Comes Domestici Praesentalis* (i.e. commanding Household Division). All seemed set fair for JJ to move on Ravenna, to take his brother Augustus into a crushing embrace and the affairs of Italy into his firm and competent hands.

It didn't happen like that at all. Sarus the Goth (hero of Fiesole; diddled by me at Valence; turned against Stilicho, or his minions, at the Massacre of Pavia; disillusioned by the pogroms, but still at heart loyal to Honorius) was lurking in the hills South of Rimini. He was more loyal to his Emperor than his Emperor to him, and he took it on himself to kill Allobech.* The news reached JJ. News, too, that Jovius had triumphed in the auction room and that Uldin and his 'Rent-a-Huns' were on the march to Honorius' side. Edobech was mad keen to avenge his brother. He wasn't scared of a few Huns, not even 10,000. JJ, alas, was. Trembling, not only with fright, he turned back towards Arles and safety.

When this dismal news reached me, I knew exactly what to do. The first thing was to send a message to Ginger, saying 'Hold on for me, I'm on my way'. The next was to 'settle' Spain – no major problem there. It was a peaceful country, which was why we kept no standing army there. But how to hold the Pyrenees? Even the *Honoriani* had now been mostly withdrawn. A 'Rufinus-style' solution was the only answer. Rufinus had been willing to surrender the Peloponnesian Morea* to Alaric and his Goths, just to get them out of the way. In the same way I had to surrender part of Spain to the BFBs. They would have to be given Galicia in the first place, because it was nearest. I'd tell them they were there as federates, and that they could stay there in peace as long as they were good. Hoof them out later.

The next bit of business was more controversial for a 'loyal' Roman. Convinced, as I was, of JJ's terminal incapacity and also that I was the little 'Mallet of God', I decided to set up an independent Spanish Empire for the time being. I couldn't stay to play the role myself, so I set up my son,* young Max, as 'Augustus' of Spain. I thought highly of him. His job would be to hold Spain and its mines, to promote good government while I was away, and to look after Titia and her daughter.* I was off to Ginger and Alaric. Just me, and my divine mission. The date? May 409.

By the end of May I had caught up with Alaric and Ginger in Tuscany – also, happily, with young Aëtius and Jason. The Conference of Rimini had broken up in useless anger. Alaric, persuaded by the Chancellor, Attalus, that payment of the promised bullion was quite impracticable, had suggested instead that he would withdraw if he were given an annual subvention in cash and kind, and also the Provinces of North Illyricum and Noricum as a permanent home for his Goths. As an afterthought, Ginger had persuaded him to add the request that he be appointed Commander-in-Chief (Stilicho's old job). He, henceforth, would be Honorius' and Rome's defender. Honorius' reply enraged the Goth: 'After the Stilicho debacle I will appoint no Barbarians, no *Arians*, to high military office ever again'. When I arrived, Ginger and Alaric were planning their revenge for this double insult. As they had heard about Jovius' success in hiring the 'Rent-a-Huns' I managed to persuade them to have just one more try at negotiations. 'Maybe you were a bit greedy, in asking for Illyricum,' I said. 'Strategically, Rome can't concede that. As to your Arianism, maybe we could get a team of Italian bishops to lead your next embassy, and to intercede for you. I bet I could get my old friend Paulinus of Nola to take part. You need rations more than Honorius needs peace.'

So we had one more try, but Fate was not on our side, though Augustine would say that God was. The news that tipped the balance was the arrival at Ravenna – where Honorius was on the very brink of boarding his galley and fleeing East – of 4,000 fresh troops* from New Rome, under the command of that Constantius to whom I referred in Book VII. (Stilicho had sent a desperate appeal for help just after the Massacre of Pavia, and Olympius had instructed Honorius to renew this appeal at the same time that he wrote to young Theodosius appointing him Augustus.) One of Constantius' first acts, on landing at Ravenna, was to kill poor Olympius. Now, Jovius had the New Romans and Sarus massed around Ravenna, and the Huns on the way. To make matters even more cheerful, Heraclian had sent some overdue tribute from Africa, all gold vessels and ornaments, and ready to be minted into lovely *solidi* in Ravenna, so that the soldiers could be paid.* Inevitably, Jovius instructed Honorius to send Alaric's bishops packing.

'With these raving lunatics at Ravenna, our only hope's the Senate,' said Ginger. 'We've got to get there before the Huns.' So Alaric and his Goths marched for the second time on Rome, and, of course, Ostia. Rome was getting tired of famines by now, and capitulated immediately. The Symmachi were the leaders in the new dispensation; they detested Honorius equally for his piety and for his incompetence. A new 'senatorially appointed' Augustus was plainly needed. Alaric quite agreed. Their joint candidate? None other than Flavius 'Priscus' Attalus, recently Chancellor, currently Prefect of Rome. Attalus was known to, and liked by Alaric. Like us Marcians, he was a Graeco-Roman; unlike us, he was probably a true Flavian, for the Senate to accept his name, *Priscus*.* He had been a successful Vicar of Asia, and was now on transfer in the West. He would be around my neck for the next five years – a sagacious but glib adviser.

The Symmachi supported Attalus as a pagan. With Augustine, as it were, at my elbow, I thought I should shove my oar in, and Alaric had him hastily baptised (as an Arian; 'tant pis'). The Senate, hurriedly convened, appointed Attalus Augustus of Rome and of Italy – Honorius would remain 'Augustulus' of Ravenna. Attalus' first act was to appoint Alaric *Magister Militum*, as he had sought. He also appointed me Count of the Domestics. Yippee! He next despatched Alaric around Northern Italy to win them to his allegiance, and to inform Honorius of their new joint status. There was the little matter of a purple robe to sort out – by custom, this should come from the Senior Augustus. The Senate could vouch for the loyal adherence of the 'Mezzogiorno' to the new dispensation.

'Don't trust Attalus too far,' said Ginger. 'You need better security for all Rome's promises than a *cingulum aureum*' (gold belt; insignia of a *Magister Militum*). 'We asked, once, for young Eucherius as a hostage. Now that he's dead—' (he wasn't, but Ginger didn't know that; neither, thankfully as it was to prove, did Galla Placidia) '—I think you should demand the Princess Galla. The Senate may be assured that we'll treat her with proper respect.' We duly got her, and I was put in charge of this lovely young lady, while Alaric went off to his duties in the North.

The next problem was caused by Heraclian in Africa. Attalus had read the Gildo lesson aright: that if Rome was to have peace and bread, its African food supply must be secure. In November 409 Attalus sent a small body of all-Roman troops to Africa* to secure Heraclian's adherence to Attalus and Rome. The mission was a failure. In January 410 Heraclian killed its leader and proclaimed his allegiance to Honorius. In the same month Attalus, quite the 'Imperator' now, marched on Ravenna, where Jovius, under cover of accepting Attalus as co-Emperor, accompanied him back to Rome. There Jovius started to poison Ginger's confidence in him, and Attalus completed the good work himself with an 'own goal'. Attalus had sent a further mission of arms and money to Africa to call Heraclian to order. Too little, too late. Heraclian saw them off decisively, and in misguided loyalty to Honorius, cut off Rome's food supply yet again. (Augustine would have said Heraclian was not misguided, but God-guided. Had they, perhaps, been talking?)

Alaric, hearing of all this, came up with Attalus at Rimini and demoted him to private life. He then tried – we all tried – to come to terms with Honorius, but Sarus managed to put a stop to this promising initiative. In a futile gesture, Alaric and I surrendered our gold belts to Honorius, humbly petitioning that we might receive them back again from the '*authentic* Augustus'. The date? June 410. Alaric and Ginger were now desperate. Alaric had so far received neither the promised ransom, nor honourable pasturage in Illyricum or Noricum, and it seemed clear that only the Senate could grant either. For the last time, Alaric turned on Rome. '*Penetramus ad Urbem*,' urged Ginger. 'This time we won't stay outside the Walls. But first, to put Uldin and his Huns in balk.'

Naturally I was sent on this tricky assignment – after all, I knew the Huns. With me were two hostages, as earnest of good faith: none other than young Aëtius, Son of the Eagles, and his young companion Jason. (They were to spend two exciting years as hostages of the Huns, being treated very much as 'sons of the King' and even swearing blood brotherhood with his sons Bleda and Attila. Bleda had a most amusing dwarf called Zercon,* whom he later sent to Aëtius as a present – but I digress.) I was able to persuade Uldin to agree to wait on the touchline, for he was still awaiting payment of the sums promised by Jovius (his last employer). In return, Alaric undertook to see him paid. So, in July 410 began the last fateful march on Rome.

On 24 August 410, Alaric, Ginger, Galla Placidia and I stood on the heights of the Pincio and surveyed The City. Aurelian's newly-refurbished walls flared, menacing, in the early sun. It was a poignant sight, and Alaric's heart was heavy at what he had to do. Rome of the Kings, Rome of the Consuls, Rome of the Emperors, Rome of the Apostles and Saints waited tearfully for her fate. None wept more deeply than the pious ladies of the Aventine, where Marcella and other noble ladies were still at their posts, as the history books will movingly tell you. Crafty old Morgan had already made her escape to Sicily, together with Melania the Holy Terror.

Rome was now in the midst of her third blockade in three years. Yet again her citizens were bargaining with one another for rats and vermin; yet again some were considering cannibalism. My rich Christian friends had already given away all their last stocks of grain to feed the suffering people. Suddenly one of them could bear it all no more; this was none other than dear dear Faltonia Proba,* my old Mendip friend and mother-in-law. She knew that Alaric was no mere barbarian from the forests but a Christian and an adopted Roman; she knew that Ginger was Uncle Ted's daughter; maybe she even knew that I was there with young Galla. She sent us a message: 'The Salarian Gate is open; be quick, and be merciful.'

**So fell Rome.**

We were less than a week in Rome, but Alaric was determined to get his money's worth, and this could not be achieved without some hefty strong-arm work. We tried to spare, and on the whole succeeded in sparing, the churches, but the populace were, inevitably, rather roughly handled. Among them, one pitiful casualty was dear old Aunt Marcella, who joined the Saints and Martyrs in this continuing 'Massacre of the Innocents'. We really took all the old pagan temples to pieces, and Augustine would surely gloat* to know that the Chi-Rho now shone unchallenged on the despoiled *fana* of smouldering Rome. Inscrutable indeed are the ways of God.

Having done minimal damage to Rome and recovered at long last his promised ransom money – all he had ever sought – Alaric set himself to restoring the situation. If he could now deal with Heraclian, as Attalus had failed to do, and restore Rome's food supplies, he could present himself afresh to Honorius as the saviour and guardian of Rome. On 30 August we set out on the long march South to Sicily, *en route* for Africa. We passed through Nola and managed to get our men to spare Paulinus' convent. Ever onwards we trudged to *Rhegium* (Reggio) where an ill-omened accident occurred. Alaric had unfortunately contracted malaria during the march through Campania, and much of the time we had to carry him in a litter. His armies were already crowding onto the ferries for Messina when a gale struck, a powerful *Tramontana*. Many of the overloaded boats overturned at their moorings. Others broke loose, smashing their neighbours. Some went on fire. A scene of chaos ensued.

Such accidents are common fare to seamen, and quickly repaired. Less easy to repair was the heart of Alaric. I have said that he was sick, and often in high fever. To the extent that he was Roman, he shared the credulity of the pagan Romans; to the extent that he was still a Goth, he knew that there were gods in the forests, who could be angry, and need to be appeased; to the extent that he was a Christian, he knew that a Christian heretic had just sacked the Holy City. 'This *Tramontana* is an omen from Heaven,' he cried, 'whoever Heaven's Inhabitants may be. I must return to Rome to seek purification of my guilt, by whatever rite.' Nothing would dissuade him.

Dismayed, we carried the delirious man back northwards, together with his train of men and loot. At Cosenza, on the little River Busento, Alaric gave up the ghost. Alaric, who had tried so hard, first to save, then to spare Rome. Poor brave Alaric, who should have fathered Romano-Gothic Emperors and thus paved the way for a peaceful entry into the Middle Ages. Alaric the Vizi-Goth was dead. He had reigned over them for twenty-eight years.

His fellow Goths mourned their King with howls and keening. Then they set out to give him worthy burial in the way Goths bury Kings, even Christian ones. There would be a great funeral pyre by the Busento. There, surrounded by all his treasures, would Alaric go to his ancestors. His treasures would be buried, with his ashes, in the river. All that precious ransom, the whole Nibelung hoard, would lie with him.* Chiefest of all his treasures – Ginger his wife – would accompany him to the Gothic Valhalla, in what the Indo-Aryans would call 'Suttee'.* Their mingled ashes would be enurned and buried in the river bed, together with the treasure. Then the waters of the Busento would return to their accustomed course, and, with them, all memory of the events would be washed away. To make sure, all the slaves engaged in the work were killed at the conclusion.

In Book X, did I not promise you Götterdammerung? Here, we are at the close of the third Act. It's not the Rhine, of course, and Ginger's not Brünnhilde, though the Romancers and Wagner may here borrow her.* All I will say is that, after a night of appalling anguish, Ginger did rouse herself to the heights of true heroism, and insisted on hurling herself, unaided, onto the pyre. So ended the 'Aventure of the Two Drowned Lovers'.

To only *one man* was entrusted the secret of their resting place, and of their hoard. That man was Alaric's successor as King of the Vizi-Goths.

**Shall I bear the sceptre well?**

# BOOK XV

## *The Headless Huntsman* (AD410–411)

The Goths were in great despair, after the death of Alaric. They had followed him, their womenfolk always in the covered wagons at their rear, all the way from the Danube. All they had ever sought, from Valens, from Uncle Ted, or from his sons, was somewhere to live. For all his charm, and his heroism, Alaric had failed to deliver. I think that's why they turned to me. I was a Roman, and knew their ways. I was a Count in Rome's army, more or less. I was Alaric's brother-in-law.

It was with tears running down their rough cheeks that they raised me on their shields as an honorary Goth. 'Ataulfus King, Ataulfus King!' they cried – the nearest their Teutonic larynxes could get to 'Adelphos'. 'Lead the Goths to peace* and we will follow you.' Had not Augustine commanded that as my next task? Sigesarus, our Bishop/chaplain, duly crowned me with Alaric's iron circlet, and the Goths did me homage, man by man. Last of all, young Galla came and placed her hands between mine.

'Think of all their poor wives and children,' she said. 'Surely it's time they had rest and a home. They don't *want* to be enemies to the Romans, I'm sure.'

'For you, my dear lady,' I said – for I was becoming very fond of her – 'for you, and I think for Rome's sake too, I will take them back as suppliants to Honorius. Maybe your prayers will have some force with him.' So our demoralised throng turned back by the road we had so recently trodden.

Before we left I had two things to do. The first was to send a message to Heraclian, to say that the Goths were no longer enemies of Rome, and that the Roman Senate had returned to Honorius' obedience. Let food be sent to Rome, and quickly. The second reminded me more of my grisly 'Aventure' at Askalon. I meant no harm to Alaric's and Ginger's ashes – they at least would continue to rest in peace. It was Attalus however, who was still tagging along with us, who made the point to me. 'Whichever way the dice fall when we reach Honorius, it would strengthen your hand if you were not ill-supplied with money. Your Goths would probably lynch you if they found out, but I think your duty to them requires you to recover that hoard of gold and valuables. We'll do it at night, with the aid of some of Galla's Roman servants, and I'll give you a hand.'

'Good thinking, Attalus. Stay with me if you like; you can be useful to me.' So the deed was done, and no Goth was allowed to weigh Galla's baggage!

In January 411 we were once again marching on Rome. My Goths thought a bit more looting no less than their due. It was Galla's tearful entreaties which saved Rome. I found I could not resist her. Indeed, I loved her. It was too absurd. Here I was, nearing the end of my fiftieth year, a widower and the father, besides, of five children by Elissa and Doxy outside the marriage bond. Only months ago I had become the father of yet another son, by my own daughter. You would have thought I'd have learnt my lesson. But, somehow this was different. Although she, too, was young enough to be my daughter, I revered Galla. She was beautiful, with her aristocratic features and rich chestnut hair, but she was also royal. She was, after all, Justina's granddaughter, and that had to count for something. But she was Uncle Ted's daughter too – born to command. I would fain serve her as her knight, if she'd have me. Suddenly I'd found a different sort of love. Did she perhaps feel some warmth for me? I thought God and Augustine could smile on this romance – yes, we are now into Romance, and the tide is flowing strong – and maybe the little 'Mallet of God' still had a key role to play.

Now that Serena was dead, Stilicho was dead, Ginger and Alaric were both dead, the future of Old Rome, and of the Western Empire lay in this young lady's hands. If I were to be her cavalier, and at the same time were to reconcile in my person the Barbarian Goths and the Romans, maybe an era of peace could come? Of course Rome had to be spared, as far as it lay in my power to control my Goths. But if Galla and I were to marry and have sons, they might rule the Goths in the name of Rome, and Rome with the support of the Goths. Was this a mad dream? I had to be gentle and circumspect. I would do nothing without Galla's consent and Honorius' blessing. Legitimacy and propriety were my new aims.

We headed therefore up the Via Flaminia from Rome and paused for a while at Rimini. Galla will be remembered in the Commedia dell'arte as 'Flaminia', later to be ousted by 'Columbine'. I, of course, was Harlequin, the leader of the 'Wild Hunt'.* When our horsemen and covered wagons rolled through the countryside, as we had since Calabria, the populace didn't forget us* in a hurry.

At Rimini the locals assured me that Sarus my old enemy and *his* Goths were still safely stashed away in *Picenum* (South of Ancona). I thought Honorius might think it threatening if I took my Goths too near to the Sacred Presence, so it was with only a small bodyguard that Galla and I made our way to Ravenna. My mission was twofold: first to seek the Princess Galla's hand in marriage, second to seek a permanent home for my Goths.

Honorius received us amiably enough in his vague way. If it wasn't a matter of poultry breeding or of religion he was never much interested. His advisers looked after his political will for him, and his chief adviser remained Jovius. Now Jovius was doing a pretty good job, all considered, and I hoped he would favour both my aims. I had forgotten that it was I who took his son, young Jason, and delivered him somewhat cavalierly into the hands of the Huns. Jovius had reluctantly ceded him to Alaric, for Rome's sake, as security for Rome's 'ransom', but that debt had now been paid in full, and Jovius naturally wanted to see his son free.

The snag was that Uldin and his 'Rent-a-Huns' had not yet been paid by anyone, and while Huns were second to none in their love of *solidi*, Rome's – and Ravenna's – treasuries were completely bankrupt. To make matters worse, New Rome had sent my old friend, (and alchemist and therapist) Olympiodorus over, with a request that Jovius return the 4,000 crack troops which they had sent to Honorius' rescue in 409, and which had indeed more than stabilised the situation.

Their commander, Constantius III, was with them at Ravenna. Would to God he had been elsewhere. Readers beware: JJ is Constantine III; John-George is Constans II. Now we have 'Constantius III', the interloper. To avoid confusion I will refer to him henceforth, vulgarly, as 'Stan the Inexorable', an epithet he will well earn.

I had long, rather wary, discussions with Jovius. He was most reluctant to return Constantius and his men; there were all too few trained and disciplined 'Roman' soldiers around in the West. However, I can claim the credit for cutting the Gordian knot. 'Why don't you offer Anthemius Uldin and his 10,000 Rent-a-Huns in exchange for Constantius and his 4,000 legionaries? I'll ante-up the necessary cash from Alaric's spoils, which you can then have coined. Anthemius will be responsible for their future pay, Olympiodorus, after consulting his masters, can take the cash to Uldin, and free your Jason, and also young Aëtius. My reward for all this will be the Princess Galla to wife.' Alas, it was not to be quite so easy. Jovius was determined to restore the entire Western Empire to Honorius' obedience. (Thank God he didn't know I was 'Gerontius', the Emperor-maker of Spain.) He therefore wanted to see JJ toppled. So did I.

'I shall advise His Serenity,' said Jovius, 'that if you are to be worthy of the Princess Galla, his sister, his heiress, and his ward, you must do some signal service to the Roman State. You must dethrone your brother, without gross expenditure of Rome's assets, and if possible without bloodshed. I myself am a Gallo-Roman of one of the oldest families of Clermont Ferrand. My people long to be once more the loyal subjects of a *worthy* Emperor.' A wry glance here towards Honorius.

'And if I do all this, what about my Goths?' I asked.

'Spain has room for them I expect,' said Honorius in a surprising intervention. 'Meantime they can play around in the valley of the Po as so often before. Enough pasture there. But first I want your brother's head on a pike, yes and that son of his too, before you can take your Goths across the Alps.'

This was about the second time in his life that this rather unexpected man had played the Augustus.

'And then I can wed my Galla, Serenity, or should I say, Cousin?'

'Yes, then you can wed her – if she'll have you.'

Why was this fellow Stan looking so furious, I wondered? He was sulky at the best of times but, just now, his looks could kill. Had I perhaps a rival?

When I thought it was time to withdraw, Honorius bowled me a fast one. 'My sister Galla will remain here with me, during your mission, Cousin.'

'Not so fast, Serenity,' said I. 'Jovius wants me to surrender to him a large sum of money to pay the Huns. I accept the challenge you have set me, but I too need some security. Galla may remain with you until I return with the money. In exchange, she then comes back to my custody. While I am away in Gaul I have in mind lodging her, with a guard of Goths suitable to her status, at the Villa Sirmione, which is hers under Justina's will, and which is agreeable at this time of year.'

Young Stan was looking daggers when Honorius gave his consent to this. I was glad I'd insisted on the bodyguard of Goths. Poor Cinderella, still a pawn for others, even now the Ugly Sisters were dead. So it was arranged. I made a hasty dash to Rimini, and returned to Ravenna with the promised money – I now thought of it as Galla's dowry. Jovius handed it on to Olympiodorus with a despatch for Uldin, and another for Anthemius.

With him, Olympiodorus took another document, one which I must confess was no more than a work of fiction. Those who read it might have seen the influence of Josephus, for I had the stories of the Maccabees, and Josephus' own autobiography very much in mind. Olympiodorus and I were chums – that's why he agreed to help me. You see, absolved or not, Little Merlin had some scruples where Galla was concerned. Honorius said I and my Goths might well end up in Spain. That was where they well remembered 'Gerontius' and his all too compliant bedfellow, 'Lot's daughter', or Ursula. I was brave enough to make a clean breast of my amatory misdeeds to Sneezy, but somehow

I didn't fancy telling Galla that the man who hoped to marry her has been guilty of incest with his own daughter. Time to kill off 'Gerontius' and his 'little bride'. Time they were written convincingly out of the script. So, shamefacedly, I turned for the last time to my pen as a tool of disinformation, and wrote the pious romance of the mutual suicide of Gerontius and Nonnichia,* the little Nun. Shades of 'Get thee to a nunnery', since Ursula was, for the moment, Ophelia (*Opellia/Ulpia* in Latin). John would soon tell me that she did indeed intend to become a nun, as Bride or Bridget of Kildare, amongst other names.* Later, as 'Hamlet', John would have another Ophelia, alas.

I don't think Olympiodorus was fooled for a moment, but he engaged to spread the tale around New Rome where all the historians were. I would enlist Max's aid to do the same job in Spain. I didn't think that Galla would ever know. Heigh Ho.

With Galla duly restored to me, we rode back together to Rimini to collect my Goths, and to head North for the Po. Galla was very sweet to me, almost deferential. Could it be that she did love me? Her short stay at Ravenna seemed to have made up her mind.

'My Lady,' I eventually dared to say, 'you can see that cousin Honorius is of a mind to approve our marriage. It rests with you then, and only you. My Princess, my Darling, will you take this ageing knight as your wedded husband.'

'With all my heart,' cried Galla, and flung her arms round my neck.

It was evening, and we were approaching *Forum Livii* (Forli). We found a church there, and a bishop* to bless us. (This bishop was of course Catholic, not Arian.) The presiding minister of any established congregation was still called bishop at this time;* over the centuries they would prove amazingly upwardly-mobile in status, rising eventually to become Prince-Bishops. Whatever will Jesus make of that title?

Attalus and our small retinue of servitors stood witness, and our wedding* night was at the inn there. As I now write, I can say without hesitation that this was, if not the first, the best and greatest love of either of our lives, mine or Galla's. Perhaps that was why, against the odds, I did not consummate it that night.

'I want to wait, my darling, until I have done a great deed worthy of you. I want to make you not only Queen of the Goths but *Caesar*'s wife.' (I had hopes Honorius might award me this status in gratitude for what I was about to do for him.) 'Wait for me a few months, while I settle accounts in Gaul.' So we fondled and were tender with one another, and each dreamed their own dreams.

Another few weeks saw Galla lodged at 'Joyeuse Garde', to be further brightened by her presence, while I hastened over Montgenèvre with a few *numeri* of Goths and Scolani to see what I could do about JJ. He had to go, but he must not die. I could not kill my brother, be he drunk or mad, just to please Honorius. Whoever's head graced the pike on my return, it would not be his. But how was I to work the trick? One thing I'd decided. I'd try to pick up my Burgundians again, when I was back in Gaul. I ought to be able to detach them from JJ's party, if they hadn't already detached themselves. What a thing it was, to have a pay chest at my disposal!

April saw me heading down the Rhone from Lyons. Yes, dear Eucheria the Pious Maccabee was long dead alas, so the 'Holy' Round Table of Jerusalem was all mine. I visited her tomb, and paid my affectionate respects to her and St Justus.

As we approached Vienne, we came up with some Burgundian troops who were guarding it. They were delighted to see me and quickly changed sides. I waited to see who they were supposed to be guarding. The 'siege', if you can call it that, took some seven bloodless days. When the white flag went up and we went in, who should I find but John-George; the Augustus Constans, no less.

Well, I made a show of treating him with severity, and then let him fade into my retinue. We were overjoyed to be together again, and to catch up on all the news. I told him about Galla; he told me about Ursula. All well there, and she'd given me a little son called *Faustus* ('Lucky'), later to be Bishop of Riez, and a noted semi-Pelagian. Convent-bred, he would be one of the Romancers' famous 'Gregorys'; in fact he would be their 'Pope Gregory'.* Would I ever be able to acknowledge him? Still, Augustine had absolved me from that, so it was back to the game in hand.

John said it was absolutely hopeless at Arles. JJ spent most of the time either asleep or else roaring drunk. The provincials were voting with their feet. Any moment now they might proclaim a new Emperor of their own. 'Who, pray?' asked I.

'Jovinus,' said John. 'He's Jovius' nephew, or else half-brother. I'm not sure. He's a regular soldier, currently serving on the Rhine. A good egg, and very popular in Gaul.'

'We could do a lot worse,' said Attalus the wily, ever at my elbow.

'Just what were you supposed to be doing, John, at Vienne?' I asked.

'Easy,' said John. 'Justus sent me there. He's sent Edobech, Dad's Master of Horse, off to Thuringia to try to recruit some Alemanni of sorts. They were to meet me here. Dad's own army, a crazy mix of Spaniards and *Honoriani*, seem to be melting away. Honorius is bound to send an army soon, probably Sarus, and we wanted to be ready.'

'*I'm* Honorius' army,' said I, 'so we'd better get down to Arles and see if JJ can be made to see sense.'

So I and my little battle group made for Arles. The date? May 411. One thing about a 'funk-hole' like Arles (or Ravenna for that matter): it may be hard to take by force, but it's easy to blockade. So long as Heraclian didn't send food in by sea, it was just a matter of setting roadblocks across the four land-approach roads and waiting. My hope was that the fat cats of Arles would force JJ to capitulate well before Edobech got back. At the critical moment I'd smuggle John-George in as an emissary. That should clinch it.

Things don't always go to plan. First a seaman brought news that a *second* Romano-Gothic army was *en route* for the Cottian Alps. What could this mean? Sarus? But who else? It could only be Stan. Was I being double-crossed? Was Galla safe? The second news item, by land this time, is that Jovinus has been proclaimed Imperator – not, I remind you, necessarily synonymous with Augustus – at Mainz by the Rhine Army, and by Goar and his tame Alans. There had been a body of tame Alans, sort of Scythians, in the Roman Armies since the time of Gratian. These too were moving South on Gaul, and were expected to make for Lyons. The timing was getting tricky.

On Attalus' cunning advice I decided to make for Lyons myself and ally my Burgundians with Jovinus. When we reached Lyons* I had a new shock, for there was Sarus, my arch enemy. He had just fallen out irreparably with Honorius and, more importantly, Stan, and had fled to Jovinus with a few followers hoping to find a new master. No room for him and me in this world; I sent him rather briskly ahead to the next – a deed his brother would avenge on me quite soon. Not cricket: war. Would Ambrose see it that way?

Jovinus welcomed me quite warmly. With me, as Honorius' agent for the removal of JJ, and Attalus, still an Augustus in the eyes of some of the Senate, we seem to add a sort of legitimacy to his position. We all moved together down the Rhone for Arles. JJ would surely crumble now. It was a hot, hot summer that year all over Europe. Drought conditions, with the Rhone absurdly low. We went back, sweltering, to the siege of Arles but, even with our augmented forces, we couldn't take it. Justus made occasional sorties to test our strength, but he couldn't break out either, so it was a matter of waiting, and time was not on our side. In the middle of August I thought it time to put in my ferret. John-George was duly disguised as a rather tall peasant, and sent through the lines. His message was simple: to tell JJ that his position was hopeless, and resistance pointless. If we didn't get him, Stan the Inexorable would. He could be sure that I would spare his life, but Stan might not.

Silence fell for the next fortnight, and on 28 August my scouts told me that a great column of dust on the East bank of the Rhone betokened the arrival of Stan and his huge-seeming armies, including Sarus' Tame Goths, now under the command of one Ulfilas. Attalus said that Goar and his Alans were all for joining up with Stan. Such Romans as I had were likely to follow suit, seeing the opportunity to bring the hot and thirsty siege to an end. We were all supposed to be Honorius' men, weren't we? I'd been trumped. I knew Stan was after Galla. He didn't yet know that he was too late. If he did, he might well try to kill me, accidentally of course. My only course was to retire with my Burgundians – still loyal to me as long as I paid them – and hide myself in the woods nearby, putting it about that I was making off for Spain.* Stan was really the answer to a prayer, so far as the damned siege was concerned, but I had yet to try to save the necks of JJ and John.

Well, you can read in the histories how Stan arrived before Arles, how the gates were opened to him, how, three days later, Edobech arrived too late with his rabble of Alemans, and was quickly trounced and beheaded. Jovinus had retired prudently to Clermont, waiting while Stan did his work for him. What of JJ? John had done a truly marvellous work at Arles. Not only had he managed to sober up my terrified brother, he had recalled him to his earlier piety. Maybe they'd remembered young Eucherius Stiliconis, and his successful *clericatus* too; for it was a tonsured priest and a tonsured deacon – now that really should have ensured their safety – who surrendered themselves to Stan's 'clemency'. (Make up your own minds how wholehearted was JJ's conversion to the 'way of the cassock', when I tell you that he and John had two large-ish objects stowed in the hand baggage which Stan had allowed them to take. Not Bibles, but 'relics' of a sort – the wax portrait busts which go with an Augustus. Hope springs eternal.) Stan got JJ's authentic purple robe, but he wouldn't wear it for another ten years, and then only for ten months. Stan was a moody and violent man, quite the licentious soldier. He had heard Honorius say that the price I must pay for his consent to my wedding Galla was JJ and John's heads on two pikes. Why should Stan not pre-empt me?

On reflection, I thought Stan would hardly wish to offer to Galla, as a wedding present, his hands all bloodied with her cousins' blood. He was a Christian of sorts, too, or Honorius wouldn't have had him. I thought he'd send them back to Honorius for him to do the dirty deed himself. I decided that the best I could do was to watch the roads from Arles carefully, and try to shadow JJ and John if they emerged. Unbeknown to me, another was also watching them: young Aëtius, Son of the Eagles. Olympiodorus had duly negotiated his freedom, whence his new name 'Ελευθερος* ('Uther' the freed-man), and he had been making his way westwards towards Gaul and liberty. He had crossed the Rhine *en route* for the Meuse, and was in fact approaching the Casa Belgica when he found himself caught up in a forest fire. Naturally he made for the nearest river (the Lesse), and that was how he came to rescue Elissa (Brünnhilde), senseless, near-suffocating, upon her rock. Did their lips meet then? No. He managed to carry her, and to lead the rest of the household, including not only my Gawain and Eugenia, but also Ursula and little Faustus who were staying with them, to safety. By and by he got them to shelter in Trier, still recovering from yet another sacking by the Riparian Franks.

It was there in the Gaste Cité that Elissa and Ursula showed their gratitude to their deliverer in physical terms (in what the Romancers will call 'The "Aventure" of the Fier Baisée').* Aëtius must have thought of Horace's words, *O matre pulchra filia pulchrior*: 'O fair mother of a fairer daughter'. This was not the time, however, for the handsome eighteen-year-old to take matters further.* His whole aim was to rejoin his unit, the Auxilia Palatinae/Scolani. Keen cadet, young Etzie. His enthusiasm spilled over onto young Gawain, the 'wild boy of the Forest'. Gawain wasn't quite as rustic and simple as the Romancers will make young Perceval, nor did he think Aëtius was an angel, but he did resolve to follow his lead and take up a military career, in which he is to distinguish himself greatly. He would end up as *Magister Militum* and *Patricius*; only to lose his life most gallantly in an ambush on the River Lawen* in Flanders, six years after the battle of Châlons where Aëtius and Theodoric turned back the hosts of Attila and saved Western civilisation for a while.

The two 'Percevals' worked their way up the Rhine past Mainz, missing Jovinus' elevation, and on to Strasbourg where they fell in with Edobech on his recruiting mission. Arles seemed to be where the action was, so to Arles they went. On arrival they quickly joined the legitimate duke, Stan the Inexorable, and were soon back among Aëtius' fellow *paladins*. They were to serve Stan for the next ten years, through the usual upward progression for cadets, in Spain, Gaul, Germany, even Britain. Aëtius, watching, saw his kinsmen shipped off to their fate at Ravenna. He would not have been proud to know himself kin to two former soldiers who hoped to cheat death by taking the tonsure. Just as well he still did not know that JJ was his father.

As I surmised from the size of his army, Stan had bigger fish to fry than JJ. Honorius (or rather Jovius who was still in power at Ravenna) had ordered him to sort out the problem of the BFBs. These were still milling around in Gascony, but a portion had accepted the opportunity I had given them to cross via Roncesvalles into Galicia where Max, trying to reign at Saragossa without an army, could do nothing about them. As I watched Stan's army prepare to move off westwards, I rather feared for young Max.

One day I saw what I was waiting for. Two chariots, a closed carriage, and a posse of guards left Arles heading up the Durance. All the familiar way we tailed them, keeping cover and distance. Up over Montgenèvre; down to the Po; along the great route for Milan and Ravenna. At Milan they were handed over to the Prefect, Seleucus,* while we watched anxiously at the Praetorium gates. Thank God, servants know how to talk, but we learnt alarming news. A posse from Ravenna had been installed there for several weeks. Jovius had sent them to bring in the usurpers dead or alive, but he had indicated, as they boasted, that dead would be preferable. Jovius had of course heard of his nephew's bid for power in Gaul. He was a passionate Gallo-Roman, and far from being bedazzled by his master at Ravenna, he was secretly preparing to transfer his allegiance to Jovinus, hoping to live out an honourable retirement in his homeland, ably administered by his kinsman. To this end JJ, as a legitimate wearer of the purple, had to die. Nothing less would do.

We continued to keep the Praetorium under surveillance, the while the outline of my rescue plan became clear. This boozy little gang should be easy to trick. Honorius should have his promised heads on pikes – I'd present them myself, yes and claim his assent to my wedding to Galla at the same time. All would go like the Commedia dell'arte, like Sir Gawayne and the Grene Knight, like Bercilak the giant in the Irish legend of Bricriu's Feast.* It was a trick I used to do in the old Saturnalian games at the Casa Sic, and which I'd worked up into one of my best tricks during my time as a travelling juggler and clown in 386. John used to be my partner at the Casa Sic and knew the trick well; all we needed was the opportunity.

We didn't have to wait long. Our chance came when the posse turned in, to spend the night at one of the *mansiones* (Post Houses), which lay at intervals along the greater Roman roads. This one lay just South of the Sirmione peninsula. Better and better; I had Galla and sanctuary just up the road. We knew, from following them for so long, that the Captain and guards did themselves well at table. Not so the prisoners; piously ascetic, they had to pretend to be.

Waiting until we thought the guard would be mellow, we broke our cover for the first time and checked boldly into the same inn. We introduced ourselves as travelling Gaulish merchants, and were loud in our criticisms of the ruin which Constantine III's corrupt and flaccid rule had brought on our homeland. 'Death's too good for the pair of them,' we cried, and they fell right into our laps. Over a few more jars, we swore to take revenge on the traitors to His Serenity of Ravenna the very next day. There should be a ceremonial execution, before all the citizens of Benaventum (now Peschiera where the River Mincio flowed out of Lake Garda). We 'merchants' would pay for the erection of a proper scaffold, for all the populace to see. We would even be glad to take off them, for the honour of Gaul, the actual duty of beheading the miscreants. No soldier gladly takes his place in a firing squad, so our offer was gratefully accepted. It will be no accident that the 'Vita St Cadoc' will have Cadoc 'die' at Beneventum, for John will be Cadoc.

It only remained to make contact with JJ and John and, thanks be to Bacchus, we achieved this. It was then that John handed over the two wax busts to us. Whew, what a bit of luck; now we could fool anyone. With all the preparations to make, it was late afternoon when JJ, his 'head' wobbling with fear above his ample white surplice, stumbled up onto the scaffold to meet his doom. Gosh, was I hot and sweaty underneath. Didn't I tell you in Book IV* to remember that JJ was a whole head taller than me? It was his 'wax head' that I was now wearing. JJ was uneasily watching, disguised, in the crowd. 'Safest place for you to be,' I said. John-George, also disguised, was up on the platform with me, ready to play his practised role as executioner. All the 'Beheading Game' myths start here. John, as I once reminded you, was pseudo-Gawayne, of 'Grene Knight' fame. Here too were the origins of so many 'Kephalophore'* Saints. Can you identify them?

The smallest of my squad was dressed up as 'John', again with two heads. John did a bit of 'Fee, Fi, Fo, Fumming' to amuse the crowd, while I wobbled convincingly. Then with one great swipe John decapitated me, the while I burst the bladder of pig's blood which I had concealed on top of my head and we gave them a real gory sight. My men dragged my carcass offstage, while John repeated the act with his own 'better half'. The 'heads' were stashed in a bag (later to be switched) and solemnly sealed by the captain of the guard. Then it was back to the 'Motel' for much merriment and liquid celebration.

Meanwhile, JJ and John were slinking up the isthmus to the Villa Sirmione and Galla. Alas, I was not free to join her yet. I still had to dig up some *real* heads to stand in for the wax ones. Two recently dead redheads were needed. We could bash them about and henna them to increase the similarity. After all, they wouldn't be expected to be exactly 'daisy-fresh' when Honorius looked at them.

**Figure 33**
Joyeuse Garde:
Sirmione the sanctuary
© Edizione Poiatti

Jovius was still, just, in charge at Ravenna when the heads were transferred to pikes* and borne in to Honorius' presence. I followed, now in full Roman rig, as soon as I thought the coast was clear and the guard paid off. I explained that JJ and John had capitulated to me – well John did, didn't he, if not at Arles? I fibbed, as if we were the best of friends and comrades, how Constantius was now *en route* to clear Gaul and Spain, and that he had asked me to escort the usurpers to Ravenna. I said I reckoned I had now fulfilled all my tasks. What about the promised home for my Goths? Honorius had no choice but to concede this. 'An Augustus always keeps his word,' he said pompously. 'You may find a home for your Goths in *Gallia Narbonensis*' (that's Provence West of the Rhone).

Yippee! 'On what basis, Serenity?' I asked.

'Oh, the usual thing for federates. I'll write to the Praetorian-elect* telling him to let you have as much waste land as he can find, for free, and that he shall compel the landowners to sell you up to one third of their existing holdings at half market value. As you'll be taking on their defence, their rates will go down. Just as well you seem well supplied with money.'

'One last thing, Serenity,' I said. 'We may have money but we can't eat it. It may be several years before we can support ourselves from our new lands.'

'I can't be bothered with all these details,' said Honorius. 'Tell the Praetorian I said you should be looked after. He can buy in additional stocks from Africa.'

'Before I leave you, Cousin,' I ventured, 'I think I should tell you that we are now brothers-in-law. I have already married Galla, but I have not made her wholly mine as yet, as I wanted to ask a favour of you. How would you feel about making me your Caesar? Then I should be truly worthy of her, and I could serve you well.'

'Nothing doing, I'm afraid,' said Honorius. 'I've had quite enough competitors for a lifetime. Nevertheless you have served me well; now go and serve her. Can't think what she sees in an ancient titch like you, Uncle, or should I now say, Brother?'

In this cheerful mood we parted, for the last time as it was to prove. The heads were despatched to Carthage* to be placed on the Town Gates. Heads of usurpers were customarily sent to Carthage as an awful warning to the guardians of Rome's food supply not to think they could get away with revolt. It didn't seem to stop them trying. Cousin Augustine could have seen the heads there, also his sidekick Orosius.* Augustine would have had neither opportunity nor inclination to look closely. Just as well, knowing JJ as he did. There the heads joined those of Maxentius, Theodosius, Maximus, and other failures. I would be sending two more of my own along shortly.

In high spirits I made my way to the Villa Sirmione for my long-delayed honeymoon. Now came the Kingdom, the Power, and the Glory.

For ever and ever?

Hardly.

# BOOK XVI

## *The Promised Land (AD411–415)*

Christmas at the Villa Sirmione was a jolly affair. Not only were Galla and I besotted with each other, but JJ and John were both in excellent form. I twit JJ that he's King 'Ban' of Benwick, the banned (outlawed) Augustus of Lake Benacus (Lake Garda), as the Romancers will remember him. JJ was really a new man, thanks to John-George. That twenty-eight-year-old had real spiritual power, even if he did have trouble with his libido – and who doesn't have that? It was only 'duty' plus vanity plus booze which made JJ an Augustus, and now he had surrendered all three. This left him where he was before: a 'Born-again' celibate Christian lawyer with marked administrative gifts. Gosh! They weren't half in abeyance while he was at Arles!

His first instinct was to go back for a while to Little Benedict, now at Cassino. I assured him that this was too dangerous; as a failed Augustus his head was still in danger in Italy if he was recognised. The same went for John. We agreed that, cowled as monks, they would slip away to Genoa, and then take a ship to Sicily. I knew Morgan was still there, as well as Genesius, my actor son. I hoped they would make it safe to the Casa Sic.

I digress, to follow them there. Morgan had aged a lot, with all the troubles in Rome, and the damage to her properties in the Mezzogiorno, where I fear my Goths' 'Wild Hunt' must have cost her many years' rents. Ageing, too, was the presence of two refugees from Rome, 'Melania the Holy Terror' and 'Coelestius the oily Lebanese'. (Another nearby refugee, Rufinus*, had even seen the smoke of our burning ships at Reggio.) Wasn't Melania a Christian Socialist? Hadn't she read Ambrose's sermon on Naboth's vineyard? Hadn't she followed Jesus by selling all she had and giving to the poor? Nightly she thumped the scriptural message into John – one which will always be a stumbling-block for rich Christians (Matthew IX.21–24, etc.). In the Sack of Rome, Augustine saw God's verdict on Rome's *paganism*; Melania, God's verdict on Rome's *wealth*.

Under Melania's compelling influence John – whom future theologians will rightly remember as the Sicilian Briton* – turned his Ciceronian prose to the cause of Christian Socialism and wrote a number of alarmingly political

Christian tracts; tracts which were to win him, JJ and Coelestius banishment from the Empire.[1]

The little group of clerical refugees decided to cross over into Africa (to which their recently published works had not yet penetrated). They were kindly received at Carthage, but to avoid encountering Augustine they resolved to go on a pilgrimage to the Holy Land.* There, for the moment, I must leave them to return to the Villa Sirmione.

Where were Max and Titia (John's wife), and my little Alice? Stan had toppled them at Saragossa, but had allowed them to retire into private life, and they were doing the 'poor relation' act around friends in Tarraco. Stan had 'settled' Spain and the BFBs rather cleverly by means of 'divide and conquer'. He had dispersed them by lot: the Asdingi and Suebes to remain in Galicia; the Siling Vandals to move to *Baetica* (Cordova); the Alans split, half to *Lusitania* (Portugal), the remainder to *Carthago* (Cartagena) on usual federate terms. His task in Spain accomplished, Stan crossed to Tangier, as Count of Tingitana *and* joint Count of Africa so that he could keep an eye on Heraclian. Honorius really seemed to be ruling at last. Elissa and Eugenia were at the Casa Belg. Aëtius and my Gawain were serving *scolani*. I think that's all the quiverful accounted for, and that I can relax and enjoy Galla.

And so indeed I did. Sirmione was not only a safe stronghold, with its long narrow isthmus ending in a drawbridge (and no ordinary drawbridge for it was to become Lancelot's 'water bridge'), it was also the most delightful love nest, even as Catullus hymned it so many years before. Warmed by braziers, Galla and I relished the winter sunshine in the belvedere, whilst reading Catullus and suiting the actions to the words. We also had frequent dips in the hot swimming bath endlessly fed from the boiling spring – yes, here was the Romancers' Fountain of the Boiling Spring.*

Soon the passes would be opening and I would have to think about my Goths and their trek to the promised land, but for now, life was very good.

---

[1] In an earlier footnote I told you about the Arian heresy. Now, because it will likewise affect all our lives, I must say something about the infant *Pelagian* heresy which will take its name from JJ. For Cousin Augustine's pen had not been idle since he and JJ had talked God around Trastevere, and his well-publicised thoughts were hardening. If God's Grace (which, as he described so frankly in his *Confessions*, had forcibly transformed him from an incorrigible lecher into a contented celibate) was *that* irresistible; if it was as irresistible as God himself from whom it emanated, what room could still be left for man's *free will*? What indeed? That will be the crux. JJ's opinions were still those of the Augustine he had known. Using his old *nom-de-plume* of 'Pelagius'* JJ took up his pen anew to answer the new Augustine; but his principal co-author, alas, was Coelestius. Now Coelestius was as provocative a writer, in matters of theology, as John in matters of polity; the resulting works would be damned as heretical by Augustine and the whole Western Empire would reluctantly agree to confirm Augustine's verdict.

In the last week of March 412 Galla and I went to Pavia to round up my Goths. As we headed North for Montgenèvre, Galla travelling in a horse litter with bodyguard, and the baggage cart with the treasure chest close behind, there must have been some 60,000 of us on the move, including the women and children. Quite a cavalcade. All peacefully-minded, even my armed Gothic cavalry. There was still snow on the mountain pastures, although the road had been cleared. Gosh! The montagnards were going to rook us for fodder. Everyone, since Hannibal, crossed the Cottian Alps via Montgenèvre. Why? Because there was fodder to spare. It was the only Pass that had.

We continued our trek via *Vapincum* (Gap) making straight for the Rhone valley where, as instructed, I would cross the Rhone, continuing South on the right bank. We would then pause at *Heraclea** (St Gilles), over against Arles, to await further orders – and, hopefully, food – from the Prefect. As we approached Valence we came up with the whole body of my Burgundians who had been milling around North of Arles since I dashed off to play the beheading game for JJ the previous year.

It was Attalus who persuaded me that I should leave the Goths to him for the moment, and lead the Burgundians instead to the train of Jovinus in the North. Crafty, yet patriotic statecraft this. Attalus didn't think Honorius would or could, or indeed should, unseat Jovinus in North Gaul. They needed a strong governor since the Rhine needs guarding for Rome's sake as well as Gaul's. The Burgundians seemed to hanker for their Northern climes. 'Put them to Rome's service, and get them out of the way at the same time,' said Attalus. 'You know they'll follow you. Aren't you their King?' Gosh! I'd almost forgotten that.

So I led them up to Trier, and left them to their duties. Jovinus promised them federate status in the Palatinate,* so they're happy. While I was up North I made a quick trip to the Casa Belgica, and found it deserted, but I'll tell you that story later.

By mid-June I had rejoined Galla, Attalus and the Goths at 'St Gilles'.* I found out that Honorius had appointed one John – not our John-George of course – as the new Praetorian of Gaul. He had been *Primicereus Notariorum* in 408 and had been on the embassy to Alaric about Rome's ransom and hostages, ending up favourably disposed to the Goths. This boded well, but it boded even better when I crossed over to Arles to see him.

'Look,' said John, 'I've got your commission here from His Serenity. You're hereby appointed *Magister Militum per Gallias*, with orders to take your Gothic cavalry and clear the remaining Barbarians out of Aquitaine and push them over the pass to Roncesvalles. Then close the pass with a good guard. There are still a lot of the BFBs messing up the Gascony, and His Serenity wants to see at least South Gaul restored to his obedience, to a peaceful existence, and to the payment of those almost forgotten things, taxes.'

'Write to him, then, that I've already done him a similar service by evicting the Burgundians from Lyonnais,' I said, and told him of my crafty transaction with Jovinus.

'Don't know quite what to do about Jovinus yet,' said John. 'Until such time as Honorius can demonstrate that he can offer Gaul better, safer government than Jovinus can, or Constantine did, an awful lot of Gallo-Romans will continue to support Jovinus.'

So John and I parted, thinking that we understood and liked one another a lot.

I had a gorgeous scamper around Aquitaine with my Goths. We went right up to Bordeaux, then got our brooms out and swept the Vandals down to and over the Pyrenees. By the end of September I was reunited with Galla at St Gilles. Now I was a hero. 'King of Kings,' my Goths called me. The locals were enthusiastic too. They contributed a fund to put up a triumphal column to me. It wouldn't be as big as my ancestor Trajan's, more like the Romano-Teutonic columns (*Jupiter-saüle*) up the Rhine. The Franks will call them 'Perrons', and I would leave another 'Perron Merlin'* for them at Liège in due course. One of these days John-George, too, would have his own 'Perrons': one in Strathmore, another in Kent.

Funds permitting, my St Gilles Perron would have a statue on top, and we planned reliefs and inscriptions* for the base – touching relics of our happiness. The local yeomen, the Anatilii and Arecomici, wanted to thank me for making St Gilles my capital. Bit premature, I'm afraid; only my temporary base. As soon as I could get my promised rations from Arles* I'd be making for Narbonne. Meantime, the locals were making a killing out of us for food. At this rate there wouldn't be much of the Nibelung's gold left by the time we got to Toulouse.

So passed the autumn and winter at St Gilles. Galla was pregnant, so my dream was about to come true. Where's the grub? Excuses, excuses; that's all I get from John the Praetorian. Of course he couldn't deliver what he hadn't got. I wondered what Stan was up to in Africa, for that's where the food was.

**Figure 34**
Merlin's 'Perron' at Liège

Before Christmas we heard some news. Heraclian was Consul for 413, and Stan was coming to Italy with him. This was a sop, really, to appease Heraclian, who was feeling his oats a bit in Africa. Not a big enough sop, as things turned out. Stan did not attend the 1 January Inaugural in Rome; instead he made straight for Ravenna, where, since the departure of Jovius, there was a curious power vacuum which would last for the next ten years. Honorius already mistrusted Heraclian as a pagan, even when he was a loyal one. Now Heraclian was less loyal. Honorius' latest laws* against the Pagans and the Donatists in Africa, following Augustine's first Council of Carthage,* had just about split Africa in two, and Heraclian was tending to support the Donatists as the patriotic party. You could say Stan poisoned Honorius' mind against Heraclian. Stan also popped in a bit of poison against me. He told Honorius I was a secret supporter of Jovinus, and thus an enemy, that I was no more than a tool of Attalus. Grain ships duly arrived in Marseilles, to meet a fresh instruction from Honorius to Praetorian John that I was to be denied them. John got the sack too. Heigh Ho.

What would you do? What I did, of course. With some squadrons of my Gothic cavalry, I descended on Marseilles to help myself. My luck wasn't in. We weren't 'sweeping barbarian rabble' this time. Marseilles not only held the grain, it held some fresh Roman legionaries, under one Castinus as *Magister Militum*. Castinus had a young Tribune with him, who knew, not only from Stan, the charms of the Princess Galla. His name was Boniface and he was a Turcius.* His brother was Turcius Apronianus Rufus Asterius (whose daughter would in due course marry my Gawain), and thus a kinsman of Sneezy and mine. Boniface would become the first component of the Romancers' Tristan. He was indeed the 'Ill-made Knight' ('boniface' means 'well-made', as he will bemoan to Augustine,*), threatening even to become a monk. Finally, he got and wed Isolde (Galla). The second component of Tristan would be Aëtius.*

We met with a strenuous defence, but could probably have taken Marseilles and our prize but for Boniface. This young hero led a desperate counter attack straight at me, downed my horse, and while I was on the ground ran me through with his lance. He was lucky enough to wound me severely in the groin – I was never the same man again. My Goths had their hands full, rescuing me and giving first aid. We never got our grain. It was a sorrowful, wounded knight who returned to Princess Galla, and to Attalus.

Galla cherished me, and by April my wounds had healed and I could sit a horse. But where to go? I turned to Attalus as usual for advice. 'If you're going to get the promised food, if the new Praetorian's going to make the promised lands available to you in Narbonne, you're going to have to win back Honorius' confidence. You'll have to do another great deed for him, to show your loyalty. Top Jovinus for him, and win him back North Gaul. Your Burgundians there are still loyal to you at heart, and so are your Goths. Ride North, Your Majesty, there's no other way to go.'

So, in May, I rode North on this fairly desperate mission, and this time my stars, and Galla's prayers, were sufficient.

After a quick *coup d'état* at Mainz* I was riding South with one head on a pike, that of Jovinus' brother and co-'Augustus' Sebastian. My nose had been put seriously out of joint when he was appointed instead of me during our earlier transactions over the Burgundians. Oh Ambrose, oh Augustine, was I merely vindictive in killing him? Surely the 'Mallet of God' can't afford to be too squeamish? Fettered on a horse behind me rode the disconsolate Jovinus. I handed him, and Sebastian's head, over to the new Praetorian, Dardanus.* He then topped Jovinus too, for symmetry, and sent the heads to Honorius. Soon they, too, would grace the walls of Carthage. Dardenus wrote about my exploit in a favourable guise, and received permission to admit me into Narbonensis and grant me lands there. Food, as promised, would be delivered to me when I reached Narbonne.

By the Autumn of 413 we were safely installed at Narbonne, the provincial capital, where Galla was safely delivered of our little Theodosius (Theodosiolus). There lay the *heir* to the thrones of Rome and Gothland, the best hope of the Western world, but where were the food ships? Alas, this wasn't wholly double-crossing by Honorius and Dardanus. Heraclian, hearing that Stan was slanging him at Ravenna, had rushed back from Rome to Africa, had imposed yet another food blockade on Rome, and had raised an Armada and army with which he actually landed in Italy and marched on Ravenna. Heraclian was massively defeated in Umbria,* and killed, but Rome's food supplies for 413/4 were in no better shape than ours. Once again they bargained for dogs and rats; once again we bought loaves of bread for gold coins. I did not know about Heraclian's blockade, and thought it was the malice of Stan the Inexorable which I still had to circumvent. Once again it was Attalus the wily to the rescue. His plan was so devious I could neither fault it nor entirely understand it. Here's an outline – remembering that we thought it was *Stan* who was standing between us and our food.

I was to write plaintively to His Serenity in Ravenna, and the original was arranged to miscarry *en route*.* A copy would be sent to Dardanus. The letter would set out the great deeds and benefits I had performed for Honorius, and the understandings between us over rations. As a further earnest of my perfect good faith and future good behaviour I was to undertake to hand over to His Serenity his sister Galla, whom I had been 'holding as a hostage'. (Don't forget that Stan didn't know of our marriage at Forli; he only knew Galla as a long-term hostage, perhaps still available to him, and I knew Dardanus would copy him the letter.) On hearing that the rations were actually being discharged at Narbonne, I 'promised' that Galla would be dispatched towards Ravenna, under an escort to be sent by Honorius.

It was about Christmas 413 when I despatched the letter, which completely misfired. Not only was it disingenuous and incorrectly aimed, the original accidentally fell into the hands of my Goths and caused an uproar. They adored Galla – they'd put up a memorial to her at St Gilles – and now there was doubt as to whether I was truly married to her and hence whether the precious young heir to the Gothic throne was legitimate. Attalus had got me into this and, to his credit, he got me out. He admitted publicly that the letter had originated from him, and was a purely political manoeuvre. To assuage the anxieties of my angry Goths, he arranged that Galla and I should have a fresh public and Royal Wedding at Narbonne, by Roman and by Gothic rites, and that this should be celebrated by their own (Arian) Bishop, Sigesarus. Fountains would flow with wine, largesse would be tossed about, soldiers would receive donatives. Any ill-will and confusion would be washed away in toasts to Galla and me, and to the young Prince Theodosius. So in January 414 the marvellous party* went ahead.

We sat down the next day with aching brows – all save mine, for in accordance with my vow I had stuck to water – to await the promised supplies from Honorius. They never came. Instead came Stan with an army, determined to win his bride by force of arms, and by blockade of the seaports. By March the food situation had become so critical that I saw no choice but to move. There was now no Augustus *in* Gaul save Attalus, who still retained a shred of legitimacy since the Senate had made him, and only Alaric had unmade him. I decided to reign in Attalus' name, and to award myself new lands in Aquitaine. Plenty of food there. Sorrowfully I led my Goths away from Narbonne. The King of Kings looked quite tarnished. But they needed food, and they followed.

We were not long left in peace. We had hardly been settled at Bordeaux for three months when news came that Stan was coming at us with a huge army, cavalry and infantry. This was bad news. You can ride down good infantry with horses, but they get up, reform, and fight on. My Goths were discouraged, worried, and their morale was low. There wasn't much fight left in them.

It was Galla who gave me the strength to struggle on. 'I still believe in your star, my beloved. I abhor that coarse brute Stan – save me from ever falling into his hands. And there's our little Theodosius to think of. One day, together, we'll still win him an empire.'

So we moved South yet again, leaving nothing but 'scorched earth' behind us. Perpignan was our goal; thence we would cross the Pyrenees into Tarraco, maybe even meet up with Max again. Behind the Pyrenees we could enjoy a Spanish Empire and wait for the tide to turn. The pain from my wound gnawed at me, and I felt old and worn out. We limped along to Barcelona, and there the event happened which broke my heart, and nearly Galla's: Little Theodosius died. A sudden fever; in three days the poor little baby was gone. No hope, so far as I could see, of begetting another. The funeral just about finished me. How low can one get? Had God no further task for his 'Little Mallet'?

It seemed not, for Spring brought news that Stan the Inexorable had crossed the Pyrenees and had also turned them by sea. Soon he would be upon us again. The whole military strength of Western Rome waged war for the sake of one woman, in order to obtain a forced marriage. Did Stan call that Romantic? My Goths were muttering. There were some new faces among them, whom I didn't recognise. Were they spies? Did they come from Sarus' lot? Suddenly there was talk about the camp that I murdered Sarus, most loyal of all the Goths. So I did but I thought only my Burgundians knew. The noose was tightening on me, and Galla – yes, and on Max and Titia and my little Alice, for we have all met up. Attalus piled on the agony. 'You're done for. Alaric failed to deliver. Now you've failed to deliver. The Goths'll get you soon, and go over to Constantius. They've got to eat from someone's hand.'

Galla was very grave, yet serene. 'My darling, I care for your dear head more than my own. My head is safe anyway; no one dare harm the daughter of Theodosius the Great. I have been a hostage most of my life. Perhaps I can now play hostage for you. You know I will always be faithful to you but, for now, the safety and welfare of all the Gothic women and children depends on my letting Stan *think* he can win me. I shall play that card for as long as it takes to win a settlement for the Goths. You must go into hiding and recover your health. This'll blow over. Then we can get together again. Never fear, I'll be able to keep Stan's paws off me.'

'My darling, you know I'll never leave you to that beast. I'll die at your side rather than that.'

In the event that's just what I was to do, or as near as dammit. We went to Mass the next day, which was a Sunday, but my thoughts were chiefly on my plight. After the service Bishop Sigesarus took me on one side. He told me that Sarus' brothers Sigeric and Wallia were actually in the town, and muttering vengeance. 'Your Majesty must flee immediately, and take your family with you. You can get away by sea.'

'I'll never flee my enemies, Bishop, I'll face them, in God's strength, and do you pray for me.'

Maybe he did. I returned to Ingenuus' house which he had put at my disposal as my palace. As on so many Sundays, I drifted towards the stables to give my horses a nibble of grain, and that was where the assassin,* Sarus' loyal batman, got me; right by Galla. Dagger in the back. Got my lung, I think. Was this the end?

Max and my servants managed to get the assassin, and he paid the immediate penalty. Galla had me carried into the house, coughing blood and almost speechless. 'Leave it all to me my darling,' she said. 'I'm sure you're going to live. Just leave it all to me.'

I could do no else. In the darkness which descended on me I could hear much muttering, then the voice of Sigesarus. He knew a bit about medicine. As he bent over me to shrive me, he whispered: 'I think you're going to live. Don't worry. We'll smuggle you away. Now for your big deathbed scene, please. We've got to convince the Goths.'

I was carried out onto the portico, and there before a crowd of loyal and mourning Goths I made my last farewells to them and to Galla. Dashed convincing. They, like me, thought it was for real. When I came to, it was to the rocking of a ship, and the cool hand of young Alice on my brow. Ataulfus had been written out of the script. I was never to see my darling Galla again in this world.* As I dictate this, I foresee that young Gawain will reunite us in the grave,* and that will be good.

It was to be four years before I heard from the lips of young Aëtius-Tristan how he conducted the Princess Galla-Isolda by sea to an abhorrent marriage to Constantius III* ('King Mark'), together with the full tale of her heroism and her sufferings. Be sure I will tell it all at the proper time, but for now, the ship was taking me where it willed, and I was struggling in the antechamber of death. To be brief, the ship, or was it ships, carried us ever eastwards, round Italy, and landed us eventually at Corinth. Here, Alice and her maid found us rooms ashore, and there they nursed me slowly back to health. There, too, Olympiodorus came on me, during his official travels, and set about putting me back on my feet.

'You may not have been very careful of your body,' he said, 'but at least your brain seems unaffected. Work's the best antidote for a broken heart, and I've got just the job for you. How would you like to be "Heraclitus Professor" of Science and Philosophy at Athens University? Anthemius has put it on my list to find them one, and from what I remember of your work at the Convent of the Resurrection you should be able to do it on your head.'

'I don't care what I do,' I said. 'I'm a shadow of a man now.'

'Then do what I say,' said Olympiodorus. 'Think of young Alice. You owe her a good education, and in time a fine husband.* Reckon she saved your life; now do something for her.'

What else could I do? Heraclitus was one of my Ocean College heros, as the great exponent of *energetic power* or *δυναμις*, expressing itself in movement; Democritus (his great opponent), favoured *matter* and the status quo. Only Plato, (in his '*Σοφιστης*') would be able to find a *via media* for them, although in his quaint way old Doc Heron was having a damned good try.

I took yet another name for my new role – 'Professor *Leontius*' (a Greek proper name from my old Latin 'Leo' of Book V), was what my students on the Areopagus* would call me for the next five years – and I did indeed give little Alice a splendid education, at my very knee – and not only mine. When I could rustle up the necessary one hundred *siliquae*,* I sent her for a term to study in Alexandria with Orion the Grammarian (not to be confused with JJ). Alice-Eudokia the 'Well-taught' ('Ευδοκια, not 'Ευδοξια), was indeed to prove a brilliant scholar. What other girl living could put the first eight books of the Bible* into Greek Hexameters? What other girl would want to? She was really special, in brains and looks.

So passed my next few years in the greatest university of the present world. I was above the rush of events. I had had too much of them. I had time to think: time, perhaps, to save my own soul. What is a soul? Only five years in my ivory tower, and all eternity to win.*

Lest, like me, you lose track of events here, I will use a bit of hindsight. I said earlier* that I had found the Casa Belg deserted. Whatever had happened to Elissa and Eugenia? It was like this. You'll remember that JJ had sent Edobech North to improvise an army of barbarian scallywags to come to the defence of Arles, and Edobech had really dredged the bottom: disaffected Franks (Salian and Riparian), Alemans, Quadi, Suebes; anyone who would bear arms in the hope of gain. Edobech had fallen, Arles had fallen. I said earlier that mercenaries don't give extended credit. Unpaid and ugly, they had turned back towards their homelands, and when they were approaching the Ardennes Elissa thought it was time to move. The date? March 412. She went in the first place to Rouen, hoping for support and advice from Cousin Vic. Now Vic had been chafing ever more uneasily under the yoke of Pope Innocent's Ultramontanism. Had not Ambrose been his spiritual and foster father, and Milan the very epicentre of his spirituality? Who and what was this 'Successor of Peter' who presumed to judge Vic's orthodoxy* and to control his missionary activities?) Vic was not at Rouen, for 'Archbishop Victricius' had walked out on his see in a most uncanonical huff.

I told you in Book XIV that the *Civites* (citizens) of Britain and Armorica had responded to the Saxon threats, from 408 on, by setting themselves up as independent Roman republics. The *Civitas* Councils of Britain and Armorica had gone on to form two Great Councils, either side of the Channel, to coordinate justice, fiscal policy and, above all defence. Now, some thirty years earlier, Valentinian I had established officers called '*Defensores*' to protect citizens' rights and to act as arbitrators in minor disputes. Very often, the men chosen had been the local bishops. More recently, by Ordinance of 18 January 409, Honorius had enacted that these *defensores* in every city must henceforth be Baptised Christians. Following Honorius' latest law, it was almost inevitably the Bishops who were appointed *defensores*. As the Imperial Magistracies foundered under stress of 'bagaudism' or barbarism, the Bishops were thus left standing out as isolated beacons of just government. It was in this situation that Archbishop 'Vic the Popular'

(*Publicola**) was invited to assume the Lord Presidency of both the two new Councils.

What should be Vic's title? Livy was no help to them here. All Livy could offer was 'Dictator', and that was hardly apt. Augustus had called himself *Princeps*, but then Augustus had started the rot. Eventually they settled for *Praepositus* (Provost*), and *Primus** (First Consul). In Livy they also found precedent to award Cousin Vic a 'Perpetual Consulate', and it was in that rank and capacity that John wrote to him from the Casa Sic in 412: '*Honorificentia tua, opto te semper Deo vivere et perpetui consulatus honore gaudere*'. ('May your Honour live in God, and enjoy a happy Perpetual Consulate'.*)

Cousin Vic was currently in Britain as Lord Protector* of the British Commonwealth, and it was there that Elissa found him. By and by he settled her and Eugenia, together with their faithful German bodyguard, at Dorchester* (Sinadon), on the Thames. They kept in touch with Ursula and baby Faustus, who were living, as they had every right to do, at Glastonbury, and there were visits in both directions. A great peace seemed to have fallen on the luckless West. The Barbarians all round were somnolent, like a beast of prey digesting its spoils. Only in Spain, where poor Galla's fate hung in the balance, and in Africa where Cousin Augustine was plotting JJ's downfall, were there still threatening stormclouds. The storms will break in the next Book, if I am spared to write it. As I write this, I know that I shall not live to finish these memoirs; I know too that my young Gawain will complete them for me. But there's still thirty years to go, and I and my scribes will do our best.

Heigh ho.

# BOOK XVII

## *Odium Theologicum* (AD415–421)

I use hindsight again in this book, so as to give you the tale in order since, in my grove of academe, news of the great world came to me only in fitful gushes. Let me go back first to 412. We left JJ and John *en route* for the Holy Land, but Coelestius remained in Carthage, and was soon made priest. His sermons caused remark. He actually dared to challenge Augustine's definition* of 'Original Sin'.[1] Battle was joined and synods summoned. Coelestius, excommunicated, fled to Ephesus in 414, where he continued his work as a priest. In Africa his 'heresy' was fathered on JJ/Pelagius, whom he acknowledged as his teacher. At the end of 414, while I was traipsing wearily out of Aquitaine, Augustine sent Orosius, his young Spanish assistant to Jerome in Palestine on a heresy hunt. Now Jerome's Achilles heel was any aspersion on his orthodoxy. For this he had demolished his friendship with Rufinus; for this he was now to break off relations with JJ. Meanwhile, JJ had been living quietly in Jerusalem,* in Melania and Rufinus' convent on the Mount of Olives, reverenced by most as a pious Christian sage. The exception was Orosius, who, in his letters back to Augustine, taunted JJ not only for his corpulence but also (rather unfairly) for being one-eyed.

Suddenly JJ was up before a Patriarchal Synod at Lydda, charged with heresy. Two unfrocked Western bishops, Heros of Arles and Lazarus of Aix, joined Orosius in the prosecution. The proceedings were a shambles. The Westerners knew no Greek, the rest no Latin, and JJ had to act as interpreter for both sides. He was triumphantly cleared, and his supporters went and roughed up Jerome at Bethlehem, by way of continuing the demonstration of Christian

[1] I must be brief in this. Augustine held that, thanks to Adam's genes, we have all inherited a hopelessly fallen nature, and are no more than a 'mass of perdition'. If Adam had not disobeyed, he and Eve would have lived on in interminable perfect chaste intentional obedient fecundity. *Now* our fecundity is made damnable by lust, and our lives are terminated by death. God's *irresistible* grace will 'save' those whom He has elected in His inscrutable judgement for salvation, and will be withheld from those predestined to damnation. Jesus, therefore, only came to 'save' the already 'Elect'. (These propositions are spread over more than one book.) Augustine's chief argument for original sin is that there would otherwise be no point in baptising babies. Bravely, Augustine did not shrink from the logical inference that unbaptised babies must go to hell!

brotherhood. Pope Innocent the Ultramontane wrote pained commiserations to Jerome, Orosius returned fuming to Augustine, and war was declared. I don't know whose side I'd have been on at the time – Augustine was still, as I thought, my spiritual director, and I didn't know how his theology was evolving. (When I did eventually discover this, I chose to float free, spiritually, and to plough my own furrow.)

At the end of 415 JJ sent John back via Crete to Italy, bearing with him a letter to Demetrias,* daughter of my former patron Olybrius and thus Faltonia's granddaughter (see App. 7), on her taking the veil. This letter was copied to Augustine who found it instinct with heresy. From then on JJ was a threatened man. He and John were lucky to escape Augustine's vendetta with their lives. John settled on one of Morgan's properties in Bruttium where, for a few years we leave him practising and preaching Christian Socialism. Augustine did not like that much either.

The 'Pelagians', as I must now call them, had now fallen foul of Augustine on the irresistibility of grace (Pelagius); on the indelible genetic taint of original sin (Coelestius); and on the admissibility of worldly wealth (John-George). The Donatist schism had taught Augustine that where the Church's disciplinary measures were proving ineffective, one should have recourse to the Civil Power, and he did not hesitate to take such action again in this instance. (His abuse of Luke XIV.23, and of the 'forceful' conversion of St Paul on the Damascus Road, would provide the justification for the massacres of the Albigenses, and would be the very foundation charter of the Spanish Inquisition.) Do not rush to think I misjudge Cousin Augustine. Read for yourselves the whole appalling letter,* addressed, interestingly enough, to Boniface, and make up your own mind.

Meanwhile, what was happening to my Galla? On my 'death', Sarus' brother Sigeric seized the throne, which he held for just long enough to 'bury' me before he was in turn assassinated. Just time to humiliate the gallant Galla in public by forcing her to walk six hot and weary miles behind the coffin while he ambled behind her on his horse.*

Eric's ungallant behaviour to the Goths' beloved Queen probably contributed to his prompt supercession. The Goths then elected a kinsman, Wallia, as King, and he treated Galla respectfully during the thirty months of his reign. He first fought Constantius in Gaul, and was defeated. Next he raised an Armada, and attacked Africa, always in the quest for food, but gales destroyed his fleet. By January 416, desperate, Wallia was forced to sue for peace. Constantius made harsh terms. Wallia must surrender Queen Galla, and he must also do Rome a service by subduing the remains of the BFBs in Spain. On completion of this, and the handing over of Galla, the so-long promised corn would be made available.

Wallia did as he was bid, and July saw Galla traded for 600,000 measures of corn in an undignified swap. She was duly handed over, with an escort commanded by none other than young Aëtius under instructions to convey her safe to Rome to prepare for her marriage. Aëtius – *Roland* the *scolanus*, *Aux. Palatinus* or *paladin* – commanding some *Honoriani* for Constantius, was captured at *Roncesvalles* by the BFBs in AD412; severely wounded whilst trying to escape, he had nevertheless managed to reach Barcelona shortly after my 'death'. There, he had been lovingly nursed back to health by Galla and was itching to rejoin his regiment. When, in times to come, you read the Romance 'Song of Roland' you should be aware that in it 'Charlemagne' is Stan, who is also Wagner's 'King Mark'. Why is Aëtius to be called Tristan; and why to be called Roland? I'll tell you later.

Back in Rome, for three months Galla prevaricated desperately, hoping maybe for news from me. But could this have saved her? Had she not interred my coffin in Spain? Was she not plainly a widow? Had the Goths not received their corn? Yet could she perhaps do one last favour for our beloved Goths? Human sacrifice, that was my Galla.

While Galla was selling herself dear, Stan was not idle in Gaul. Naturally I loathed the beast, but I had to admit he was serving Rome well.* He had now settled Africa and Spain, and Central Gaul was virtually clear of Barbarians. What about recovering the independent Commonwealths of Armorica and Britain to Honorius' obedience? Further Gaul (from the Seine to the Meuse) he took in hand himself; Armorican Lyonesse (from the Loire to the Seine) he deputed to Exuperantius,* father of my Cabinet Office chum Palladius, and later Vicar, then Praetorian of Gaul. To **recover Britain,*** he utilised the services of a young Duke called Ambrosius Germanus. Yes, dear reader, this was none other than Eustathius Aurelius Ambrosius Placidus Germanus, Macrobius' son and St Ambrose's grandson, JJ's youthful novice at Subiaco and John Cassian's copain in the desert, in Rome, and at Constantinople. Students of British history will call him 'Ambrosius the elder'; Irish scholars and hagiographers will call him St Patrick, but that comes later.

The coast was clear for Germanus (as it will be convenient henceforth to refer to him) to act, since Cousin Vic had died a few months previously at the end of 415* and lay buried at Caernarfon*.

By the end of 416 Stan was ready to return to Rome to celebrate a mini-triumph, mount the Capitol as Consul, and two days later to wed his scowling bride. (Did my sneering enemy Taurus do him a panegyric or an *epithalamium*?* He'd had the job since 'Claudian' stepped down.) Not long after this Stan was made *Patricius*.

The next step for Stan was the purple robe; for Galla, motherhood – Romans can't duck duty. In 418 she bore him a daughter, the famous Justa Grata Honoria, better known as 'Honoria the Whore'. As a disturbed teenager she would confound diplomacy by proposing marriage to Attila the Hun. She who would die, after marrying both my Gawain **and her own son by him,*** as the revered St Geneviève of Paris.

Finally, on 3 July 419 Galla bore Stan a son, the future Augustus Valentinian III, but for this she would manage to extract a *quid pro quo*, for Stan agreed to give the Goths their promised land in Aquitaine and Narbonense, with Toulouse as their capital. The last of Alaric's and my demands were at last met, and the Goths remained there happily until the time of Clovis.

**Figure 35**
Honoria the Whore as Augusta
© Trustees of the British Museum

I return to the crusade against 'the Pelagians'. In 416 Augustine had assembled two Councils of bishops, at Carthage and at Mileve, and they expressed their dismay at JJ's acquittal by the Council of Lydda the previous year and excommunicated JJ and Coelestius. (Augustine was never a metropolitan in Africa; he led from below, by sheer energy and force of rhetoric.) When the Canons of these councils were sent to Pope Innocent for 'his approval', they were naturally accompanied by a covering letter from Augustine. JJ also wrote to Innocent protesting his innocence. Innocent, as I have hinted above, was an 'Ultramontane' Pope. He was very keen to improve the *status* of Rome, as against Milan (doubly prestigious* as the former seat not only of the Court, but of Ambrose), or against Rouen for that matter; or most particularly against Carthage – for far too long the African Church had been a law unto itself. Innocent was flattered to be referred to in this way by the Africans and he thought best to endorse their findings, adding his excommunication of JJ and Coelestius for good measure.

Two months later Innocent was dead, and his successor, Zosimus, was a Greek. Now, although the Eastern Church was very willing to tie itself into knots at the drop of a hat about the Trinity, or the Dual Nature of Christ, they did not recognise the self-taught Latin provincial theologian of Hippo as an authoritative Christian pundit. They did not at all believe in Augustine's 'Original Sin'; they *knew* man had at least *some* free will. At this very moment Augustine promulgated his latest dogma of 'Predestination' in a letter to my old friend Paulinus, who passed it on to Pope Zosimus. Zosimus summoned Coelestius to Rome (JJ at first sat tight in Palestine), and, after hearing all parties, restored the Pelagians to communion, and wrote severely chiding the African bishops for amateur heresy-hunting and lack not only of charity but also of common sense.

We are now into 418. The Africans had appealed to Rome, and they had lost. What would Augustine now do? '*Appello Caesarem*,' once cried St Paul:

'I appeal to Caesar'. So, on 30 April 418, it fell to Flavius Honorius Caesar Augustus to decide for the world, once and for all, the fateful questions of man's free will *et al.* He chose to banish JJ and Coelestius severally outside the boundaries of the Empire, on pain of their lives, which meant in practice that they must henceforth live beyond the Danube or the Rhine, or perhaps chance certain persecution in Persia. With the recovery of Britain they were no longer any too safe beyond the Channel. JJ's and Coelestius' followers, including of course John-George, the 'Sicilian Socialist',* were only to forfeit their property and civil rights, but John was in particular disfavour because his most famous pamphlet, *De Divitiis* ('On Wealth'), contained the ringing call '*tolle divitem*', or 'Soak the Rich', which the authorities rightly thought politically inflammatory. It was really Melania, however, who should have borne the responsibility for John's 'Ciceronian' invective. He was only the pen-pusher – she was the prophet. Poor Melania the Holy Terror was deeply guilt ridden – nay, obsessed – by the disproportionate wealth of the Senatorial classes, as compared with the poorer classes. This was not all their fault. We had an Inheritance Tax of up to 25%, but you could dodge this altogether provided your estate was left within your close family. The *Clarissimi* (the *Hons*) mostly lived in the country, dodging Rates, and intermarried. Inevitably they got richer and richer, like my Anicii.

Discovering rather late in the day that he was involved not in theological controversy but in high Imperial politics, Zosimus turned coat and sent a circular letter to his Italian bishops condemning 'Pelagianism'. Eighteen bishops, Julian of Eclanum among them, refused to subscribe to it and were deposed from their sees. Julian went on arguing the toss with Augustine by correspondence for another two years, and many think he had the best of the argument. He had to flee just the same. The views of the Gallic bishops may be inferred from the laconic entry in the *Gallic Chronicle* for AD417: '*Praedestinatorum haeresis, quae ab Augustino accepisse dicitur initium, his tempore serpere exorsa*' ('at this time the heresy of predestination, said to originate from Augustine, began its spread'). It would continue to spread down the ages, to Calvin and John Knox, and then to the eigtheenth-century Jansenists. In the latter case it would be belatedly disowned by the then Pope. The Council of Trent came down as semi-Pelagian, or, if you like, semi-Augustinian, and the row smouldered on. Oh that people would read Plato!

I would not bother you with all this theology, were it not that it was to have such a marked psychological, and indeed geographical, effect on my nearest kinsmen. You will see the results in action shortly.

Mid-July 418 saw two interesting developments. Stan had been so impressed by what he saw and heard of the workings of the two Great Councils of Britain and Armorica that he decided to make this a pattern for Gaul too. Centuries ago, Augustus had set up the 'Forum of All The Gauls', to hold an annual Eisteddfodd at 'Croix Rousse', Lyons. Stan thought something rather more practical was now in order. Accordingly he established a 'Great Council of Gaul' at Arles, to meet regularly and to discuss public issues. A constitutional novelty; my Goths, now resident Federates, were to be represented on equal terms with the Gallo-Roman *Civitatae*. That same month 'Duke Ambrosius', the probable author of this scheme, was ordained as 'Bishop Germanus' of Auxerre, a post he was to hold for the next thirty years, with a distinction reminiscent of St Ambrose, his grandfather. Indeed, he would better his grandfather by being appointed Consul for AD421.

The following year, 419, brought me my first hard information from the West for four years. It came in the person of primrose-locked Aëtius, Son of the Eagles, now twenty-six years of age and a most impressive young man, despite his lack of inches. He had tracked me down in my ivory tower thanks to Olympiodorus – perhaps the only man who knew where I was. Indeed it was Olympiodorus who had got Aëtius his present promotion to be Prefect of New Rome* – a job usually held by a rather older civilian, *en route* for the Consulship and retirement. But the competent Anthemius, himself *en route* for retirement, thought that a soldier was needed at this time. You'll remember that the Hun locusts still pressed on Thrace, and that Anthemius was surrounding New Rome with towering new walls. But the defences still needed to be perfected, and Aëtius would play a useful part in this by identifying the need for ample stored water so as to enable a long siege to be withstood without stress. Thus he built a huge reservoir up near the Adrianople Gate* and made improvements to the gates and sallyports, especially in the Northern salient, whilst learning a bit of politics and economics at the same time.

It was Aëtius who told me the sorry tale of Galla and Stan. He also told me how JJ and John were now on the run from Augustine. (Next time I meet JJ, if ever, I shall twit him as 'King Ban of Jerusalem'.) He also told me that my old enemy Taurus, who was Prefect of Rome in 414,* had returned home to Cahors, and that my old chum Palladius had completed his second tour as Praetorian of Italy. Finally, he brought me the sad news that dear old Morgan was dead.* In her last weeks she had told him who his father and mother were. That had given him something to chew on. Dear Morgan. She'd been part of my life since always. She'd been anchor woman for the whole family and a real lifesaver for Aëtius and Gawain. But for her, Little Benedict might still be at Subiaco. I didn't think she'd ever given religion, pagan or Christian, much thought. Science, astronomy, herbal medicine, family life: these had been her fields. Wonder where she's pre-destined for? Wonder how she's left all her money? I'll write Uncle Theo. He'll know.

There was other gossip from Aëtius. In Aquitaine, Wallia had died after a valuable innings. Guess who they'd selected as his successor? Obvious really – young Theodore, Alaric and Ginger's eldest son. He would reign as Theodoric I, King of the Vizi-Goths* and his friendship with Aëtius, despite heavy strains, would bear rich fruit at the battle of Châlons (in AD451) against Attila. Aëtius confirmed that the last he had heard of Ursula, she was a nun in Ireland on Cousin Vic's recommendation, and that Vic actually clothed her himself. If four years was long enough for John to purge his errors, I reckoned Ursula would be back in circulation quite soon.

'What about Elissa?' I asked. Aëtius didn't know. He thought she was still in Britain with Eugenia. 'What about Titia? Does she know she's now the wife of an heretical exiled deacon?'

'Dunno,' said Aëtius. 'Maybe they agreed to separate.'

'What about John-George?'

Here Aëtius had some news. 'He's in New Rome. Cleared out of Italy pronto in 418. He's hiding up in the Convent of the Resurrection, fuming against Augustine. Much good will it do him.'

'How do you find my Alice?' I enquired.

'Too much of a 'blue-stocking' for me,' replied Aëtius. 'I'm just a simple soldier. As you know, my schooling was a bit interrupted.' This was just as well. They were a bit too closely related by current standards. I'd have to find her a husband jolly soon, though. She was pushing twenty.

My Chair at Athens University came to an end in 420 and, for Alice's sake, I decided to try our luck in New Rome. I had got contacts there after all – wasn't Theodosius II my cousin-german, as also his sister Pulcheria? Now there was quite a girl. You may wonder who was taking hold of the reins of the Eastern Empire, now that Anthemius had retired. Pulcheria, that's who. She had been made Augusta by Anthemius on 4 July 414 when she was only fifteen, and at once grabbed herself the role of Regent for her thirteen-year-old brother. She would not relinquish it* in his lifetime, or after. Theodosius II didn't seem to mind a bit; he was such an extraordinary mixture: a compulsive penman, he compiled and wrote most of the *Codex Theodosius* as his personal contribution to good government and posterity; while in his leisure hours he played polo on horseback and other virile games at night.

We took a modest flat – it had been years since any of my British rents came through to me, so I only had my earnings – and set about 'fishing'. Impecuniosity was part of the ploy. Since Morgan's death, there had been quite a bit of money around to go for because, knowing that Sneezy had left me well looked after, Morgan had singled out her grandchildren as principal beneficiaries in her will. Relying on Honorius' confiscatory laws against the 'Pelagians', amongst whom Morgan could be deemed to be included, my two eldest boys, Max and Genesius, had decided to jump in and grab not only their shares but Alice's too. In this way the boys had tried to do down Alice, but Alice, on becoming Augusta in 423, would repay this injury in a fine display of Christian forgiveness by making Genesius Prefect of Eastern Illyricum and Max Minister of Munitions.* I can forgive Max a bit. He was in dire financial straits, but I never had much use for Genesius. Something wrong there?

It was as suitors, therefore, that we forced ourselves on young Theodosius, and tore him away from his files to dispense some justice. I never seriously expected him to write immediately to Honorius, his uncle, to remedy matters. What happened was much better: he fell instantly for Alice. A blue-stocking was just what he admired – and she looked good too. Pulcheria was no less smitten by Alice, and it was she who named her *Eudokia Athenais** (the well-taught Athenian girl). Pulcheria set out do some matchmaking, and soon the nuptials were arranged for 7 June 421, a full Augustan wedding, Public Holiday, St Sophia's Cathedral, the lot. What a clever Dad I am.

The only other events of 420 were the news of Jerome's death at Bethlehem and an attempt on Aëtius' life. The assassin was some sort of cleric, as you can tell by his name, *Kyriakos*.* This crazy fellow accosted Aëtius as he was going into St Sophia's on a Sunday, under pretence of presenting a petition in the form of a scroll, but inside the scroll was a dagger. Aëtius being very alert and fit, escaped with a minor wound, but he would remember the trick and use it later with dire effect. How the ghosts of Greek tragedy haunt my family.

Aëtius dined with me shortly after. 'I don't like this town,' he said. 'Do you know what I've found out? That goon Kyriakos was an agent of the Palace. I put him to the usual tortures and he sang merrily. They say "Hell hath no fury like a woman scorned". Those three sisters, Pulcheria, Arcadia and Marina are murder. All this piety and sanctity by day. It's very different after dark* I can tell you.'

'What happened, then?' I asked.

'It was Arcadia,' said Etzie. 'You know she's got a palace in the Ninth District* up beyond Uncle Ted's Forum. "Lives out" as it were. Had to dine there. Lots of wine, which I don't much go with. Tried to seduce me. Don't fancy her. Nothing doing. "Sorry Ma'am; sorry Cousin". She looked daggers at me when we parted. Next stop, Kyriakos and a real dagger. He says he'll sign on as my taster, 'cause next time it'll be poison.* Pulcheria "lives out" too. They say she's currently having it off with John, our John you know, up at the Convent.* I think I want to get back to soldiering PDQ.'

'You should have made quite a bit of money by now as Prefect,' said I. 'And you've inherited a lot more from Morgan. You probably don't want to serve under Constantius with what there is between you, but by all accounts he won't last long the way he's drinking. Why don't you "Go West Young Man" and look after your interests?'

By now I had quite forgiven Aëtius for worshipping Galla. I trusted her so much that another admirer quite pleased me. No room for jealousy there; just a great sadness. Etzie and I parted excellent friends, but my mind was busy. I wondered what sort of marriage I was letting my Alice in for. Worth it, maybe, to become an Augusta? Maybe she'd be allowed to 'live out' too.

By the end of 420 John's love life with Pulcheria in New Rome was becoming rather fraught and he was not sorry to see something of his two daughters, and maybe try again with Titia. I had intended staying on for Alice's wedding, but Pulcheria had made it clear that my presence was not welcome. Theodosius' bride, a future Augusta, shall wed him from a Palace. From *my* Palace. The populace will not wish to be reminded, as the nuptial chariot draws up at a humble boarding house, that she is only the daughter of an indigent professor.'

I could take a hint as well as the next man. I wouldn't have left her, though, had I not been satisfied that it was a real love match. Theodosius doted on her, and she on him. Would she take up polo? My Ursula would have, but Alice was no athlete. Somehow, between them, they'd keep Pulcheria at bay. My concern was to keep the wolf from the door. It was time to collect my rents in person.

All this time (and we're now into 421), I knew nothing of what had happened to JJ. It was to be seven long years before I found out, and I don't want to spoil that story, but I will say here that JJ had returned to the Teuton Forests as 'Wotan the One-eyed Wanderer'. He didn't know, as I had heard from Aëtius, that, thanks to Morgan, he and I were the new co-owners of the Casa Sic. He couldn't go there anyway. He was 'Friar Tuck the Fat Outlaw', 'Old Jowlie' (Faramund, from Φαραγξ)* or even Pharaon Dandde,* the 'purple-wattled guinea-fowl'. All these names would resound down the centuries.

Spring 421 saw three 'exiles' of sorts take ship from the Golden Horn. Aëtius' cistern had been formally opened and was in course of filling. I had made fond farewells to Alice, and beggared myself to buy her a trousseau. John, sporting a Novatian habit, with cowl (so he could retain his ruddy locks) and a bag of books, was making a discreet getaway. Aëtius was in civilian clothes. All of us were glad to be clear of New Rome. Yippee, no more eunuchs.

We made first for the Casa Sic (John hoped he would be safe from Augustine there), arriving just in time to attend the funeral of dear old Uncle Theo. What a Trojan that man had been to the Western Empire and to the whole of Western Civilisation. I supposed more money would wash our way eventually from his estate. Meantime, I helped myself to his telescope as a keepsake, and some of his books.

After the funeral, impressively taken by the Bishop, I was able to take young Aëtius and my Gawain down into the family catacombs* and show them the tombs of their Marcian ancestors.

Now Aëtius was off to Rome, to take possession of Morgan's palace on the Quirinale, and his many other estates.* Meanwhile John-George, as an arch 'Pelagian' was beginning to feel uneasy. There were too many of Augustine's friends around – notably Hilarius, the Bishop, who had been the first to sneak* on John's socialism. So John and I decided to make for Britain, he for security, I for my rent-roll.

When I got back to Glastonbury who should I find in residence but my dear Ursula, with my badge of shame, little 'Faustus-Gregory'. Shame? I'd been absolved from that, hadn't I? Even if I was parting company from Augustine on theology, it was as a Bishop that he had absolved me, and that should be pretty indelible. I put the shame behind me, and enjoyed the toddler.

John was delighted to see his sister too. They'd always been very close to one another. *Too close*, perhaps?*

'Where's your mother?' I asked.

'Haven't heard anything from her for over a year,' said Ursula, 'but you know what she's like. She would insist on going back to the Casa Belgica, which has been liberated from its Barbarian occupants. No wars on there at the moment, so far as we know, and the shooting's never been better.'

So we all enjoyed ourselves, and I started to build my observatory up on the Tor, had trouble, however, with Uncle Theo's telescope, and in order to redesign it I needed rock crystal. That's how we came to instal ourselves for the summer at 'Tintagel', the Dun of (Achilles) 'Agel' which, indeed, took its name from John. He would be very active there and around, as St Nectan. Ursula, too, as St Julyot (variously

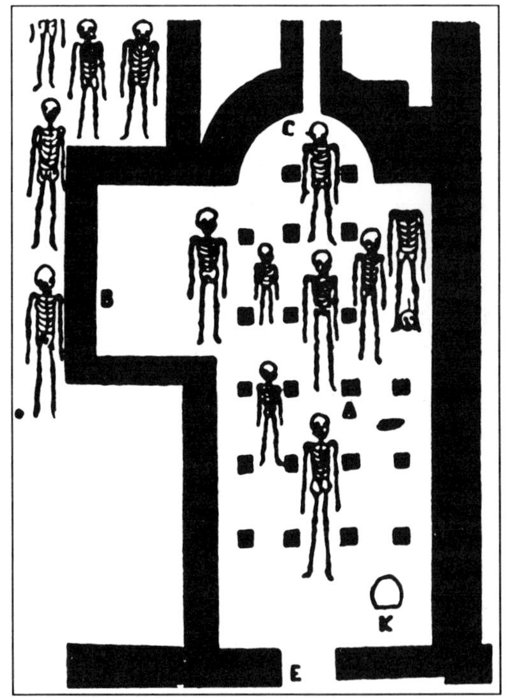


**Figure 36**

The Casa Belgica: Barbarian skeletons in the former Bath House

© Prof Raymond Brulet

spelt).* Besides names, they would leave copious archaeological evidence there for all to see.* In the cliffs were rock crystals and even, usefully, arsenic. As many would find in the future, Tintagel is an ideal summer holiday home; that and more, for it has impregnable natural defences, approached only by 'Lancelot's sword bridge'.

Here I set up an 'Esplumeoir'* or *scriptorium* for our bookwork, complete with central heating, as well as a laboratory and workshop for my experiments and metalworking. We made ourselves really comfortable, and I found myself, with John's and Ursula's help, back in the Quest of the Holy Grail. All we needed was Elissa's presence, and it could have been twenty-four years before. But the quiverful were adult now, and we were soon to have a reminder of this. I suppose it was my fault, for it was I who had written to Aëtius, and invited him to visit us in Britain.

I had expected to entertain him at Glastonbury, but had no reply. The slaves knew where we were, however. It was a blustery night in late October when the unknown horseman blew his horn on the headland to have the drawbridge let down, and we welcomed Aëtius, now unmistakeably 'Uther Pendragon'* to his destiny. We made him very welcome, and over dinner I could see him eyeing Ursula expectantly. I did not know that they had already met nine years previously at the Gaste Cité as 'Siegfried and Grane',* but then Ursula was Grane (Gratiana IV), and she had been previously wooed as Grainne* by Diarmid-John. How incest stalked my family; maybe that's why legend would never let go of us.

A few nights later, Aëtius was in bed with Ursula. Did I disguise him as John? What need? Did I give him a drugged nightcap of forgetfulness? Again, what need? She was nine years his elder, but petite, and in perfect shape. That night saw the conception of Galahad the Younger, who would 'achieve the Holy Grail', and much more. He would be the penultimate, but the most famous, of the line of Arthurs, and in him all but the most sceptical and minimalist of historians would place at least *some* credence. Of his battles Nennius would try to write, and Gildas obliquely praise him as the victor of the siege of Mount Badon. All I will say here is that he was born in mid-July 422 in the Villa Simbruina at Subiaco, and would thus be, technically, a 'Latin'.*

At Tintagel 'Arthur-Galahad II' was conceived, but to the best of my knowledge he *never* lived there. If I tell you his name was *Carpilio II*, classical historians* will be able to identify him as Aëtius' son of his first marriage, and will know something of his story. If I tell you that his name was also *Cerdic* alias *Coroticus*, founder of the House of Wessex and in some sort the maker of England – whom Calpurnianus Patricius (St Patrick II) would one day excommunicate – British historians can have a field day redating them both.*

If I go on to tell you that Aëtius promptly married Ursula you will realise that as an officer and a gentleman he could do no other. We started this book with theology. We have ended it with Romance. More than time for a breather.

Heigh ho.

# BOOK XVIII

## *Judex Maccabeus?* (AD421–426)

Midsummer 421 saw two happy events, at neither of which was I present. On 7 June, Theodosius II and my Alice were wed in Constantinople. Tell you who *was* there – my Gawain. Since he joined up with Aëtius in 411 he'd been serving mostly on cross postings in the East, as planned career development. He'd served a bit in Palestine with the old Xth Legion *Fretensis* with whom I'd fought so long ago at Carrhae (see Book IV). He enjoyed looking around the Holy Places, as I did. I was glad I had lent him Eucheria the Pious Maccabee's journal, since one day he'd be remembered as 'Palmerin d'Oliva', the pilgrim of the Mount of Olives. He'd be a Tribune soon, and return to the West, where he'd be Oliver to Aëtius' Roland.

The other event was the birth of Carpilio-Cerdic which, as I mentioned in the last Book, took place at Morgan's old summer palace, the Villa Simbruina, where Aëtius has been biding his time taking seisin of his inheritance.

The reason for this low profile was that Aëtius got back to Italy to find Constantius involved in yet another mini-triumph, as a result of which Honorius rather grudgingly ordained him Augustus on 8 February. Now he was co-Emperor of the West. *Cave canem*, but I must say, I thought he deserved it. We left him in the last Book restoring North Gaul and Britain, and he'd spent the last two years doing again, and well, the job which Augustus attempted centuries ago. Augustus saw that if Britain's frontier was the Rhine, Gaul's frontier was the Elbe. The trouble was he couldn't hold it and nor could any of his successors who attempted it, down to Julian, down even to JJ. 'Show of force and a treaty' seemed the best we could do across the Rhine. Now Constantius had done it, even if too late to prevent the second sack of Trier. He hadn't just locked the stable door, he had fenced the paddock. Some of Stan's wars and battles in Saxony* would rightly score among 'King Arthur's victories', for **Constantius III, was at that moment, Arthur. He was even married to 'Guinevere'** (III)!

Constantius' triumph and ordeal didn't last long. In May he got a rude rebuff from New Rome. Sent his bust back, that's what they did; won't recognise him as Augustus. (From the grave, Doxy struck back, by the hand of Pulcheria;

the kettle blackened the pot.) Aëtius had told me Constantius was hitting the bottle good and hard. The knowledge that his wife-and-love hated and despised him can't have helped. The discreet contempt with which the Palace courtiers treated their 'uncouth' Augustus made him paranoid. Now came public humiliation from New Rome. Revenge was a must. Like Stilicho and Serena, long ago, he thought of war on the East. War was really the only way he knew of expressing himself. The courtiers slyly sent jug after jug into the den where the Augustus and his cronies were plotting their drunken campaigns. Cirrhosis did the rest. On 2 September 421, poor Stan – who had tried so hard to win love, and won no more than glory – went to his distinguished ancestors, and Galla was free. She buried him in a great plain non-committal sarcophagus, for which she built a beautiful Mausoleum – still extant – at Ravenna. On his death, one Castinus took his place as *Magister Utriusque Militum*, Commander-in-Chief, and dominated the next five years of history. For better or worse, civilian government had petered out in the West and military rule held sway.

Castinus had been *Comes Domesticorum*, commanding Household Troops – my old job of 409–10. As such he was responsible for the Palace Guards at Ravenna, and naturally saw much of Galla, indeed he was probably Galla's appointment. His successor, around the purple petticoats, was a smart young-looking Guards Tribune, now Count,* none other than Boniface, he who had wounded me at Marseilles. He had since won great renown as a fighting soldier against the hostile Berbers of the African mountains. He had fallen in love with the *idea* of Queen Galla in 412 but then he had married another, loved, and been widowed, in that order. In his grief at the last event in 417, he had intended forsaking the army and becoming a monk. He had consulted with Augustine and Alypius at *Tubunae*, and they had given him the same advice they gave me eight years previously.* 'Forget your self-centred concern with your own soul and serve God by doing your duty as a Christian Roman soldier.' So I had; so he did. That's how the personable widower came to be the 'cavaliere servente' of the Augustus' widow. What would come of this? Truly the ways of God are inscrutable.

Meantime, John-George, who had left us at Tintagel armed *inter alia* with St Andew's knee-cap (a relic he had picked up in Crete when he was there in 415), had arrived in Fife eager to evangelise 'Britain-beyond-the-Walls'. He had resolved to complete Glorious Dad's, and JJ's, work as 'Niniani' by evangelising *all* the Picts and Scots. He'll be Kentigern II, the Monk (Mungo). He'll be Daniel Fab (Daniel the Less: Daniel 'Isaf', whence St Asaph). He had been welcomed by the Southern Picts* as their bishop/*defensor*. Soon, they also made him their *Regulus* or under-king (St Rule).* Flushed with success, he next went over to Ireland (as Diarmid*), only to leave it, after some evangelisation, for Iona* (as Columba).

I myself was rather preoccupied with the ways of God. I found John-George had this effect on me. I kept thinking of him using his exile to evangelise the

Picts of Fife, as I sat at Glastonbury working on my telescope. Ten years of Constitutional Consular rule by 'Archbishop Vic' had left a mark on the politics of Britain. (It is time I revealed to the scholars among you that Victricius was Bishop Fastidius,* the recipient of John's letter,* and his father-in-God. He was that first 'Vortigern' who first invited tame Saxons* into Britain. '*Fastidius*' is loftier than '*Superbus*' which would be John's own epithet when he came to the same job as Vortigern III '*Tigernicus*'.* But first I would have my little turn as Vortigern II.)

I foresee something of the same sort under one Oliver Cromwell, in the same character of 'Lord *Protector*' of the 'British Commonwealth'. A sort of high moral earnestness, and an attempt to conduct public life on Christian principles was there, at the top at least. The trouble was that at the grass roots most people simply hadn't heard of Jesus, and remained totally heathen. John's example burned my conscience. There was a practical incentive, too. Now that Constantius had restored our obedience, with whatever reservations, to Honorius, we expected the legions to defend us, and Rome to pay them. By the same token, Rome expected some tribute from Britain, in cash and in kind.

I had not a letter, but a visit in person from Exuperantius, now Vicar of Gaul, about all this. 'Claudius,' he said (we were of course friends), 'you see how I'm placed. There isn't just now a Vicar of Britain; don't want to put all the County Councillors' noses out of joint, especially when they've been doing such a good job for the last ten years. The Praetorian* therefore holds me in some sort responsible for Britain, and, alas – for both of the Saxon Shores, but I have no power over the *Civitates*. I do have some authority, however, over Britain outside the *Civitatae*; that's to say over the military areas and the new provinces of Britain. I want to make you Rector of the Valentias, and of Armorica including the Saxon Shores. I have neither armies nor money to give you, and I seek for tribute. Is it a deal?'

'Most certainly not, old friend,' I said. 'You yourself admit that Rome does not dare at this moment to appoint a Vicar of Britain, nor provincial governors under him. I'm a landowner and taxpayer in this country, and I have been a councillor. We will play it the new British way. I will return to politics, if they'll have me. I will put the needs of the new and frontier provinces to the Great Councils. If they entrust me with any responsibility, that's up to them.'

'But what about my tribute?' asked Exuperantius.

'You'll have to *earn* that by sending us some troops,' I said. 'Rome's bled Britain white for troops. I know it was my own kinsmen for the most part, Grandad Max, and JJ who did it. Even so, it's time we had some of the *Honoriaci* back, and the *Honoriani*.'

So we parted without either getting what we wanted, but the seed was sown, for a few months later I was a Councillor and Magistrate for Caerwent, a Civitas Capital (or County Town) in my sphere of influence. I thought I'd give Eastern Britain a miss this time round. I rather fell down there! Thus it was with the title of *Judex* and with the command of police as 'Protector' *cum tribunicia potestate*,* that I went with the Great Council's authority to reorganise and evangelise Valentia. I don't know which aspect pleased them most, but the number of churches* we managed to establish during those few years of mission was phenomenal by any standards outside 'The Acts of the Apostles'.

I started my mission at St Maughold's* in the Isle of Man, which had been founded by and named after Glorious Dad, and was ideally poised to command the whole Irish Sea Province. John joined me there from Fife, where he'd given his own name **Angus** (Eugenius) to Strathmore. We then went over to Southern Ireland for the really difficult bit. Ulster had had an introduction to Christianity from Dad, and from all of us on our earlier visits, but the South had been neglected. Now we commenced the 'Pre-Patrician'* evangelisation of Eireann by St Sechnall* (that's me as Senex Calchas) and St Ail-be (*Ælius Benedictus*), with John as Auxilius (for Achilles), Budoc, Kevin/Kieran, Declan (John as *dei colanus* – St Collen II), and Tigernach* (Tigernicus). After my life with the Goths, maybe I was a bit sloppy about Arianism; after his life with JJ and Coelestius, John could not be described as less than semi-Pelagian. Did we, nevertheless, do a good job? We certainly taught the Irish peasants a bit about Jesus, and founded not a few monastic settlements and schools. The last are important. Look what an effect Ocean College had on Cambria, and indeed on Ireland. It was time they had schools of their own – Clonard and Clonmacnois for a start. Did John and I amuse our students with presentations of our Atellan charades? Was our most popular turn our, by now well practised, performance of the 'beheading game'? You'll have to ask their grandchildren.

Legend will say that I had a row with John, and that he left Ireland for Iona* under a cloud – like John-Mark in Acts XV.38 – but in fact we parted by agreement. Iona – which even takes its most common names from John – is the staging post for the Great Glen and Inverness, which we had agreed should be John's goal for his evangelistic campaign of 422. Legend will there have him convert King Brude,* but John in fact *was* King Brude, and within six years the Picts put up a magnificent 'Perron' to their Most Christian King and former 'Regulus'. I foresee that you will yet be able to admire the thrilling key panel of this at St Andrews,* (see Fig. 37 on next page) where it will form a major exhibit in the Cathedral museum.

Meanwhile I was Cormac (Coronac for *coronatus*), crowned Prince and Bishop of Cashel, where centuries ago it seems – I'm sixty now, so it's actually forty years – I once held petty sessions as Procurator; and Elissa was with me as the 'Morrigan'. Maybe the crozier's mightier than pen or sword. I've done the lot.

One last event of that year would ultimately prove more fruitful than any of our little efforts, for it was then that Honoratus* founded the great Monastery of Lérins, off Cannes, a nursery of learning for saints and bishops. My own Faustus would one day be abbot there.

**Figure 37**
John-Brutus-Daniel, with his 'Hamlet' (knife), apes Gilgamesh!

422 saw me reporting back to the Great Council of Great Britain on a mission pretty well accomplished: 'Romanitas' reaffirmed, 'Christianitas' enhanced, and even some tribute coming in. It was at this juncture that the Great Council of Armorica, hearing of my exploits, wrote asking if I might be seconded to them for a year or so for a similar mission, in the course of which I might perhaps cast my eye over their mineral resources with a view to some tribute. I set out that very Spring for the Cotentin, and put in for a few days to Guernsey ('the island of Quirinus') and Jersey (which my ancestor Constantius I had named 'Caesarea'). The former bore some fruit, since just inshore on Sark, I located a lode of argentiferous lead which they agreed to work. On to Aleth (later St Malo – after me), and then SW for the Monts D'Arrée where I found another vein of silver-lead. Finisterre had no minerals; didn't have much at all. But legend had it that the Phoenicians bought tin in 'Cornouaille', so there might

be some stannary companies to be revived. Sure enough, I found the relics of the tin industry in the valleys of the rivers Blavet and Oust (Pontivy to Ploërmel) and did some panning and exhortation there, but I feared Exuperantius wouldn't get very fat on tin. Jesus came off a bit better, as I preached the 'Good News' in my leisure hours and managed to found quite a number of churches.* But my efforts were nothing to what John-George was to achieve after my retirement and death. Truly, he'd be the apostle of Brittany, just as my grandson Calpurnianus '*Patricius*' would be the apostle of Ireland.

422 also saw great and confusing events abroad, as I learnt in time from Aëtius. The BFBs were creating trouble again in Spain, especially the Vandals in Baetica. Castinus mounted a massive task force to subdue them. Large numbers of cavalry would be called for. Boniface, as *Comes Domesticorum*, would be the man to lead them. Boniface, however, was reluctant to serve *under* Castinus. He expressed views, which alas were to be proved well founded, as to Castinus' military competence. Whether Castinus would have succeeded in his expedition with Boniface as his loyal lieutenant we shall never know. Very likely he would. He had a higher opinion of Boniface than Boniface had of him. As it was, his expedition was an expensive flop.

What was Boniface up to? What indeed? It is with pain, even now, that I dictate this. First of all, I would have you know that my Galla loved me best and most. I shall always know that. She hated Stan. I know that too. On Stan's death a great new trouble befell her. Honorius, who had had two of Serena's and Stilicho's daughters to wife without really noticing, now in his dissipated dotage (he was all of thirty-eight years old) noticed that he had an attractive half-sister, and in public he would make embarrassing amorous advances to her and paw and caress her. To whom could she turn, as one would to a brother, for protection? But again, which comes first, the chicken or the egg? Who was ever at Galla's elbow; who was it that slept outside her door? Who but Boniface the Beautiful, the winsome guardsman. Was Honorius maybe only acting a part to ensnare her, like Hamlet's Player King? Was Galla *enceinte*? Was yet another Imperial heir on the way to threaten Honorius' tranquillity?

The answer to all these unpleasant questions was to be found in Boniface's actions. What gave the show away was that Boniface the Beautiful sailed at once for Africa where he set himself up as some sort of tyrant. First Gildo, then Heraclian, now Boniface. What did he intend? Not, probably, what happened. That was, that Honorius suddenly expelled Galla, with her two children Honoria and little Valentinian, and maybe her guilty secret,* by ship to Constantinople to her not-so-loving nieces. Bag and baggage, they were gone. Boniface was left gazing East with his mouth open, unable to help his lady, certainly unable to place her on the throne of Rome as Augusta; free only to rebel against his sovereign if he now still chose. This was not what he had set out to do. He stood still and foolish in Africa for the next three years, doing some harm and considerably less good. Meanwhile in Ravenna Honorius was going the way that self-indulgent Augusti go who don't take exercise.

With the departure of Boniface, Castinus appointed Aëtius as *Comes Domesticorum* and *Cura Palatium* in his place. Had Galla not been sent away, Aëtius would now have had the right, if not the duty, to sleep at her door – two 'Tristans' alternating, like something out of the Commedia dell'arte. Instead Aëtius had long chats with Castinus. Castinus was really worried. 'You can see for yourself that we shan't have His Serenity with us for more than another twelvemonth,' he said. 'Then Old Rome's got the succession problem we have always feared. Next in the running, young Valentinian, aged three. Big deal. Not much help looking East, even if we wanted to. All petticoat government there. Pity, now, that we toppled all His Serenity's competitors, Constantine, Constans, Jovinus, Sebastian, Maximus – Attalus, unless he's still around. He was no good anyway. Wherever is Rome to look in this extremity? As you know, Rome prefers an Augustus "of the Blood"* if available. But who's left?'

'I have heard tell, Sir,' said Aëtius cautiously, 'that there is still one Western Augustus around: Constantine's son Julian-Constans. I heard he did not perish at Vienne, as was thought. He has been Caesar and led armies in action. He has ruled Spain for a time, not without success. True, he never got a purple robe in his own right, but maybe his father's would fit? He's about the right age. If I could find him for you, would you and the Senate think this a good idea?'

Etzie, of course, knew only too well where to write. 'c/o Aurelianus, Villa Glasdunum, Britannia Secunda. Please Forward'. It took Castinus a month or two, however, to sound out the Senate. The opinion of the Symmachi was vital. All still staunch Pagans, despite all Augustine's and Orosius' efforts. Indeed, Symmachus Jr had been prefect of Rome only four years previously, and Taurus four years before that. You just couldn't keep the Pagans down. The Symmachi didn't want a woman – 'Un-Roman', that. A descendant of Uncle Ted? – 'Tool of the Bishops, look where that's landed us.' A descendant of Constantius I, and of Maximus – 'Now you're talking!'

So it was early Spring when John got his marching orders from Rome to 'stand by'. Now don't forget that John's a Roman, nor that he was ordained both Caesar and Augustus by (albeit unauthorized) imposition of hands, before ever he was ordained deacon or priest.* Duty, that trumpet, called; moreover, would God not be able to make use of a Most Christian Emperor who really thought the poor more blessed than the rich? How would the Sermon on the Mount sound from the Capitol?

From Inverness to Rome's quite a hike, but by June 423, as ever in monk's habit (more of a habit than a disguise really), John was 'in position' and seeking news around the Aventine and Quirinale. Meanwhile, on my return from Brittany, I had been elected *provost** of the Great Council of Britannia for the ensuing five years (following in the footsteps of Cousin Vic). It therefore fell to me to look after all John's interests in Arctic Britain: his catechumens, his donations of land. I was also holding the missionary endowment of Melania,* and the offerings of the faithful: I was having some military and civil trouble with the Galloway Picts and Scots, and I was trying to collect some taxes for central government. Cormac 'Il Magnifico' had become Lucius Hiberius *Vectigalis*. In all, I had some accounting and identity problems. Who'd be a Prince-Bishop? Maybe I'd have done better to accept Exuperantius' offer of a 'Rectorship'.

On 15 August 423 Honorius died, as expected. Thanks to Constantius, the last few years of his reign had been quite successful. He had ruled mostly through others, but occasionally one had been aware that there was someone there, which was more than you could say of Arcadius. Uncle Ted was right at the terrible birthday party, though. Basically they were two puppets. At this juncture John cast aside his cowl and was acclaimed by the Senate as their new Augustus.* As you will notice, the Senate was slowly resuming its old powers and role, to match the current political vacuum. Next stop, Ravenna, where he was reunited with Titia,* and received by ambassadors. I'm glad to say all the West accepted John gratefully, save Africa, where Boniface was carrying a torch for Galla. It was now Aëtius' duty to sleep outside John and Titia's bedroom if required!

So passed 423. 424 went off in tranquillity. No laws, no wars. Castinus got his reward with the Consulate. Boniface had not cut off Rome's corn supply. John's Busts had been sent to New Rome. What would Pulcheria say? At first she said nothing. But she was moved by the presence of Galla and little Valentinian, clearly the rightful heir. Would not 'Theodosius the Penman' be the right Regent for him? Could not the Empire manage again under a sole Augustus? If he had been another Uncle Ted, the answer could have been 'Yes'. In the event, the answer was a muddle. No reply was sent to John, but a start was made in building up troops in Dalmatia with a view to dispossessing him. News of this was soon sent to Ravenna, and John took countermeasures. By way of trumping their hand, he sent Aëtius to obtain the services of Uldin and his Rent-a-Huns. Their numbers had increased during the previous fourteen years and it was more than 10,000* Huns who followed Aëtius from Pannonia to Ravenna the following year. Sadly, they arrived three days too late.

425 opened uneasily. Rumours were that Theodosius II had amassed a huge army and armada at *Salona* (Split), opposite Ravenna, under General

Ardaburius I and his son, Aspar. (Gosh, how well Theodosius was served by his principals; Anthemius had here picked some real winners for him.) In March they set sail for Aquileia, where Aspar's fleet arrived after a rough passage. His father's ship, setting out late, was caught in a *Bora*: the notorious NE gale of the upper Adriatic, once experienced, never forgotten. He was driven, helpless, across the Adriatic, and was shipwrecked at Ravenna. He was taken to John who treated the distinguished old gent with the greatest affability, treacherously repaid. Ardaburius abused his parole status to spread alarm among John's army, stressing the huge resources of the East now bearing down on them from Aquileia; they did not know how closely the relieving force of Huns was following behind them. Ravenna was highly defensible, and could easily have held out for a month, but thanks to Ardaburius and his war of words, Ravenna capitulated instantly.

John was taken back to Aquileia, where after a bit of public humiliation in the arena, he was punished by having his left hand chopped off. They made quite a neat job of it, and he lived on. When he got back to Britain he was known as (Cambrian) Ludd, *llaw ereint*,* (Erse) Nuada argetlam. Both mean 'Nitonius Silver Hand', as who should know better than me, for it was I who made John's artificial hand. You'd hardly know, because he generally wore gloves.

So ended a grandson of Ishmael's brave attempt at the throne of Rome. We're tryers aren't we? Any of us, we thought, from Glorious Dad down, could make a better fist of it than the opposition. The ways of God are inscrutable.

Ardaburius and Aspar were clement. Or maybe it was their fellow Roman General, none other than my own Candidianus. Candidianus had been one of Vic's couriers.* Joining the army in Gaul – my army, as it happened – he was best man at my posh marriage to Galla at Narbonne. He had then been cross-posted to the East, where he had risen to be Pulcheria's *Comes Domesticorum*. He was a thoroughly humane and balanced chap. Castinus took all the blame, and exonerated Aëtius wholly; indeed he commended his services to Pulcheria and Theodosius. He himself was lucky enough to be granted exile, which he took, *most oddly*, by fleeing to Boniface in Africa. Whatever was in his mind? In his place a chap called Felix (his wife Padusia was one of Galla's 'ladies-in-waiting'), was appointed Commander-in-Chief, and the next five years of military rule in the West were down to him. A nasty piece of work, Felix. Aëtius, in self-defence, would have to have him murdered just five years later.

All this I heard from the chastened lips of John himself when he dragged himself back to Ireland the following year. 'That's done for me ever trying for Empire again,' he said. 'Worse, the bleeding swine have done for me as a priest. You know that, by the Canons of the Council of Nicaea, a mutilated man can't be a priest.'

We both believed this at the time. Later, having looked them up, I found he could have obtained some sort of dispensation, as it had been involuntary.

'Well, you'll just have to serve God as a good Christian layman,' said I. 'Had you thought of going on the Council? I hear there's a seat coming vacant at Wroxeter.'*

I use hindsight to give you the next bit. You'll be wondering what happened to Galla. So was I. When Pulcheria gave the signal in February 425 to despatch the Armadas of Salona on John, Pulcheria also took the decision to send Galla and young Valentinian back, both as Augusti, she as his Regent. Two women would rule the Romes of East and West for the next twenty-five years. Uncle Ted's pledge had come true, and Cordelia had come into her birthright. Who was Prince Charming? Was it Eucherius? Was it I? Was it Stan? Hardly. Boniface? Maybe. What about Aëtius, Son of the Eagles? Eventually, yes. One thing was certain: Galla was born to rule. My Goths had sensed that. She took ship from Constantinople in February 425 – not reliable sailing weather. They struggled boisterously along by the usual routes and havens. They were not destined directly for Ravenna, lest the issue of that battle was still in doubt or adverse. They were making instead for Gaul, for Arles; or if their reception there seemed in any doubt, they would make for Narbonne.

Of one thing Galla could be totally sure: her Goths would greet their beloved Queen with rapture, but that was not to be. Neptune decided otherwise. They had rounded Sicily, taken on water in Sardinia, and were approaching the Isles d'Hyères near Toulon, when the *Levanter* (the local equivalent of the *Bora*) struck – very likely part of the same storm which had shipwrecked Ardaburius. Like him, there was nothing to do but run helplessly before the wind and pray for a soft landing.

That's how 'Mary Magdalene' and her companions came to be washed up on the beach at Les Stes-Maries-de-la-Mer in the Camargue on the Rhone Delta. Legends about them will abound. They had a very frightening experience, and it has to be said that it put the fear of God into Galla's heart. She vowed a great vow, when she was still at sea, that if she were saved she would erect a memorial church at Ravenna* for herself and *all* her family, loved and unloved. She would be a better more forgiving, more Christian, more moral woman.

They were picked up eventually by local fishermen, who took them to Marseilles. There Galla met John Cassian, there they talked God day and night; there Cassian reasoned her out of her Arianism, even suggesting that her shipwreck was *just* punishment, both for this and for her misbehaviour with Boniface. 'Jesus would have surely stilled the waves for you, if you had given him your whole allegiance,' he said.

No wonder Galla now saw herself as Mary Magdelene, as Pelagia the Penitent and as many other reformed sinners. (The 'Pelagia' is one of the most precious and beautiful of the religious *novellae* which John Cassian had brought with him from the Desert, then in the library at the Convent, and often read at mealtimes. There Galla heard it, and was just about hit for six.) Behind Marseilles she would do her fabled 'retreat' in the cave of 'La Sainte Baume'. Henceforward she would be a new woman. Whoever loved Galla from now on must love her as a pious Catholic Christian, and she was not less but more lovely for that.

In due course news came that John had gone, and that the throne of Ravenna awaited her. By August 425 Galla was settled in at Ravenna, and starting to embellish it with churches and oratories. She was putting herself straight with God, too. She summoned Boniface from Africa to 'make an honest woman of her' (in what will one day be called a *morganatic marriage* – what are we to make of that term?) as *Pelagia*'s husband. Boniface would hereafter know her only by that name, and Aëtius after him.

**Figure 38**

Galla/Pelagia wears her crown to wash John Cassian's feet, while St John Evangelist looks benevolently on

October 425 saw Aëtius working his passage back into favour by relieving Arles from some marauding Goths belonging to his cousin Theodoric. For this task he used a small party of his own trusty Huns, who were Rent-a-Huns no more but regular Roman soldiers. These were Aëtius' private army of Gurkha *cavalry*, if I dare envision, and you imagine, such a concept. They were really tame then, but later on, thanks to Honoria the Whore, and under Attila's sole and unbridled leadership, they reverted to being locust Huns.

Don't forget that Attila and Bleda were Aëtius' blood-brothers and Aëtius was an honorary Hun. That's why, on his return from Arles, Felix would send him and all his Huns with a doctor's mandate to recover the North.

Why did it need recovering? Hadn't Stan the Inexorable been given a triumph for fixing it? Barbarians don't stay fixed; that's the trouble.

So ended my sixty-fifth year. I'd had an exhausting life. I would only continue to make history myself, and to a limited extent at that, for another five years; then it would be the cloister for me. My torch was already passing to other younger hands: the Gawains, the Percevals, the Galahads, Lancelot and Guinevere, Tristan and Isolde. I would sit in my cloister and write poems* about them. But I had some last roles to play, and the next book should despatch them.

Heigh ho.

# BOOK XIX

## *Family Business (AD426–430)*

Before I start on AD426, I will hark back for a moment to two events of 424 and one of 425 which concerned me. The first event of 424 was the sad news of the murder of Hypatia, Sneezy's and my beautiful instructress at Night School in Alex. To succeed old 'Thugophilus', Alexandria had elected yet another 'thug' Patriarch called Cyril. His hands were ostensibly clean of the murder, but even his friends could not say that he regretted it. The second event was the murder at Arles of my old friend and boss Exuperantius, father of my 'copain' Palladius, who had gone on to succeed Agricola as Praetorian of Gaul. Dreadful news; what a lawless age we seemed to have moved into. His successor was one Armatius, whom I didn't know, but as he was one of John-George's appointees, he would probably be OK.

In 425 came news of the death of Aëtius' former Hunnish host, Uldin (or Ruas-Mundjuk). This gentleman-barbarian and pagan had served both Christian Romes really rather well. To the glee of Catholic historians, he was nevertheless struck, memorably, by lightning. Bleda and Attila were now Joint Kings of the Huns. How long would they manage to coexist?

**Figure 39**

Cordelia truly Augusta – note the Chi-Rho on her shoulder



Galla prospered piously in Ravenna, passing mostly ecclesiastical legislation. One of her laws proscribed not only heretics, but also Manichees. Could she have had Augustine in mind? Julian, Bishop of Eclanum, who was exiled for supporting JJ, had denounced him as the '*Punic Manichee*'; John Cassian, Galla's new spiritual director, also got it in the neck from Augustine. Augustine spent the last three years of his troubled life trying to answer Julian's strictures.*

Lover-boy Boniface – no, I mustn't call him that, he was Galla's 'lawful' wedded husband; Galla didn't know she had two husbands still alive – Boniface wallowed indolently in African intrigue, with a bit of lechery on the side. His military duties against the Berber tribesmen and the insurgent *Circumcelliones* – the 'bovver-booted' rump of the unfortunate Donatists – seemed quite forgotten. Trouble about governing Africa? Too many opportunities for the corn monies to stick to your fingers. Felix was very worried about him and Africa, and about Old Rome's precious food supply. Finally, that year Felix summoned Boniface to Rome (**not** Ravenna, note) to give an account of his stewardship. There were whispers of impeachment. A well-wisher sent a warning letter to Boniface that he risked great danger in coming to Rome, and this letter, later discovered and fathered on Aëtius, would earn him his nickname 'Palamedes' after the character in Homer's *Iliad*, who was stoned to death by the Greeks on account of a forged letter.*

Whoever wrote the letter, Boniface was in a 'Catch 22' situation. If he came, he risked discovery and dishonour. If he did not come he was an evident rebel. He decided to stay put, but hurried to Augustine to pour out his troubles. Augustine was ill at the time, and barely saw him. But he wrote a magnificent pastoral reply, which Boniface was too far gone to benefit much from. If, at times, I seem to deprecate Augustine rather harshly as a theologian, just read this letter* and see what he was still capable of as a priest and as a pastor. Even so will the Romancers' hermits – Amytans, Augustine, Gurnemanz – counsel their young and more than usually errant knights. There for the moment we must leave Boniface sweating.

Meanwhile in Britannia 'Lucius Maccabeus' was still holding the fort for the Great Council in my second term as 'Provost', and as *Judex* for the Civitas of *Venta Silurum* (Caerwent), while John-George had won himself a seat as representative for the *Civitas* of *Uriconium* (Wroxeter, by Shrewsbury). Troubles soon beset us both. Pictish* pirates (from Ulster and Galloway I'm sorry to say) had been raiding both shores of St George's Channel ever more boldly, and were now misbehaving in the Bristol Channel. (You'll have twigged by now how St George's Channel got its name. Should I now help future scholars by telling them that *these* Picts talked 'Goidelic',* or 'Latinate' Erse, which they had learnt from all the Agricolas who had subdued them. When in the future my Cambrians write about the 'Gwyddel Picti' they will **not** mean Irishmen.)

These Pictish pirates, then, had made a raid on the Vale of Neath, and had continued eastwards and burnt Ocean College to the ground. When they left, sated, they took with them as prisoner the then Head Boy, none other than young Calpurnianus '*Patricius*', my grandson by Consentia. No one knew what had become of him.

Now, '*Patricius*' is no normal Roman name; it's *the* top Roman honorific, below the Sacred Family itself. In my grandson's case, however, it was a true *agnomen** or Ocean College nickname given him by his mates because, as a pukka member of the ancient patrician *Gens Calpurnia*, he had bluer blood than any one else could hope to claim. It made my own pretended membership of the *Flavian Gens*,* seem really rather mere.

Duty, and love for my old Alma Mater, made me promptly refound Ocean College on a safer site some miles further East, at a place which would actually take its name, of Llancarfan, from John rather than me (Llan-'*Cuaran*',* for *Coronatus*). Wasn't John 'King Brude' of Pictland, and would not other crowns come his way? New Ocean College would be just as good as its predecessor, its scholastic repute being maintained by a succession of eminent scholars for another seven hundred years. John was its first headmaster,* and later, Visitor. Would he teach them 'sound' Catholic religion? Or would JJ's (Pelagius') very own son, 'the Sicilian Briton', give the syllabus an unorthodox tinge?*

To us, as we worried for him in March 426 in Silchester, where the Great Council held its working meetings, came Aëtius via Richborough. You will be able to read in Geoffrey of Monmouth (a distinguished later Llancarfan alumnus), how I persuaded them that Britain needed an equivalent to the *Croix Rousse* at Lyon; somewhere where the Brits, like Augustus' Gauls, could have a giant annual Eisteddfodd on 'Britannia Day', to celebrate their national feelings (and you'll soon realise why and when this came to be called St George's Day). Where was this 'amphitheatre of all the Britains' then? Stonehenge, of course.

Stonehenge was, therefore, my third *tabula ronda* or Round Table, on the site of the ancient Celtic **Prytaneion*** which gave Britain its name. No, I didn't bring the Stonehenge 'Blue Stones' from 'Little Ireland' in Menevia, but with my trained prospector's eye I *did* recognise their unique geological origin near Prescelly. Latter-day *Druids* won't be wholely wrong in their imaginings, though they may be wholly ridiculous.

We were amazed to see Etzie and not less amazed at what he had to tell. We had left him working his passage back to favour with Galla and Felix as *Comes Domesticorum*, and we had heard that he had won 'brownie points' for his exploits against his old fellow-hostage (and my successor), Theodoric, King of the Vizi-Goths in the relief of Arles. Poor Goths – they were still short of food, and Boniface wasn't helping them much.

'I'm here on a very special mission from Felix,' said Aëtius. 'You know he's having trouble with Boniface and the food supply. Looks permanent. Time to cut Rome's losses. He's remembered Stilicho's brainwave. Britain shall again be the granary of Old Rome. Britain supplies Rhine Army and Arctois with their food. *Germania* and *Belgica* ship their produce to Lyonesse. South Gaul ship theirs to Rome.'

'That's all very well,' said John, 'but this isn't 397. We've grown up. Since 417* we've been an independent Commonwealth within the Empire. If Rome wants our produce she'll have to pay the full market price. Then, something might be done.'

'Of course Rome'll pay,' said Aëtius. 'That's the least of the problems. We've even had to pay for our African grain recently. No, the problem is military. You see, New Rome's exacted quite a price for putting Galla and Valentinian back on the throne. It's back to Diocletian's* old division of the Empire. They've confiscated Hungary. Worse, they want all my Huns out – their families, that is. I've got to find a new and permanent home for the Rent-a-Huns. What do you think I'm doing on the Rhine at Xanten?'

'You tell us,' we said. 'We're all at sea.'

So Aëtius went on to explain Felix's master plan. Felix wanted to 'settle' the NE Frontier up to the Elbe. Stan the Inexorable had recently conquered it. It was now time to Romanise it, as all my family had so long striven to do with the Valentias. The Saxons and Norsemen would have to be tamed or ejected, and fighting would definitely be needed – hence the Huns. There was no need for an 'Antonine Wall': the Elbe would serve well as a frontier.

'When I've straightened out Arctois right up to the Baltic,' said Etzie, 'Felix says I'm to push the Huns across the Elbe and tell them it's their new home for ever and ever, and please may I issue an invitation for the covered wagons containing their wives and families to roll North to join them?'

'Ripping idea,' we said. 'What's the catch'?

'Catch is that, apart from a few *comitatenses*, I haven't got any troops to push the Huns onwards across the Elbe,' said Aëtius. 'They're loyal to me all right; damned loyal so long as I pay them. I don't think they'll want to leave me. That's where you come in, Uncle. You see, the only other troops we've got in the North are your old Burgundians; the ones you flogged to Jovinus. They're contented federates, sitting in the Palatinate around Trier. They'd turn out all right to defend Trier, if needed. But get them hiking up to the Baltic with me? I don't see it happening. Unless...'

'Unless they'll turn out for me,' said I. 'I read it now. You think I've still got some pull with them because, years ago, I was their King Gundahar.*

'Well, you can see how I'm placed,' said Aëtius, 'I can't do my task for Rome – don't you still care a bit for Rome? – unless you help me. We're going to make history yet again, and keep the West free for centuries. You'll find Felix will know how to express Rome's thanks to you when we succeed.'

'Well,' I said grudgingly, 'I'm an old man now, and John here's got a gammy hand. But once a Roman always a Roman. Count me in. We'll have to get leave of absence from the Council though.'

That's how three Arthurs (me, as former warden of Elissa, John, though he hadn't won the title yet, and Aëtius, Son of the Eagles, at that point very much the *Imperator* Arthur*) crossed the German Sea in April 426 to campaign in the forests,* which were infested with Giants and Leprechauns* (*Lepores coronati*). A delightful addition to the squad was my very own Gawain, now a full Tribune commanding a Cohort of Palatine troops. He was now devoted to his half-brother Aëtius, though they didn't see eye to eye at first. A real 'Oliver' to Etzie's 'Roland'. (*Oliver* means someone who has been to the Mount of Olives, as Gawain had.)

Time to tell you about *Roland*. This is short for (Teutonic) **Gui**[don]-**Römerland**. As Aëtius rose to ever dizzier heights of power, with no title save *Magister Utriusque Militum*, the Teutons found a less tongue-twisting nickname for him. They called him the *Guide** (as in 'be Thou my guardian and my guide') of the lands still living under Roman Law. The French Romancers will call him 'Gui-romelant' (get it?), shortened to *Guirom*, then corrupted to Guiron.

There will be further Romance confusion with Gerin/Garin (of Chartres/of Lorraine) who was 'my Gawain', corrupted from *Quirinus*. This was Aëtius' nickname too, but then weren't both lads brought up by Morgan 'La Dame du Lac' in her palace on the *Quirinal*? Don't blame the Romancers too much for the mess they'll make of it.

There was one more very young man in our squad I should mention. Only a cadet, his name was Majorian, and he would be Augustus one day – and quite a good one.

On my way down to Worms to seek my Burgundians I was delighted to meet up with Ursula, whom Aëtius had left, with a bodyguard of trusty Huns, in a very nice *domus* in CCAA (Köln*). She had a dear little boy, just four, called Carpilio after his mother, the same that was conceived that wild night at Tintagel. (He's 'Cerdic', remember? Will he too go on to be Arthur? Not half!)

The Burgunds followed me, and I followed Aëtius. Restful to be under my nephew's command. Attila and Bleda were in joint command of the Huns, and with them rode Bleda's grotesque dwarf Zercon,* whom Bleda would quite soon give as a present to Aëtius. Did the Huns suspect we were going to double-cross them? Not yet.

Meanwhile, in Spain, something dire was happening. The Vandals, under their King Gunderic, had conquered Seville. Not content to gloat there, they had actually taken to the water, and become pirates. First they raided the Balearics.

Then, more ambitious, they crossed over and raided Mauritania. Boniface did nothing. Where would this end? Galla, in Ravenna, built churches and legislated for priests. Felix and the Senate ruled at Rome. It was becoming more and more like Livy. *Floreat SPQR*.

Under Aëtius' cool command our Saxon campaign went off faultlessly, and by the close of the campaigning season we were back at Köln, and reunited with Ursula. Despatches were exchanged with Rome, throughout, by fast courier, and a reply from Felix soon reached us. The Senate was much gratified by our success, and were pleased to ratify Aëtius' recommendations that I should be made King of Saxony (as 'Alberic'), and also of the Romans living among the Salian Franks (as Clodio-n). The latter's Western frontier was now extended to the great road leading North from Le Cateau via Cambrai, Arras and St Omer, leaving the block of land covering the *trajecti Britanniae* (cross-Channel ferry ports) firmly in Roman hands. Felix's rescript concluded with congratulations to our General. The Senate would know how to express their appreciation next time he was in Rome. (It was at this time that I established my seat at *Dispargum** – now Doesburg by Leuven.)

John was to be made High Admiral of the revived Saxon Shores, now extending from the Isle of Wight to Jutland, and even round the corner into the Baltic as far as Elsinore.* Would he enrol some *tame* Angles into his fleet? (We Romans didn't take kindly to the water in general.) Would he allow some of them a base in the Isle of Thanet? Would he live to regret that day bitterly, and carry an odium for it worthy of Pontius Pilate? Or was it Cousin Vic who should properly carry that can? I'll tell you by and by.

I retained my status as elected Guardian (Æd-*ward*) and Provost of the independent Britains. If Aëtius was the 'Arthur' of the day, who was I? All I can tell you is that the Britons thought I was a *major turannus* or Vortigern; not the first, nor the last to be so named. John-George would succeed, even displace, me as 'Vortigern III, *Tigernicus*.* Would my Franks remember me as 'Charlemagne II'? Once I had tried to become Augustus. Then I was 'King of Kings' – bitter memories there. Then I was a Prince-Bishop. Now, no one could really say what I was.* I had a lot of reponsibility and influence, but very little real power – like a constitutional monarch.

So 426 went out in a blaze of self-satisfaction. 427 didn't start so well. Taking advantage of the absence of the Burgundians, many of whom were still in Saxony on garrison duties, the Riparian Franks from the upper Main and Neckar decided to cross the Rhine and occupy the Palatinate. For starters they sacked Trier, the poor old Gaste Cité, for the third time that century. City of the Phoenix*, I called it (many Romance revelations here). On hearing of this, Aëtius and I turned quickly South to deliver what remained of it, taking my Burgundians and Gawain's cohort. They really were indomitable, and were rebuilding already and talking about repairing the Arena for the following year's Games. Among the ruins we came across Elissa and Eugenia.

None of us were getting any younger but, apart from her teeth, Elissa was still in remarkable shape, still 'Ye Gods what a torso!'; and, despite my receding and now virtually white mane, I was no slippered pantaloon* myself. Titchy, but ever-youthful. *Vitalis** – that's me.

Eugenia was now thirty, and had spent all her life to date at Elissa's side. What had that meant for her? Alchemy, astronomy, and athletics, that's what. No time for men,* and in any case, no men around.

I switch for a moment to Africa. On hearing that his NE and Northern frontiers were in good order, Felix felt able to take on Boniface. The latter had been declared an Enemy of the State, and Felix sent an army under no less than three generals – at least two too many in my view – with a high-ranking diplomat, to try to bring him to heel. Now here was a strange coincidence: the Vandals had suddenly started to raid not just Mauritania but Africa, and in some force, yet Boniface did nothing to defend his own patch. At the end of the year Gunderic the Vandal died, to be succeeded by his lame ill-tempered bastard half-brother Gaisaric. Now when *his* turn came to sack Rome, he'd give us all a new word: to *vandalise.*

I was glad to be with Elissa again, and quite took charge of her and Eugenia – in so far as anyone could be said to take charge of Elissa. She knew Ursula was well and happy at Köln. Gawain had gone off West, with his cohort and my Burgundians, to Metz* to round up the displaced Palatinate refugees and, with their help, to swing anticlockwise through the Vosges, sweeping the Riparian Franks back to where they belonged. Was their King Pharamond with them, and would he return meekly to his capital at Rothenburg ob der Tauber?* In fact Pharamond was not with them, but they were far too many in numbers for Gawain to shift, so he dug in, and sent word to Aëtius for reinforcements. All Aëtius could do was send to Bleda and Attila for help, and he and the Huns were soon on the way to Gawain's aid.

That's how another King also met his end near the end of 427 – none other than 'Pharamond', King of the Riparian Franks. With us all pushing – Romans, Burgunds, Huns – the Franks made off southwards and were allowed an easy passage across the Rhine at Speyer. Plainly they were making for the *Agri Decumates*, the no man's land of the Swabian Alps, 'twixt Rhine and infant Danube, where all the scallywags of the Empire seemed to hole up. Aëtius was in command, but we were all in the hunt. Rather fun. Not so funny was the weather. The German winter was hard and snowy, and both armies were just about immobilised. However, Aëtius refused to retire into winter quarters. 'If I can't beat them in battle just now, I must quickly teach them a lesson they won't forget,' he said.

'They've been good quiet federates since the time of Julian the Apostate,' said I, 'and no trouble 'till that bleeding Pharamond came along. Maybe if we could "take him out" that'd knock the stuffing out of them.' (See how quickly this old man was trying to imitate the young men's talk. Chameleon, that's me.)

All this would be surprisingly well recollected in the Romance *Song of the Saxons*, and in even more remarkable detail in the Grimms' *Märchen** of the 'shoemaker of Lauingen'. We're all in there. The latter, *Henfwil* 'Old William' is of course me – the 'Golden Shoemaker' of the Third Branch of the Mabinogion. No time here to clear up for you all the ancient confusions behind that word 'shoemaker'. If I tell you the residual word is *gold-maker*, that'll have to do for now.

The place was right for a battle; indeed one day the battle of Blenheim would be fought nearby, on the little River Nebel. Was this when my Burgundians* would become *Nibelungs*?

So the plot was hatched. It was Aëtius who remembered Kyriakos' assassination attempt on him outside St Sophia's; it was John-George, who had come South from Hamlet-land with Attila and the Huns, who was chosen to do the deed which my Gawain would one day record;* and it was I who gave the plan my experienced approval.* John was suitably disguised, as usual in monk's habit and cowl, and was sent with an 'embassy' through the lines, a dagger duly concealed in his envoy's 'letters of credence'.

Did 'Hamlet' not recognise his father? You don't always recognise someone who you have every reason to think is somewhere quite different, especially if years have passed, and their appearance and clothes are much altered.

So, by a trick, and by mistake, yet another Oedipus slew his father. Poor old JJ. He died, as he had lived, still at the 'Edge of Battle'. He was 'Bendigeid Vrân', *Orion Benedictus*, Constantine Augustus. His head was buried on and with him. What happened to his wax bust,* the famous 'talking head', is another story. I wouldn't dig up the Tower of London for it, whatever the Mabinogion will say. Why not try Madame Tussauds?

'***Irish King slain in the Alps***',* the 'Ulster Journal' for January 428 would read. Would John have it in for his Uncle Claudius when, not so long afterwards, I married his mother? (Elissa here plays 'Gertrude'.) Elissa did *not*, as Brünnhilde or *even as Dido*, jump onto JJ's funeral 'pyre', for Ginger had already performed that feat for her, in honour of Alaric. Moreover it was JJ-Siegmund (Sigurd), not Aëtius-Siegfried (Sigvrid*) that Elissa was mourning. Shakespeare will not get it really quite right in his *Hamlet*. Moreover, typical tragedian, he'll kill us *all* off at the end of the play, in order to get us off stage. In real life we lived on, each with our own tragic thoughts to bear.

We returned, sombre, to Worms where Elissa was awaiting us. Aëtius had brought Ursula down from Köln when he had joined us with the Huns. What we then did may seem very strange to you, but we were all in a very strange mood. It was John's idea, really, that we should arrange a double wedding. 'The Jews would say you should marry your brother's widow and raise seed up to your brother, but you did that ages ago. How about de-bastardising* all of them, particularly my sister Ursula? Aëtius, too. He didn't have a proper Church wedding after that night at Tintagel, just a *mensam et thoram* job. As for me, I've just killed my father, though I did not intend it. I think we all need a bit of absolution and blessing for the future.'

So took place the Second Act of Wagner's *Götterdämmerung*: the Double Wedding at Worms of the *Nibelungenlied*. It wasn't at all the vengeful business he makes of it. We were all in our way penitents, for there was a lot of adultery, incest, and now murder to be absolved. Aëtius was so depressed that he would ever after be known as Tristan, Latin *tristianus*, the 'sad man'. The Romance chickens are really thudding home to roost aren't they?

Aëtius didn't have long to mope, for with the thaw came news that there was more trouble in the Swabian Alps. The vanquished Franks had pushed out a veritable nation of mixed Norse refugees – Angles, Saxons and Jutes – who had taken root in the *Agri Decumates.** This rabble had moved SE and were currently harassing Augsburg.* So the younger soldiers of the party were on the march again, leaving their elders in their winter quarters. I found my bride Elissa very edgy and preoccupied: none too happy about her soul and a bit guilt-ridden. It wasn't her original unchastity with me that pushed JJ into intemperance, nor into celibacy. The former was a mixture of ambition combined with high living, the latter the effect of Augustine plus Little Benedict. Morgan may have been a better mother, but Elissa hadn't done badly. I really didn't think she should reproach herself in any way for how things had turned out. However, once Elissa had got her head down there never had been any stopping her. She felt that Ursula was much more relaxed after her four years in Eire as a nun, and that even John seemed to have a 'curious serenity'. She decided that she must do a bit of real penance before absolution really felt real. So, she resolved to become a nun. Should it not be in Ireland, like Ursula and John? Ursula had the answer to this.

'I think you're getting a bit rheumatic for that climate, Mummy dear. Why don't you do a spell at Bishop Salvius'* convent at St Maurice-en-Valais* at the foot of the St Bernard? Better still, why don't you lay up Uncle's remains among the martyrs graves there?* Just the place for him.'*

So it was all arranged, and at Easter 428 JJ's body was solemnly transferred to the very martyrium tomb whence the original martyrs had been translated. Elissa accompanied it, in deepest mourning and took up her residence in the anchorite's cell high in the cliff above. (No wonder Lancelot won't be able to get his horse up that path.* Just you try!) Here she would mourn awhile as the Romancers' *Sigune*; as Isabella, *Elissa bella* with her 'pot of Βασιλ' – '*King*' JJ in his 'urn' – and pursue her spiritual destiny.

Ursula returned to Köln to look after her little Cerdic. John headed back to Denmark to his Prefect's job* there, taking with him – surprise, surprise – his own daughter Eugenia. My God! I hope that's going to be all right; but I'm hardly the man to caution him. I went back to all my responsibilities in Britain, Germany and Flanders, leaving my Gawain in charge of my Burgundians in the Pfalz.

Elissa didn't last very long in her mountain cell. Perhaps it was pneumonia, but in ten months she too was dead, and Gawain buried her in the same martyrium tomb, beside *her* very own and first Arthur. So that was one Guinevere, the original one, by whom I shall not sleep the long sleep. Gawain found an old cistern in the ruins* of the Roman *vicus* at Massongex, a few kilometres North of the Frontier Post, which made an excellent sarcophagus (see Plate 11). On it he set the inscription:*

*NITONIAE AVITIANAE: CLAR:FEM.*

*VASSONIUS GELLIANUS; ET*

*NITONIA MARCELLA, ET*

*NITONIUS POMPEIUS, FILII*

*M. MATRIS CARISSIMAE. M.*

which translates as: 'To a mother's memory, the Hon. Nitonia Avitiana (Elissa): Vassonius Gellianus (Gawain the yellow); also Nitonia Marcella (Ursula) and Nitonius Pompeius (John the leader), her children'.

Aëtius made a clean sweep of the Norsemen, pushing them all the way back into John's territory whence they originally came, and where John was awaiting them. By the end of the year he had completed his task, and was summoned to report to Felix at Arles. Just as well he took his Huns with him, for he used them to earn yet more 'brownie points' by a successful skirmish near Arles, where he managed to drive off some marauding Vizi-Goths, still under his old comrade Theodoric. Six years later he would have to secure peace with them by a diplomatic marriage,* but for the moment he was still married to Ursula. Or was he? The tragic answer would very soon be 'No', for when Aëtius received the promised summons to Rome to receive the plaudits of the Senate, he sent Attila and Bleda back North, their destination Pomerania. On the way they passed through Köln. Naturally they looked up Ursula, and her Hun bodyguard, and naturally they all had a few jars. That's how Ursula met her disgusting and pitiful death in what will one day be called a 'Gang

Bang'. Never trust a Hun. To avert Aëtius' predictable revenge they took an unscrupulous precaution: they took away little Cerdic/Carpilio as a hostage. He spent *years* as a hostage in Hunland. Well might Aëtius be styled Tristan II.

429 saw some changes up in the North. The miasma of Pelagianism, not untinged with Arianism, emanating from 'New Ocean College' at Llancarfan was perturbing the British Bishops. Of how St Germanus was sent over to assist them theologically,* you can read in his *Vita* by his disciple Constantius; you can read, too, how the Soldier Saint led his army against the Picts in Gwynedd; but you'll have to read between the lines to find out all that passed between Germanus, John and I (all cousins of sorts). Suffice it that he straightened out our theology and churchmanship once and for all. I was a pretty good theologian, but Germanus really knew his Bible. I couldn't argue with that. He thought that, at the age of sixty-eight and repeatedly widowed, it was about time I was put out to grass. He called a special synod at *Bremium* (later called 'Llanddewi' Brefi, after me), where he announced my appointment as Archbishop of Wales. When I climbed onto a mound to respond, a dove obligingly settled on me. I couldn't argue with that either. So it was retirement for me. There was nothing left for the rest of my life but to serve Christ full-time (as St David). Maybe I should have done it earlier.

Germanus also scooped up and took with him Ursula's and my son Faustus, now nineteen and reared at Glastonbury. He was sent on to the monastery at Lérins, where he met up with young Patrick Calpurnianus. Germanus gave me a right telling off for laying my daughter, and agreed to adopt Faustus as his own son, since there was no way I could legitimate the lad. Still setting things to rights* like a fairy godmother, Germanus, on his way home, gave a solemn benediction to John-George, whom the Council had agreed should succeed me as 'Vortigern III', Provost of Britain.

There's not much more to say about 430, except that in Africa Cousin Augustine breathed his last. His end was the more sad since Boniface, his protegé and the defender of besieged Hippo, was at his side, for Boniface, the 'Ill-made Knight' had reaped the whirlwind for his follies. To support himself against a tidal wave, as he saw it, of Roman armies and generals, he had actually invited Gaiseric and his Vandals (now 'sea wise') to come to his aid. They came; they conquered; they stayed. By and by they sacked Rome. They were Arians, so all Augustine's laborious efforts for Orthodoxy in Africa fell to the ground. In Augustine's day, North-West Africa had nearly three hundred Orthodox, and a like number of Donatist Bishops. In a few years there would be only eighteen. Then Islam will come. Oh Lord, how unsearchable are thy ways.

Meantime, I put my heart and soul into *my* religion, and got back to the

*Laus Perennis*, or continual office. I made a special point, too, of my Lent Retreats; maybe if I'd stuck to them I'd have made fewer mistakes.

It was good that the younger men were taking over, but I foresaw that I had about twenty years to live, so there was still plenty for me to do.

Time to peer at the stars; time to set down my own contributions to the *Liber Gradalis* (or *Book of the San Graal**) on the nature of *pneuma* or 'gases'. They're definitely not air. You can smell them but not see them. They do funny things. I even managed to liquefy some of them briefly.

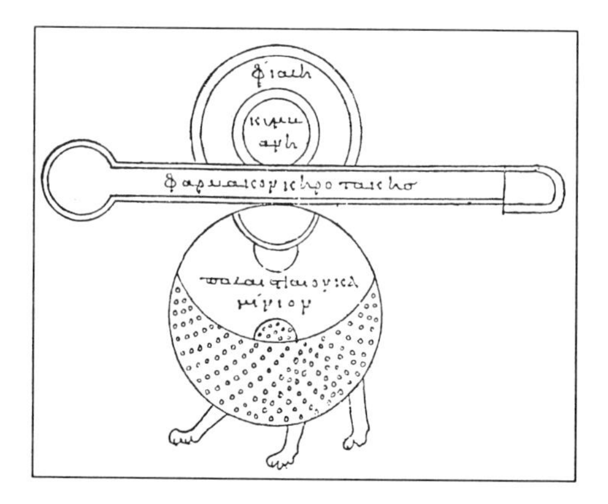

**Figure 40**
Faraday will think he's the first to liquify gases; but Berthelot here indicates that the Greeks got there first

Eventually they will take their name from me as Χαος,* 'Sir Kay'. Would Doc Heron be proud of me?

Time to see how my 'Dionysius the Pseudo-Areopagite' sits alongside the Gospels. Time to try to see where JJ went wrong, yes and Augustine too.

Nestorius is now Patriarch of New Rome ... I hear that he's getting into trouble with Cyril the Thug over his unwillingness to agree that the Blessed Virgin Mary actually gave birth to God the Father...

Heard all that in the pagan religions... Cybele 'Great Mother of the Gods' we called *Her* when I was a Reader at Lyons University...

I don't find all this lies too well with the Gospels. I *must* think some more about Mary...

Maybe my training at the Convent of the Resurrection was for a purpose...

Funny to think that the citizens used to call it the 'Swan' Convent, because it was in the *Cycnus Regio* of Constantinople...

Maybe I'm Lohengrin, the *Swan Knight*...

**Maybe this is my own swan song.**

Easter, AD447, note by Merlin's faithful scribes Basil and Anthony.

*Our master had been growing increasingly doddery and infirm recently, and his old groin injury gave him ever-increasing trouble. Frankly we weren't sure he would last the winter into 447. He finished dictating this book to us by the beginning of Lent, when in accordance with his invariable practice, he laid all work aside. He seemed unusually down and dejected in Holy Week, muttering on about all his sins. On Maundy Thursday he attended Mass for the last time, and insisted on washing all the brethren's feet, though he was barely able.*

*On Good Friday* we had some little trouble arousing him and persuading him where he was. When we told him that it was Good Friday he gave a great yell, the loudest we have ever heard man produce. 'Oh my Jesus!' he cried, 'it was I who betrayed you; I who drove in the nails. Yet, in your mercy, remember me when you come to your Kingdom.'*

*Then he gave another great yell, something like a grotesque laugh, and blood poured from his mouth and nose. Something had burst in his head. That's how he died. He was a strict but kind Abbot to us monks.*

# BOOK XX

## *Epilogue, by Sir Gawain* (AD430–453)

(*recte*, Q. *Flavius* Claudius Eugenius Meropius *Merobaudes**)

What am I to say about my old Dad? He's said it all already; but then he would! I didn't really know he was my Dad when I was a child. Didn't know people had Dads. (Didn't know they had Mums either; it was all rather a confused upbringing.) 'Uncle Lucius' was often at the Casa Sic for holidays of course, and I remember he used to play with us, and tell all sorts of tall stories. I found out later that they were just about all true. Then there was Morgan, and Aunt Elizabeth,* as my 'stepmother' liked me to call her, in the Forest of Arden. And then came the army.

So I didn't really get to know my Dad until I was thirty-three and we soldiered together 'twixt Rhine and Elbe. From then on, Aëtius followed the Eagles, and I followed Aëtius, and am still doing so. But it was a real treat to visit Dad whenever I managed to get some leave, at Glastonbury or St David's, or the Isle of Man, or wherever he was in his Diocese. There he taught me a lot, and he taught me to love him. I won't go on about this. I'll just say that he was the most learned man I ever met, and the funniest, and in the end the best of fathers. He was keen to finish this book, although he foresaw he wouldn't. On reading it so far, I find he's left me an odd legacy by prophesying my own death – but even soldiers must die sometime. The best tribute I can pay him is to finish it for him up to his death. I'll try to follow up the many loose ends he left dangling into the future, and to follow his expository method.

When Dad died (as brothers Anthony and Basil told you, on Good Friday 447) he was still dictating the events of the year 430, so I will take up from there. I'm not trying, as he was, to write a full family history in strict chronological form; so I may follow up people and what happened to them, without minding if it gets a bit out of order.

The first person I'll follow up is Galla. We left her moping in Ravenna, while Boniface reaped the whirlwind in Africa. Not even with the help of armies from Rome, and a substantial detachment from New Rome under Aspar,* could Gaisaric and his Vandals be expelled. Africa was lost to the Western Roman Empire for ever.

I should say that Aëtius returned to Rome in 431 to his promised Roman Triumph, but first he had to 'take out' Felix, his predecessor. Now Felix had been promoted Patricius in 430, when Aëtius became Commander-in-Chief. Felix could hardly be said to have pulled off his African assignment, but Aëtius had gloriously pulled off his 'Arctic' one. Padusia, the wife of Felix, was jealous, very jealous, and Padusia was Galla's Lady-in-Waiting.* Two attempts were made on Aëtius' life, and the hand of Felix was seen behind them. Do two wrongs make a right? I'm not the man to blame my beloved brother. He acted in self-defence, as I see it. The Senate saw it the same way, and fell over themselves to laud Aëtius. He was 'Mr War and Peace', Mr Sieg-fried, victor in war as a successful general, as he had been victor for peace as an adolescent hostage. Now who was jealous? Was it Galla? Or was it 'Lover-Boy' working through Galla? Dad would have said the latter, and I agree with him.

Whoever was pulling the strings, at the end of AD431 Galla (as Augusta and wife), rashly recalled Boniface intending, on his arrival, to make him Commander-in-Chief in place of Aëtius! Nevertheless, on 1 January 432 in Rome *Flavius* Aëtius (now that he knew his father, he knew his *Gens*; so did I – I was *Flavius* too), ascended the Consular Chariot (or *Charpente* or *Charrette*) for the first of his three Consulates. Why was Guinevere III (Galla) so angry with Lancelot (Aëtius) for travelling in a '*cart*'? Because it was the consular 'cart', and because, for her, he was the wrong occupant. Galla desperately wanted Boniface for Consul. Moreover the Senate had given Aëtius a full Triumph in the old Republican style, so he was now a full *Imperator*. He'd exchanged the Duke's red spear, *Lança-rote* (Lancelot) for the Emperor and Field Marshal's baton (Fr. '*tronçon*'*). It was just as well he kept hold of the spear though, as you'll see.

Meanwhile Boniface, 'Enemy of the State' and bungler of Africa, returned to *Ravenna* to be 'rewarded' with the insignia of his new office by Galla and the infant Valentinian III jointly, as was their prerogative. Galla had finally nerved herself to sack Aëtius and he was allowed to retire into private life at Subiaco where, once again, murder attempts were made on him. What would you do? Fight, of course. Galla was just under Boniface's thumb, and Rome was being made a mockery of. So, outside Rimini the armies met. Aëtius' forces lost the day, but Aëtius won it. Following this battle, the option of settling civil disputes by single combat would be *de rigueur* for centuries.

It wasn't planned as a single combat. The armies were there, and engaged; their leaders, brave men both, were at their head. They met, clashed, and Aëtius succeeded in giving Tristan a mortal wound with his long spear. Boniface-Tristianus lived on for three months in much agony, but died in the end. Like

Isolda – nay, *as* Isolda – Galla just made it to his death bed, to receive a strange and very chivalrous last request from Boniface-Tristan. He was 'for the dark'. **Should Galla ever wish to marry again, there was one man, and one man only whom Boniface-Tristan would wish her to consider. It was Aëtius-Tristan.** So died the lovable but 'Ill-made Knight'. Galla did not sing this Tristan a '*Liebestod*'; nineteen years were to pass before she did that,* and then it was for my brother. Even then, he outlived her and is still alive as I am halfway through writing this epilogue, interrupted as my pen* always is by matters of war and state.

So that's 432, and that's Galla. On Boniface's death, she shook off the love-miasma he'd cast on her, and got back to governing the Western Empire, this time in full collaboration with the Senate. Aëtius was restored, made *Patricius*, and became her most loyal and trusted servant. By and by, and without the need for any love potion, she came to feel first respect, then attraction, and finally love for the man who had killed her latest lover.* When the time came that she could have wished to marry him, Aëtius was no longer free; for he had contracted an unhappy political marriage* in 434 with the sister of Theodoric, King of the Vizi-Goths by way of cementing a treaty with him. Did he love Galla? Of course he did. I could have myself, if I'd been in the 'Royals' League, and if I had not already made my own love match – for, like Dad and Sneezy, I too married my General's daughter (Boniface's niece), Asturia.

If I tell you that 'Asturia' means 'Sparrow Hawk' you'll see how I earned my nickname of 'The **Knight of the Sparrow Hawk**'. I did win her in battle, too – call it a joust if you will – for after serving him for a time in Savoy, Aëtius had sent me off to Spain under General Asturius, whom I was to succeed as Commander-in-Chief. I'd even get to be *Patricius* too. Must be the genes!

In this way, some twenty years have gone by around the old battlefields. My brother has kept the peace from Dalmatia* to the Elbe, and we have kept the lid on the BFBs in Spain – not just as Roland and his Oliver, but as Garin (Quirinus) and his Bego (Bagaud, from my Ardennes days). Africa's gone for ever; which makes the old Stilicho Plan for food from the 'Arctic' a constant preoccupation.

So did Dad and brother John get on in the independent Arctic? Only so so. After Ambrosius-Germanus had won his famous 'Alleluia Victory' of Easter 429, and he had put Dad out to grass, he went over to the Western Isle to straighten out the theological mess which had resulted from Dad's and John's unsupervised evangelistic efforts. Wild wet Hibernians, he found, reeking of Arianism (semi-), Pelagianism (semi-) and Neoplatonism (semi-). Germanus wasn't really a 'semi-' man. Black and white for him. John, who went with him, said you should have seen him trying to explain the doctrine of the Trinity to the country folk by brandishing a three-leaf shamrock. Anyway, he cleared the island of the serpents of heresy.

John himself was more than fully occupied in baptising the newly Catholicised converts. He must have done thousands; indeed after this they called him 'John the Baptist', John *Bedyddiwr*, to be remembered, importantly, as **'Sir Bedivere I'!**

On his return to Gaul, Germanus put in a recommendation to Pope Celestine that a proper Bishop should be sent to 'the believing Christians in Ireland', and Celestine's deacon Palladius was ordained and sent, but died soon after. The way was finally clear for my own nephew Calpurnianus 'Patricius' to take on the job, and devote his life to being the Apostle of Ireland. He'd escaped from his captivity in Ireland, met up with Germanus and Faustus at Lérins, and was finally chosen – he said it was reading one of Uncle Vic's old letters* that inspired him to volunteer – to succeed Palladius. Religion apart, Ireland slumbered, perhaps because John (as St Ruadan the Red*) unfortunately introduced both Scotland and Ireland to the joys of Dad's distilled cordials, from which it was only a short step to whiskey, the water of life (*aqua vitae*). That kept them pretty somnolent.

The Picts were quite another matter. Be they Caledonian Picts or Galloway Picts, they were neither settled nor loyal neighbours. Indeed they tended to ally themselves with the fair-haired sea-going Saxon raiders, whom the Irish called the *Finn-Gael*. I must now mention the Danes. The Cambrians called the Norse inhabitants of the Cimbric Chersonese (the Horn of Denmark) the 'black pagans', and the Irish called them the *Dubhthach* (the 'black' race). John, as High Admiral* of the Saxon Shores, with a naval base at Elsinore, made the mistake of employing increasing numbers of his newly-Romanised Tame Danes and Frisians to defeat the Picts and Saxons. Cousin Vic had already paved the way by employing Tame Saxons*. How ever would John then get rid of them all? Adopting the Danish horned Viking helmet as his battle gear, he earned from the Irish the name 'Finn Benachus'* ('WhiteHorns'). More, they would call him *Cernunnus* after the old Celtic stag god, and this survived at Kells (*Ceannannas Mor*).

Now you know why the *Vita Germani* called him Elafius, the 'timid stag'.* For the moment (AD 428) he was winning golden opinions* from the Council, and working away at Dad's scientific studies. Tintagel had now become an important scientific research establishment.*

You'd think all was set fair for John to be the greatest 'Arthur' of the whole long line, but the complexities of the situation, combined with his own, all too human, libidinous weaknesses led to a tragically different outcome over the following twenty-five years. I said I might follow people up 'out of order', and this is a case where I feel compelled to digress, so as to tell you about John's decline, fall, and – God be praised – return to respectability, nay even perhaps sainthood. In telling this sorry personal tale about my first cousin, I am also telling you the tale of the final 'Loss' of Britannia* to the Western Empire and its conversion into 'England' by the Anglo-Saxons.

I'll tell the story briefly, as is my wont. Dad told you in his last Book how Germanus persuaded the Great Council to appoint John-George 'Vortigern' (as it will be convenient here to call him). John duly transferred his naval headquarters from Jutland to London River, and commenced operations against the rebellious Saxon seamen in Thanet. These were Cousin Vic's 'gamekeepers', now turned 'poachers' in a big way. Intended to protect the *trajecti Britannici*, they had quite gone over to the side of their fellow Saxon pirates, thereby putting Britain's links with the Mainland Empire in jeopardy; and now they were even encroaching NW towards the Medway. The Council appointed John as *Dux Bellorum* (Cat-tigern) and in a series of spirited battles,* by land and sea, John penned them up again in Thanet, and reduced them to their former obedience. For this service the Council voted him a gorgeous commemorative 'perron' which was duly erected at *Regulbium* (Reculver*) where the Saxons could always have it in view.

John's valedictory charges from Germanus had been, first to foster Britain's 'Romanitas'; and second to keep the Pict and Scots quiet.* To the first end he had restored Britain's continental links; now for the Picts and Scots. He will be too much blamed for calling in his Baltic Fleet for this task. No one foresaw at the time that they would choose to stay in Eastern Britain, where indeed they are still pullulating. Circumnavigating Britain (like, indeed as, the Irish Maelduin), Admiral John returned triumphantly to London, leaving yet another 'perron' behind him in Fife. He was forty-seven years old, and the Council's pet, with his 'bouffant' red hair, blue eyes, dashing freckles and close-trimmed beard. Could they refuse him, like Vic, a 'Perpetual First Consulate'; should they not rather welcome it? Should they not name a Gate (Ludgate) after him, even as he had renamed the River Gate (Billingsgate) after JJ?

**Figure 41**
Vortigern himself, Christian First Consul

So passed 432, and 433. Despite John's little frontier difficulties, the Britains were enjoying a golden age of prosperity. They paid no tribute, and they got splendid prices for their grain. Dad's farms, now mine since he became Archbishop, were appreciating steadily in value, but I was well content to live on my pay. One thing I'd inherited from Dad, though, was his poetic talent, and I wrote quite a bit in my times off duty. Already I had done panegyrics* for my brother. I'd even got my own bust in Poets' Corner,* just like Dad. But I must get back to John.

434 saw John busy around Cornwall and the Valentias: minerals were one preoccupation, family piety the other. John built a host of memorial chapels in memory of Ursula and of Uncle James (JJ) all over the place, and continued to establish monasteries, such as the Bangors of Gwynedd and Ulster. 435 found John pious, attractive, competent, successful, and single, for Titia had alas died in Cornwall in the Spring of that year.* To her funeral, to support her widowed father, came Eugenia from Elsinore, where she had been living. I blame his own fatal invention of whiskey, as much as anything, but honestly, you'd have thought after Dad's misadventure with Ursula – about which of course we all knew – that John would have had more sense, or else more self-control. And now John had done it too!* Worse – at least I think it was worse, but I'm not quite sure – John had been quite open and brazen about it. He'd actually married the girl, his own daughter by his own mother, and justified himself by saying that 'in heaven there will be neither marrying nor giving in marriage'. I couldn't see Germanus letting him get away with that, if and when he heard about it, but that wouldn't be for a few years yet.

Tell you who did hear – Dad himself.* His distress was pitiful, and his anger terrible. He wrote John a letter, which he copied to the Council, denouncing him in biblical terms* as a monster of depravity. Now there were a lot of bishops among the magnates on that Council, and John didn't wait to be sacked or excommunicated, so he took off for Armorica, with Eugenia, and raised the flag of rebellion.* It was as Tybalt of Tintagel, Theobald the 'bagaud' that he raised Brittany against Rome.

Aëtius soon got wind of this, and early in 436 he sent Litorius to put matters to rights. Thank God I was in Spain, or I might have had this unsavoury task. Before he had completed the job Litorius had to divert his forces suddenly to Narbonne to raise yet another Gothic siege, and John used this opportunity to attempt to spread the 'bagaudic' revolt eastwards towards Belgica and the Ardennes. The Salian Franks of Flanders, Dad's old Kingdom, received him with opportunistic enthusiasm, and Aëtius himself was forced to intervene. At the celebrated skirmish of the Vicus Helena,* Aëtius, and his young cadet Majorian, actually interrupted a happy family reunion – young Cerdic's marriage, or at least betrothal. For Cerdic had been freed as a hostage by Attila on the latter's receiving Honoria the Whore's love letter, and had found his way to Flanders. Majorian thought it funny to carry off Cerdic's bride – a sixteen-year-old cuckolds a fifteen-year-old – and Cerdic fled back East to Attila. But the wedding guest of honour fell right into Aëtius' hands: this was John-George-Tybald, no less.

It was to Galla's clemency that John owed his life and pardon. Aëtius would have done his Roman duty, even against his brother, but Galla had mercy on the young, or rather not-so-young mother. 'Pelagia the penitent' knew how to be merciful to unwonted mothers – hadn't she been expelled to Constantinople for just this? Eugenia should be allowed to rear her son (John II *Pompeius* 'Riothamus'*), at least until he was weaned. John, also apparently chastened, might return to Britain as a private citizen, but should keep out of Gaul. So 437 saw John and Eugenia back at Glastonbury, quietly farming and evangelising. They were not destined to be left in peace for more than three years, for in 440 the Council summoned him from retirement to advise them on the Saxon problem.

I said that Attila and Bleda, with their Huns, were then milling around Saxony, ostensibly under Aëtius' control. Huns were not naturally kind to Saxons – or indeed anybody. The Saxons had been pouring across the North Sea to their cousins in fat fertile East Anglia. They left as refugees; they arrived as unsolicited federates, ready to become invaders if thwarted. John was now fifty-seven, maimed, humiliated, civilianised. No more, for him, the red spear ('Peredur') of a 'Cat-tigirn'. John counselled appeasement, and the Council agreed. A conference was summoned to discuss a treaty with the Saxons – the famous 'Night of the Long Knives'* – with partition of some sort on the Agenda; yet another 'Rufinus-style' solution, as it were. The Saxons played it dirty, and negotiations were broken off. Now the Saxons burst into outright civil war and devastated Britain westwards to the Irish Sea. Terrified, the rump of the Council turned to John yet again, to negotiate the best peace he could. The result was dire. The Saxons agreed to take virtually the whole of Eastern Britain; Deira, plus whatever the Southern Picts hadn't already taken of Bernicia; Elmet and Lindsey westward to the Pennines; East Anglia, Kent and Middlesex, save London which was to remain a free city. So fell Britannia in AD442,* leaving British 'Romania' as what might be called the 'Celtic Fringe'.

John himself decided to carve out a 'Kingdom' for himself West of the Severn, in what would be called after him Gwrtheyrnion (Salop, Powys, Brecon, Buillt, Dyfed). To him in 446 came Germanus, now fully apprised of all the terrible events. There Germanus solemnly excommunicated, cursed and banished John from human society. There Germanus yet again carried off the progeny of miscegenation (John Riotham), and sent Eugenia off to her final retirement. John Cassian had been dead for over ten years, but his double Convent of St Victor at Marseilles flourished. The women's section was across the harbour from St Victor, right in the 'Red Light' area. Fallen women to be saved by the bucketful. Marseilles needed cleaning up. On Germanus' advice Eugenia was sent there, and there she would die in the aura of sanctity.*

Old Germanus still cut a lot of ice among the Brits. Faced with this total ostracism, John fled across the sea to Brittany, initially as St *Maledictus* 'Maudez', the accursed; as *Cunomorus* 'Comorre' the accursed; as Bluebeard; but later, as wind of his penitence got around, as St Paul Aurelian and many other saintly names*. He would work his passage slowly back to forgiveness, to respect, to veneration even. Seems there's no one Jesus can't do something with, if the spirit is willing. Thank God I'm a Christian* – and that, I think, I owe to Dad.

Coming back to my own life, after following poor old John like 'Don Giovanni' to the gates of Hell and back, in 434 I was *Comes Domesticorum et Cura Palatium* at Ravenna, following in the family footsteps. I saw quite a bit of Empress Galla, still mourning tetchily for Boniface; I saw even more of her son and daughter Valentinian III and Honoria, in their new palace just down the road which I also had to guard. Valentinian was by this time a spotty fifteen-year-old, while Honoria was a delectable sixteen. When she was nine, and on a visit to Paris, Germanus had blessed her and encouraged her to take the veil when she got a bit older. He didn't live to see that day, but I just have. Petite, with soft fluffy brown hair, white skin, sparkling eyes: she was a real handful, I can tell you. She climbed all over the *Silentarii*, telling them how handsome they were. She climbed all over me. Did we have another Doxy on our hands? Worse yet, I had her in my bed. I see now why they recommend eunuchs for palace duties. Self-protection really. So I was sacked, or at least hastily transferred to combatant duties. Honoria was sent off in disgrace to her 'pious' Aunties in New Rome – that's Pulcheria, Arcadia and Marina – and there she was to give birth to my natural son **'Childeric'** ('King' of the *'Scheldt'** as you'll all remember him). Galla said she wouldn't speak to me ever again, and I had quite a bit of explaining to do to my own Asturia.

My combatant duties took me back to Aëtius' side in the Pfalz. The Burgundians were misbehaving there. Some 'Federates' they! Aëtius thought the best thing was to move them right away from the Rhine. If they couldn't keep the Riparian Franks out, maybe the best thing to do was to let them in, in place of the Burgundians. So, as usual with Attila, Bleda and their trusty Rent-a-Huns, we fought and smashed the Burgundians, and I was deputed to lead them South and settle them in Savoy. They would move further South in time, reaching Arles in the end and founding a powerful duchy. It was at this time that Honoria sent her provocative love letter, with an engagement ring and a lock of hair, to Attila. Whatever would come of this?

Aëtius continued to dash about, 'firefighting'. Now it was Bagaudic unrest in Armorica; now the Vizi-Goths playing up in Narbonensis; now his very own Huns misbehaving in the Auvergne. I was always with him. When up North, I used to slip over to see Dad, and at that time found him very mellow. He was deep in his 'Philosophy' (Science, or even Alchemy as he said the Arabs called it). 'My dear son,' he said, 'I think I can see my way even beyond Doc Heron. He was going to demonstrate the Incarnation in a test-tube. I'm on my way to displaying the whole Trinity of *Energy*, *Matter*, and *Gas*. "Three is One and One is Three". Athanasius was right. Plato was right. Parmenides was right. *One* is *All*. 'Εν το Παν.'

'I'm a simple soldier, Dad,' I said. 'You know I can't follow you when you go on like this.'

'But you *must*, my boy, you must. You'll be the custodian of my copy of the *Liber Gradalis*; you'll be the keeper of the Holy Grail after my death.* Even if you can't understand, you must at least preserve it. Bury the two books with me, in their covers;* my book, and old Eucheria's *Book of Mary.** I've left some other evidences, too, for those who come after with open eyes. Back to the tricks old Onesimus taught me on the Nile so long ago. I want you to come with me to the Isle of Man. There, I've got something to show you.'

It was misty Autumn when we set out for the delightful island, but Dad amazed me, the way he put to sea in the haze. 'Is this blind faith, Dad? Or have you got something up your sleeve?'

'Faith be damned,' he said. 'Come and see what I've got in the cabin. I call it a 'compass'; an idea of Uncle Theo's I've worked up. Years ago I wrote about the lodestone* which always points North. I've tied one onto a piece of wood floating in a saucer and now I always know where I am, even in a fog.'

That's how we came safely to the Northern harbour (Ramsay bay), and were soon at Dad's monastery (St Maughold's).

'Tomorrow,' he said, 'we'll go off to the South end of the Island; that's where I want to initiate you.' So we sailed to the South-Western harbours, and a little further, and there, just offshore, lay a little islet, as it were a calf* to its mother cow. 'Here I've spent some of my Lenten Retreats,' said Dad. 'I've brought John here too. Not Germanus, though. He's too prim. When you've seen and *understood* this you'll know what Jesus meant in John III.5–10. Wasn't He talking to Nicodemus the Arimathean?* Am I, too, a *Master in Israel*? Even if what I've just told you goes over your head, initiates of the future will find chasms of meaning in it. So, one day, may you.'

Dad took me into a little chapel on a hillside where was an altar with a reredos behind of carved slate. All quite small. 'What do you see, my Gawain?' he asked.

'I see Christ crucified upon the Cross,' said I, 'with the soldier with the spear piercing His right side and the sponge-bearer reaching up towards His left. He looks very strange, though. I thought the soldiers had stripped him of all his

**Figure 42**
'St David's Magic Altar'...
© Manx National Heritage

clothes. Yet he's wearing some sort of hieratical garment with rich designs; and He's got some sort of fantastic ornament on his chest. Is it a Jewish High Priest's Ephod?'

'Not bad for a first look,' said Dad. 'Now let me mark in some of the designs with these coloured leads which I've brought with me. Then you shall see the pictures speak,* even as they used to speak to the initiates in the Egyptian Temples. Then you shall see more than they could teach me even at Eleusis. Watch carefully, my Gawain, stage by stage.'

Here Dad outlined for me the brazier or *καμηνιον*, in *white*, and the flames or *φωτας* in red, constituting the first 'muance'.

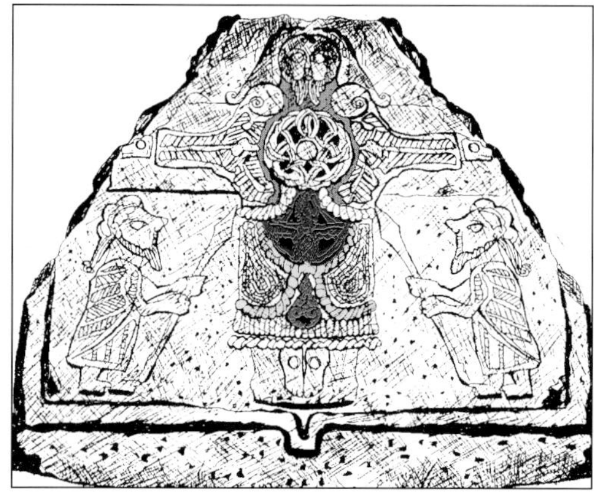

**Figure 43**
...of the five 'muances' (Nos 1 and 2)

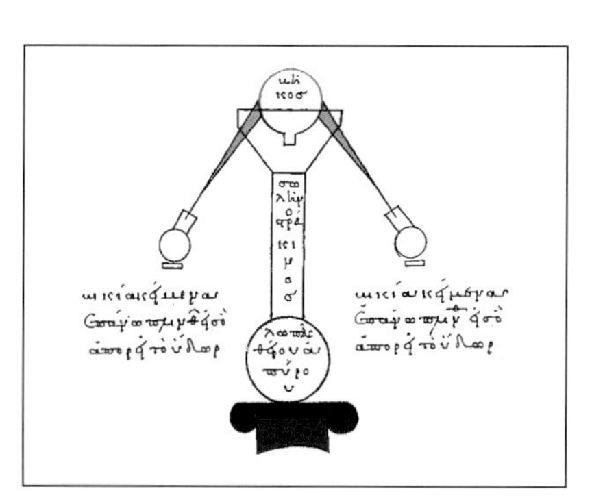

**Figure 44**
Zosimus' 'Dibikos'

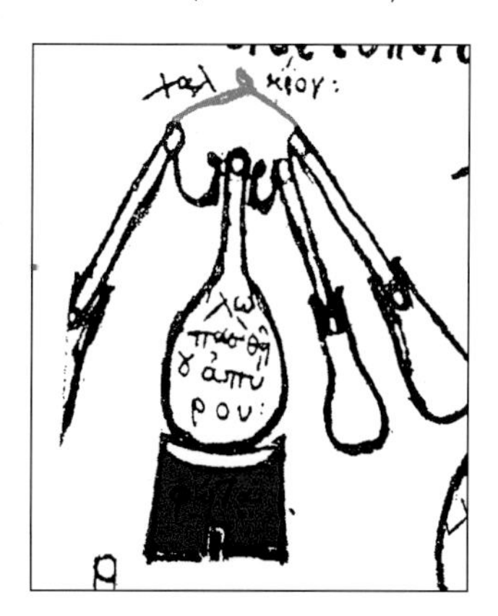

**Figure 45**
Zosimus' 'Tribikos'...

The Calf of Man Crucifixion is already illustrated at Plate 15, and Fig. 42. As will there be seen, most of the right hand side is missing. My artist has therefore prepared a line drawing, shown as Fig. 43, in which the right hand side has been restored as a mirror image of the left. If we then extend the two spears, the resemblance to the *Διβικος* from Marciana MS 299 (Fig. 44) is most striking. But this is far from the whole story, as the Clonmacnoise Crucifixion sufficiently indicates. There are two more *διβικοι* also in the Marciana text, and not glossed, at p.193 of the same Codex, and, *highly relevant to what follows*, there is a *τριβικος* Fig. 46 adjacent, ascribed by Zosimus to Maria the Jewess. Fig. 60 has therefore been so prepared by my artist as to restore the right hand side on the lines of the Clonmacnoise* example (see p.328 in the Commentary), so that the whole operation of the 'tribikos' for the purpose of fractional distillation or sublimation may be grasped.

He went on to outline in *white* the *φυαλη* or phial poised above the brazier on a conical chimney. This constituted the second 'muance'.

'What's the funny little object like a toad, above Jesus' feet and below the brazier?' I ventured to ask.

'Just the bellows, you fool,' said Dad, ever the practical metallurgist of Book VI. 'However else can you expect to make the *twankie dillo* glow?'

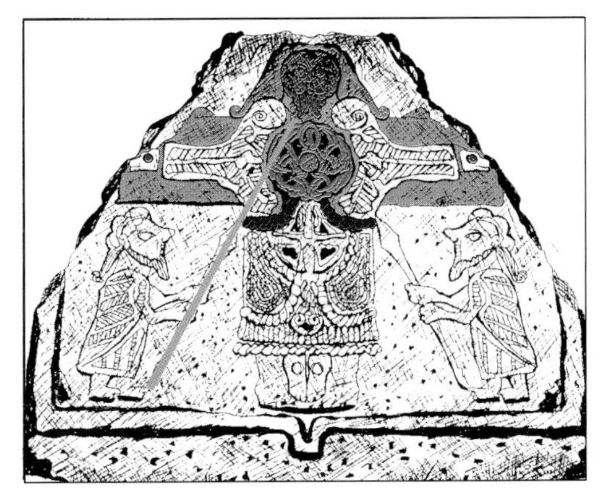

**Figure 46**

... in five 'muances'; here No. 3

Now Dad outlined the phial again, held just above the ceramic chimney or *σωλην ὀστρακινος* by a great wooden crossbeam or *πηκτος*. But this time he added a bell-shaped copper stillhead or *ἀμβιξ χαλκιος* on top, which he said Mary rather cheekily called a *μασταριον* because it somewhat resembled a bosom. To complete this third 'muance' he completed in red and extended the left-hand spearholder.

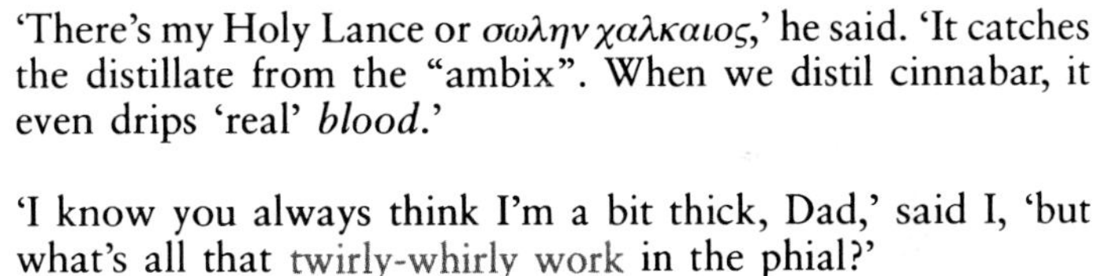

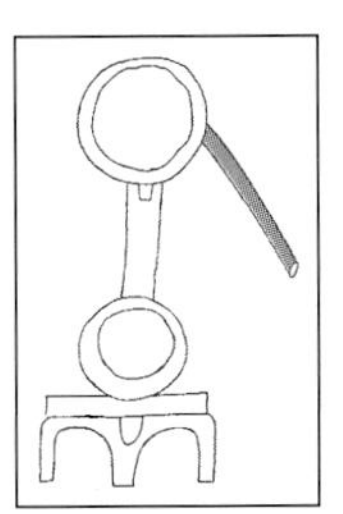

**Figure 47**

A Still...

'There's my Holy Lance or *σωλην χαλκαιος*,' he said. 'It catches the distillate from the "ambix". When we distil cinnabar, it even drips 'real' *blood*.'

'I know you always think I'm a bit thick, Dad,' said I, 'but what's all that twirly-whirly work in the phial?'

'That's Cleopatra's "dragon" devouring himself, like the "Fenris Wolf". I've shown his head, too, peeping out of the left-hand end of the crossbeam. When he's finished *digesting* the ingredients we place in his heated stomach, they'll ascend as *πνευμα* or gas into the "ambix" – which here stands in for *ὁ ὀυρανος* or *Heaven*.'

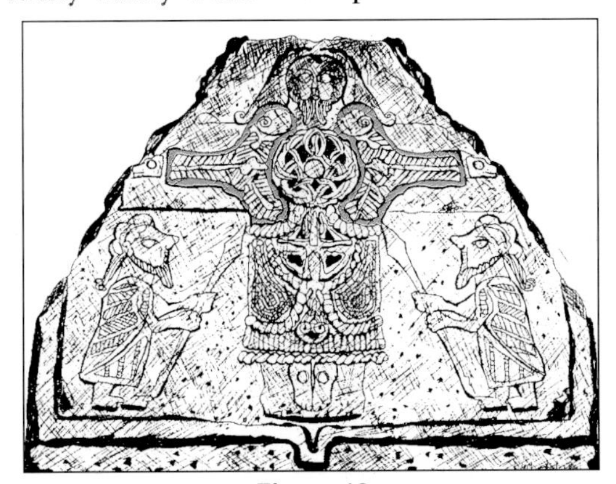

**Figure 48**

... here 'muance' 4

'Go on, then, Dad, I'm enjoying this. Why's He got such funny shoulders and pectorals in your picture?'

'To explain that I'll need a fourth "muance",' said Dad. 'Don't you think the phial's likely to topple over unless we give it some cunning insulated and padded brackets λωπαστηροι, to rest in?'

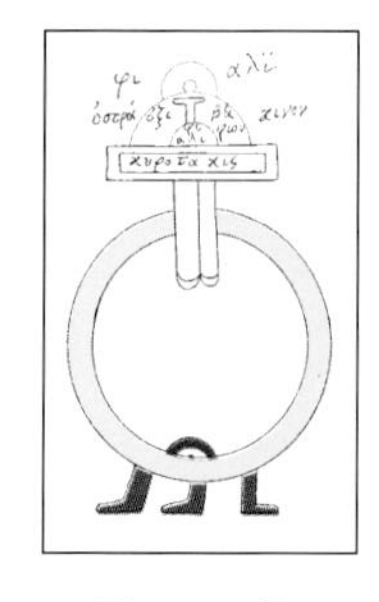

Figure 49
Ambix or 'Aludel'?

The working of the 'dibikos' has now been amply demonstrated, and it is time to turn to the concurrent activity of the 'tribikos'. The whole explanation is from Zosimus in the *Liber Gradalis*. All that is necessary is to 'make the pictures speak', and this we will continue to attempt.

Dad's fifth and last 'muance' was a bit beyond me. At long last the right-hand spearholder came into his own, with his 'sponge' held right up to Jesus' mouth.

'Forget all the other markings,' said Dad, 'and just concentrate on His head.'

'Looks rather like a turnip, Dad,' said I. 'And I don't much fancy His two "kiss-curls".'

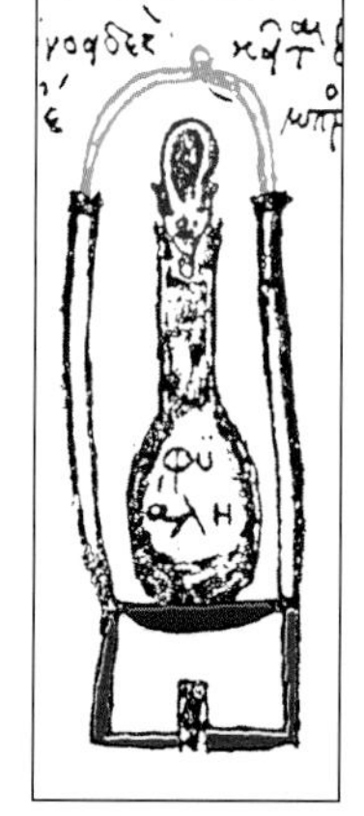

Figure 50
'Cosmic egg'?

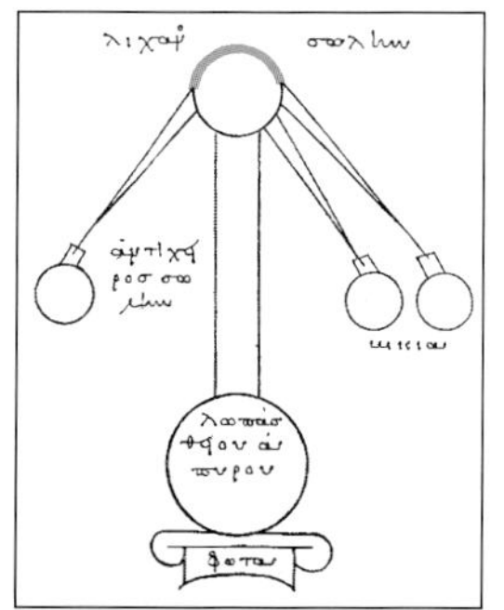

Figure 51
'Tribikos'...

'I'll outline the "turnip" in red,' said Dad, 'because it really should be made of glazed ceramic refractory. It's a pierced hollow stopper or plug; my Arab successors will call it an "aludel". The two "curls" are the inner lip which turns the heavier condensed sublimate, which lodges therein, back down to the "spearholder's" funnel. What's he catching then, my Gawain? **The salt of the God Jupiter Ammon**, no less. Useful stuff, *Sal Ammoniac*!'

Figure 52
... the fifth and last 'muance'

So I watched, and so I saw, even as it is described in the Great Book (Irish, *Cuilmenn*), and maybe I even saw the Holy

Trinity itself in five 'Muances'.* I might have understood more if I'd only had the nous, and the courage, to ask the right questions,* but then, unlike my brother John-George, I was never an Ocean College man. Maybe he would do better when his turn came.

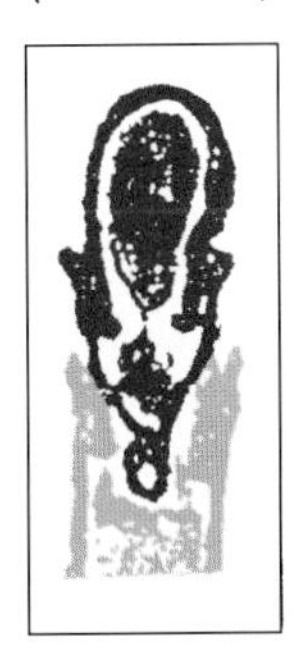

**Figure 53**
Zosimus' 'stopper'

So ended my enthralling lesson in applied chemistry. There was just one question I was burning to ask, but I knew Dad thought I should have 'twigged' already, and would be hugely disappointed if I only asked now. I'm only a simple soldier. I'll try asking you instead. **What on earth has all this to do with Jesus?**

Alchemical symbols, from the *Liber Gradalis*, or Holy Grail. QED.

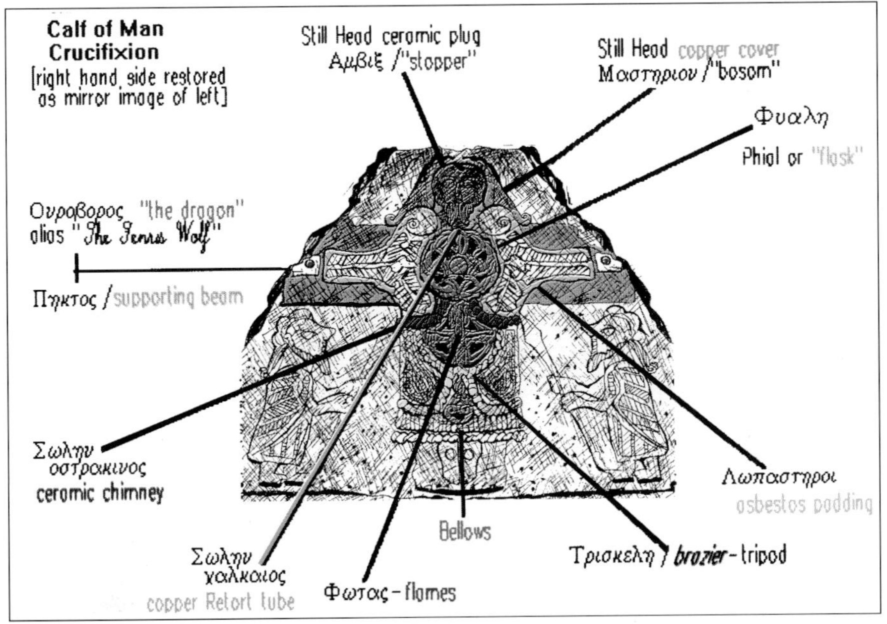


**Figure 54**
'Εν to Παν: Three in One, and One in Three

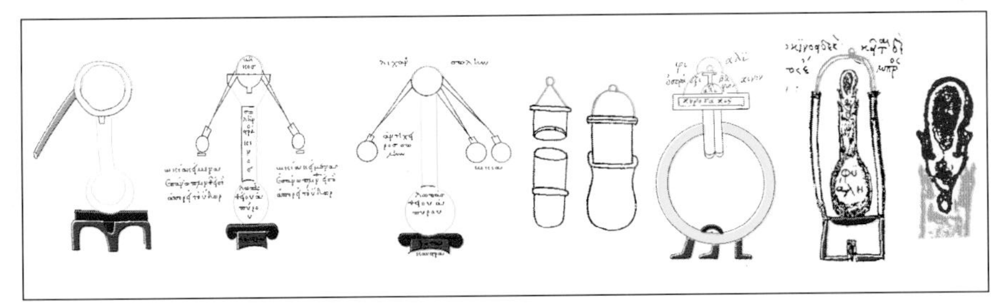

**Figure 55**
The Holy Grail revealed

Anyhow, we washed off the red and white lead, and left the slab for those with eyes to see, and we rowed back to the Island; and there it remains.*

I could not help noticing that Dad was in great trouble with what the Authorised Version will call his 'reins'. Old man's disease, combined with lesions from past infections and wounds. His attendant, one of his novices, helped him regularly by passing a hollow reed as a catheter, but even this was starting to cause him much agony. I felt really sorry for him.

'If you really want to help me, dear boy,' he said, 'take advantage of your next posting to the East – you must surely be due for one – to go to the Swan Convent and try to get me some ether. Either that, or obtain for me the formula and apparatus for making it. It's not much fun having the 'Sacred Lance' passed up my most intimate parts as things are at present. I begin to long for the end of it all. Be quick for me if you can.'

In the event I was not very quick, but neither was I too late; for don't forget that, like my brother, I too am 'Perceval' (Parzifal) a son of 'Doxy/Persē. Between then and Dad's death I haven't got a lot to tell you. It's his story I'm telling, and, apart from the John fracas, his old age was peaceful, and apart from all the pain, serene. His old loves, and his old enemies were all gone. That happens. Did he still think of Galla, and did she think of him? I, for one, didn't feel it was my duty, while I was still around the Palace, to tell her that her second husband was still alive. '*Ora favē*,' we Romans say: 'make a favourable noise with your mouth'. Vulgarly, 'keep your trap shut'.

My brother Aëtius went on from strength to strength and Consulate to Consulate. In 437 he celebrated his second Consulate, to be crowned with the singular honour of a special Statue and inscription* in the innermost courtyard of the Curia – the *Atrium Libertatis* – witnessing the grateful thanks of the Senate, and also of Galla and Valentinian III. Inevitably he went on in 446 to his third Consulate. Barring Marius 532 years earlier, no private citizen before has ever had the prestige *and* the money to take this on. In Britain John got into ever increasing difficulties with his sex life and with the Saxons, as I told you above, and shortly before his final ostracism in 446 he, with Dad's support, persuaded the Council to send yet another appeal for military help. Aëtius was a bit cool about this. It was years since the Brits had paid tribute, and they were rolling in money. Let them get themselves out of their own hole. However he did suggest to Germanus, twice already the rescuer of Britain, that he might pop over and give them some fatherly advice, and not just theological.

Germanus came, with his son Germanianus, also (like so many of us) called Aurelius Ambrosius, and currently Duke of Armorica and the Nervican Tract. Bishop Germanus returned to Armorica while his son stayed on and did what he could. One of the things he did, which in an unexpected way was to bear rich fruit for Britain and for England, was to bring a young officer of his called Cerdic to Britain to meet his supposed grandfather – not just supposed, actual – Ursula was Dad's eldest daughter. It was his own father Aëtius *Eleutherus* (Uther) that Cerdic couldn't remember. Following the flight from his abortive wedding, Cerdic had been received coolly by Attila, had found his way back to Germanianus in Armorica and had joined the army. He was a bright young man, if a bit uneducated. He wanted to know more of his family, and Dad was the right man to tell him.

So it came about that at Christmas 446 young Cerdic, with only one half of his paternal grandfather's signet ring (i.e. JJ's ring, inherited from Doxy via Morgan), as the time-honoured recognition token, turned up at Cardiff for the 'Aventure of the Sword in the Stone'. I was an eye-witness, because I'd managed to make it back with my precious phial of ether. If I tell you the sword's name was '*Gram*', Sigurd's (ie. JJ's) sword in the Volsunga Saga, and that 'Gramma' is Greek for 'Word' not 'sWord', I think you'll have it all. The sWord had to be 'drawn' from a (gem)stone set in an 'anvil' (corrupted from Latin *annulus*, a ring). In other words, only he whose *signum* was engraved on the reunited ring could claim to be the rightful future 'King of Britain'. Dad, as Merlin, was just the man to validate young Cerdic's claims; indeed, thanks to Merlin, Cerdic would eventually be King Arthur, 'Hammer of the Scots', reconciler of the Saxons, and founder of the House of Wessex.*

Dad was overjoyed to meet his grandson, thus, in his old age. I think, with his prophetic gifts, he could see the young man's future greatness. He did all he could, in a few short days, to initiate him into the secrets of the Holy Grail, to prepare him for his hereditary role as Galahad II. I'm afraid, like me, it mostly washed over Cerdic's head. Uncouth and forest-educated, he too failed to ask the right questions. These things can't be hurried. One has to reach 'years of discretion' before one can usefully be initiated. Still, Dad sowed the seed there. All that was left for him to do was die, and his last Lent was only weeks away. Brothers Anthony and Basil have already written that story for you.

All I'll add is my own soldier's tribute to him; fittingly, in 'Gothic' slow march tempo:

**Réxne quúmdam sápientíssimus,**

**Réxque futúrus opínatíssimus,**

**Hic jácet Artúrus ínclutíssimus.**

But the '*hic jacet*' bit must await this, my final postscript.

For, while my brother Aëtius was anxiously mobilising to face the invasion of Gaul by Attila and all his Huns, Galla sang out her '*Liebestod*' in Ravenna, the full last measure of her love for her last and greatest Tristan. She had ruled the Western Empire for twenty-five years.

She had made it abundantly clear that she did not wish to rest in her own mausoleum in Ravenna, alongside her detested husband Constantius, and her hardly less disliked brother Honorius, nor did she or the other two long remain there. It was Aëtius, returning mournfully the following year from his historic victory of Châlons-sur-Marne, who persuaded Valentinian to bury her in the Imperial Mausoleum in Milan.

And I must claim the credit for exhuming Dad from Glastonbury and placing him alongside Galla, his last and greatest love and 'bestest Guinevere'. There, in this Year of Grace AD453 they lie forever intertwined.

**Figure 56**
Galla and Merlin ... at peace in Milan

***Explicit vita Merlin***

11 Elissa's tomb at Agaunum

12 John George, as Daniel, King Brude and St Regulus

13 John-George ‘realised’ by Arthur Hughes

Courtesy of National Museums & Galleries on Merseyside

14 Aëtius yet guards Bremen and Saxony
Courtesy of Bildarchiv Foto Marburg

15 St David's Magic Altar of the speaking pictures Courtesy of Manx National Heritage

16 The Arms of Merlin
Courtesy of The Heraldry Society

17 Claudian's inscription as Poet Laureate

Courtesy of Soprintendenza Archaeologica delle Province di Napoli e Caserta

18 Aëtius' inscription as 'Siegfried'

Courtesy of Istituto Archeologico Germanico, Roma

# COMMENTARY FOR THE CURIOUS

**Important:** Opening references (eg 153.5) are to the page where the **key phrase** quoted appears (and where it is followed in the text by an *). Where there is more than one such reference to the Commentary on a text page, they are numbered serially; hence the above illustration refers to the 5th asterisked Note on page 153.

xxiii.1 **amazing Placidia** Scholars will expect to find Professor Stewart Oost's 'Galla Placidia Augusta' 1968 in the Bibliography. But I have deliberately included only works cited, hence Oost's famous work, being wholly secondary, wins no place. Moreover, his adoption of E. Stein's c.1925 anti-Aëtius interpretation needs re-evaluation in the light of A. Bartoli's 1946 discovery of the Aëtius inscription, and even of his own student F. Clover's groundbreaking study on Merobaudes. Both these latter are deservedly in the Bibliography.

Notwithstanding, Oost's anxious apology

> 'To my knowledge there is in English no full-length account of her life ... In attempting to supply this omission I have been *painfully aware of the omissions and lacunae in our sources*; it is for this reason, to give the reader fair warning ahead of time, that I have subtitled this interpretation '***A Biographical Essay***'. In trying to put together and explain the scattered and disparate data that survive concerning Galla Placidia I have found myself obliged to construct *bridges of inference* to a degree *well beyond what is customary in other areas of history* where the evidence is much thicker, as it were'

could as justly have been written by the present author, despite the ampler range of primary sources utilised by him.

1.1 **born** No evidence on this. St David's Day, 1 March, has been arbitrarily selected for reasons which will only become fully obvious in Book IX. See also p. 94.

1.2 **Babylon-on-Nile** Apollinaris Sidonius, Carm IX l.274, gives Canopus in a poetic sense, perhaps generic for Egypt. I have utilised Canopus at page 1 but have preferred Babylon here with reference to Pickford in Loomis (1959) p. 348.

1.3 **short head** Hence Wolfram in his *Parzival* will call him 'Protesilaus'.

1.4 **Gratiana** Gratiana III, 'Little Mother' was Magnus Maximus' daughter by Grata Valentia Marciana his first wife, herself the sister of Valentinian I, Augustus.

1.5 **Gilvus** This '*Gil*' prefix – the root, as in *yel*-low – occurs in Bartrum (1966) as Gil-das, Gilfaethwy; in Spence (1913) as Gil-bert (1) and Gilla Dacar (2); in Amadis de Gaula as Cil-dadan. All are Merlin, save Gilbert who is his son Vassonius Gellianus, of whom much more in due course.

1.6 **Tussock ... of hair** The Brothers Grimm in Sagen No. 424 tell that the Merovingians were once called 'the hairy ones' because they had a brush of hair up the middle of their backs like the wild boar. We may here have an allusion to the *signum* of the XX *Legio Valeria Victrix*. The Grimms' source here is Theophanes Confessor, writing in his monastery on the southern shore of Sea of Marmora, about the time of Charlemagne's coronation AD 800. He supplies this information about Charlemagne's rather dubious ancestors, using *χριστaται* and *τριχοραχαται* for 'hairy ones'. Sagen 424 goes on to recount the begetting of Merovech by a 'sea monster something-like-a-bull', beneath which we may discern 'Meroveus' and Comm. p. 268, 32.1, 'Taurianus among the Roman names of Gilbert II and his father, Merlin. Gilbert II himself will be more easily recognised as Gawain II (Welsh *Gwalch mai* – the Sparrow Hawk) – see Text, p. 241.

**Figure 57**
Meroveus the Taurocamp

1.7 **Carpilio** From Latin, *capillus*, hair. Our authority here is Renatus Profuturus Frigeridus apud Gregory of Tours II.7. I have assumed that the intrusive 'r' results either from scribal corruption, or else a barbarising provincial spelling. The Romance trouvères confused this with *Capreolus*, a Roe-buck. Hence the reference in Grimms' Sagen No. 538 to the hind (Nitonia Marcella Carpilia Ursula) who wet-nurses Siegfried's (and her own) son Carpilio II (Cerdic/Arthur) in the Ardennes. We shall come up with them there in time.

2.1 **quite a story** As her family background is of such continuing relevance I should clarify this nickname. Her real name was Julia *Aureliana Marcella* (see Appendix 6). From the days when M. Claudius Marcellus defended Syracuse against Hannibal, the *Aurelii-Marcellae* (an illustrious branch of the widespread Aurelian Gens) had owned the best lands of the **heel** (Apulia, which the ancients called *Calydonia*), and the **toe** (Bruttium) of Italy. That's why the road to those parts is called the *Via Aurelia*. The **foot** (*πους*) of Italy naturally faces the 'Αντιπους of Sicily, together with a large part of Eastern Sicily, which, with its adjacent islands, constituted the Antipodes to Graeco-Romans of the time. Hence the legends of 'King Arthur in the Antipodes' to which Loomis 1956 devotes a learned and useful chapter. (The Southern Hemisphere Antipodes were predicted by Crates of Mallus in 150 BC but did not make their debut for another 1800 years).

On Marcella (***Morgan***)'s marriage to Honorius Sr (***Glorious Dad***) some of these properties came to the Marciani, particularly the estates around *Tarentum*, *Rhegium* (Reggio), *Sicilia Peloritana* (around Messina), and a large tract of *Sicilia* ***Ibleia*** called the *Agri Morgantinia*. Thus, by marrying the co-heir of Casa Sic and its surrounding forests, *Marcella Morgantina* became virtual Queen of Eastern Sicily. Hence, Romance authors will remember her sometimes as Queen 'Iblis', more often, wrongly, as '*Morgan la Fée*'. You will learn the true identity of the latter on p. 65.

2.2 **famulus** As I am breaking new scholarly ground here, I give full references. See the article 'Marcian' in Pauly-Wissowa, esp. Nos. 11–12, 18–22, and 25 (in which I agree with Contarelli's conclusions), 27, 29–31 *et al.*

2.3 **Ulpian Gens** This claim occurs not only in Claudian VIII.19 *et al*; it is expressly stated by Sex. Aurelius Victor Jun. *Epitome, apud* Clinton 1850 p. 124. Subsequent confusion of *Trajanic* and **Trojan** descent was a gift to poet and trouvères alike.

3.1 **family trees** See Appendices 1–9.

3.2 **Catacombs** The Marcian crypt and catacombs at San Giovanni, Syracuse, may be seen to this day.

3.3 **Marcianopolis** Now Sumen (Kolorovgrad) Bulgaria.

3.4 **Vicar of Britain** Martin (Ammian XIV.5). For variants of the name Marcian see Pauly-Wissowa: 'Marcian', esp. 11–12.

4.1 **Cousin Julian** See Appendix 1 for the relationship.

4.2 **Godfather Basil** If, as is likely, the names of St Basil's sister and of his grandmother (Macrian) indicate kinship to the Marcian families the proposed relationship of godfather is not implausible. His brother St Gregory of Nyssa was named, like so many of the leading Cappadocian Christians of those days, after the famous St Gregory 'the wonder-worker' of Neocaesarea (Niksar), also just in Cappadocia. Finally, Basil's sister-in-law was Theosebea, whose brother Zosimus of Panoplis – if it is surely he – by writing the forerunner of Marciana MS 299, is of major importance to the history of **alchemy**, and thus to the main thrust of this book (see Comm., p. 286, 99.2).

4.3 ***excrementum*** Translated by Farrar (1907), Vol. II, p. 20.

4.4 ***Dies Lustricus*** Baptismal and Naming Day. Egbert (1896) p. 84 cites Festus, Plutarch, and, appropriately, Macrobius.

5.1 **Christian Padre** Thirty years later it certainly had its own Bishop/chaplain (one Apion) who signs a petition as such in AD391 to Theodosius I. 'Leyden Papyrus Z', in Leemans (1885) t.II, *apud* Berthelot (1888), Vol. I, p. 8.

5.2 **theologian** See esp. Farrar (1907), Vol. I, pp. 248–341. Cyprian lauded infant baptism, and infant reception of the eucharistic elements; the bishop as viceroy of Christ by apostolic succession; sacramental efficacy *ex opere operato* – that is, irrespective of the intent of the recipient – but only by the hands of an ordained Catholic minister for *extra ecclesiam nulla salus*. There was only one Holy Catholic Church in his day. Unsurprisingly, he stoutly opposed the supremacy of the Bishop of Rome (Stephen), as Basil later opposed Damasus.

5.3 **Cousin** Conjecture from Commentary 4.2 'Basil' above.

5.4 **Theodore** All that is written of him here and later comes from Tillemont (1701), Vol. V, p. 107 and p. 702, and from Eunapius *apud* Clinton (1845), Vol. I, p. 361, col. 3. The relationship is my own informed conjecture, based on the totality of the research underlying this book. Scholars are invited to keep an open mind at this stage.

5.5 **Maximus** Later self-styled 'Heron', by which name we will henceforward refer to him to avoid confusion with Magnus Maximus. Cynic philosopher and magician. If, as I prefer, we are to believe him the same as the bogus Patriarch of Constantinople who bamboozled first St Gregory Nazianzus, and then St Ambrose at the Synod of Aquileia, we must assume he eluded the death penalty in AD372 (See Clinton (1845), Vol. I, p. 479, col. 3 and Tillemont (1701), V, p. 110.) Otherwise we must assume two contemporary 'Christian philosophers' of the same name and the same Houdini-like character, which seems unnecessary.

5.6 **Eucheria** See Appendix 1. See also Commentary, p. 273, 53.1. For both of them it was their second marriage.

6.1 **Casa Sicelis** I have taken the name, as best I can read it, from the masseur's loincloth in the Palaestra mosaic (Room 13 on the 'Villa Casale of Piazza Armerina' plan).

6.1 **Palace** This suggestion neatly resolves the apparently conflicting witness of Ammian and Chrysostom, set out in Tillemont (1701), V, p. 702.

6.3 **Morgantina** Former home of the fierce 'Morgetēs'; a Greek city (brilliantly identified on the shoulder of the Sierra Orlando by the late Kenan Erim, and excavated by King Gustav of Sweden and the Princeton expedition), which named its whole locality.

6.4 **Eucherius** Refugee in Britain c.375–9. Restored to favour by Theodosius I. Consul 381. Praetorian Prefect of the East 384. (See Clinton (1850), Vol. II, p. 124).

**Figure 58**
'Casa Sic' masseur
© Edizioni Poligraf

7.1 **picture** Which can still be seen in room 21.

7.2 **Maximian's wing** Rooms 20–4 and 26–8.

7.3 **Milan** Still visible in her mausoleum, now in the chapel of San Aquilino, within San Lorenzo in the Palace.

7.4 **Apollonius** 'Apollonius of Tyre' (*Gesta Romanorum*, Cap. 153). I shall revert frequently to this *Geste*, from which Shakespeare has drawn his 'Pericles'. Since most readers will own a Shakespeare, I will not epitomise it here.

7.5 **Family album** See Loomis (1959), p. 68 re. Arthurian 'pictures' as a feature of Morgan's palace. He gives the underlying references.

7.6 **Hippolytus** Schismatic Bishop of Ostia c. AD220. His statue is in the Vatican Gregorian Museum. This reference is to his 'Refutation of all Heresies', the so-called *Philosophumena*, Bk. IV, 32 and 35. (*Encyclopaedia Britannica* XI text articles 'Hippolytus' and 'Conjuring').

8.1 **Marcians on the Mother's Side** See Appendix 2.

8.2 **Maximianus** Geoffrey of Monmouth (HRB) always calls him Maximian. Gildas (Cap 13–14) calls him Maximus. Nennius (HB) jumps both ways in Caps 26, 27, 29 when the same Emperor is clearly intended. It is not easy to doubt that his full name is Maximianus Maximus. We find this confirmed in Tillemont (1701), Vol V, pp. 55–8 who gives us the facts as I have used them, mostly from the reliable Ammian. 'Maximus' is a Roman military title, as we find in Eusebius, xvii, 5. See Williamson, 1965: 'Edict of the three Augusti of AD308, where Galerius has held 11 local "maximus-ships".' It would well suit a Roman Military Vicarate of this period, implying that the Vicar was authorised to, and qualified to, command troops. I have used it accordingly. 'Maximian' is the evident root of (Welsh) 'Macsen'. Suddenly we know a lot about 'Macsen Wledig'.

9.1 **Basil and Anthony** Blaise and Antoine of the '*Prophecies de Merlin*', per Loomis (1959), p. 352 and of course Paton (1926). The other three scribes may be taken as allusions to Merlin himself, and it may be to Merlin himself ('David the harpist') that the Irish High Crosses will owe their fixation with the Desert Saints.

12.1 **Dispargum** *Not* Duisburg on the Rhine. As so often, Tillemont (1701, V, p. 639) is right. See also text p. 230.

12.2 **Celtic (i.e. Doric Greek)** The received view is well summarised in Chadwick, N. (1970), pp. 43–6, where the divergence from standard Greek is assumed to be prehistoric. But neither Caesar (*Bellum Gallicum*, I.1), nor Tacitus (*Germania*, Cap. 3) should be overlooked. Moreover, surviving Celtic placenames indicate that the version they spoke was akin to Doric.

12.3 **Dual Title** One thinks of Fritigern, and later most notably Alaric for the Goths; and even, incredibly, Attila for the Huns.

12.4 **'The Stranger from the Elbe'** 'Albis Hostis' (Teutonised) is the best attempt I can make at this name. A later barbarian, Andragath, is plainly 'Ανηρ ἀγαθος. But if we look for 'Arbogast' in Greek, we get 'of the dainty stomach'. Not very promising.

12.5 **Little Mother married him** See Bartrum (1966) p. 130, n. 14, on which I base this statement, reading 'Gratiana (III) Arbogasta' for 'Gratian Aurbost'. That she is Magnus Maximus' daughter and that she has been married to *Tudwal I ap Morfawr* (Honorius Sr, 'Glorious Dad', *Keeper of the Wall*) is also here confirmed.

13.1 **Count of the Saxon Shores** Presumably Count Nectaridus who Ammian says was killed in the troubles of AD367. The command at this time covered both the Northern and Southern shores. 'Dad' is Honorius Sr, eldest brother of Theodosius I the Great, father of Serena. See Zosimus V, 4.2 and Claudian himself, *Serenae* l.96 (*apud* Clinton (1850) p. 125). He would be a bit young to have succeeded Nectaridus, but could well have served under him. The thrust of this book is to identify him with Llŷr Morini of the Welsh genealogies (see Bartrum 1966) where he appears as Marini, and a connection with the Pas-de-Calais, where the tribe of the Morini were located in Caesar's day, would not be inapt. Is he not Chaucer's 'Sir Topaz (T. Ulpius) of Poperinghe'?

13.2 **Patricius** There is no direct evidence that he held this honour, but it would be very likely in an officer of his rank and background entrusted with so great a responsibility. I choose to credit it.

13.3 **The Mounth** Welsh Mynydd, Latin *mons*, the first 'y' being pronounced as in 'bun'. Jackson has pointed out (*apud* Thomas 1981, p. 74) that British Latin, as surviving in inscriptions and via Welsh, 'would have come from the speech of an educated or conservative reservoir of society ... perhaps upper-class and "haw-haw".' Assuming, therefore, that 'top Romans' pronounced Latin *on* with a short clipped 'u', '*mons*' would come out as '*muns*'. This applies particularly to proper names like Constantine, often abbreviated in speech to Conan. The Welsh say and write 'Cynan'; the Bretons write it 'Conan' but pronounce it short, as in our own day Cholmondely is pronounced 'Chumley'. Think also of Bromley and Coventry. Most aptly of all, of Conan Doyle. It's a class thing. (In the Welsh genealogies Constantine also appears as Custeint, the 'u' being short as in 'crust'.)

13.4 **put forward** Tacitus, Cap. 24.

13.5 **cousin** Valentinus per Ammian, Zosimus, Jerome *apud* Clinton 1845 p. 472. The relationship is highly probable in the circumstances.

13.7 **Carausius II** Frere (1974, pp. 390, 402) follows Kent (1957) up the blind alley of a *terminal* date of AD358. Some flans and dies for remodelling or overstriking, could still have been available ten years later. The Evans coin (NC s.III(7) 1887, p. 191 *et seq.*) remains an oddity. Sir Arthur Evans' conclusions are undoubtedly too wild, but they are not as stupid as Sutherland (NC 6.5, 1954) suggests. There is room for yet another Carausius (III or IV: see Commentary, p. 300, 153.6), and that will be the point at which to suggest the provenance of these few unique flans. Sutherland is wrong to rely on there being no Caesars after Julian. See Olympiodorus in Clinton (1845), p. 568, which is pertinent in other ways as well. The coins have yet to tell their full story.

14.1 **Patrick's Isle** As much ink has been spilt on the problem of St Patrick as on almost any other issue. Was there more than one St Patrick, and when were they? The current state of play is well reviewed in Thomas (1981) pp. 295–346, and this book supports his preference for a late Patrick, drastically amends his views on St Ninian and postulates an earlier Patrick (not sainted) in Count Theodosius.

14.2 **Middle and Western Hibernia** The southern stronghold, Cashel is Latin *castellum*. Less easily recognisable is the Northern stronghold of 'Emain' Macha (Navan fort by Armagh) until we trace it via Welsh *Amddiffynfa* to Latin *Ambidefensio*, a stronghold. Central, and to be encountered later, is the 'Royal Hall' of Tara. But the Vita S Ruadan gives us its earlier spelling Temorah, mediaeval Irish Temuir, or even 'Teach Miodhchuarta', in which we can recognise the Welsh Ty-Mawr (Great House) from Latin *Tectum Major*, a great covered dwelling or hall.

14.3 **poets or geographers** The references are too numerous to mention. Claudian, aptly, uses it constantly. Ptolemy the geographer also uses it as a matter of course, and Ammian at 21.7.7.

14.4 **implications** The Anglo-Norman Romancers will carefully refer to '*le Roi Artus*', meaning the ruler of the '*arctois*' (the North) – of whom we shall find not a few in these pages. The Welsh will prefer 'Arthur', for '*arcturus*', a significant variant of the foregoing – see next note but one below.

14.5 **Cunedda** For 'Cun', see Comm. p. 261, 13.3. In 'Edda' (Old Welsh '*Edag*', and cf. Icelandic *Edda*) we have a compound of 'Welsh' root '*eti*', offspring, heredity, and '*ach*', race. We find analogues in Irish nomenclature. I read this as meaning '**of the race of Constantius the First, Chlorus**' and therefore applicable to any of his claimed descendants, and this is well confirmed by Bewnans Meryasek (1966).

14.6 **Panegyric** This is conjecture, inspired by Welsh Genealogies. No trace of such a panegyric survives; it would have been a '*gratiarum actio*' in any event. All that I here contend is that **Arthur** may well be poetic shorthand for a **Protector of the North**, and more specifically, as I shall show later, Protector of the **Bear** herself. This disallowed, the name Arthur floats meaningless and unidentified, since I find no link with that L. Artorius Castus on whom other scholars have found a precarious foothold.

15.1 **Pelagius** Latin and Greek 'of the high seas'. We speak of 'offshore', as opposed to coastal, sailors. A pelagian isle was by definition offshore, out of sight of land. Sicily, the Isle of Wight, and the Isle of Man are not 'pelagian'. The Orkneys are; Ireland was, until the establishment of the Valentias.

15.2 **Praeses** This distinction in title of Governor, from the Notitia (Occidentalis I, 120 and cf. 77), gives a valuable clue to the location of the Valentias, on which so much has been written. I am glad that this book does not require me to locate the two Caesarienses. The spade will find the answer one day.

15.3 **Tara** See Comm. p. 262, 14.2, Middle and West Hibernia.

15.4 **Saunas** See Weir (1980) pp. 80, 81. It is not contended that all are of Roman date. Some may be earlier, others surely later. A near-contemporary account is in C. Apollinaris Sidonius, Bk II, 9, to Donidius (Anderson 1936, pp. 458–9).

15.5 **Bomium** See Margary (1957) II, p. 58.

15.6 **Road** Numbering per Antonine Itinerary (Margary, ibid). Now the A48. The college is known nowadays as Llantwit Major; by a quaint coincidence the modern Atlantic College lies two miles to the West.

15.7 **Coleg Theodosius** Caradoc of Llancarfan (*apud* Iolo MSS, 1888, p. 422) is worth quoting here. 'The College of Theodosius, in Caer Worgorn (Vortigern) was not a monastery, but rather an enfranchised school, to exhibit and teach the distinguished knowledge and exalted sciences that were known in Rome...'. Other references in the Iolo MSS make clear that the seven liberal arts, the Trivium and the Quadrivium, are intended.

15.8 **Heliodorus** We know his father's *cognomen* was Theodosius. Socrates (H.Ecc. V.22) makes him c.380 become Bishop of Trikka. I further identify him with the Novatian Bishop of Constantinople 384–95 whose son Chrysanthus II later succeeded him in that office. See Pauly-Wissowa 1894, 'Marcian' 12 (A and B).

15.0 **Dolorous Stroke** In the 'Suite du Merlin', whereby the blight fell on Logres. Loomis (1959) p. 333, etc.

17.1 **AD370** The narrative is from Ammian *apud* Tillemont (1701) V, pp. 55–8.

18.1 **Odometer** A distance-measuring instrument of the *Mensores Decempedatores Gromatici* (Text article E.B. XI Edn). Whence, 'Sir Gromer Somer Jour' of the ME Romance 'The Wedding of Sir Gawain and Dame Ragnell'. A vivid description of the odometer is in the (Irish) 'Wooing of Emer', where Lug (Merlin) makes Cuchulinn (John) run behind the wheel. (As you see, I agree with Rolleston.) All per Loomis (1927) p. 318.

18.2 **Astronomy** Back to Wolfram's *Parzival*, Cap. 9, and much Welsh tradition.

18.3 **Language of Hercules** 'Partholon' himself, or rather themselves. Myceneans from Tiryns, *ὁι παραθολοι*: cf. the incised daggers of Stonehenge (Atkinson 1956, Plate XIIA). They spoke Doric Greek, to judge by the surviving place names.

18.4 **Verrenianus and Didymus** Sozomen calls them 'O*νοριου συγγενεις* from which a later historian has improperly called them 'the sons of Theodosius', to the confusion of all since this is genealogically unacceptable. As Sozomen says, they are cousins-german. Heliodorus looks the best choice as their parent, and this would allow their rather odd actions, best summarised from the sources in Tillemont (1701) p. 555. Freeman (in EHR I, 1886, pp. 65 and 66) admits to floundering here.

19.1 **'Prentice Imitations'** I suggest that these novellae, mistaken for fact, account for some of the trouvères' wilder flights of fancy. Particularly in the *Gesta Romanorum*, in Sir Eglamour of Artois, Guy of Warwick, the Eastern scenes of *Parzival*, but in so many other Romances where hack classical motifs (mostly from Ovid) are dressed in wild Oriental garb. That the trouvères also found much that was fact, this book attempts to show. For example 'Sir Eglamour' is JJ as *Agricola Majorus*, and his son 'Sir Degrabell' is John-George as *Tigernus Bellum* or 'Catigern'. 'Artois' speaks for itself.

19.2 Θολοξ See Commentary p. 263, 18.3. By tradition Partholon was the first invader of Ireland (Nennius H.B., c.13). Partholon's hitherto inexplicable precursor in Irish legend, the 'Lady Caesarea', will be explained by the inscription on Comm. p. 308, 192.2. Irish trouvères have confused Hibernia with Hiberia.

20.1 **Coins ... still there** See Carson and Kelly, Vol 77, C, pp. 35–55.

20.2 **Southern Picts** The 'problem' is discussed by P. Hunter-Blair in *Studies in Early British History (SEBH)* (1954) pp. 166–8, with references. Earlier Scottish scholars had less doubt on the point.

20.3 **Alban's Horse** My conjecture.

20.4 **Honoriani** Shown in the Notitia, Seeck (1876) under the command of the Magistri Equitum Praesentalis, Oc. VI, 60 and Galliarum, Oc. VII, 74 *inter alia*. Some of them are to fight for Constantine III and his son in Spain, AD408.

20.5 **Slav troops** Vandals (Wends). Frere (1974) p. 252.

20.6 **market gardens** Where once stood the church of S. Maria della Porta Fulcorina, 'St Mary of the thieves gate'. An unsavoury area in those days, now fast coming up.

21.1 **at Tours** With deep regret, for she is deservedly one of my heroines, I part company from Norah Chadwick on the Tours issue, and from her followers. The arguments are regurgitated in the 'Whithorn Volume' (Dumfries-Galloway Nat. Hist. and Antiq. Soc. Proc. XXVII, 1950, p. 46 ff.) and Chadwick in *SEBH* (1954) p. 200. N. Chadwick relies too heavily on the negative evidence in the Miracula poem (Levinson in *Antiquity* 1940, pp. 280–91) in rejecting Ailred (AD1154–86) whose testimony is to me convincing. I am glad to have W. D. Simpson on my side. But O. Chadwick (also in *SEBH* 1954) further attempts to demolish Ailred and Simpson on two inadequate counts. First that a 'Martinian' dedication at Whithorn *must* be subsequent to Bp. Perpetuus' dedication of a basilica to him in AD461. His circular conclusion is hardly persuasive, to put it gently. Second, that 'it would be incredible that a visit to Tours before the end of the fourth century should have caused an *immediate* [my italics] dedication of the church. If this were true it would make Whithorn the first church in the West to be dedicated to anyone but a martyr or confessor, which is very unlikely' (Chadwick, p. 181). 'Incredible' has soon waned to 'very unlikely'. Hardly less 'unlikely' (and breaking similar new ground) is that St Severus should have published in AD392/3 a best-selling cult-provoking *Life of St Martin* (the non-martyr, non-confessor as O. Chadwick would have him, carelessly limiting the meaning of the words) well within the Saint's own lifetime. Should Severus have meekly awaited Bp. Perpetuus' *imprimatur* in AD461? I think N. and O. Chadwick have left Ailred quite undamaged, and have felt free to develop my model of Ninian utilising very different sources.

21.2 **Catelli, κυναρια, Ceneu.** These three affectionate nicknames litter the early Welsh genealogies (Bartrum 1966, Index) and mistaken for proper names, even Saints, have caused limitless confusion. *Catellus* is a true Latin word (vulg. for *catulus*) meaning 'puppy'. Kunaria and Ceneu, are from (Greek) *κυων*, dogs. The Welsh prefix Cun- is often confused with Con- or Cyn- (see Comm. p. 261, 13.3). Ceneu has come to be confused with 'kin'. The Welsh Herald-Bards fell right into the 'proper name' trap.

21.3 **Eunapius** In the *Vita St Cadoc* (*apud* Baring-Gould 1877 for 24 January p. 364, and Wade-Evans 1944, pp. 48–9, albeit Merlin and Eunapius are here not unreasonably confused), we are told of the arrival at a school in Wales which precedes the foundation of Llancarfan (and which in context must surely be 'Ocean College',

Llantwit) of a famous Latin rhetorician. The *Vita* tells that this 'doctor' had more pupils than money, and that famine reigned in his school. It is gratifying, therefore that Gratian gave him a salary increase on 23 May 376 (per *Codex Theodosius* for that year). As to my identification of Eunapius, perusal of the comprehensive chronological list of 'Men of Letters' in Clinton (1850, pp. 310–5) shows him as overwhelmingly the strongest candidate, and his literary works fit more convincingly into the life-experiences here envisaged than any other candidates. This, I hope impeccably drawn, conclusion is strikingly confirmed by Bartrum (1966, p. 216, line 17), where 'Eunapius Hall' (Ocean College) emerges convincingly from its disguise as a Welsh ancestor!

22.1 **laboratory equipment** Copiously illustrated in MS. 299 of the Biblioteca Marciana, Venice, and in this book in Figures 17, and 43–53.

22.2 **Praetorian Prefect** All per Tillemont (1701, p. 691).

22.3 **Welsh Tradition** 'The Dream of Macsen Wledig' (many translations).

22.4 **Vicar of Britain** If Icarus really 'fell' in Britain, he should be the original of Geoffrey of Monmouth's Prince Bladud (*Bleiddud*, 'vulpine', Ulpianus). Geoffrey (HRB. II v. 10.) brings him to earth in Bath, with, as it were, a splosh. Council of British Archaeology Report RR90 (Casey & Davies) on Segontium confirms the (recent) discovery of a 'magnificent palatial building set in its own grounds within the fort precinct – probably the residence of an imperial procurator of high standing'.

23.1 **'Bishop Peregrinus'** All this flows from my acceptance of Ailred (*supra*). The name translates as 'Bishop Pilgrim' (not, of course, of the Nibelungen Lied's Passau *Bataviensis* on the Danube; there may however be genuine echoes of Batavia proper here). We should not therefore be too surprised to come on him again as the heroic Archbishop Turpin (T. Ulpianus, after 'rhotacism') of the 'Song of Roland' and the Charlemagne cycles, although by this time he was long dead, and only his relics and example were left to inspire the participants.

23.2 **Duke of Moesia** Ammian and Zosimus *apud* Clinton (1845, p. 484). He is de Boron's enigmatic Moyses, Moys (Moses) who was unworthy to sit at Joseph's Grail table and was 'swallowed up by the earth' (interred) at Constantinople in February AD395. (See also Comm. p. 295, 131.2).

23.3 **Meriadoc** We shall find it used copiously by Geoffrey, and a Romance of him as 'Le Chevalier aux Deux Epées'. The latter title is of course '*peditum equitumque*', at whatever command level, right up to *Magister Utriusque Militum Praesentalis*. We shall encounter other bearers of the title, notably JJ and John-George: see HRB Vols 9–16, and Bartrum (1966, p. 180, l. 47–52). The latter, also, as Cornish St Meriasek (Bewnans Meriasek 1966).

23.4 **Consuls** My conjecture. The Gracchi, as forerunners (albeit as tribunes). More recently, the Gemini (Rubellius and Furius) in AD29; and later, the Anician brothers as successors AD395.

24.1 **remembered in Britain** Nennius (or his chronographer), is obsessed with this date which he uses anachronistically and in erroneous contexts at HB c. 6, 31, 5

24.2 **Murocincta (Vienna)** Scholars have had some trouble looking for Ammian's 'Villa Murocincta'. I suggest *villa* here in the type of the 'Villa Publica' in the Campus Martius at Rome; I further locate it at Vindobona whose walls have been established by the archaeologists and which fits the geographical parameters imposed by the texts. Such a curiosity as a walled (i.e. fortified) rustic villa in the right area suitable as a refuge for the Imperial Family at this time would surely have achieved some other mention in history and/or have left some discernable archaeological trace. Valentinian's route towards the troubled front-line area would have taken him past Vindobona still firmly in Roman hands. Vienna seems the obvious choice.

24.3 **Charge of Cruelty** Geoffrey of Monmouth (HRB V, v.13) has picked this up. It is too easily inferred from Ammian that Maximus was actually put to death. I contend that he escaped (see Comm. p. 263, 17.1).

25.1 **Bishop of Verulamium** Thomas (1981) reviews the state of current scholarly opinion (pp. 48–51) and, in my view rightly, rejects John Morris' date of AD209 for the martyrdom. Thomas (p. 44) points towards a later date, and I have taken this further than he probably envisaged. My model accommodates those elements of the Turin Passio which misled Morris. The martyrdom of Becket and its resulting nationalistic cult form a strong analogue.

25.2 **tattered ... ἀμφιβαλος** 'Personalised' in legend as St Amphibalos. Here is the Welsh 'Gwrwst *ledlwm*', the *vir Augustulus* of the tattered cloak.

25.3 **'Apollonius' ... long hair** Maponus as the Celts called him; cf. Lochmaben, and the Locus Maponus stone (Frere 1974, p. 367). There is much about Maponus, *Mabon*, in Welsh tradition, but have you looked closely at Apollonius of Tyre? Or – hold on tight – Polonius in Hamlet? Just stay with me and all shall be made clear.

25.4 **Merovingian descendants** Long fair hair, cf. Gregory of Tours (HF 11, c. 9).

25.5 **Gwri Gwallt Euryn** The 'little chap' with the golden hair (Goldilocks) in the 'First Branch' of the Mabinogion.

25.6 **Milon** Suggested father of Orlando in the Romances of that name. Appears in many guises, in the same company, in *Guerino il Meschino*.

25.7 **Ovid** Metamorphoses VI, 241. This reference is to the sons of Amphion (equated in ancient times with Arion as possessor(s) of a wonderworking harp). Further corrupted in the Chanson de Geste of the Four Sons of (H)Amon. The key reference here is to the 'pro-Boniface' poet of Apollinaris Sidonius' important (and highly engaging) poem IX to Felix, lines 279–88. I shall contend in due course, that the works of the 'Boniface' poet survived in Gaul at least to the ninth century and were an intermediate source for much of the Romance material, 'Arthurian' or otherwise. The likeliest candidate as the 'Boniface' poet is Claudius Rutilius Namatianus, whose home was in Southern Gaul, and may well have been a Cadurcan (of Cahors). See Sidonius (ibid) l.28. His literary efforts can hardly be confined to the surviving fragment of the *De Reditu Suo*, which reads like a swansong, but which by poetic excellence qualifies him as the first of Sidonius' three poets. His known background and political and religious attitudes also fit admirably.

25.8 **Nibelungs** This suggestion may not appear so fanciful in the light of the foregoing. Remember too, the death of Gunnar the harpist (Gwyn Aurelius) in the Volsunga saga. The point will be developed. I have never liked the somewhat 'Ciceronian' derivation from the '*nebulones Franci*' in Waltharius (of Aquitaine), itself deriving from Eumenius' panegyric to Constantius I, pp. 296/7, Cap. 17.

25.9 **Gloyw** Variously spelt. See Bartrum (1966, Index), Gwyn Gloyw, Gwynllyw *et al.* Teutonic gives us *Loh* (now archaic) for the same meaning. Whence Lohen-grin.

25.10 **Vasso** See Gregory of Tours (HF. I, c. 32). The Puy-de-Dome (one of the Monts-esclair), conspicuous, bald, snow-capped all winter, is aptly called *gleaming* in

Gallic (from Sanskrit root *vas*, shining). This epithet appears in Mael-*was* (see text p. 63) and Bartrum (1966, Index). Also various Romances in the epithet of Kay the Va*vasseur*, but most importantly of all in an inscription at which we shall arrive in due course (p. 234).

25.11 **Nitonia** From Latin *nix*, snow. We shall see by and by who she was, and who were Sts Nectan, Neithon, Nidan etc. (Bartrum 1966, Index).

25.12 **Imposition of hands** *χειροτονια*. Literally, 'the holding out/up of one's hand in a vote'. By extension, the phrase is used of 'constitutionally legitimate election' both in Hellenistic Greece (see Josephus, Ant.ii 2), and Imperial Rome (see Olympiodorus *apud* Photius, where the suggestion is that John-George's appointment by JJ as Caesar, then Augustus, was unauthorized). The phrase occurs unexpectedly but correctly in 2 Corinthians VII.19, and again, more normally, in Acts XIV.23. If the 'show of hands' provided legitimacy, this was next physically transmitted by the 'laying on of hands' or *ἐπιθησις*, again per Acts, and all the New Testament, as also in Leviticus and Numbers.

25.13 **purple smock** There was no time to obtain the necessary consent from Valens, but on the latter's death in AD378 there was no one in Constantinople to gainsay this ordination, which thus became legitimate.

26.1 **Medusa head** This is the Romancer's 'Laide Semblance'. See Comm. p. 283, 81.3.

26.2 **spell out answers** The Tabula is described in Ammian and other authorities (*apud* Clinton 1845, p. 478). It is also described by the hermit Trevrizent (Merlin) to Parzival (Gawain II), when imparting the secrets of the Graal (in Wolfram, Cap. 9 with a final reference in Cap. 16).

26.3 **the scheme was hatched** I think this reconstruction satisfactorily reconciles the conflicting views of scholars on the reasons for Count Theodosius' execution.

26.4 **Baptismal chrism** (Hence also *Nitonius*?) We are told that, as was common at that time, Count Theodosius was only baptised '*in extremis*'. Easter was the major time for baptisms. I have chosen Maundy Thursday for effect, but the date must be about then.

26.5 **Caesar** Thus I absorb the witness of Morris' Turin MS, the 'Fleury' *Passio*, (Thomas 1981, p. 49).

27.1 **white hope** Honorius/Alban ('Augustulus') really had a strong claim to the Empire of the West, had he been willing to enforce it. See Appendix 1.

27.2 **Balin and Balaan** Variously spelt in the Romances. The 'Suite du Merlin', (*apud* F. Bogdanow in Loomis 1959, pp. 329–33) gives Balain and Pellean, which latter we may recognise as Pelagianus (equally applicable to either brother). The 'dolorous cop' is by definition a *colpus*, a buffet with a hand not a weapon. The Holy Lance is an intruder in **this** story, although as we shall see in Book XX it does have to do with a later Pelagianus (Merlin Amfortas himself).

27.3 **as his rage** Theodosius I was famous for his uncontrollable rages (see especially Claudian, Carm. XXX Laus Serenae, l.135–8. See also the tumult of Callinicum (AD 389). Worse still the massacre of Thessalonica, AD390, both in Farrar (1907, II, pp. 160, 164–170). As we watch him on his knees, ailing, ravaged, distraught, on the Bora-swept hilltop during the battle of the River Frigidus (AD394) (see Tillemont 1701, pp. 378–9), we may well think of Shakespeare's King Lear (Pelagianus in Greek) raving in Act III upon the blasted heath. And we may conclude that the author of Cap. XXI of the 'English *Gesta (Romanorum)*' (Douce's name for Harl. MS2270) was right in naming his 'King Lear' Theodosius, and in making him an Emperor. We shall see next who 'Goneryl', 'Regan' and 'Cordelia' were.

29.1 **my own children** Aurelius Ambrosius Theodosius Macrobius is the only one we know of. This identification is likely prosopographically and apt genealogically. He could, of course, be Satyrus' son; if not he must be a cousin. His dates would be c.360–440. His history, which is on record, plays an intermittent part in our story.

29.2 **bringing them up as his own** Claudian, XXX *Serenae* I.104, pp. 116–8.

29.3 **Regan and Goneril** Goneril is reasonably enough 'the fair Aurelia'. Shakespeare has fixed Geoffrey's tale too firmly in our minds for me now to correct the other two as I should. Cordelia is from the Welsh *Greidiol* (Cinderella); burning, ardent (as in coals). The proper identification is undoubtedly Thermantia (Greek for 'warmly glowing', 'fiery'). The *Gesta Romanorum* do not name the daughters, but Geoffrey of Monmouth has named them for us and it is too late to change. So the youngest sister, Galla Placidia (Regina, Regan – Augusta indeed) has become Cordelia, Cinderella, leaving Thermantia as Regan (usually played on stage as a redhead). So be it, for the rest of this book. The folk-tale of the glass slipper may be less fanciful than it seems. A pair of Roman glass slippers dug up in the Severinstraße in 1971 in perfect condition are exhibited in the Römisch-Germanisches Museum in Köln. They resembled plastic 'flip-flops', and perhaps by chance they bore the Casa Sicelis House Badge, as worn by 'Uncle Ted' in Plate 5 and Fig. 7; and prominently displayed in the Casa Sicelis and at Old Morgantina itself.

30.1 **Melania** See Appendix 6; Maximus' beloved only son Victor will be killed in Book VII.

30.2 **Ward of Court** The references, mainly to Jerome, are in Farrar (1907, II, p. 238).

30.3 **Sabines** Wolfram (*Parzival*, Cap. 13) gives 'Gramoflanz' (Aëtius) and his supposed father Irot (*Tiro*) (Merlin) the title 'King of Rosche Sabins' with a palace there. Wolfram-the-dyslexic is a great man for anagrams. Try it as 'Morgan-Pfalz' and you won't be far off. You will see in Book XIV where Morgan's palace in Rome really was, and in Book XVII who inherited it.

31.1 **Tatius** Just keep 'Achilles Tatius' the naughty ('Greek') author of the Aventine in mind for now. See Comm. p. 294, 129.3 and p. 298, 148.3. When Pretty-boy George is a libidinous highly literate late teenager on the Aventine he might find a bit of 'soft-porn' not altogether untimely.

32.1 **real bull** Taurus. Hence Merlin, as his brother, can be called Taurianus (see Comm. p. 258, 1.6). Scholars in this field may think of Bevis of Hamton, of (Irish) Bôdb I, II and III the Red; and, with a slight gulp, of Dorian Grey!

32.2 **tiro** Wolfram's Irot, although he has wrongly applied this to JJ and not to Merlin.

33.1 **'Strong arm'** (Welsh, *Vreichvras*; French *Briebras*). The latter may be a misformation from the Welsh, confused naturally with *Brisé*, broken. 'Strong arm', is the unquestionable sense, and here it may be useful to set right an ancient Romance confusion. The Emperor Nero was not so called because he was black, or dark, or even noticeably swarthy. 'Nero' is *Sabine* (strictly, 'Samnite') for *strong* (Welsh '*nerth*', strong).

The Romancers will have much ado with 'black knights', with 'perilous' chapels of 'black hands'. Wrong language: **Oscan, the language of the Sabines,** gives the answer.

33.2 **Vizi-Goths** In the Gothic language 'Vizi' means 'Western'; as compared with the 'Ostro-' or Eastern Goths who, under pressure from the Huns, are pressing westwards behind them, and with whom we shall come up in Book VI.

33.3 **unlock many doors** The 'g' of Fritigern is of course, soft and aspirated. Taking an appropriate example (gwyn-*tigernus* 'the fair tyrant') we derive (in varied spelling). Teutonic Gun*dahar*, Gun*dacar* (Gun*dicar*ius) (but **not** Gunter, which is 'Quinterius' from Quintus-Gawain (see Comm. p. 289, 107.1); Cambro-Hibernian (Gilvus-***tigernus***), Gilla*dacar*, **Gil***das*; Welsh (Constantine-***tigernus***), **Cyn**-*deyrn*; **Lucius** (*tigernus*/catellus) *ddyrn***lug**. The latter (in Romance) is Leo*degrance* and we have Welsh *T*(r)*ahayarn* or Talhaiarn, familiar as Traherne. The ramifications are endless.

33.4 **Constantius I, Chlorus, and Galerius** Per Orosius VIII, Cap. 25. Kipling gets it right in Puck of Pook's Hill, Cap. 5, and although he errs in many subsequent details in this and the next two chapters, they remain a towering feat of historical re-creation, one might almost say, of clairvoyance.

34.1 **Augustus** At Sirmio, 16 January AD379.

34.2 **Celerinus** See Tillemont (1701, V, p. 631). His prime source is, not inaptly, Claudian himself (Epithal. Palladio c.m. XXV 2.3, 6, 72–91, and NB i.93). I venture – do not yet call me too bold – to identify him with 'King Archistrates ("C-in-C" in Greek) of Cyrene' of the *Gesta Romanorum* CLIII , and also to make him father not only of Bp. Synesius (of whom more anon) but of Merlin's first legal wife. Tillemont is unable to date the relief of Carrhae with any certainty. I need a battle for Merlin to win his spurs, and have ventured, harmlessly I think, to appropriate Carrhae, together with the incident of Celerinus spurning the Empire, which latter may belong to the earlier ancestor referred to in Claudian (ibid.) i.75–82. As to the propriety of seeking reliable historical material in romantic fiction, Seeck has shown the way (in Philologus 1894, 52, p. 442 *et seq.*), and has earned the 'imprimatur' of Bury (Gibbon) (1897) 111, Appendix 27. Aptly, again, Seeck's quarry was Synesius. This is not the place to justify myself further.

34.3 **Carrhae** The original of Wolfram's Zazamanc although his details are much garbled.

36.1 **'Berenice the Golden'** Now Um-el-Ketef. Not to be confused with Berenice in Cyrenaica, nor with Berwick-on-Tweed and North Berwick.

40.1 **Paphnutis** Now Dakka; home of St Paphnutius (of Council of Nicaea fame), and of Paphnutia the well-known alchemist.

40.2 **Decurion** In the Glastonbury traditions 'Joseph of Arimathea' is sometimes described as '***nobilissimus decurio***'. Leland rightly concludes that this is not the man who buried Jesus, 'but some eremit of that name'. Merlin, as we shall see, well earns the epithet Arimathos ('very wise') Matholwch ('Lucius the wise'). I have shown in Book VIII how he could have acquired the name 'Joseph'. The ranks of Nobilissimus and Decurio would have been applicable from AD409 and AD379 respectively. Merlin was a *curialis* again from time to time after 405.

40.3 **optio** In the sense of Assistant. There is no exact translation for this word. At the lowest level it could mean no more than batman. A General would have his *optiones* as Aides-de-camp. A tribune (Colonel) would have his adjutant. Aide is the nearest we can get.

40.4 **Magister Militum** At this stage he would only have been *MM per Orientem*. Later, as we learn from Claudian (C.M. XXV, i.84–91) he became *MM Praesentalis*; Commander-in-Chief.

40.5 **huge voice** Barrectus. Whence Wolfram's 'Baruch' in *Parzival* (Cap. 2). See also Nash-Williams (1950 no. 285) for a stone (lost) at Tomen-y-Mur, where we shall find Merlin in the next book. Merlin will one day establish an observatory on Cader Idris, of Idris Gawr or (unmutated) Cawr, meaning 'of the huge voice'. By the same token he will be known as St Cawr.dav(id).

40.6 **stammer** There is a tradition that Merlin, and perhaps his father, had a stammer: *μογγος* in Greek, *Let-iaeth* in Welsh. We find the giant Fa*mong*omad in Amadis de Gaula, and cf. St Mungo (Kentigern). For Llŷr (Πελαγιανος) Llediaeth see Bartrum (1966, Index). A derivation from Μοναχος rather than Μογγος would be equally acceptable, since Alban, Merlin, JJ and his son were all for a time monks. The latter will in time be presented to you as the historical **Vortigern.**

42.1 **Maximus ... Vicar of Britain** Britain at the time was, as we know from the Notitia, a military Vicariate, hence governed by a 'maximus'. Our Maximus may be presumed, from his career, to have launched his rebellion of AD383 from a senior position. The vicariate seems a plausible conjecture. His practical military experience to that point seems confined to a brief and menial spell in the service of (probably) Count Theodosius (Pacatus Paneg, XX 1, and Zosimus IV 35: the former calls him *statarius lixa* – see Bartrum 1966, Index, 'stater'). We may safely distinguish him from the incompetent General of AD377 who by inflaming Fritigern and his Vizi-Goths brought on the catastrophe of Adrianople. This would be altogether too odd a posting for the disgraced Praetorian Prefect of Gaul of the same year. My solution of exile followed by rehabilitation seems more plausible. As Military Vicar he would have been responsible for repelling the incursion of the Picts and Scots AD382 in 'Pseudo-Prosper'. Would that scholars had accepted Hodgkin's appellation of 'Pseudo-Prosper'. Since Bury, we are condemned to refer to it as 'the anonymous Gallic chronicler of AD452, *Chronica Minora* p. 617 *et seq.*!, or the '*Gallic Chronicle*' if we are being slapdash. I mean that chronicle which scholars of the seventeenth to the nineteenth centuries called '*Prosper Tyro*' (as opposed to Prosper of Aquitaine) and which I surmise could very properly be called the *Chronicle of Lérins*. I shall return to this suggestion.

42.2 **'Elissa'** In mythology, another name for Dido. Virgil gives her a sister, Anna, a brother, Pygmalion, and a former husband, Sychaeus, murdered by Pygmalion. These fancies will all plant seedlings in the minds of the trouvères. Cf. also 'Elsa' of Brabant, and 'Essyllt'.

42.3 **Incest** Readers may think me obsessed with this transgression, which will recur in the life of Merlin, and will positively rampage in the life of young John (as Don Giovanni). The choice is not of my making; the Romance sources are riddled with it, and the genealogical locks will only open with the aid of this key – see particularly Appendix 9. The Church of the day sounded an equivocal note on degrees of affinity, but was clear that sexual relations between those of whole blood were unacceptable.

42.4 **Gaisarix** This correct form displays '*Caesar-rex*' in Vandal guise. Historians generally remember him as Genseric.

43.1 **tricks of disguise** Merlin is remembered as a Protean shape-shifter (cf. Cu Rui in Bricriu's Feast, Gantz 1981, pp. 232, 245, 247, 251–5. See also L. H. Loomis in Loomis 1959, p. 530 *et seq.*). This is not perhaps too early to mention Alberic and his Tarnhelm, an early camouflage net; a 'magic' **cowl** if you like. We shall hear more of them.

43.2 **Serapeion** Eight years later this wonderful library was to be broken up by an edict of Theodosius the First and pillaged. We should not assume that no books survived.

43.3 **compass** The latter in text p. 247. Merlin's poem on the lodestone is in Platnauer (1926) *Carmina Minora* XXIX (Birt, XLVIII). The 'quadriga episode' is in Quodvultdeus *apud* Braun 1964.

43.4 **Zosimus of Panoplis** His surviving alchemical works are in Marciana MS.299. Although I have felt justified in making him brother-in-law to Merlin's godfather St Basil, I have not made them meet, although they may well have done.

43.5 **camouflage** Zosimus gives an example of these hidden symbols among the inscriptions in Egyptian temples (Berthelot 1888, trad., pp. 45, 233). I shall give, towards the close of Book XX, an example nearer home and purporting to be the work of Merlin himself, in which we shall actually see displayed the five '*muances*' of the Holy Grail which King Arthur is recorded as seeing reveal themselves in turn (see Comm. p. 328, 251.1).

43.6 **Marculinus** Brachet (1868) (trans. Kitchin, 1882) gives the transition from *marculus*, a little hammer, with his usual impeccable lucidity. He will be our guide with some other names which puzzled the trouvères.

43.7 **Mercury** I postulate use of the amalgamation process at this time. Egyptian mercury was obtained from cinnabar from Asia Minor. (In his 'Titurel', Albrecht von Scharfenburg has actually turned the latter into a Grail Knight, 'Sir Sennabor of Cappadocia'.)

44.1 **synthesis** Merlin's son Gawain will publish this as the works of 'Dionysius the Areopagite' (or pseudo-Dionysus), remembered in Paris as St Denis (see Comm. p. 309, 198.1).

44.2 **Crypheus** The order of the junior degrees in Mithraism is variously given by our authorities. For brevity I have had Merlin clear the three degrees of 'Υπερητουντης in one bound, to become what some today would call a Master Mason. The Mithraic elements in Masonic ritual are patent. We should remember too, Arthur's imprisonment for three nights in the 'dark prison under the stone' in the Welsh Triads (Tr.1 in Notes to Lady Guest's *Mabinogion*, 1906, p. 406 and Loomis 1959, fn. 8, p. 46). The Grail Knights too, have alarming adventures in dark 'perillous' chapels with tombs and slabs, although, as I have suggested in Comm. p. 269, 33.1, they were probably trying to refer to the 'chapel' of **Perillus the Strong,** the famous Sicilian metalworker of Greek myth. Think, too, of the 'Siege Perilous', the 'Pons Perilous'; also of Shakespeare's *Pericles*, the *Gesta Romanorum*'s 'Apollonius' – that's where Shakespeare got the name from.

44.3 **Leo** Confused by the Cambrians, too, with Gloyw/Nitonius. *Llew*, a lion; *Llyw*, glowing. Very many references here in the Welsh genealogies (Bartrum 1966, Index, especially Llywarch, Llywelyn, Gwynlleu and Gwynllyw, Bywyr Lew).

45.1 **Virgil of Naples** Wolfram (Cap. 9, 35–2. Wolfram gets this, and the relationships right, but mediaeval fabulators have transferred much of Theodore's lore and 'magical' prowess to the author of the *Aeneid* on the mainland. See also the whole of Claudian's Panegyric on the Consulship of Manlius Theodorus, where l.39–41 and 66–112 are of particular relevance. Note also l.126–34 and 326–30. For the problems of translating Greek philosophical terms into Latin, see C.Ap. Sidonius' prose preface to Carmen (XIV), Polemius paragraphs 1 and 2. In the light of all this I think the two next paragraphs are hardly audacious.

45.2 **Hadrian's tower** Now the 'Torre del Filosofo', high up on Etna.

45.3 **movable platform** Hence Gawain's adventures with the marvellous bed in the Castle of Marvels. There is a vivid and thorough description of the 'perilous' bed in Wolfram (Cap. II). (Hence too the damsel of Montesclaire whom he rescues.) Merlin's Camera Obscura (referred to in text p. 7), is again splendidly described in Wolfram (Cap. 12). This invention had to await the introduction of the convex refracting lens. It may be noted here that rock crystal is found not only in the Alps, but also notably in the vicinity of Tintagel and Snowdon.

45.4 **Procne** (and of the Romancers' 'Hirondelle') Gerlinte is also found in Teutonic myth as Chelinde, Sieglinde; and in Agnellus, Bishop of Ravenna, c.839, as Singleida, Agnellus (Vitae Pontificum Ravennatum, *apud* Hodgkin 1860, I, p. 453) calls her Galla Placidia's niece. In fact they were step-cousins (see Appendix 4).

46.1 **coaster** Common practice at this time of year. A good account is Claudius Rutilius Namatianus, *De redite suo* (AD 414) l.179, *et seq.*

46.2 **Spice Trade** I have made Satyrus a merchant, partly to account for his known wealth, partly because of the story of his winter voyage and shipwreck. Only a man well acquainted with the sea would have gone offshore outside the sailing months (see Namatianus, ibid., l.221). We know, from Ambrose's own writings, that Satyrus had practised as a lawyer, and was to become governor of a province. There is time for this after the present episode.

47.1 **Pygmalian's** It is no chance that Pygmalion King of Macedonia (Thrace) appears in the Romances of Palmerin d'Oliva and of Primaleon-y-Polendos. Merlin commanded in Thrace AD386 and JJ was Master of Horse there in AD393. The ghost of Ovid, mediated by Sidonius' Cadurcan poet (probably Namatianus) lies heavy on the trouvères.

47.2 **Great Bear** Ovid calls Ursa major and minor '*magna minorque Ferae*' (in his *Tristia*, iv. 3.1), whence the '-vere' of 'Guine*vere*'. *Fera* is not only a bear, but any wild animal such as might be encountered in the forests of the Ardennes (Forest of Arden). Ursa Minor would become **Ursula** as a proper name. I shall identify her and her 'eleven thousand' companions in due time.

47.3 **Paulinus** of Nola In calling him Merlin's mentor I am relying partly on Rhygivarch's *Vita David* (see Comm. p. 275, 58.1) partly on the evidence of the Trescawen Stone, so brilliantly read 50 years ago by Sir Ifor Williams and the young Raleigh-Radford. (RCHM Anglesey, 1937). Line 3 of the inscription can be read in my sense, but there are alternatives, geographic and hagiographic. Either way I dispute the '*hic jacet*' and place this stone among that group of 'Falsae', most of which save the Drustan stone (Fowey) are listed in Morris (1977, Note 124.2) and all of which I ascribe to the chauvinistic activities of 'Maelgwn II Gwynedd', who, if indeed he existed, seems to have been a keen Neo-Arthurian. (There could be a case for ascribing some or all of these stones to the time of Merfyn Frych in the ninth century, however.) My reference to the Te Deum is opportunist. We do not know that Niketas visited Italy before AD400 (although he would have had sufficient reasons to visit the 'Pope' of Milan before that date). This is, however, a convenient literary point at which to air it. I have only allowed myself two other such chronological liberties, in Comm. p. 269, 34.2 (Celerinus spurning the purple), and p. 279, 68.1.

47.4 **Remesiana** Now Bela Pelanka, near the Yugo-Slav border.

48.1 **Lake Benacus** Whence the Romancers will rightly extract 'King Ban of Benwick'; JJ will get 'banned' there, and nearly lose his head in 411. Lancelot (Aëtius) will rename it 'Joyeuse Garde' after 432.

48.2 **Castra vetera** The foundations of the amphitheatre are adjacent and San Lorenzo Maggiore, with the famous Colonnade, form part of the Palace remodelled, I contend, by Justina into an Arian place of worship and mausoleum AD385. The Castrum lay to the East with its Campus Martius.

48.3 **Military provinces** Teutonic: *Herepp*, *Hreppr*, *Hreappe*, *Herupe*. Whence 'Rape' as a Saxon land-division. Whence also Herupe near Bayeux in Normandy, and the Herupians of John Bodel's *Song of the Saxons* in the French *Gesta*.

49.1 **Agricola** The third of this name treated here. The first: Julius Agricola, Conqueror of North Britain. The second: Count Theodosius who completed the task. The third: Merlin's brother JJ, later to become Constantine III Augustus, later still to become Pelagius the heresiarch. There is a lion (Orosius) lying in that path, but do not worry, he will not bite when we reach him in 29 years time in AD408. See text p. 187 where Leo the friendly lion saves Agricola's head, and Comm. p. 306, 187.2.

51.1 **Old Cole of All** I derive Coel, Coillus, Cole from Agricola. But an alternative derivation is offered in Comm. p. 277, 62.5.

51.2 **charcoal** The charcoal burners shipped their product to depots near to the Roman roads, where their memory survives in innumerable 'col*d* harbours'.

51.3 **Bononia** Also, *Portus Gessoriacum*. Here is the Romancers' 'Portles*guez*', later still confused with 'Portugal'.

52.1 **Rampant Boar** A splendid representation on a tile in Carlisle Museum.

52.2 **Acheloös** Many confused Romance reverberations here, notably the 'wicked enchanter Archelous' in Esplandian. Also Archemais.

52.3 **'Pan the goat'** This rustic divinity, Greek ὁ Παν, will be hopelessly confused by the witches and warlocks of the future with 'Pan the All', Greek το Παν, a supreme being to whom Merlin, in his alchemical researches, will give much devotion. See text p. 246.

52.4 **Rome's being cheated** Pacatus, in his Panegyric of June 389 to Theodosius, depicts Maximus as a rapacious enforcer of tax laws.

53.1 **Eucheria** See Appendix 1. Also Eutheria, Aetheria, Egeria, Euheria (no way Silvia of Aquitaine). I propose her as a Jewess, and as Theodore's second wife, without authority, save such as may present itself in this book. Valerius, seventh century monk in Galicia, in an Eulogy (addressed to his fellow monks at the Vierzo mountains of Cantabria, N. Leon), refers to Eucheria as 'a native of Ocean's Western shore', which covers the whole Western fringe of the Roman Empire. Not knowing Theodore's full 'CV', we cannot judge just where their paths might first have crossed.

53.2 **her diary** See Wilkinson (1971) in Bibliography.

54.1 **camp concerts** The amphitheatre is still extant. Another, aptly, is at Tomen-y-Mŭr.

54.2 **Oscan vocabulary** Recognisably a Latin tongue, but of the 'P-Celt' branch. It was the pronunciation rather than the vocabulary which Merlin had to teach. Native Britons should not have found it difficult. Morgan, as an Italian, would have been fluent.

54.3 **Casnar** Oscan for 'white', 'hoary'. Latin *canus* (Horace) *canities*. Probable root of Welsh *Gwyn*, Irish *Finn* (for 'fair'). See Bartrum (1966, Index).

54.4 **Miles Gloriosus** Hence 'Sir Kay' as a braggart, in Romance. (And St Magloire, St Malo, but John won this title too.)

54.5 **ancestor Hadrian** Count Theodosius Sr married Thermantia Aeliana. It is not clear that Aelius Hadrianus had any direct descendants in his 'pre-Antinous phase'. Hadrian was, however, responsible for reviving the Atellan farces.

55.1 **a Harlequin** cf. (Oscan) *Hereklui* for Herculeus (see Comm. p. 279, 55.6). Whence, Erek, the Erle-König, and the onomastic confusions in the Mabinogion with Harlech. See also King Herla, in Walter Mapes' Nugae, and Hellekin in Adam de la Halle (per Loomis 1959, p. 536). The 'Wild Hunt' is yet to come in Book XV.

55.2 **brother's keeper** The Welsh *cyfarwyddion* will get this tale of wife-swapping a bit wrong in the 'First Branch' of the Mabinogion. Merlin is '[C]Arawn' (*coronatus*); JJ is 'Pwyll' (the Apulian) – both names yet to be accorded. 'Hafgan' is Magnus Maximus, and 'Pwyll' was 'fighting with him in the North' in the sense of fighting on his side, not against him. Merlin keeps faith with JJ over Elissa, for now anyway, as the disguised 'Pwyll' does in the tale. The resonance of Cain and Abel looks forward, as well as back.

55.3 **Wells** Then Fontinetum. 'Suspected' but not yet found, per Rodwell (1982) in BAR (Brit, 102, p. 52). Excavations under the Bishop's palace should uncover it. I suspect another near Shapwick for reasons which will emerge.

55.4 **Faltonia's three sons** She is the famous Anicia Faltonia Proba. Faltonius Petronius is better known as Probus II. The relationships of this family are set out in Appendix 7. I have selected the Marshall's Elm Villa for Olybrius (NG.ST(31)4834); the Bradley Spring Villa (ST(31)4931) for Probus II; and the putative Shapwick villa for Probinus. All this is conjectural. There are plenty more villas in the area which would serve.

55.5 **the Estuary** I propose '*Aestuaria Regio*' for Somerset and Gwent, corruptly read in early mediaeval times as '*Aestiva Regio*' the 'Summer' Country or Gwlad yr Hafod. Silly name, 'Somerset'.

55.6 **Faltonius a little younger** See Apps. 5 and 7.

56.1 **Atecotti** 'Southern Picts' (see Comm. p. 264, 20.2). When we recall that the Romans pronounced 't' as 'ts' we may conclude that the Atecotti are the same as the 'Scots'. *NIL OBSTAT*?

57.1 **cemetery** Most notably at St Maurice-en-Valais. But Verulamium and indeed Fontinetum should not be forgotten, nor Poundbury (Dorchester) where Sparey-Green has revealed much cognate material (BAR, Brit.102, 1982, pp. 61–76). Cemeteries around Cologne will bear fruit too.

57.2 **Casa Belgica** The Casa Belgica was an imperial hunting lodge, built originally by Tetricus, second of the independent Gallic emperors of the third century. Used by Constantine the Great, and by Magnentius (Justina's first husband), it passed to the Valentinians and thus remained Justina's till her death in 388. It was Elissa's favourite home, and she was to spend much of the rest of her life there. However it was Justina who won it its surviving name of the Forteresse de Hauterecenne – 'of the High Queen'. My deductions as to its origin and occupation are based on the archaeological reports, and specifically the coin-find analysis in 'Ardenne et Gaume' *Monographie* 12, 2nd Edn, Bruxelles 1978, pp. 82–3. This monograph also appears as Vol. XIII of *Publications d'Histoire de l'Art et de l'Archéologie de l'Université Catholique de Louvain* (Louvain 1978). The single cache at the 'barrage' of three *solidi*, one of

Valentinian III, and one each of Constantine III and of John, **is surely highly significant**. I include in Figure 59, for completeness, the excavation working plan of the Baths site. The whole monograph deserves study, and the site is well worth visiting.

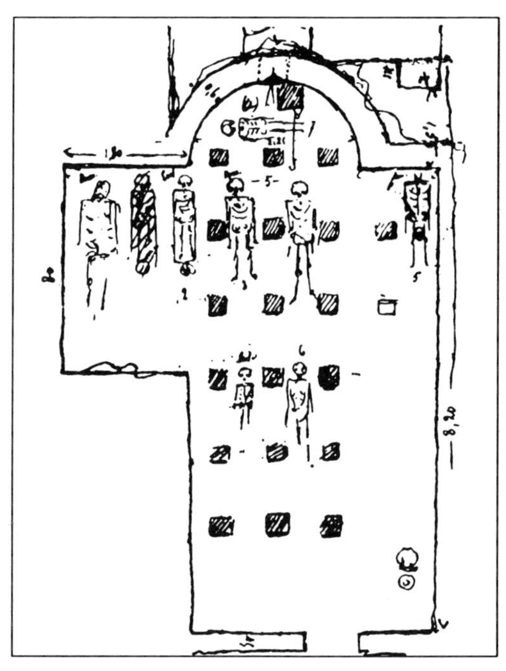

**Figure 59**
The Casa Belgica at Furfooz:
Baths excavation, working sketch
© Prof Raymond Brulet

57.3 **Dolaucothi** Named after Merlin. Welsh, the 'meadows of Cothi'; see Bartrum (1966, Index) 'Corthi', perhaps from Welsh *coet*, 'wooded', 'silvaticus' or even 'Sylvestris'.

57.4 **the 'Ring'** Wagner was one of Merlin's best popularisers. The reference here is to the scene in *The Rheingold* where Wotan wrests the Ring from the dwarf, Alberic.

58.1 **Ædonius the rich** The Vita Sancta David of Ricemarchus (d.1099) (Wade-Evans, BCS University of Wales Press Board, Cardiff 1944, Cap 38, p. 160) gives 'David' two disciples: Aidanus (read **Ædonius**) **and** Scutinus (read Scutarius), '*qui et **Scolanus** aliud nomen habens*'. In my view all three are Merlin/**David**, although he will not acquire the latter soubriquet until Book IX of this work.

58.2 **Kassite** See Lindsay (1970, p. 213). (Lindsay's authority appears to be Forbes' *Studies in Ancient Technology*, 1970, l.125, but his *apparatus criticus* leaves much to be desired.) 'However did they get here'? Well it's a long story. The Irish 'Cin Drum Snechta' calls them 'Scythians' (meaning no more than *pelliti* or leather-clad barbarians). Archaeologists tend to call them 'Beaker' or 'Necked-beaker' folk. Both sources associate them with tin, and the dawn of the Bronze Age. I contend that they are Kossites, people of Kiss, the tin people. The ancients sometimes call them 'Scythians'. They are Elamites of Susiana (Elam 'land of Cedars', home of Gilgamesh) who, c. 1780 BC, seized Babylon from the Sumerians. Aeschylus (Persae 16), Strabo (xv.3.2), call the Fourth Principal Tribe of Susiana 'Cissii'. Other classical authors call them 'Cossaei'. Cuneiform inscriptions call them 'Kassi'. Their Old Sumerian ('Akkadian' is the semitising name for it) language is Altaic/agglutinative, and positively non-Semitic. (Note: tin is Sanscrit 'Kastîra', 'shining'.) The Kassite kings issued boundary stones called (in Kassite) 'kudurru' which are strangely reminiscent of the Pictish Class I stones with their diagrammatic symbols (e.g. solar), heraldic beasts and status symbols generally. The Kassite artistic, linguistic, and legendary links with Pictland are really most puzzling.

58.3 **Eudaf Hen** The Welsh 'Dream of Macsen Wledig' makes Helena's father (*recte* grandfather) Eudav (Octavius Theodorus) ap Caradawc, the latter Constantius I

Chlorus, while Merlin is also Octavius (Eudaf), bungled from Nennius HB 24, also ap Caradawc. The *cyfarwyddion* have confused the two Eucherii, and Uncle Icarus is plainly intended.

58.4 **Amlawdd I 'guletic'** Welsh '*ym llodd*' or '*clod*' is Latin *cum laude*, 'praised'. γυλετικος is plainly of Gallic origin, cognate to (Heraldic) *gules*, French *gueule* and Latin *gulae*, all with the same sense of 'red'. I postulate, with some conviction, that all the Welsh 'Wledigs' were redheads, and that the word does not in itself mean 'ruler'. (Casnar is a special case, because of his traditional red costume on stage.)

58.5 ***Procuratores montium*** Mine managers. Merlin, as *Procurator Metallorum*, is responsible for the product.

58.6 **Moray Firth** This campaign is inferred from the sudden appearance of Northern Picts (Taefali) in the Notitia. If such events went back to Severan times they would surely have left some epigraphic evidence in the intervening 200 years. About this time, too, the brief sixth Province of Orkney (*Orcades*) emerges in the *Laterculus* of Polemius Silvius (Seeck 1876).

59.1 **Medionemeton** 'Nemeton' is a Celtic name meaning not just a grove but a Druid grove. It means 'place of judgement', from Νεμετωρ, 'a judge'. The latter word is recalled in 'Giudi' from the Latin *Judex*, 'a judge'. Hence also the Welsh epithet *Eiludd* (modern Eliot) for twin-judge '*duumviri juri dicundo*' (see Bartrum 1996, Index). The name is found all over Britain and Gaul, and the Celts even took it as far as Ankara in Turkey (formerly Δρυνεμετον). Here in the clearings among the great oaks the Druids, under divine auspices, worshipped, taught, governed and presided over currency, such as it was. Is this why Merlin may be remembered as a Druid – Erse '*Daire*'?

59.2 **Cunedda** This means 'descended from the Emperor Constantius Chlorus' and was first applied as a name to Count Theodosius. However, *all* their descendants are entitled to it.

59.3 **Ides of March** When Brutus and his fellows slew Julius Caesar.

60.1 **Great Constantine's grandson** See Appendix 5. Pacatus says that Maximus' ancestry is unknown. In making him the conjectural son of Crispus I seek to account for his pride and ambition, and some support is given to this by the St Crispin legends, and by the annual procession at Stirling in honour of 'King Crispin'. JJ and Merlin would thus be 'Crispiniani'. You may believe it or not, it is not that important. Suffice it that the Welsh sources are insistent that Macsen was a Constantinian.

61.1 **Pentheselea** Queen of the Amazons, whence 'Thessala' the conniving nurse of Chrestien de Troyes' 'Cliges'. We shall come up with this Proto-Romeo/Juliet story again in Ireland (see Comm. p. 302, 167.1 and p. 313, 208.7).

61.2 **Servanus** On p. 14 I postulated Severus as a *cognomen* of Count Theodosius Sr, so as to allow Severianus as a filiative for his two sons, and to tie in with Prosper of Aquitaine Chron, entry AD429. I cannot, by my thesis, have 'Glorious Dad' (St Alban) present at the birth of 'Little John'. I have therefore assumed 'St Serf', foster-father of St Kentigern in the 'Vita', to be one of his disciples, hence 'Severiani'. He could, of course, be a retired veteran of the Legio XXX Ulpia Trajani Severiani, and have come by his name that way. Of course the *Vita Kentigerni* may be wrong, but as it is all we have I have tried to use it.

62.1 **tattooing** For a thorough examination of probable Pictish tattooing customs see Thomas (1963) in *Archaeological Journal*, Vol. CXX, esp. pp. 88–93. Fig. 15, p. 92, is particularly relevant, esp. in the context of John. See also text Figs. 37, 41.

62.2 **Melrose** I have no particular grounds for postulating a hospital here. The Traprain Law and Culross stories are from the *Vita Kentigerni.*

62.3 **hair ... more foxy** One day he will give his name to Reynard the Fox, and Rinaldo in the Charlemagne cycle. Charlemagne means no more than 'Great Man'. Constantius III and Merlin are among the candidates.

62.4 **one day** Indeed, yes: as Joannes, precariously Augustus at Ravenna, AD423–5.

62.5 **'three Collas'** 'The wild boars' (Irish, 'the colaigh', or 'Collas').

62.6 **Red Hand** The 'Red Hand' remains the badge of Ulster to this day, and an onomastic legend has arisen to explain it. I think my explanation is more likely in every way than the Irish legend. For 'Collas' see above; also Comm. p. 273, 51.1.

62.7 **Taifali** Ptolemy calls them Ταιζαλι, but the *Notitia* securely identifies these very units by this name at this date. (The *Notitia* Oc.XLII.65 gives '*Taifali gentiles pictavi*', and four other unit references. I do not accept Seeck's tendentious gloss on Pictavi as '*in Gallia*', i.e. Poitou).

62.8 **Carrantuohill** Merlin derives the name from 'King Tudwal', 'Crowned Keeper of the Wall', or else 'senior *Judex*'.

62.9 ***Boreum* Promontory** The Northern headland. Ptolemy's coordinates are none too clear and the correct name may be the *Vennicnium* Promontory.

62.10 **Kassite overtones** See Comm. p. 275, 58.2.

63.1 **centres of population** Ptolemy's Ireland is conveniently accessible on p. 20 of the handbook to the *Ordnance Survey Map of Roman Britain*, 3rd Edn, 1956.

63.2 **a Northern and a Southern Kingdom** Ptolemy (see note above) gives two inland towns the name of Regia. The Northern one is probably Armagh, the Southern, perhaps, Lough Gur.

63.3 **Muig's Half** Cf. Eochaid Muigmedon (for 'myrmidon', the hordes of Achilles, or indeed of any 'meriadoc').

63.4 **Deisi** The 'expulsion of the Deisi' will linger long in Irish and Welsh myth and in archaeological remains. Now I give you a date for it. Think, too, of *Des*mond and of Decies.

63.5 **Maelwas** See Comm. p. 267, 25.10

63.6 **Cu-Chulain ... Scolan's 'hound'** Here the Ulster Cycle of Legends leaps to life; and St Collen the First (i.e. Merlin), 'Sgeolan' himself, and his brother Brân (JJ) are themselves the 'hounds' of Finn I, Mac Cool (Glorious Dad). By confusing coincidence St Collen II is Cu-Chulain as Declan, *dei colanus.*

64.1 **Ogham ... island ... Northern lough** Near the door of St Patrick's chapel, on Inch-agoill (*Insula Achill*) in Lough Corrib, stands a cross-pillar bearing Ireland's oldest inscription in Roman lettering. It reads: 'Lie LUG ÆDON macci MENUEH' – 'the stone of Lucius Ædonius from Menevia' which could be either Wexford or St Davids in this context (Weir 1980, p. 150). Weir thinks the stone was recut from Ogham. **This is not the moment to speculate whether Merlin was the inventor of Ogham.**

64.2 **Grianan Ailech** Something has gone badly wrong with this name in course of time. Modern Erse offers the interpretation 'rocky solarium' which won't really do. Hesitantly, I draw attention to Old Irish *Aerech* – Princeps, chief, cf. Indo-Aryan *Arya* 'best'; Gk. ἀριστος, Teutonic *Ariovistus*. Grianan (Welsh *Rhiannon)*, Grainne, will in due course be put forward as a corruption of **Gratiana**, and I have awarded Merlin the filiative Gratianus in right of his mother. (Roman prosopography thus parallelling the concept of an 'heraldic heiress', with family representation by quartering.)

64.3 **Gratian ... not a pretty tale** The murder of Gratian is irreconcilably recorded by the historians. In the most hostile version Andragath pursues him to Lyons in a closed litter, pretending to be his wife Laeta. Thus disguised he gains access to Gratian and strikes him down. All somewhat out of character for both Andragath and – at this homosexual stage in his life – Gratian himself.

64.4 **Constantianus** The *Codex Theodosius* (*apud* Tillemont 1701, vol. V, pp. 731, 221, 301) gives us his career as Vicar of Pontus, AD382/3 and Praetorian Prefect of Gaul, AD389. I have interposed a Vicariate of Britain AD385 to mark his Westward trend. We do not know who Constantius III's father was, but he needs must have one. I have tentatively made him the son of the Praetorian of Gaul, which seems not improbable.

64.5 **Domitian was right** It was the Emperor Domitian, or more probably his advisers, who prevented Agricola I from conquering Ireland.

64.6 **St Indracht** Whom I mentioned in my Introduction. In Erse the letter *n* eclipses a following *d*. St Ind.racht, 'the fair Rector', is associated at Glastonbury with St Benignus and St Dominica. Benignus is alternative for '*liberalis*' (Welsh '*hael*'). It should not be confused with Benedict (see text p. 75) who is JJ. It is 'Little John' who will win the epithet '*liberalis*' (Nudd Hael, Rhydderch Hael – see Bartrum 1966, Index).

64.7 **Finn Mac Cool** For Finn Mac 'Cumhal' see the Ulster Cycle, where 'Glorious Dad' Honorius Albanus, son of 'Agricola' and founder of the Fenians, will be easily recognised. (I prefer my derivation from Colla – see Comm. p. 277, 62.5 – to the customary derivation from Irish '*cumhal*', a 'slave-girl'.) Merlin is then Finn Demna, the 'daimonic' Seer.

65.1 **Pennants** My allocation of pennant colours to the three troops is arbitrary. The *Notitia* 'blazons' the shield-badges of a very large number of units in traditional heraldic tinctures.

65.2 **Rathmore** (Ptolemy's S. Rhegia). No prizes for spotting the Roman road here.

65.3 **many others** I have just named four. To these may be added: from the *Saints' Lives* (by date): Bridget 1/2, Columba 16/3 and 13/11, Cecilia 22/11, Dominica 5/2, Dymphna or Genebern (Guinevere) 15/5, Euphemia II 16/9, Gudula 8/1, Juliana or Julyot 16/2, Lucia 13/12, Madern or Madron 17/5, Marciana 9/1, Maura 15/1, 13/7, 2/11, 30/11, Modwenna 6/7, Nennock or Nonnichia (Comm. p. 305, 181.1) 4/6, Regula 11/9. Also Carpilia (Comm. p. 258, 1.7, p. 280, 70.5, p. 293, 123.4).

65.4 **Great Queen ... Mor-rigan** *Regina majora*, or v/v.

65.5 **Queen ... Máb** The Irish 'Mo-', which we will come across in innumerable Irish Saints' names, is from *meum, mea*; the -'ábh' is for 'Avitia', even more clearly recognisable in modern 'Mavis' 'mea-Avitsia'.

65.6 **little King** Guivret le Petit, Jauffroi, Gottfried (but not yet – see Comm. p. 304, 177.1). A major character in Chrestien de Troyes' *Erek*. Little will Chrestien know that Merlin is both characters: 'Erek' from 'Heracles' in *Oscan* (per the Tabula Agnonensis in the British Museum) (see Comm. p. 274, 55.1). Oscan is a language of what will be called the **Brythonic** or 'P-Celts', who pronounce their vestigial 'digamma' with a p/v/bh sound: Latin is for the **Goidelic** or 'Q-Celts' – who pronounce that same 'digamma' with a q/k/gh sound. All are still talking 'the language of Hercules'. You may also keep in mind Gun.ilde's champion Memering, 'the smallest of Christian men' in 'Ravengaard og Memering' (Wagner's Mime).

66.1 **Chersonese** Greek for promontory. The Tauric 'Chersonese' is the Crimea, the Cimbric '*Cherson*ese' is Jutland. The *Curzon* family derive from the Cotentin or Westernesse (cf. Romance of King Horne). 'Ness' for promontory has continued, through Saxon and Old English, right to the present day.

66.2 **Charlatan Heron** My proposed association of Heron with Priscillianism, perhaps as the enigmatic Marcus, is conjectural but not, I think, unlikely. When we reach Book X we may feel that Merlin's use of the epithet 'charlatan' is less than fair.

66.3 **Martin's ... protest** On his last visit (AD 387) to Trier, his biographer tells us, Helena entertained him in a way which reminds us not only of Jesus and the Syro-Phoenician woman but even of the woman at Emmaus with the precious ointment. Plainly he made an enduring impression on her.

67.1 **Jerome's nastier suggestions** Migne PL IX.1305 and X.26. Also Ep. XXII.30 and Ep. XIV.

67.2 **Septuagint** The famed, and as it was claimed, divinely inspired Greek translation of the Old Testament (second century BC) which is – very significantly – the version used in all the New Testament references. As Jerome was to discover, there are many departures from the Hebrew.

67.3 **Basilica Thecla** or Basilica Nova. Ambrose himself recounts the tale in his Ep. XX. Both the Basilica Nova and the adjacent Basilica Vetus were invested with troops, and it was in fact in the latter that Ambrose kept his musical vigil.

67.4 **deft clericatus** JJ is to attempt this at Arles (AD 411) and Glycerius in AD474. Eucherius Stiliconis had a paganising reputation at the time, but in the extremities to which he was reduced in 408, took sanctuary in a church. Zosimus records, somewhat doubtfully, that he nevertheless failed to save his life. If this is correct we should look for another Eucherius (see Comm. p. 321, 233.4) to become Bishop of Lyons.

68.1 **Tomi** I have adapted the sad tale of Gerontius' humiliation and punishment from Zosimus (*apud* Tillemont 1701, V, p. 259). It may be that Zosimus indicates an officer of greater seniority than Merlin could have held at this time, and that another Gerontius is intended. If I had believed this I could have transferred Merlin's own humiliation and penitence to some later episode, perhaps AD396.

69.1 **as only she could** Claudian, *Serenae*, CM.XXX (Birt XXIX) l.137–139.

69.2 **no money** Compare (Welsh) 'Aneurin', which means 'no gold'. The Welsh often refer to 'Gildas-Aneurin' (see Comm. p. 257, 1.5, p. 269, 33.3); also to 'Aneurin' as 'Taliesin', he of the 'radiant head' (Goldilocks). Compare also (Teutonic) 'Kein reich' (i.e. Heinrich/Henry) meaning 'no wealth'. Hartman von der Aue, Wolfram von Eschenbach's arch rival in the Arthurian field wrote, unknowing, of Merlin in his popular *Der Arme Heinrich* to which I shall return (see Comm. p. 302, 166.1). All the foregoing characters are Merlin.

69.3 **Paulinus** See Comm. p. 272, 47.3.

69.4 **Therasia** Cf. Gerasina Queen of Sicily in the Ursula legends (Golden Legend J de V. 21/10).

69.5 **Saints** Baring-Gould (1872) has him on 22 June. His letters are in Walsh 1967.

70.1 **Keepsake ... Angevin stater** I have chosen to accept the coin as an authentic relic of Lucius Merlin, the defender in AD428 of orthodoxy v. Pelagianism and solicitor of Germanus' AD429 and 446 missions to Britain. (For the AD446 mission see Comm. p. 322, 235.1 and 235.2). I can just about see in its 'Angevin' origin a precarious *stemma* for Wolfram's (or better, Kyot's) opportunistic glorification of the House of Anjou. Take this, or leave it, as you will. The coin itself is the famous 'King Lucius' coin (cf. Bede I Cap. 4). See Ussher (1639) *Antiquitates*, V, iii, p. 58, and Numism. *Chron.* II (1849) p. 153 with reference to Speed. Also Ruding (pl.II.26), Blanchet (Fig. 192, p. 302) and Muret et Chabouillet (No. 6725). It is now in the Hunterian Collection at Glasgow. Many arguments, reared in earlier days on this coin (of which I have a cast), founder on examination: even the eye of faith cannot discern Ruding and Speed's crosses thereon. It seems certain that the coin they saw was of the Parisii (see Comm. p. 277, 62.1 re. Thomas, Figure 15). Another representation is in Lombard-Jourdan (1989) Plate 10, p. 120, where the author goes on to draw from it some very tendentious conclusions about Constantine the Great's *labrum*.

70.2 **Heliodorus' robe** Fully described in Chrestien de Troyes' *Erek*, lines 6739–6809.

70.3 **St Illtyd** The *Vita* has been printed, with an English translation. The Latin, however, in Wade-Evans (1944 – from Cotton, MS Vespasian A XIV ff. 43b–51) should also be read, since it evokes many resonances. I am aware of **the radical consequences of this earlier dating for Illtyd,** which necessitates redating so many of the Saints *vitae* on which the early history of Brittany, and of sub-Roman Britain finds a precarious chronological foothold.

70.4 **famous St Patrick** Son of Calpurnius Jr and Constantia (Consentia, Concessa). He is St Patrick Jr. His *agnomen* of 'Succat' may here be usefully explained. It was his Dalmatic or gentry tunic, Greek σακκος, Latin *succa* or *sucta*, perhaps the very garment of *ingenuitas*, which he confesses so pitifully to having had to sell. I identify St Patrick Sr (whose Irish mission has been conflated with St Patrick Calpurnian's in Irish legend) as St Germanus of Auxerre, paving the way for Palladius' abortive mission of AD431.

70.5 **Molossian** See Grattius, '*Cynegetikon*' (c.10 BC), l.196.7. Grattius also gives us '*petranius*', where we shall recognise one of John's Roman *agnominae* (later, by scribal confusion, rendered 'paternus'). Typically, Claudian is fond of the term 'molossian', and there are several references to Molossians in the *Saints Lives*, most aptly in the *Vita Sancta Kebii* (Wade-Evans 1944, Secs. 17 and 18, p. 246). Aptly, because Cubi (for *cubicularius)* is John and the 'she-goat' (*capriola*) is Ursula. Moreover John (in typically Romantic schizophrenia) is also Maelgwn I (Gwynedd?), Μεγαλος κυνος (from κυων) the Great (Wolf-)Hound; Melkinus of Glastonbury; **Alains le Gros** ('alain' meaning 'hunting dog', mastiff, in Old French). The Irish will make him into a saint as St 'Molasrian', the original **Irish wolfhound** (famed Irish exports since Caesar's day, and of unforgettable appearance).

71.1 **Marcellinus 'the born loser'** See *Claudius Marcellus*, Appendix 6. Pacatus loosely calls him Maximus' brother, thereby causing confusion. Brother-in-law is the relationship.

73.1 **bacaudism** Thompson (1977), in his tendentious attack on Stevens, has nevertheless some relevant, if incomplete, remarks about 'bacaudism' (see Comm. p. 292, 121.2).

73.2 **Conan ... Meriadoc** See Comm. p. 265, 23.3, p. 277, 63.3 Geoffrey, HRB, tells a ferociously garbled tale of the wives of the British legionaries (which has become intertwined with St Ursula and her eleven thousand virgins), working up a hint in Nennius' HB §27. Geoffrey's Conanus Meriadocus, however, is (mostly) John-George who had nothing to do with this episode. If we take Nennius' chronology as correct, and the Emperor as Maximus, JJ lies most naturally as the 'Conan Meriadoc' of *this* tale.

74.1 **Magister Epistolae** We have only the Romance of the 'Emperor Octavian' with the two twins 'Sir Octavius Jr.' (Merlin) and his brother 'Sir Florent[issimus]', 'sold to the Emperor **Clement** at Paris for some *solidi*', to make us wonder whether at about this time Maximus made JJ Caesar.

74.2 **missed Elissa** If Elissa's other name is **Dido,** JJ here plays the role of Aeneas to a tee, and 'Aeneas of *Lugdunensis*' translates into Old Welsh as 'Elydyr Lydanwen' (see Bartrum 1966, Index, where Aeneas figures too in his own right). No wonder the Romance and saga makers will insist on giving Elissa a funeral pyre.

74.3 **a brief monasticism** At Cassiciacum, 4 miles north-west of Varese near L. Maggiore. Autumn AD386. Augustine's *Confessions*, IX 3. (The reference to Monica and alcohol is in *Confessions*, IX 8). For Augustine's intimacy with JJ see his Ep. 146 which presupposes more than a casual acquaintanceship (see Comm. p. 293, 124.2).

74.4 **Faltonius Benedictus** See Comm. p. 274, 55.4, and Appendix 7. I do not lightly tamper with the dating of the Benedictine foundation legend. Nor, I think, do I injure it in any way. Our sole authority on Benedict is St Gregory I's *Dialogues*, and the only dating of the Cassino Benedict is by Totila. Gregory is an hagiographer not an historian. Benedict is a common enough name for a saint, and there is scope for more than one at Subiaco and Cassino. If I am right, the Faltonii would be the Lords of Nursia intermarried with the Anicii from whom Gregory himself descends. He could have had family traditions of the Sagro Speco to add to the information he received from the Cassino monks. May the thesis be left open for the duration of this book.

74.5 **one on Free Will** See Farrar 1907, II, p. 471 and citation therefrom. Augustine here expounds what was to be Pelagius (JJ's) own position on Free Will, with great lucidity. In AD427, nearly 40 years later, Augustine specifically withdrew this opinion (*Retractiones*, i, p. 23) and continued to write in a strictly Predestinationary way until the end of his life. His ultimate views were to inspire Calvin and Jansen.

75.1 **the Anio** A few miles above Subiaco.

75.2 **Brân Bendigaid** Also, Custennin Bendigaid (Bartrum 1966). Custennin for Constantine, a name JJ will not assume until AD407.

75.3 **Apulia (and Messina)** See Comm, p. 258, 2.1.

75.4 **house party** Including, according to St Gregory's *Dialogues*, Bk. II, six other nubile lasses. The scene is charmingly depicted in Plate 16 of the Rome 1628 edition of St Gregory.

75.5 **saunas** See Comm. p. 263, 15.4.

75.5 **to Cassino** Here I fall in, cheerfully enough, with the received Benedict legend.

75.6 **Tarentaise** If the *Vita* of St James of the Tarentaise is to be relied on, it is just possible that Benedict moved on to Lérins (as Honoratus). But Gregory (*Dialogue* II) says Honoratus was Benedict's *successor* at Subiaco – odd in itself in the light of the legend – and he throws in a 'Constantine' as his successor at Cassino and, for good measure, a 'Valentinian' at the *Lateran*. Probably the somewhat generalised epithet '*benedictus*' is the cause of the confusion, if such there be.

76.1 **Te Deum** cf. the 'Latinus' stone at Whithorn. Thomas (1981, pp. 283–4). (See also Comm. p. 272, 47.3.)

76.2 **poem about Jesus** 'De Salvatore'. Claudian, CM XXXII (Birt XCV).

76.3 **Novellae** See text p. 19, and Comm. p. 263, 19.1.

76.4 **huge literary industry** Evidenced in the huge volumes of the Bollandists, of the Benedictines, and of Colgan.

76.5 **Onesimus** See Book V. Conjectural. Zosimus was writing some miles down the Nile, and Onesimus could have been in contact.

77.1 **St Peter** 1 Peter, III 15.16.

77.2 **educated pagans** cf. Augustine's correspondence with Maximus of Madaura and Longinian. In fact the first ten books of the *City of God* were written to confound the Pagans.

77.3 **What is God?** **'What'**, not 'Who'? Recall Parzival's heartbroken outburst '*der Waleis sprach: "Wê, wâs ist Got?"*' (Springer in Loomis 1959, p. 227).

77.4 *ἀριμαθος* Remembered by the Welsh as *Matho*-lwch, and again as 'Math ap Mathonwy', 'Wise, Son of Wisdom': the clerically-minded Romancers will rashly identify him with that Joseph of Arimathea who buried Jesus.

77.5 ***Liber Gradalis*** ***The Book of Steps*** (cf. the 'step' visions of Zosimus in Berthelot 1888, pp. 117–20 and Sherwood Taylor 1976, pp. 57–60). This definition of the Graal allows room for various wonder-working images of apparatus and their products to surface under this or allied names in the confused imaginations of the Romance writers. Sherwood Taylor is an admirable introduction to the whole topic, but a complete reading of Berthelot (as re-presenting the underlying MSS) is inescapable for the serious student. He is not that long, nor that obscure, unlike the voluminous and chaotic writings of later alchemical authors to the present day. More of this in Book X.

78.1 **Theodosius** History, and Literature, will remember him as *Macrobius*, 'the long-lived', clearly a later epithet. He was Vicar of Spain in AD394, and most importantly Governor of Africa with Heraclian in AD410.

78.2 **Placidus** See text p. 75.

78.3 **Probus' villa** Identified as the Bradley Spring villa. Probus is Faltonia's son from Book VI, and also St Benedict's cousin, as there mentioned.

78.4 **later myths** cf. *Vita Gildae*, and most particularly the Mabinogion where the angry JJ/Brân wades across the St George's Channel to recover his bride.

79.1 **'To each cow its calf'** King Diarmaid's (Little John's) famous dictum in the 'copyright' dispute with Colum-Kill (*Colum*ba, A*chill*es, Little John again) in Irish myth. The copyright issue was probably the ownership of John-George's Cathach Psalter. Should it go back to JJ, or even Cousin Vic, together with Ambrose's psalter from which it was copied. In the event it remained in Ireland and is now in the Royal Irish Academy as MS 5n.

79.2 **Holy City of Sarras** Supposed final home of the Holy Graal, or rather the Sacred Lance, in the *Queste de Saint Graal*, mentioned also in *L'Estoire del Saint Graal* (texts identified in Loomis 1959, pp. 303, 313). The name still survives in Lyons where Fourvière borders on the plateau of 'Sarra'. Nothing to do with the Saracens, as the crusading Romancers will think. It appears on an inscription from Poitiers – see CIL XII (Nîmes) 5686–785, referred to in Holder vol. II, 1370 and Holder vol. II 341–2 gives us '*Justina quem peperit Sarra*', which is my justification for Comm. 80.2 below.

79.3 **Praetorium** Since 1896, the Basilica of Notre Dame de Fourvière.

80.1 **take up my Mithraism** Augustine, no less, is our informant that there were not a few Christian Mithraists at this time: '*usque adeo ut noverim aliquo tempore illius Pileati sacerdotem solere dicere "et ipse Pileatus Christianus est"*'(Augustine, Homilies on St John (vii.6) in Migne, PL Vol. 35 1. 1977 on).

80.2 **Avitian palace** See Comm. 79.2 above.

81.1 **place of worship** Originally the Basilica of the Maccabees. Eighty years later Bishop Patiens will rebuild it sumptuously and re-dedicate it to St Just. 'Titular' means an endowed church, usually under the patronage of the bishop. Cf. the 'titular' churches of Rome.

81.2 **papyrus** 'Cleopatra and the Philosophers' (Berthelot CAG 1888, trad. pp. 281–3. Gk 289–99. English extracts in Sherwood-Taylor (1976, pp. 55–6). This comprises sections 17 and 18 of Marciana MS 299 long since missing but which Berthelot has largely supplied from other MSS, e.g. Paris 2327, 2252. Other portions are recalled in the Latin '*Turba Philosophorum*', originating probably in (Kyot's) Toledo, whose ultimate source is lost – or is it? See Comm. p. 286, 98.1.

81.3 **ouija board** See Comm. p. 267, 26.2.

81.4 **Labyrinth** See text p. xxxii, and Comm. p. 288, 104.1.

82.1 **'our theme'** See text p. 77.

82.2 **Maccabee** Specifically, a descendant of John Hyrcanus, Ruling High Priest who died in 105 BC, 'of the course of Joarib' (David's line). I identify him as 'John the Archpriest', alchemist, whose sayings, extracted by Zosimus Panopolitanus, are in Berthelot CAG 1888, trad. pp. 252–6. See also Judas Maccabeus and the Laide Semblance in Sommer's *Vulgate* (ii) p. 231 (in Loomis 1959 p. 338) and also Comm. p. 267, 26.1.

82.3 **Tertius 'Synesius'** From Greek *συνίημι*; here, perhaps, conveying 'born in rather quick succession'.

82.4 **Gaudentius** Father of Aëtius, per Renatus Profuturus Frigidus, *apud* Gregory of Tours II. 8. (Not to be confused with Gaudentius bishop of Brescia.)

82.5 **Thaliarchus** See Horace, *Odes*, Bk. I, 9, v.2. This epithet, corrupted to Tallwch, Talorc etc., marks the father of Tristan/Aëtius. See also (*Gesta Romanorum*, CLIII) Apollonius of Tyre's 'Taliarchus', and the 'Taliard' of Shakespeare's *Pericles*. Nothing to do with the Pictish King 'Talorcan' of AD653–7 – a man of Orkney as his name tells us (Orkney was tributary to King Brudei, under its own 'regulus').

82.6 **arts of the table** *Gulae et ventri deditus*, writes R. Profuturus Frigidus (*apud* Gregory of Tours, HF ii, 9). See Comm. p. 313, 209.2 for **the very important reverberations of this.**

82.7 **'limerick' to JJ** In Claudian c.m.L. (Birt LXXVII). (Translation Platnauer in Claudian, Loeb, 1922.)

83.1 **Serapeion** In 390 (Clinton's dating) the great Temple of Serapis, and an adjacent Mithraeum, were demolished on Theodosius' orders. A basilica of John the Baptist replaced them, for which another of John's heads, supposedly preserved by Athanasius, was duly found. There is no indication that Theodosius explicitly ordered the dispersal of the Library, but this certainly ensued.

83.2 **grisly business** The Romancers' 'Aventure d'Ascalon le ténébreux', whose importance they stress but are unable to describe or explain. I have not elected to 'bury' Theodorus in the extant painted late Roman catacomb at Askalon, thinking that, as a vanquished usurping Augustus, he might only have received menial interment.

84.1 **lapis lazuli** The ancients called this 'sapphire'. Today's emeralds and sapphires to them were *beryls*. The terminology is here in transition. This is St David's magic sapphire altar – see below.

84.2 **legends will persist** *Vita St David* (Wade-Evans 1944) Cap. 48, p. 163.

86.1 **house of the sons of Promotus** The story from Zosimus V, 3 (*apud* Tillemont 1701, V, pp. 429–771). That it was a house of ill-repute is my own inference from the Count John story and Aristaenatus (Comm. 87.1 below).

86.2 **no name** The Romancers' '*C'il sans nom*'. Also Galvaginus, Walwen (whence Gawain) from 'Eugenius the sallow' Galba Eugenius. ('Owain the adulterer' or 'Little John' is sometimes, wrongly, called Gawain, especially as Gawayne and the Grene Knight. He was nobly born in legal wedlock and the Welsh remember him as Daniel Vab '*dremrudd*' from his ruddy freckled complexion. The confusion will be explained later.) See Comm. pp. 289-90, 109.3.

86.3 **burning their old huts** A first-hand account of Hunnish life and ways is in Priscus' account of his embassy AD448 to Attila, conveniently translated in Hodgkin (1880) II, the key reference at p. 82.

86.4 **Lake Balaton** An inland 'sea'. See Comm. p. 258, 1.6. The 'Merovech' there referred to is, *recte*, Meroveus. JJ (Meropeus the First) and Merlin's son Gawain (Merobaudes) are understandably confused.

87.1 **Λαικας** Per Aristaenatus 'scriptor eroticus', Consul in AD404, the year of her horrible death. She is the Romancers' '*la Reine qui meurt en grand douleurs*'. The full pitiful account is in Georgius Cedrenus (c. AD1100) who uses earlier Byzantine sources. Obstetrics seem to have been the Achilles heel of contemporary medicine.

88.1 **Aëtius** 'Little' Aëtius would be Ætsel, 'Etzel' of the Nibelungenlied, 'Hettel' of other sagas; not unreasonably confounded with Attila at a later date. We *know* nothing of his appearance, but from these diminutives we perhaps conjecture that he was of small stature.

88.2 **Eugenius** The historians know nothing of his origins, which must nevertheless have carried some weight. My conjecture is based on physical resemblances (coins and the British Museum's apotheosis ivory, probably commissioned by Symmachus). Berthelot CAG 1888, trad., p. 40 hesitantly awards him a recipe for alloying gold.

89.1 **falconry** See Comm. p. 316, 216.8, and Fig. 18.

89.2 **Chlamys** Theodosius had recently consigned the toga to near oblivion.

91.1 **auburn** See Plate 9, and text p. 29.

91.2 **Gothic fashion** You may study this on the medallion of Theodoric the Great, the Ostro-Goth, in the Museo Nazionale in Rome. Also on the column of Theodosius in the Hippodrome of Constantinople, where all the Gothic contingent wear it. Indeed Alaric is almost certainly portrayed there, but the reliefs are now too weathered to make him out.

92.1 **dining-room** The full ground plan of the Palace has not yet been recovered. This description is modelled instead on the Belvedere Triclinium at Sirmione.

92.2 **Uncle Ted kept a good table** The menu is collected from Apicius. Our witnesses are Zosimus, Philostorgius, and S. Aurelius Victor Jr *apud* Tillemont 1701, V, p. 393, which I have followed conscientiously.

93.1 **prepossessing** His coins are indefinite, but the Rothschild cameo fully confirms my description.

94.1 **little David** Later **St David.** My thesis is that this is when and how Merlin acquired the 'David' epithet. The Welsh remember him primarily as '*Dewi Sant*' the magician saint. The Irish High Crosses show an extraordinary concentration on David as harpist, and **this may have given rise to the Harp as badge of Ireland.**

95.1 **essay** (Berthelot CAG 1888, trad. pp. 409–15. Vatican MS Cp, p. 378. My attribution is conjectural, but not improbable as this book will maintain.) The tract is dedicated to Uncle Ted and contrives to be at once quaint and informative. Modern scholars, since Berthelot, have been at a loss to explain and translate *ἰοσις* which appears in this tract and elsewhere. May I help them out? *ἰος* is Latin *venenum*, venom (especially of serpents). It means an exudation or encrustation (including rust and verdigris), unlike water in that it carries a 'kick' or sting (cf. *μεμφομαι*, whence Pindar 0.6, l.79 calls honey '*ἰος ἀμεμφης μελισσαν*', the harmless 'venom' of bees). Thus it includes the newly-discovered strong acids, and 'iosis' is the process of exposure to the strong acids, generally resulting in oxidisation. More of all this in Book X. See also Comm. p. 288, 103.2 and 103.3.

95.2 **clown** Merlin is in fact the Fool in Shakespeare's *King Lear*. Shakespeare created him, and Edgar, and Edmund (Ædonius) to do justice to Merlin's multi-faceted personality. Conversely, in that play, he conflated Galla and Ginger in Regan. The whole action of *King Lear* thus takes place between April 393 and January 395. Shakespeare had more to say about the characters in this book in other plays.

97.1 **Convent of the Resurrection** Taking van Millingen as my topographer, I locate the Novatian church on the ridge above the Golden Horn, from the church of St Theodore at the top to St John de Cornibus by the harbour, North of the present Suleymanyeh Mosque.

97.2 **tutor of the royal princes** An informed guess. Heliodorus had been tutor of Valens' daughters, Anastasia and Carosia. Arcadius and Honorius had first Themistius then Arsenius as tutors. On the latter's departure to become a Desert Father, it does not seem unreasonable that Ted should have turned to his experienced brother to carry on the ungrateful task.

97.3 **Bishop Wilberforce** 'Soapy Sam', Bishop of Oxford 1845–69, of Winchester

1869–73. Perturbed but not dismayed when in 1851 his brother-in-law (Cardinal) Manning, his three Wilberforce brothers and his daughter and son-in-law all followed Newman into the Roman Church, he set out to stabilise the Church of England, reviving Convocation and founding Cuddesdon Theological College. He thus played a major part in restoring the confidence of the Church of England.

98.1 **Eucheria's papyrus** See Comm. p. 283, 81.2. Yet another version of this survives in an Arabic tract of Ibn Umail, and in a Latin translation (1192) from the Arabic called 'Calid and Morienus'. The transmission is from Constantinople (per Nestorius?) to Nisibis, where Sergius of Rasain translates from the Syriac into Arabic, to Morien, and thence Westwards to Toledo, where some works were translated into Latin.

98.2 **twin Cathedrals** Twin basilicas were very much in fashion at his time. Bologna shows a good example at St Stefano and there are others at Metz and at Paris (Sts Etienne/Geneviève); while the substantial remains under the Cathedral in Geneva have recently been discovered and marvellously displayed.

98.3 **Patriarch** Heron held this office following an irregular ordination, for barely 24 hours. Next came St Gregory Nazianzus for an uneasy month; finally, Nectarius picked up the bits.

99.1 **Bolos of Mende** (in the Egyptian Delta) The alchemical works in Berthelot CAG ascribed to Democritus, and commented upon by Synesius, are his. My tendency is to identify with him Aristobulus of Paneas (Caesarea Philippi) fl. c. 160BC, one of the Septuagint translators in Alexandria. Very much a 'Maccabee' family hero, we find links here with Cleopatra-Mariamne (see below) the celebrated alchemist, and the Blessed Virgin Mary's mother.

99.2 **Zosimus of Panoplis** Compiler and redactor of the earlier alchemical tracts forming part of Berthelot CAG (and redistributed, under 'authors', by Berthelot himself). See Comm. p. 259, 4.2. He must not be confused with Count Zosimus the Byzantine Historian of the third quarter of the Fifth Century, whose work this book so closely follows.

100.1 *ἀκοιμετης* There is perhaps an allusion to this in Claudian's lampoon on Hadrian, the sleepless Egyptian of text p. 119. It is worth noting that the customary Latin for this is 'Agrippa' (Welsh Griffith) and the sense links with '*Γρεγορειτε*', 'Gregory' of text p. 123. All these names circle around the Romance legends, and in the Celtic 'Bangors', in which connection, St Fillan 9/1 (John-George) St Columba and St Kentigern (ibid.) all are recorded as chanting the psalms 'by companies'.

100.2 **humble pie** See text p. 126, and Comm. p. 293, 126.1.

100.3 **bleaching powder** In the margin of p. 112 of *Codex* MS 299 we find an interesting 'aludel' glossed '*καρκινος δ' ἐπι Λευκωσεως*' (and see Berthelot 1888, CAG I, p. 149). Although no actual recipe for this survives in CAG, the *Summa Perfectionis* (AD1300) of the 'Latin Geber' (see Comm. p. 320, 232.5) is the first MS we have which treats of Aqua Regia (Nitric and Hydrochloric Acid mixed). Having traced all (save Chinese) alchemical ideas back to a confluence at Constantinople in the Fourth and Fifth Centuries, I am reasonably sure that they would have encountered chlorine there in the course of their distillations and sublimations, and the MS 299 gloss appears confirmatory of this. (The Chinese were well into goldmaking by the mid-Second Century BC, and would have welcomed the Seventh Century AD Nestorians the more readily if they brought them some of the 'missing chapters' of the *Liber Gradalis*. But that's another matter.)

101.1 **speciality** 'Cordials' they were called, from their therapeutic effects. I think they were the source of many of the Romance notions of the 'feeding' Holy Graal, the Still seen as Cornucopia. That the Graal should have actually dispensed 'meats' seems a grotesque misunderstanding. The 'bleeding Lance', could well be a memory of distillate dripping from a retort. If mercury be sublimed with sulphur the resulting vermilion drops would much resemble blood; indeed there is an actual 'recipe' for making vermilion in this way in Berthelot (CAG 1888, trad. pp. 39–40).

101.2 **quotation** *ἐιπε πως κατερχεται το ἀνωτατον, και πως ἐγγιζει το μεσον προς το ἀνωτατον ἐλθειν και ἑνωθηναι το μεσον, και τι στοιχειον ἀυτοις. και πως κατερχονται τα ὑδατα ἐυλογημενα* (Berthelot 1888, Greek, p. 292). The full thrilling explanation is given by Cleopatra-Mariamne herself, and the whole passage alarmingly resembles the 'Questions of Bartholomew' (to Mary) in the Apocryphal New Testament (M. R. James 1924, pp. 170–20). There are other resonances of Cana in Galilee in Berthelot (1888, II, p. 263) which I here give only in Greek: *πορευου κατα το σπηλαιον του 'Οστανου, και ὁρα των ὑδατων τα ἀγγεια ἐις πληθος ἀυτω παρασκευασθεντα και ποτιμου ὑδατος πληρωσας*; cf. John II. 6: *'Ησαν δε ἐκει ὑδριαι λιθιναι ἐξ κειμεναι … χωρουσαι ἀνα μετρητας δυο ἠ τρεις. Λεγει ἀυτοις … Γεμισατε τας ὑδριας ὑδατος: και ἐγεμισαν ἀντας ἑως ἀνω.* How the Holy Family came to be so closely involved in alchemy is a matter best reserved for my next book. All I would say here is that the terminology of the day was thoroughly familiar to Jesus.

101.3 **Summer Palace** Hebdomon Bakirköy on Cape Magnaurus.

101.4 **Agricola and Vitalis** Their church, and most of their relics presented by Ambrose (although some in Florence), survives at Bologna. Am I being perhaps unnecessarily cheeky in this suggestion? I think not. Ambrose had not only 'invented' the relics of St Gervasius and St Protasius, but invented their legend. He was capable, in all piety, of 'inventing' these latest martyrs. We do not know he so named them, nor why.

101.5 **fellow Cambrians** See Comm. p. 319, 231.2.

101.6 **home from Chalcedon** The sources diverge. One puts the Head at Panteichion (Pendik) 16 miles South of Chalcedon on the Sea of Marmora, nevertheless in the Province of Chalcedon. Valens had made an earlier attempt to obtain it.

102.1 **St John in Trullo** In the Fener Quarter. Here Ted was able to see the Head deposited, and to salute it, as he left by the Adrianople Gate on his last doomed journey to Aquileia and Milan. Socrates confirms that he had it with him at the Hebdomon Palace until that time.

102.2 **Pelagius** (the alchemist) Berthelot (CAG 1888, trad. pp. 243–50), and a reference by Olympiodorus on p. 96 (ibid.). Look forwards, too, to the Romance Kings Pelles, Pellinor, Pellehan, Pellean, Parlaam, and other variants of *Pelagianus*, and see Comm. p. 267, 27.2. There is a further suggestion of JJ's alchemical activities in 'Háva mál', second poem of the 'Elder' 'Edda' (edach) in Old Icelandic (l. 138ff., ***apud*** H. M. Chadwick '"The Cult of Othin", an essay in the ancient religion of the North', London, C. J. Clay, Cambridge University Press 1899). There is a 'visionary' quality in this poem like the alchemical visions in Zosimus of Panoplis, especially the poor little man of copper in Sherwood Taylor (pp. 58–9) who suffers grievously, yet apparently willingly, in the cause of alchemical 'purification', and ends up silvered or even gilded. And JJ is the Man of Bronze, Aeneas, Elydir Lydanwen. Did JJ write this Icelandic 'novella' at Cycnus Coven whilst working on his 'gilding' tract? And take it with him to the *Agri Decumates*? Worth considering. All ties in well with JJ/Gaudentius as Odin.

102.3 **telescope** See text p. 45.

102.4 **Lens grinders ... apparatus** Lenses were ground from rock crystal (optical glass comes later). The apparatus should much have resembled Tschirnhaus' (d.1708) 'catacaustic' machine still extant at Dresden (see Fig. 20).

102.5 **Glass mirror** The glass was backed with tin-mercury amalgam. Pliny (*Natural History* XXXVI, 66, p. 193) mentions a factory in Sidon, and a Roman glass mirror was found at San Remo. The technology was there.

103.1 **The Egyptians were right** The mystical tradition of light is fully treated in Anderson (1987), where this aspect of the Holy Grail traditions is taken back to its roots.

103.2 **dangerous fluid** See Comm. p. 285, 95.1 Cleopatra gives a 'health warning' about it, calling it a 'fiery product' (Berthelot 1885, MS 2–527 ff.138, 2–250, 163).

103.3 **Odin the Giant ... Mime the dwarf ... serpent's venom** JJ, Merlin and Ouroboros, the tail-biting serpent of Cleopatra's Goldmaking (Berthelot CAG 1888, Intro., pp. 132–3). The inner circle of the serpent bears the Greek inscription (my translation) 'This is the serpent, who has his venom in two guises'. Merlin/Claudian writes of Ouroboros (*De Consulata Stilichonis*, Bk. II, lines 426–30) in terms recalling Act II of Wagner's Siegfried. But then **Ouroboros is the Ring of the Nibelungen** as Wagner well knew. Did he know why? E. Tonnelat (in *New Larousse Encyclopaedia of Mythology*, Hamlyn 1959, pp. 252–8) makes some very pertinent remarks. (1) Earlier scholars have regarded Woden as a *jumped-up* God who 'has managed to oust the more important deities' (Tonnelat distances himself unconvincingly from this view). (2) Woden wears a wide-brimmed hat (πετασος). (3) He is **not** the Leader of the Wild Hunt (I say that will be Merlin, AD410–414). (4) 'in spite of his patronage of battles he [Woden] does not fight in them [Ailill, Edge of Battle]. (5) He wears a golden helmet [Roman cavalry parade helmet]. (6) He loses his eye to Mimir the wise dwarf in drinking from the 'fountain' [retort] of knowledge. (7) ' Odin was never considered to be an immortal god'. To this I add the testimony of Saxo Grammaticus (per Ritson, Diss. p. 30, in Giles 1841, p. xxxviii): 'Saxo ... knew nothing of any Odin but a magician whom the stupidity of the inhabitants of Upsal adored as a God'. I think I may not be too bold in designating Odin as JJ/Gaudentius in text p. 82.

104.1 **Labyrinth ... Nothing to be seen by that time** Merlin nods. Sir Arthur Evans is to uncover the whole palace of Knossos, revealing a ground plan identical to that on the Augustus coin, but not quite the same as 'Solomon's Labyrinth'. The Knossos labyrinth, adapted from the rectangular design on the coin to a circular form, but otherwise unchanged, appears twice carved on the cliff of lower St *Nectan*'s Glen, near Tintagel (see Plate 3), and again in identical form on the Hollywood stone (see Plate 2) which stood formerly at Cillin Chaoimhin (Kil Kevin, i.e. Little John) on St Kevin's Road to Glendalough in Wicklow, and is now in Dublin Museum. Solomon's Labyrynth has been inserted on the back of F102 of Marciana MS 299, Berthelot thinks as late as the fourteenth century (MS 299 is tenth century). It also appears in identical form on the floor of Chartres Cathedral. It follows the same scheme as the Knossos (round) labyrynth but has been enlarged and extended, giving the *appearance* of division into four cantons, where Knossos appears homogeneous. **It symbolises a Quest. No more. No less.**

104.2 **Askalon** A coin of Askalon was found in a private garden of Rue de Dinant,

Falmignoul in 1966. Falmignoul lies three miles West of Furfooz and five miles South of Dinant across the River Lesse. It is hard not to associate it with Merlin. The coin, now in the Brussels Cabinet des Medailles, is a bronze of Domitian. (See report in quarterly *Bulletin* for May 1979 of the *Société Dinantaise de Recherches*, p. 15).

105.1 ***Lacus Pergus*** Now the Lago di Perdusa, four miles SSE of Enna, and a mecca for water-skiers.

106.1 **Alaric** I cannot tell you his Gothic birth-name, although amateurs of Late Imperial Roman Plate may toy with the, not improbable, idea that it was 'Seuso'. 'Alaric King of the *Ala*' looks all too like an onomastic epithet.

107.1 **called him Quintus** See Comm. p. 269, 33.3; also text p. 119. This would be rather 'U' for the Constantiniani, who were really a bit 'nouveau'. However he is Merlin's fifth child, so Quintus Quintianus will have to serve awhile. (See C. Apollinaris Sidonius Carmina IX, l.290. The poem goes on to praise his support as Oliver to Aëtius' Roland, or Bego to Garin if you prefer.)

107.2 **family name** See Book I, p. 3, para 2 and App. 1.

108.1 **Transubstantiation** The Medieval Schoolmen only knew their Aristotle in a Latin version of an Arabic version of the Greek. As they saw it, to deny Transubstantiation was thus to deny the very *possibility* of any 'Real Presence', as Thomas Aquinas makes all too clear in his 'Summa'. Would that that they had known Greek.

109.1 **Consubstantiation** This was the belief of Uncle Ted (and in such case, we can hardly doubt, of Ambrose), of Nectarius probably, of John Chrysostom certainly (Clinton 1850, II, p. 521), and see Comm. p. 290, 110.1; and probably of Sisinnius, Heliodorus' successor as Novatian Bishop, and predecessor (AD 426–8) of Nestorius as Patriarch of Constantinople. The Eastern Church has remained essentially consubstantianist, holding further that such change as occurs in the elements is occasioned by the action of the Holy Spirit. Hence the 'Epiklēsis' (See John XVII.21–3 and Romans VII.11).

109.2 **bridal veil** This may be an anachronism. Some concealment, however, would have been appropriate.

109.3 ***Persei filii*** This classical allusion **opens many doors**. The key is that there are **two** 'Percevals' (however spelt) whom the Romancers have been unable to disentangle, conflating them and their exploits haphazardly. Wolfram does well in making 'Parzifal' and 'Feirefiz' half-brothers (he gets the 'vibes' of the latter name right, too, as we shall see), but is otherwise in a great muddle, bringing in the two Gawains as a third person. Basically Wolfram's 'Parzifal' is Aëtius, conflating some of Quintus Merobaudes/Gawain's *enfances* and exploits. Basically Chrestien's 'Perceval' is QM/Gawain. How does he get the name 'Feirefiz' and give that name to the *Casa Belgica* as 'Furfooz'? Simple really: Wolfram (Hatto 1980, p. 40), has his (foster) mother name him '*vair fils*' from *ferae filius* of Comm. p. 272, 47.2. He is 'Orson', the wild man of the woods, to Aëtius' 'Valentine'. Now we come to '**Peredur**' (from Welsh '*Paladyr*', a spear). Any '*Dux*' would bear one and it might well be stained red (cf. Rhun Rud Paladyr 'the Roman with the Red Spear'). The Monza ivory referred to in Comm. p. 291, 116.2 and Fig. 32 shows Stilicho in precisely this pose). There is a significant comment in Iolo (MSS 1888, p. 39 (Welsh), p. 415 (English)) that the Britons refused 'Cysteint' (Constans) son of Cystenin (JJ) as Prince (*princeps*, 'Brenhin') because, being maimed, he was no longer eligible as a 'Tywysawg [*Dux*] of the sceptre' (*imperator*). (My translation from the Welsh, as against Iolo, p. 415.) (They go on to invite Vortigern II (Merlin) to be King.) **The Welsh 'Peredur' is thus basically Little John**, pseudo-Gawain, Owein, Nitonius Pompeius Eugenius Constans, but Aëtius also qualifies as a spearholder. No wonder the Romancers are confused about their parentage, loves and deeds. I will do my best to make all clear.

110.1 **Gainas the Goth** It is worth noting that he was no mere ignorant barbarian soldier. He entered into a long correspondence with St John Chrysostom about the doctrine of 'Consubstantiation' which John handed over to his disciple St Nilus, himself, significantly, an alchemist and contributor to the *Liber Gradalis*, to deal with.

111.1 **Ephialtēs** Greek *ἐπιάλομαι*, Latin *incubo*, an 'incubus' or nightmare; also, in medieval thought, one born as the result of such an unwelcome nocturnal visitor. Hence all the 'monkish' lives of Merlin make him an incubus, and ascribe to him a fiendish origin as 'the boy without a father'. If their works were to be retranslated into Greek he would appear as 'Merlin 'Εφιαλτης'. Now, who's **'Desdemona'**(*του δαιμονου*), the demon's daughter? All shall be revealed.

112.1 **what I have already written** In the works of 'Claudius Claudianus', still in print; Eunapius survives mainly as a source of Zosimus the historian, or in Photius' epitome.

112.2 **Joyeuse Garde** After Serena's death in AD408 it would have remained in control of the *Comes Rerum Privatorum* (Keeper of the Privy Purse) and was more or less unoccupied until Galla Placidia achieved the throne.

113.1 **black robes** Echoed in text, p. 118). This is the best use I can make of Eunapius' comment (in Tillemont 1701, V, pp. 433–4), which sounds authentic, even important, but is not readily comprehensible.

113.2 **concealed by its cowl** Merlin perhaps appears in this guise on the Franks Casket (British Museum).

114.1 **own words** Claudian, *In Rufinum*, Bk. II, lines 348–439. Rather horrible don't you think? The scene is re-echoed in the 'Pelagian' letter 'De Vita Christiana' (Migne PL 40–1035(3)) and Liebeschuetz is undoubtedly right in referring the reference to Rufinus. We shall soon learn why. (W. Liebeschuetz in 'Latomus' (1967) vol. 26, pp. 440, 442–3). Plainly the 'Pelagian' author knew his Claudian. Have I got something up my sleeve? All right, I'll tell you: the 'Pelagian author is none other than John-George. See Comm. p. 307, 189.2. John-George is none other than the 'Sicilian Briton'.

115.1 **constantly refer you** In Comm. pp. 260, 7.4; 266, 25.3.

115.2 **Gigantomachia** *Γιγαντομαχια*. See Latin version lines 66–7.

115.3 **Ephialtēs and Otus** With JJ cast as *Iago*/Otus, Ephialtēs/Merlin is available for the sardonic epithet *Otello*, little Otus; Romance Otuel, Otinello etc. We shall see why and from whom ere long. *Desdemona* has already been mentioned above.

115.4 **Taurus II** Son of Aurelian (Synesius Ep. 31). The identification of Aurelian's father as Palladius *Rutilius* Taurus Æmilianus was demonstrated to Bury's satisfaction by Borghesi and Seeck (see Bury's Gibbon, App. XXVII). I think I am the first to give the poet Namatianus a father.

115.5 **Count Aurelian** He is Synesius' 'Osiris' in Synesius' 'Egyptian' squib (Bury's Gibbon, App. XXVII is explanatory). Aurelian tried to counter Rufinus' (and Ginger's) pro-Goth policy and narrowly survived Gainas' revolt of AD400 in consequence). His 'wicked' brother 'Typhos' was strongly pro-Goth. The two discordant brothers ruled the East for eight years in alternation, while Doxy sat on the fence. Both fell from power on Doxy's death.

115.6 **Flavius Alaricus** Like his brother-in-law Stilicho, Alaric would have received his grant of Roman citizenship from, and on becoming the son-in-law of, Flavius Theodosius Augustus. (Some scholars write that 'Flavius' had by now become a military honorific. Not yet.)

115.7 **Marcella's Bible Classes** Farrar 1907, Vol. II, p. 291, citing many letters from Jerome.

116.1 **six foot tall** A splendid ivory of him as '*Dux*', nay as 'Magister Militum', is extant in the Treasury of the Duomo at Monza, Milan, and is shown as Fig. 32.

117.1 **count** *Comes*, companion, peer, at varying levels. At the top level they were 'companions of the Augustus', members of his Consistory or Privy Council. The chancellors of the Public and Private Purses were Counts. Military Counts were of lower status but senior to Dukes. Some of the older Civilian Governorships were Countships (Counties), most notably North-West Africa and Tripolitania.

117.2 **Cad-wallon** Welsh, '*cad gollwng*', battle dodger; Irish, 'Edge of Battle'.

118.1 **'Enemy of the Republic'** Despite his obedience, he was nevertheless so posted by Eutropius, as cover for the later plot with Gildo.

118.2 **Illyricum** The Notitia confirms that Theodosius had made a *de facto* partition of North and South Illyricum, allotting Dalmatia to the Western Empire. Was this intended to be a temporary measure? That's what Goneryl and Regan were fighting about.

119.1 **Egyptian** Claudian calls Hadrian 'Pharius' from the famous Pharos or lighthouse of Alexandria. Presumably he, like Claudian, spent his infancy there.

119.2 **grandmother** Grandmother via Doxy; step-grandmother via JJ and Merlin (see App. 4).

120.1 **'Dame du Lac'** Loomis (1959, pp. 297f, 330f, 353, 384, 414) makes it pretty clear that 'our Morgan' is intended. I have provided an onomastic explanation accordingly. Profuturus Frigidus, *apud* Gregory of Tours (II.8) calls her 'Itala' (for *Italica)* and Augustine (Ep. 133) commiserates with her at the time of the Fall of Rome, AD410. Since Morgan is plainly intended Frigidus should have made her Aëtius' foster-mother. The Marcelli were 'Italians' (Vitaliani) of the 'Mezzogiorno', as I explain in Comm. p. 258, 2.1. 'Italica' is a personal name deriving from this.

120.2 **eye ointment box** The site of **this very singular find,** now in the British Museum, is Golden Bridge (Grid ref. S.01.38) West of Cashel, County Tipperary. The inscription has been read as (my translation): 'Marcus Jr. [probably the optician] *Zinc Eye Ointment of Dionysus*; for old scars'. (See *Proc. Royal Irish Academy*, Vol. 73C, p. 74, no. 25). A similar inscription unsurprisingly, is at Lydney – see *Soc. Ant. Res. Rep.*, IX).

120.3 **Cousin Vic** Currently still Archbishop of Rouen. Morgan forgets – if she ever knew – JJ's evangelistic spell in the Tarentaise in 390 (see Comm. p. 282, 75.6). The Apostle of the Isère, they called him. The Irish will remember him as Iserninus, Asurnai, Sorney.

120.4 **Morini** Glorious Dad is Chaucer's 'Sir Topaz [T. Ulpius] of Poperinghe', No. 4 in Group B of the *Canterbury Tales*. A pot-pourri of much material in *I Merlin* will be found in 'The Man of Law's Tale', too late in date to be serviceable.

120.5 **the Turcii** Some rather bold conjectures here, derived from Holder, which link with and explain the ownership of the famous Esquiline Treasure (in the British Museum), are developed more fully in Comm. p. 293, 127.1. Let me just hint that 'Aunt Marcella' (see App. 6 and Comm. p. 291, 115.7, was the early-widowed second wife of Asterius L. Turcius Secundus of Fiesole, and quondam governor of Tuscany.

121.1 **alchemy** During his three years in New Rome Tertius Synesius was able to make a very substantial contribution to the Holy Graal with his commentary on 'Democritus'. A long letter to Dioscorus priest of the Serapeion, probably before AD390, informs us of his intention to write this, although, if ever completed, it is no longer directly extant (Berthelot 1888, CAG, trad., p. 75).

121.2 **Peasant Revolts** (Bacaudic) The Bacaudae (from Βαχαω, 'to rave with Bacchic frenzy', 'to go ape' in modern parlance), gave the Roman authorities increasing problems from the time of Maximian Augustus (d.305) the builder of the Casa Sicelis. From 408 the revolts became chronic in the Gauls, and Spain. Thompson (1977) makes a barely temperate attack on Stevens, Myres, Morris and Frere in his attempt to prove that the British *coup d'état* of AD409 (a) owed nothing to the inspiration of 'socialist' Pelagianism, but (b) owed everything to 'Bacaudism'. I do not think he makes his points. I offer here an obvious explanation, eschewing happily for the moment both Pelagius and Bacchus.

121.3 **Lucius Wihtigils** Here we join forces with Nennius' *History of the Britons* (Cap 31). His genealogies may now be conflated, corrected, and most importantly, dated.

121.4 **Hengist and Horsa** 'Hengest' is a corruption of Eugenius, and would therefore serve either for John-George or for Merobaudes-Gawain. 'Horsa' is a corruption of 'HRoss' the 'Red' [HR]Ossa 'gylellfawr'. This makes it likeliest that **both** epithets refer to John-*anelathus*/Hamlet, later to succeed his uncle as Vortigern III.

121.5 **Lucius Hiberius** It is not clear whether Geoffrey of Monmouth (HRB) intended 'of Spain' or 'of Ireland'. As it happens either will serve, but Spain is apt to the date of this episode, which is post-AD419.

121.6 **several** See Index to Claudian.

121.7 **write her one too** 'In praise of Serena' (CM. XXX, Birt, XXIX).

121.8 **his own Basilica** Now called San Ambrogio after him.

122.1 **Oedipus ... Jocasta** Alas yes, Little John will kill his father. As to Jocasta, Wolfram gives us an Antigone (her incestuous daughter) for whom in due course I shall display both a name, an epitaph and a sumptuous sarcophagus (see Comm. p. 326, 245.3).

122.2 **the Amazon** See text p. 47. Brünnhilde has the same sporting talents in the *Nibelungenlied*, Chapter VII.

123.1 **best hunting** King Leopold I of the Belgians will build his Royal Hunting Lodge nearby.

123.2 **forest fire** My rationalisation of Wagner. Thence, c.AD 412, Aëtius/Siegfried will rescue her.

123.3 **Elsa of Brabant** Lohengrin I is Merlin: see Comm. p. 266, 25.9. Lohengrin II is Gawain II, is Q. Flavius Merobaudes.

123.4 **Genovefa of the Ardennes** The Atalanta of the Ardennes (Romance Ardanata) (see Comm. p. 278, 65.3 above). In legend she spends six years in a cave in the Ardennes, 'nourished by a roe' (*capreola*; cf. Carpilia). Siegfried discovers her there.

123.5 **Georgios/Gregorios** The alternation is shown in B.Cod Paris Graec. 2669 for Gregorios 'Pardos' Metropolitan of Corinth (see Pauly-Wissowa 'Gregory'), and more accessibly in the case of Gregory of Tours.

123.6 **Ende** Colgan, or rather his source MacCrodin, c.1390, has conflated 'Benedict' (JJ), with 'Benignus' (John) under the variants Endeus, Ende, Euda (for JJ) and Einne, Anna (for John) with disastrous effects on the family relationships therein set out. They can now be corrected.

123.7 **familiar names** (As surviving on and around Aran-Mor.) Aengus (Eugenius/Hengest), Bheanain II (Benignus), Bhreacain III (Brychan), Ceannanach (Cernunnus/Finn Benachie from his horned Viking helmet at a later stage), Cheathrais Alainn (Bedivere/Quattuor, Alainn/hound), Chiarain [C]Ronan (Coronatus), Choncuir II (Constans coronatus), Coemhen (Kervin, Kevin from Cuaran/Coronatus), Col.man mac Duagh (*Columbanus filius Dominus* [JJ]); also Loman (from Columbanus), Cubi/Gybi (Cubicularius, or else Cu-Bikanus/Merlin, CuChulainn, Eochill (Achilles and cf. Colum-*kill*), Eoghan (Owein/Eugenius), Gregory. John survives outside Aran as St Budoc (renowned), St Declan (*Deo colanus* St Collen II), St Fortchern II (*turannus maurus*), Madoc (Marcianus dux), Maelduin (Μεγαλος *Juvencus*/Juan), St Ruadan (the ruddy cf. Bôdb. III the Red, Ross the Red), and many more.

123.8 **impecunious** It was not until he acquired the income of these Estates that Stilicho could consider accepting the Consulate, since the whole cost of the resulting 'Lord Mayor's Show' came out of the Consul's private purse.

124.1 **controversy** Augustine's wanton past and his unquestioned Manicheism were not unjustly held against him. Quite a man with his pen, Augustine.

124.2 **'dearest brothers'** actually '*dilectissimo et desideratissimo*', which is almost untranslateably chummy; so commences Augustine's Ep. 146 to Pelagius. See Comm. p. 281, 74.3.

124.3 **Capriolae** See Comm. pp. 258, 1.7 and 280, 70.5.

125.1 **Celerina** See Claudian c.m. XXV (Birt LXXX).

125.2 **recently widowed** I make her the widow of Merlin's patron Anicius Probinus, Consul in AD395, to whom in Comm. p. 274, 55.4. I tentatively assign the Shapwick/Glastonbury Villa. In March AD397 Probinus assumed the Pro-Consulship of Africa, to be promptly shipwrecked in Gildo's rebellion. Whether he died in the fighting, or fled maybe to Cyrene and died of illness or a broken heart I do not know, so have not written. Certainly his promising career ends abruptly at the age of 37.

126.1 **I grovelled** Claudian c.m. XXII (Birt LXXX).

127.1 **travelling casket** Similar to the 'Muses' Casket in the famous Esquiline Treasure, pride and joy of the British Museum. The whole of Shelton (1981) is here prayed-in-aid. Shelton establishes beyond doubt the existence of the 'Esquiline' workshop, (not, in my view, necessarily on the Esquiline itself), and makes interesting links with Mildenhall and Traprain Law. Her comparisons at Plate 23 are conclusive. Plate 30, the 'Erôtes' flask, to my eye, shows considerable similarity to the Traprain

Law 'Adam and Eve' flagon. I offer here a fresh solution to her attempts to identify the various owners. The key is that 'Projecta' is an ephemeral surname, signifying one prostrate, in preparation for baptism. The rectangular casket is plainly a christening present, indeed the Lateran Baptistry can be clearly seen in Shelton's Plate 6. She is 'of riper years'. I therefore surmise that she is Æmilia Paterna, first wife of Secundus (see Genealogical stemma on Shelton's p. 34). There is room, time, and probability for him to marry as his second wife Marcella Turciae, C.F., da. of a *Vir Consularis*, wife of 'Tussius' (read Turcius) per C.I.L. X 3862 (an inscription at St Maria di Capua, which is apt enough for the Aurelii-Marcelli). See also Holder (1896), Vol. II 1994. Do we not have here 'Aunt Marcella'? She who, prematurely widowed, gave away all her jewellery on becoming a sort of lay-abbess on the Aventine. (Farrar 1907, II, pp. 290–1). The remaining inscriptions on the Esquiline Treasure, and the subject of the Damasine epitaph can now be readily identified, but this book has other fish to fry.

127.2 **Dinner service** This is conjecture – see following Note.

127.3 **Ursula** Some of it will end up in the **Traprain Law** Treasure, pride and joy of the National Museum of Antiquities, Edinburgh.

128.1 **Paula** For Paula's family relationships and story see Farrar (1907, Index).

128.2 **Bethlehem Pilgrim Hospice** The 'Xenodochium' of Farrar (1907 II, pp. 308–9) where (c. AD391) Jerome sends his brother Paulinian home to raise funds. I have felt able to assume that subsequent fundraising expeditions would have been necessary.

128.3 **Trier would be sacked** Salvian (de Gubernatoriis) is our authority for this. Unfortunately he gives no dates; I have therefore inserted these occurrences in the narrative wherever they lie most circumstantially.

128.4 **Sinadon** See Loomis (1959, pp. 371–2, 392, 513). Stirling is Froissart's candidate. Sinadon Hills above Dorchester, Oxon, could deserve support, to judge from the coin hoards and barbarian military cemeteries thereabout (Frere, in Arch Jnl 141, 1984, pp. 130–5). Romancers have a way of relocating sites to areas familiar to their hearers. Nothing new in this. The Greek bards did just the same to the Giant **Orion** when they got to Magna Graecia, making his last great leap take him to Rhegium and Sicily, where earlier, his furthest West had been Epirus. Rather apt.

128.5 **decapitating** See text pp. 109, 110.

128.6 **father of Attila** Jordanes gives us Bleda and Attila, brothers and joint Kings, as sons of 'Mundiuch'. He says they succeeded Octar and *Ruas* (*Roua*, *Regulus*, both killed in AD433), also '*sons* of Mundiuch'. The dates are unworkable genealogically. A possible solution would be to make Attila Mundiuch's grandson. Not really important, Ruas is real. Attila is real. 'Mundiuch' may well be the least real of them all – see Comm. p. 305, 183.1.

129.1 **St Declan (*inter alia*)** See Comm. p. 293, 123.7 for John's other saintly Irish names.

129.2 **Repoussé** This is how I translate 'spherulatis' (from Greek *σφυρα*, hammer and *ἐλαυνω*, drawn or wrought), in the celebrated extract from 'Melchinus of Avalon' (John-George, Mael-cu, *Μεγαλος κυων*) in John of Glastonbury. You will see how I treat this passage in the Epilogue.

129.3 **Achilles** Son of Pēleūs and Thetis (JJ and Elissa). You may sport (without improbability) with the idea that John is the contemporary 'saucy' author 'Achilles Tatius' (see Comm. p. 268, 31.1 and p. 298, 148.3). The ninth-century Romance

'Waltharius' confuses Walthar (Valteger, Vawrtigernus-John) and Hagan II, who indeed 'skulks' Achilles-style. The true protagonists are Theodoric the Vizi-Goth as 'Walthar' and Aëtius as Hagen II; but Aëtius is needed to play Siegfried.

129.4 **statue of Helios** To be splendidly depicted on a mosaic at Olbia Theodorias in Cyrenaica. (See Goodchild in Bacon 1960, p. 252). In classical mythology Helios was the son ('Hyperion II of Sicily') of Hyperion I, the Titan, assimilated to Phoebus and Apollo. The 'Amadis de Gaula' gives us no less than three Perions; the cavern scene in Palamedes gives us Febus as an ancestor of Guiron (Gawain II) (Löseth 1891; Prose Tristan etc. p. 460). I postulate a mediating source between Ovid and the Romancers in the shape of Rutilius Namatianus Taurus II, maybe in panegyrics since lost.

129.5 **thank-you letter** Claudian c.m. XXXI, Birt XL.

129.6 **Maternal grandfather** Via Calpurnia Constantia/Consentia – see text pp. 70, 167.

129.7 **St Oudoceus** See *Vita St. Oudoceus*, Bartrum (1966), with reference to the Sons of Ishmael. See text p. 148.

130.1 **A new Theatre** Goodchild in Bacon 1960 p. 250.

130.2 **Cathedral** Goodchild in Bacon 1960, p. 250.

130.3 **Nymphaeum of Artemis** Wright in Bacon 1960, p. 251.

131.1 **Theon** See text p. 98.

131.2 **Diplosis of Moses** A recipe for alloying gold (Berthelot CAG 1888, trad., p. 40). Theodosius I, Augustus was once *Dux* **Moesii** (Comm. p. 265, 23.2). He would not be the only Emperor to contribute a chapter to the *Liber Gradalis*. Caligula we know took a keen interest. Eugenius may have contributed a chapter. Heraclius contributed several.

131.3 **Gilding** A curious echo of this in Gregory of Tours, Hist. Fr. II 42.

131.4 **God-smith** Hephaestos, Vulcan, Fafner ('the waffener'), Wayland Smith, Gofan (Gobannion, Gobain) and Daedalus, doubly significant for his construction of the Cretan *labyrinth* (see Comm. pp. 283, 81.4 and 288, 104.1), and of *Icarus*' wings.

132.1 **Rhaëtia** Present-day Rhaëtia is the Grisons area of Switzerland, capital, Chur. In Roman times it had a northern half, Raëtia Vindelicia, capital Augsburg (Augusta Vindelicorum), which the Romancers bungled as 'Windsor', causing hilarious confusion in Chrestien de Troyes' *Cligés*.

132.2 **Harmonia/Serena** Serena, per Zosimus, had snatched the necklace not from the Vestal, as I have written it, but from the nearby statue of Rhea or Cybele, Great Mother of the Gods, in the Vestal's presence. That the Vestal then cursed her is per Zosimus in Tillemont (1701, V, p. 387). For Harmonia the much-cursed daughter of Mars and Venus, see Brewer, *Dictionary of Phrase and Fable.*

132.3 **Whole court to Lyons** Our authority is Claudian De Bello Getico (l, pp. 296–301). He should know.

132.4 **Count Caesareus** Synesius' 'Typhos'.

133.1 **Ouija Board** Great grandad Theodore's fatal toy, or tabula ronda. See Comm. p. 283, 81.3.

133.2 **that means death** By and by, that unreliable and somewhat unsavoury writer Procopius will hear Childebert's Franks talk of the Isle of *Thanet*, and will record wild tales of the corpses of Europe being ferried over by night to this British Isle-of-the-Dead. Some later scholars will be so foolish as to make use of this farrago failing, like Procopius, to recognize in 'Thanet' the Isle of the Saxon and Jutish *Thegns*. 'Unreliable'? Let Gibbon have the say: 'Procopius is a *fabulous* writer for the events which precede his own memory' (Cap. XXXV.vi fn. 76). 'Unsavoury'? Just read his 'Secret History'.

133.3 **'deeper than did ever plummet sound'** Here Prospero/Merlin drowns his 'magic books', or rather magic *tabula*. The scene is re-echoed significantly in (1) 'Scolan's dialogue', in our oldest Welsh manuscript, the 'Black Book of Carmarthen' as 'Dū dy varch, dū dy capan'. (This is p. 41 in J. Gwenogvryn Evans' 1888 facsimile, transcribed in *ibid* Pwllheli 1907 p. xii). *Prospero/Merlin* is here called Y'-Scolan *Scolanus*, and the key words are *'a llyvir rod y voti'* (and the drowning of a given book – Psalter?). Yscolan's unknown interrogator is, however, identified as his 'mother' in (2) the Breton 'Gwerz Skolvan', where Merlin has become (Eucherius) Bishop of 'Leon' (Lyons?) – here see Comm p. 321, 233.4. Or maybe Caerleon-on-Usk as Archbishop of Wales; see text p. 235. It is to this scantily recorded period of Merlin's career that I tentatively, but plausibly, award a lost Passio and a cultus of Julius-Pharaon (JJ) (corrupted, as demonstrated in Comm. p. 313, 209.2, to Araon), as Gildas' and Bede's otherwise unknown martyrs at 'Caerleon', Julius and Aaron.

133.4 **as it would be recorded** in the *Livre d'Artus*. Loomis (1959, p. 338).

134.1 ***Pulcherius*** He will be venerated annually on 13 March under this name; also as St Mo-Choemog, 'Dear young *Kev*-in'; see Baring-Gould (1872, March 13, p. 247). The whole '*Vita*' is full of relevant recollections.

134.2 **Lebanese** i.e. of Coele-Syria. This is my mere inference from his name. We know nothing else of his origins.

134.3 **sort of monk** '*veluti monachus*' says Jerome, Ep. 66.6.

135.1 **slew the dragon** The whole stirring account is in the *Livre des Promesses et des Prédictions de Dieue of Quodvultdeus*, second Bishop of Carthage after Aurelius in René Braun (*Sources Chrétiennes*, pp. 101–2, Les Éditions du Cerf, 29 Bd de la Tour-Maubourg, Paris) and Tillemont (1701, V, pp. 518–9).

135.2 **smash the dragon** Cf. the 'whirling enchantment' which 'Arthur' disarms in the 'Chevalier du Papegau' (e.g. Papagast the serpent). See p. 71 of Henckenkamp's edn (Pickford in Loomis 1959, p. 356); also the 'automata' (ibid. p. 354).

135.3 **Melania the Holy Terror** The return of Melania, her meeting with Cousin Vic, and her visit to Nola *en route* for Rome are vividly described in Paulinus Ep. 29 (to Sulpicius Severus). Fabre (1948, Chron. 29ff., 35ff.) dates Ep. 29 (with Eps 23 and 24) to AD400, on the assumption that the reference in Ep. 29, Cap. 14. is to Nicetas' earlier visit (correctly deduced as in AD400), and he assumes that Ep. 29 is being written contemporaneously with *that* visit. But Nicetas' visit is not referred to in Eps. 23 and 24, and it seems open from the text to hold that this reference in Ep. 29 is to Niketas' second visit of AD403. *Pace* Fabre and his followers, we are therefore free to redate Ep. 29 and therefore Melania's return to AD403. Palladius (Hist. Laus 46.5) tells us that she had been 27 years in the Holy Land (rather more than the '*quinque Lustrae*' of Ep. 29.6), having spent some years previously in Egypt. We know, too, that she deserted Italy and her son in early AD372. If we allow her and Rufinus about three years in Egypt, she will have taken up permanent residence in

Jerusalem in the autumn of AD375 and will be arriving at Naples in the twenty-eighth year thereafter, i.e. late AD403. **Much turns on this re-dating** (see Comm. p. 308, 193.1).

135.4 **spiritual director** See text pp. 47, 69.

135.5 **died on 11 November** (AD 401) For once I diverge from Clinton, who gives AD394 following Gregory of Tours, and prefer Farrar (1907, I, p. 656). S. Severus gives no date, Prosper of Aquitaine and Idatius are silent. The Gallic Chronicle (pseudo Prosper) gives AD400. All the Chroniclers' dates are accurate only plus or minus one year, as Clinton amply demonstrates.

136.1 **Lenten custom** The *Vitae* of Merlin and John-George under their various pseudonyms give ample descriptions of Lenten retreats to desert places, often offshore islands. Flatholm comes to mind, and there is room to include many of the Breton islets, notably Bréhat (See P-R Giot in BAR BS 102, 1982, pp. 197–210). Others will emerge in the text.

136.2 **Stewards, seneschals, bailiffs** Here etymologies may arouse Classical and Romance resonances: *Steward* (*stig*-ward), from Latin *Comes Domesticorum*. Seneschal from Latin-Teutonic *Senex-calchus*, aged servitor. I much prefer, however, to identify 'Kay the Seneschal' as *senex CALCHAS*, 'old Calchas the Seer' (see Proem). *Bailiff*, Latin *Bajulivus*, from Bajulare 'to be guardian' (S.OED, p. 137). The Greek for this latter, *Φερεγγαριος*, is also of interest as the source of the French Béranger, whence the Romance 'Emperor Raynier' (Renier de Vienne in the Orlando), father of Aëtius' wife, Ursula.

136.3 **epitaph ... copy** This survives in Leland's *Assertio inclitissimi Arturi Regis Britanniae* (London 1544, trans. R. Robinson, 1582, republished by W. E. Mead, 1925, in *EETS* Vol. 165). Leland, browsing in the Glastonbury Library, scoffs at the suggestion by the monks there, that the ascribed author 'Suynesius' (sic) is a botch for 'Soliacensis' (i.e. Henry of Blois, formerly of *Sully*, quondam Abbot of Glastonbury, later Bishop of Winchester). 'How', Leland asks 'can Soliacensis become Suynesius?' How indeed! Giraldus Cambrensis, and others after, will think *Secunda* means 'Arthur's second wife'. I say she was his first, and her personal name 'Secunda'.

137.1 **mountain passes** November AD400. Claudian, *Paneg, De sexto consulatu Honorii* l.455–6, and De bello Getico, l.321–429.

137.2 **without a legion** We may perhaps deduce that the Legio XX VV was at this time withdrawn from Brittany.

137.3 **soldier sons** Claudian '*De VI. Consulat. Honorii*', l.297–8. The eldest will be known as Theoderic I, King of the Vizi-Goths, and 'Walthar of Aquitaine'.

137.4 **Ginger herself** Claudian, '*De bello Getico*' l.625, *et seq.*

138.1 **hostages to Stilicho** Alaric will have his revenge in terms of hostages in a few years time when the boot is on the other foot. See text pp. 162, 163.

138.2 **statue in my own family Forum** In Trajan's Forum by the Basilica Ulpia with its two great libraries, one Greek, one Latin. This was the 'Poets' Corner' of the day. The plinth, bearing the whole inscription, is currently in the Naples Museum; see CIL Vol. 6, no. 1710; and see text p. 138 and Plate 17.

139.1 **Chateau de Vêves** My conjecture (Veuf from Latin *vidua*, a widow. Genovefa thus means 'the fair widow', the Romancers' 'la Dame Veuve').

140.1 **Coronatus** Welsh, *coronog*: Erse, Cormac, Cuaran, Kieran, Kervin, Kevin etc.

140.2 **betrothal** Prolonged study of Late Imperial genealogy satisfies me that senatorial Romans of the day, whether from social or from economic pressures, commenced breeding only in their late teens.

143.1 **Nitonius** The allusions here are to Manaw*ydan* of the Mabinogion; to text p. 25; to the very important sarcophagus of Book XIX, and Plate 11.

144.1 **John Chrysostom** Read all about him, in a sympathetic and indeed admiring vein, in Farrar (1907).

144.2 **St Anastasis** In medieval times this will be quaintly misunderstood to mean 'St Anastasia who can *deflect sorcery*', a typical reversal of cart and horse.

145.1 **miscarriage** October 6, AD404. See Comm. p. 284, 87.1.

146.1 **punning variations** See text p. 70, p. 150 and Comm. p. 298, 150.1 below.

147.1 **sanctity** More to say about its saints, relics etc., in Comm. p. 300, 154.1.

147.2 **the Arian heresy** See text (footnote) p. 42.

148.1 *ἄφλακος* This derivation for the Romancers 'Havelock the Dane' also accommodates Aballac, Afallach, Aflech (Auchinleck) from Bartrum (1966, Index), and Loomis (1959, Index). Here too is King Evelac of Sarras in Manessier's continuation of Chretien's Perceval. Best of all, here is the Beowulf's 'Hygelak King of the Geats' who has been incorrectly identified by recent scholars as Gregory of Tours' Chlochilaich (Danish King, killed in AD521 in Gaul). Beowulf the Orphan may himself now be identified and re-dated. He is John-George and he did kill many dragons, including alchemical ones. Alexander the Orphan, another 'Havelock', is Aëtius, and the Beowulf author has conflated them.

148.2 **Ishmaelites** Aptly it is the Vita St Oudoceus which recalls this; see also text p. 129, and Comm. p. 295, 129.7.

148.3 **virginity ... for young men** (especially those addicted to soft porn) See Comm. p. 268, 31.1 and p. 294, 129.3.

149.1 **glass sand** Glass was made at Colchester and near Norwich.

149.2 **Coelbren Gaer** Vast open-cast mining operations make a search for the site today unrewarding.

149.3 **Agricola** See App. 1 where I offer St Helena, first 'wife' of Constantius I, 'Chlorus', as the great granddaughter of Calpurnius Agricola, governor of Britannia in AD163. This conjecture would explain many legendary confusions and also account for the persistence of the name, not only of St Patrick's father but also in the Romance of Palmerin d'Angleterre; and again as the name of King Grallon's father-in-law in Lobineau (1863, n. 1, p. 35).

150.1 **Concessa ... Consortia** The Irish hagiographers (notably Muirchu and Probus) will pick these names up.

150.2 ***Eil-udd*** The modern 'Eliot'. Also Eliud, Ebiud, Eifudd, Ebian. See Bartrum (1966, Index).

150.3 **Siling and Asding Vandals** Their geographical origins are obscure. They behave as two distinct 'nations', but are both Wends (Pliny's Venedae) and in this connection we may cautiously remark the Veneti and the Venedoti.

150.4 **Codex Theodosius** Conveniently cited in Clinton (1845, p. 566).

151.1 **Marcus ... Gratianus** Here I bravely conflate the two phantom usurpers of the Greek authors and of Orosius. That there should be two separate failed usurpers *in Britain* within a few months, one known only by his *prenomen*, one only by his filiative, seems extravagant. That Theodosius had a brother, Gratianus, attest Ambrose's Funeral Oration for Theodosius I, and also an earlier reference in Gregory of Nyssa's Funeral Oration on the death of Flaccilla, AD386. Honorius Albanicus apart, the only brother of Theodosius we know of is Uncle Heliodorus, and he could have born the names Marcianus and also conceivably Gratianus. But, although once slightly known in Britain (as Headmaster of Ocean College) he would hardly have had a faction there; moreover, I have him well established in Constantinople as Novatian Bishop, and dead in AD395 (see Clinton 1850, p. 125).

151.2 ***Padarn Peisrudd*** See Bartrum (1966, Index). *Peisrudd*, 'red coat', could refer to any cavalry officer, or duke, or Caesar; and, as we shall see, JJ will also get this name among the Cambrians.

151.3 **good Imperial names** One major confusion by Nennius may now be put right. Giles (1847) gives (p. 305) '*de secundo etiam Severo*'; this is spelt out in the full list of emperors 'reigning' in Britain (pp. 318–20), where we find at §24 '*Octavus fuit alius Severus*'. Nennius is self-confessedly in doubt over the last three emperors; he gives Maximus twice at §22 & 23, and his 'ninth' (Constantinus, plainly Constantine III) is confused with Constantius I and Constantine I. Nevertheless, he gives us an ***eighth*** 'British' Emperor between Maximus and Constantine III, and scribes, Bards, monks and Romancers alike have taken this numerative as a name. Here is the Emperor Octavius Octavianus of Romance; here is 'Eudaf' Jr. of the Welsh. (See Bartrum 1966.)

151.4 **Lucius Fortunatus** The quite extraordinarily apt Teutonic legend is summarised, with analogies, in *Encyclopaedia Britannica*, 11th edn, text article. Hans Sachs wrote it up. There is something here of the Wandering Jew legend. Think, too, of Shakespeare's Prospero, the rightful Duke *Milanion*. We have already noticed Prospero in Comm. p. 296, 133.3 above.

152.1 **Black Forest Barbarians (BFBs)** Asding and Siling Vandals, Alans, Suebes, and Quadi.

152.2 **Rheims, Tournai** Our source is Jerome, Ep. CXXV.15.

153.1 **Wimbledon** For this conjecture see Bartlett, *History and Antiquities of Wimbledon* (1865), reissued by S.R. Publishers Ltd (1971) with a foreword by R. J. Milward. The 'Hastings' conjecture is mine and mine alone. Take it or leave it, as you will.

153.3 ***Leporello*** 'Bosom companion', as it were, of Don Juan *Tenorio* in Tirso de Molina's comedy of 1630. The 'Young Dominus', 'Don' John/Constans II Caesar, will perhaps pick up the *agnomen Antenor* (the legendary founder of Padua), during his 'Padine' reign AD423–5 at Ravenna. Antenor was famed for his 'treachery' (aptly with 'Odysseus'), whence, perhaps, the Cambrians 'Gwrtheyrn (Vortigern) gwr*theneu*. Whence, also, John's unhappy Romance role as the 'traitor' Ganelon ('Grand Alains', Alains le Gros, Gand.elyn, Middle English 'Gamelyn').

153.4 **Novatian Bishop** Socrates, VII 6 and 17.

153.5 **Imperator Augustus** It is Orosius, and only he, who dismisses Constantine's name and his military prowess alike with '***ex infima militia propter solam spem nominis sine merito virturis eligitur***'.This seems to have been the current Hippo sneer, and they were no slouches at sneering there. Notwithstanding, I have shown in Book VIII that Constantine III had held high military rank before this, albeit only as *laticlavus* (non-combatant).

153.6 **spurning ... Carausius** During which JJ, I contend, nevertheless dallied with the name 'Carausius IV', and coined a few inscrutable coins – see Comm. p. 262, 13.7. Specifically, the 'Evans coin', for which archaeologists have since found some companions, is here referred to. I claim this as JJ's, and having allowed 'Marcus Gratianus' his brief fling (as Carausius III?) these coins should now belong to Carausius IV, i.e. JJ.

153.7 **Cligēs** See text pp. 129, 207 and Comm. p. 313, 208.7.

154.1 **Trier** We don't know where JJ made for; only that he secured the Rhine. It might have been Köln where he could be St Maurus *Florent*ius, brother (Cassius from Κασις) of St Gereon (Merlin Gerontius). All these references are to the Passio of St Gereon in Helinandus. JJ also appears in the Romance of the Emperor Octavian as 'Sir *Florent*' and when we remember that Florentissimus is the honorific of a Caesar we may wonder whether Maximus did for his son-in-law in 383 onwards (see Comm. p. 281, 74.1) what JJ will do for John-George in text p. 155.

155.1 **nobilissimus to Caesar** See Comm. 154.1, above. By 'ekecheirotonia'. The initial ἐ should probably read ἀ (privative). Thus ἀ.κεχειρο–τονητος seems the aptest emendation of our source Olympiodorus, *apud* Photius in Bouqet (1869, p. 599B), signifying that (as an usurper) JJ/Constantine was not yet able to bestow true legitimizing 'chirotony' on John Constans, whose 'ordination' as Caesar then Augustus was therefore invalid at this moment. Hence JJ's manoeuvrings to obtain a purple robe.

157.1 **sort out the Montagnards** The alpine peasants who controlled the passes were necessarily something of a law unto themselves. The amiable M. B. Courtier, (*Le Vrai Visage de Montgenèvre*, Reims, c. 1984), ponders on the origins of the Pennine *République des Escartons*, established in 1343 to survive until 1713, and mentions that the then Dauphin was obliged not only to concede their independence but to purchase their goodwill for 12,000 gold florins and 4000 ducats. Things don't change, *solidi* remain *solidi*.

157.2 **tyros** Latin, *tirones*. At Colchester, AD406. Now think yet again about 'Apollonius of *Tyre*', if you will be so kind.

157.3 **cavalry** per Not. Dig. Oc. VI and VII.

157.4 **Gallic parlance** Confirmed in the Not. Dig. (ibid.).

157.5 **infantrymen** Not. Dig. Oc. V. 247 *et al.*, as Honoriani Gallicani (*comitatenses* in Gaul). A modern scholar who should have known better refers to them as a 'rustic' army, when all that was conveyed was that they answered to Decimus Rusticus as Praetorian Prefect of Gaul under JJ.

158.1 **no military establishment** None in the Not. Dig. at any rate, search as you will.

158.2 **provincial governors** See Not. Dig. Oc. I, p. 27, 65–7, 102–105.

158.3 **Verrenianus** See text p. 18 and App. 4.

159.1 **Gundahar** First-named 'King' in the *Lex Gundobada*. He is usually dated to AD411 by Olympiodorus (*apud* Photius), where he appears (with Goar) as Φυλαρχος (ruler of the army).

159.2 **ruler of the feast** Greek Θαλιαρχων.

159.3 **intelligence service** Paulinus of Nola tells of Cousin Vic's courier service, and of his own. Augustine was in constant correspondence with Sicily, Rome, and the East. Pope Innocent also corresponded widely.

159.4 **Livy** Historian of Rome from its beginnings up to the time of Augustus; hymner of the great days of the Republic. It is no coincidence at all that c. AD396 Q. Aurelius Symmachus should have been responsible for commissioning a new edition of so congenial and topical a work, nor that it became a best-seller. The 'puppet' sons of Theodosius had him worried.

160.1 **De Bello Gothico** Lines 545–8.

160.4 **Ataulphus** Idatius the Spaniard gives us the spelling Atavulfus, phoneticised as he heard it. Search for a Teutonic root is otiose.

161.1 **earlier miscarriage** Claudian could hardly have written lines 341–4 of his *De consulatu Stilichonis*, Bk. II, had Maria not been *supposedly* enceinte. With understandable caution Claudian switches abruptly to Eucherius Stilichonis.

161.2 **Jovius** See text pp. 123, 124.

161.3 **Salona** Ancient capital of Dalmatia. Diocletian's palace at nearby Split was now an Imperial *Officina* under the Mag. Off; a textile factory manufacturing army tunics (Dalmatics), later to receive their meed of veneration as ecclesiastical vestments. (Uncle Ted is seen wearing a typical example in Plate 5, and in Fig. 7.) Trogir cathedral, nearby, is perhaps to be rebuilt by a legacy from Q. Fl. Merobaudes II ('Quirinus') Patricius. About the same time (AD 462) Count Marcellinus (one of Aëtius' staff, and indeed kin) will set up an independent Kingdom there.

162.1 **statue ... inscription** Discovered only in 1946. The same inscription will also serve to underpin and immortalise his later nickname 'War and Peace' – Teutonic Sieg-Fried. Verdi made him a bass, but heros must be tenors. The key references here are in Clover (1971, pp. 36–9) which is definitive (as far as it goes) for Aëtius and also for Merobaudes/Gawain. The key words in the inscription are '*objuratas* ***bello pace*** *victorias*' (i.e. 'war and peace' or 'sieg-fried'), and cf. Merobaudes Panegyric (II l. pp. 131–2). Clover rightly states that Aëtius has not less than two wives nor more than four. You will see how I handle this later, so as to allow him two and a half.

163.1 **Quirinale** See text p. 72.

163.2 **Jason** See text p. 124. See also the early Romance of 'Walthar of Aquitaine'. Who's the third hostage going to be? Theodoric I, the ViziGoth; Aëtius' future brother-in-law. He had already been hostage to an earlier master, Stilicho, after the Battle of Pollentia in AD402 (see text p. 138).

163.3 **funeral** Arcadius had in his latter years been obsessed with the cult of St Menas of Alexandria, for whom he built a splendid basilica. We may well think that the unidentified porphyry sarcophagus now in the Alexandria Museum is his.

164.1 **Vincentius Jr** Hardly the Praetorian of Gaul 397–400. I postulate a son.

166.1 **scabbard** A mass of Romance legends of Excalibur's yet more precious 'scabbard' fall into context when we recall that the Latin for scabbard is ***vagina***. (Excalibur is not a 'sword' but a corruption of 'Mont Esclaire', whichever and ***whoever***.) I hope not to get unduly gynaecological when I point out that Ursula is 'La Pucelle de la Gaut Estrée', of the 'narrow entry', the 'imperforable hymen' – the latter very fancifully described in Chrestien's *Yvain* (v. 907 ff.) and other Romances. Romance, legend, and hagiography unite in stressing Ursula's impregnable 'virginity' and the Welsh remember her as Morwen (Olwen), 'the maiden'. Boccaccio sends her up in tasteful bawdy in his *Decameron* (II. 7), giving her nine, or (including the two 'Genuese') **eleven** lovers before delivering her, still *virgo intacta* to her husband the Sultan of Garbo, *recte* Narbo[nne]. Here are the eleven of the 'eleven thousand virgins'. Boccaccio has conflated poor Ursula with Doxy, and other loose ladies of the Courts. She was not *that* naughty. In fact the 'Queste' author shows her in a purer more altruistic light as Perceval's sister. Longfellow, (building on Hartman) in his 'Golden Legend' calls her 'Elsie' and combines her with Ursula in her self-immolation. Jacob de Voragine in his 'Golden Legend' for 25 October gives us Ursula amid a forest of names familiar by now to readers of *I Merlin*. Baring-Gould (1877) for 21 October surveys the whole Ursula 'cultus' with growing distaste, but gives us another quota of familiar names. Connoisseurs will identify most of Ursula's sisters and companions as aliases of herself. Her anatomical peculiarity (imperforable hymen) is not that rare; it will come to our attention again in the famous Russell paternity case of this century, where it was demonstrated medically that impregnation *could* in certain circumstances result without normal consummation. This may put alarming thoughts about the whole subject of virgin births into our minds.

167.1 **laugh my head off** Here is the dénouement of the 'Merlin and Grisandole' story (see Loomis 1959, p. 323). The faithless queen was Elissa (AD396) and her 'Achilles style' juvenile lover John-George. Ursula is 'Grisandole' (Chrysanthula) and here (as Vivienne-Nimue) she has ensnared Merlin, the man with the mysterious laugh.

167.2 **Gregory too** Micha in Loomis (1959, pp. 361–2) and Loomis himself (ibid. p. 476) struggle manfully with this, and Loomis (1927, pp. 331–43) gives the problem a laborious and illuminating chapter. Maybe I can simplify matters.

'Pope (i.e. Metropolitan) Gregory' is Faustus of Riez, here conceived, later brought up at the instance of a 'Fisherman' (St Germanus) at Lérins. John/*Albinus* (the latter from when he becomes Prefect of the Elbe/*Albis* and Saxony as 'Frowenus', *Fl. Eugenius* per Saxo Grammaticus), is 'Gregory of the Rock' (Aran) where Oedipus-like he lays his mother. **He *is* indeed the son of Armenios (Herrman, Pharamond, JJ).** Libido was a giant problem for him and he may well have made a pass, and more, at his sister Ursula (Marcella). Indeed Irish legend of the pursuit of Dermot and Grainne, and the testimony of Welsh and Romance legend will insist that he did. See App. 9 and Comm p. 314, 211.6, p. 317, 220.4. Merlin is Gregory, 'Curoi mac Daire', Gregory the Druid, '*Gwri gwallt euryn*' of the Mabinogion; Goldilocks in person.

167.3 **drop of alcohol** Hence St David *aquaticus*, the teetotaller ('Dubricius' to the Welsh).

167.4 **Don Giovanni** '*Mille tre*' is da Ponte's exaggeration of his 'conquests' in Spain. For Leporello see Comm. p. 299, 153.3.

168.1 **Theodosiolus** The future Emperor Marcian. See App. 4.

168.2 **next year would do?** A Greek inscription at Trier (commemorating one Eusebeia in the 8th Cos Honorius (AD 409) and 1st Cos Constantine) confirms that *JJ* did indeed take local advantage of this offer. See Freeman (1886, p. 71 fn. 2), citing Tillemont (v. 570) (ibid. Gruter 1072).

169.1 **Go back to Spain** I have based this episode on the advice Augustine gives to Boniface, eight years later in his famous Epistle 220. The dominance of anti-pagan sentiments in his thinking at this time is amply confirmed by Caps 1–10 of the *Civitas Dei* on which he is currently engaged, and by the succession of anti-pagan laws which he has persuaded Honorius to pass, notably that of 15.11.407 but continuing to 30.8.415. About this latter date he commissions Orosius' *Adversus Paganos*. Later, in colloquies with Sigisvult's Bishop Maximin in 427, he brings the Arians belatedly into his sights. I think my scenario is more than plausible.

170.1 **brother of ... Edobech** My inference. Both are Franks, by their names. It would explain much, especially Honorius' unease.

170.2 **kill Allobech** We know he was killed *for* Honorius but we don't know by whom. Sarus seems a possible candidate for the job.

170.3 **Peloponnesian Morea** See especially the 'Prince of the Morea' in the 7th Tale of the Decameron, which relates intimately to Ursula. See also Comm. p. 301, 166.1.

170.4 **my son** Olympiodorus (in Clinton 1850, p. 134) is right, naturally enough. Sozomen and Orosius fudge this.

170.5 **her daughter** John-George, the 'Sicilian Briton', in his first letter to Fastidius makes clear c.411/2 that he has now a second daughter with him in Sicily.

171.1 **4000 fresh troops** Zosimus says quite unmistakeably that it was 40,000 troops, a curiously large army for one assembled as a panic 'task force', especially one brought by sea. Zosimus may here be somewhat in error; I choose, more than hesitantly, to follow Sozomen. The size of Constantius III's command will determine his rank at this time. For Constantius, see text p. 64.

171.2 **so that the soldiers could be paid** Here is that veritable ***Beacon*** of British Historians, Honorius' famous **'Rescript' to the cities of Britain.** It reads as no more than a disappointing little aside in Zosimus (15. Bk. vi, Cap. 10). Thompson (1977, p. 307) ridicules Zosimus (*and* all his followers whom he sneeringly dubs 'Zosimophiles') as 'mutton-headed' and 'moonstruck'. Striving, nevertheless, to punctuate Zosimus' turgid Civil-Service Greek amidst a veritable cataract of genitive absolutes, we find no more than that Honorius at last met his obligations to the British (and Continental) 'Dad's Army' *tirones* by paying over their original enlistment bounties due under his two Ordinances of 406. At the same time he tells the British *civitates* to assume (financial) responsibility for their (continuing) defence. Curiously, Thompson (pp. 315–6, his guns firmly trained on the luckless and moribund Stevens), can find 'no context' for this statement. I suggest *the context is exactly as Zosimus has it*: the presence of a newly-arrived army from Constantinople plus 10,000 Rent-a-Huns all expecting donatives; continuing pressure from Britain for payment of the promised enlistment bounties; and the arrival of Heraclian's *solidi.* (Some of these even turn up, just where you would expect them, at Richborough. Even more, very recently in 1992 at Hoxne *Villa Faustini*, by Scole, where a whole paychest has worked its way into the *latifundus*-enriched Anician hoard. Gawain will say in Book XX that 'the Brits' are 'rolling in money' with Rome paying market prices for their grain.) Thompson (p. 314) goes on to mock Myres and Ward saying that Liebeschuetz had 'pulled the carpet from under his (Myres') feet'. Those who read Liebeschuetz's useful, scholarly, and temperate contributions of 1963 and 1967 will find it hard to agree, perhaps even to recognize Thompson's summary of his findings. This is that very Thompson whom (with a colleague) his disciples will in 1984 salute rather oddly as '*magister elegans*'!

171.3 **Priscus** Like '*atavis*' this hints at ancient lineage. The Attali were Kings of Pergamon in antiquity. These three names, and a coin portrait, are all we have from which to construct his career. I have done my best. He was more than a joke; initially he plainly had a substantial following in the Senate, and he retained Merlin-Ataulfus' confidence for many years.

172.1 **troops to Africa** Under another Constans, not John-George.

173.1 **Zercon (the dwarf)** He is the true grotesque original of Wagner's 'Mime' (cf. 'Memering' in Comm. p. 279, 65.6). Much more about him in the Romance 'Palamedes', and in Priscus.

173.2 **Faltonia Proba** See text p. 55, and App. 6.

173.3 **Augustine ... gloat** Augustine, *Civitas Dei*, Bk. I, pp. i, vii, gives tactful support to this conclusion, although he ascribes the credit, rather cautiously, to God's unaided efforts.

174.1 **would lie with him** Something of the Beowulf syndrome here. Redwald would not have disapproved.

174.2 **Suttee** You think me fanciful? I'm only following Jakob Grimm's 'Verbrennen der Leichen'. The Grimm brothers haunt this Commentary, and rightly, for 'Grimms Law' is very much of the essence.

175.1 **may borrow her** See Comm. p. 281, 74.2.

177.1 **lead the Goths to peace** 'Goth-peace', Gott-fried. Hence Godfrey, Geoffrey, Jaufré. See also Comm. p. 278, 65.6.

178.1 **Wild Hunt** Adam de la Halle in 1276 is our chief authority for 'la chasse furieuse' and its leader Hellekin. Many reverberations, too, in the Teutonic legends of Helle and his hunt, and Walter Mapes' King Herla. **It is time to rehabilitate 'Walter Map'** as a prime source of the Grail legends. If we can see 'Walter *Mapes*', courtier and author to Henry II as 'Walter of that Ilk', i.e. Walter III, son of Walter II son of Walter I, we may be nearer the mark! 'Walter Map', begetter of the Grail cycles, is then Walter II who could very well be Walter, Archdeacon of Oxford, source of Geoffrey of Monmouth and probable compiler of the Welsh 'Bonedd y Saint'. The 'author' of *La Mort le Roi Artu* (firmly identified as Walter Map at its beginning and its close, although modern scholars hotly contradict this), gives ages for Merlin/Arthur, for Pseudo-Gawain, and for Lancelot *around* the time of Arthur's death of 92, 76, and c.55 respectively. At the very least these accurate and unlikely ages demonstrate that the *La Mort* author had made the same historical identifications as I have in this book. The dates would refer roughly to a base of AD450, although Merlin was dead by then, and Lancelot was on the brink of assassination. If all that Walter II could leave his antiquarian-minded but busy courtier-son was a mass of ill-digested genealogical information, we can well imagine the latter turning it over to scholars better able to cope.

Maybe I can lay yet another scholarly dogfight to rest if I say that, very likely, all that Guiot de Provins was able to transmit to the self-confessedly **dyslexic** Wolfram was a large variant family tree. Family trees support family histories. Do you begin to see?

178.2 **populace didn't forget us** Rutilius Namatianus Taurus II describes ('De Reditu Suo' 1, pp. 37–42), the impassable state of the Via Aurelia, *mansios* burnt, bridges smashed. Did the Goths not also forage? Did they not loot? This of course, was on their way South. They returned, as Merlin tells us, by the Flaminia, by this time better-heeled.

181.1 **Gerontius and Nonnichia** Freeman (1886, pp. 82–3) owlishly exposes this as no more than a 'pious' novella.

181.2 **other names** See Comm. p. 278, 65.3.

181.3 **bishop** The presiding minister of any established congregation was still called a bishop at this time. Indeed, 286 Catholic bishops attended that year's Council of Carthage. They were hardly the Suffragans, Diocesans or Metropolitans of today's usage. Moreover, all Metropolitans (at least) were addressed as 'Pope' in those days, as the letters of Apollonius Sidonius evince – see Anderson (1936). Over the centuries they proved amazingly upwardly-mobile in status, rising eventually to become prince-bishops. Whatever will Jesus make of that title?

181.4 **wedding** Jordanes Get. (c.31) records this wedding, and Manitius, in *Cambridge Medieval History* (1911, Vol.1, p. 274) accepts it as **certain.** Orosius (VII, p. 40) can better be read as supporting this than as referring catachronistically to the second wedding at Narbonne in 414 so vividly recorded by Olympiodorus (*apud* Photius). If we are not to use our sources wilfully we should therefore attempt to reconcile the two accounts. This, and what follows, is my attempt. It has the major result of invalidating the chief arguments against the authenticity of the St Gilles Perron, to which we are drawing near.

182.1 **Pope Gregory** See Comm. p. 302, 167.2.

183.1 **we reached Lyons** Historians think this whole episode took place at Mainz. Olympiodorus (*apud* Photius), who is our source for this, names Mainz, in Greek, as Μουνδιακου (for Latin *Moguntiacum*), which looks suspiciously like Jordanes' 'Mundiuch', supposed father of Attila (see Comm. p. 294, 128.6). I think Jordanes has misapplied the genitive, or maybe Cassiodorus before him. As to my removing this encounter from Mainz to Lyons, Olympiodorus has moved on several sentences in his narrative. Political and strategic necessities should by now have called Jovinus nearer to his own heartlands. Jovinus, I suggest, is the Romancers' 'Doon de Mayence', cf. Ariosto's traitorous family of Maganza.

184.1 **making off for Spain** Orosius, ever slapdash, simply says he was killed by his own soldiers, somewhere. The traditional 'flight to Spain' is inferred from Sozomen's touching 'novella' of his suicide, firmly abrogated in Comm. 181.1 above.

184.2 **'Ελευθερος** (the freed-man) This will be shortened by the Romancers to '**Uther**' (Pendragon – the second to bear this name – as explained in text p. 65).

185.1 **Fier Baisée** or Dragon Kiss, or 'Kiss of the Dragoon'. See Micha in Loomis (1959, p. 371 *et seq.*, *et al.*, where Gawain II is confused with his son). If we are to thrill to all the goings-on upon the Rock and after, we can now read 'Lohengrin'. The Knights of the Swan (Wolfram's *Templeisen*) are Novatians, looking to the Cycnus (i.e. Swan) Convent on its Mons Silvaticus in New Rome as their spiritual nursery. That's where the children of Lĕr (Pelagiani) were 'turned into swans'. There are still trees in today's Botanical Gardens at *Munsalvœsche* above the ruined walls; yes, and metallurgical activities. Glass has gone elsewhere.

185.2 **take matters further** Many reverberations here. Parsifal's first 'chaste' dalliance with the lady in the tent. Siegfried's primal wooing of Brünnhilde.

185.3 **to lose his life ... River Lawen** Gawain discovers and accepts this with phlegm in Book XX. See also the *Elegy for Gwēn* of the Welsh *Llywarch Hēn* cycle. In this terse and deeply moving elegy, anachronistically ascribed to Merlin (Leo Marcus) himself and of which neither Claudian nor Pindar would have been ashamed, Gawain is killed in a skirmish on the River Llawen. This river and the adjacent River Clarence, are tributaries of the River Lys in the Pays-de-Lys (cf. Brân-de-lys) in Artois. (Froissart, who should have known better, makes the Clarence a broad river in Ireland in his interminable 'Meliador'.) The Lys joins the River Scheldt at Ghent. Amateurs of great poetry should rush for the 'Canu Llywarch Hēn' (Cardiff 1935) and, above all, read the original Welsh aloud as best they may. It always makes me cry.

185.4 **Seleucus** Tillemont (1701, V, pp. 814–6) strives manfully to disentangle the Praetorians of these years.

186.1 **Bricriu's feast** Conveniently translated in Gantz (1981). Your attention is drawn to pp. 231, 245–7, 250–1. Bricriu is John the freckled; CuRui, *recte* Gregory, is Merlin the Druid.

186.2 **in Book IV** p. 32.

187.1 **'Kephalophore'** Here are a few such saints: St Denis 9/10, Caraunus 28/5, Lucian 8/1, Regula 11/9. Several more in Ireland, where you would expect them.

187.2 **transferred to pikes** I said in Comm p. 273, 49.1 that there was a 'lion' (Orosius) lying in the path. Here's what he wrote, at Hippo, AD417 (having heard that their 'heads' were on display at Carthage, and scrambling to finish up his somewhat slapdash polemic): *Constantius Comes in Galliam cum exercitu profectus, Constantinum Imperatorem apud Arelatum civitatem clausit, cepit et occidit.* By now Orosius is at full gallop, his main task (to which the fate of a brisk list of recent tyrants, subdued for the 'pious Honorius', is no more than a footnote) completed. That this was the version current in Africa we may believe; that this should be taken by subsequent historians as definitive is inadequate. Zosimus and Eunapius close their histories before this date. Our best source, Olympiodorus (*apud* Photius) aptly gives us the fullest account (Photius, Cod. LXXX, p. 181 of the 1653 Rouen edn): *Κωνσταντινου του τυραννου και Κωνσταντος του παιδος, ὁς προτερον μεν Καισαρ, ἐπειτα δε και Βασιλευς ἐκεχειροτονητο, τουτων ἡττηθεντων και πεφευγοτων, Γεροντιος ὁ στρατηγος την προς τους βαρβαρους ἀσμενισας ἐιρηνην, Μαξιμον τον ἑαυτου παιδα ἐις την των δομεστικων ταξιν τελουτα, Βασιλεα ἀναγορευει ... Ἐν ὡ δε ταυτα ἐγινετο, Κωνσταντιος και Οὐλφιλας ἀποστελλονται παρα Ὁνοριου κατα Κωνσταντινου και καταλαβοντες την Ἀρηλατον ἐνθα τας διατριβας ἐποιειτο Κωνσταντινος συν Ἰουλιανω τω παιδι* (and why should he not be the same as John-Julian-Constans?) *ταυτην πολιορκουσι. Και Κωνσταντινος καταφυγων ἐις ἐυκτηριον, πρεσβευτερος τοτε χειροτονειται ὁρκωα ἀυτω ὑπερ σωτηριας δοθεντων, και τοις πολιορκουσιν ἁι πυλαι της πολεως ἀναπεταννυνται και πεμπεται συν τω ὑιω Κωνσταντινος προς Ὁνοριον. Ὁ δε μνησικακων ἀυτοις ὑπερ των ἀνεψιοω ἀυτου, ὀυς ἐτυλχανε Κωνσταντινος ἀνελων προ τριακοντα της Ραβεννης μιλιων παρα τους ὁρκους προσταττει* (**gave orders** that) *τουτους ἀναιρεθηναι* [they should be seized (generally with fatal intent)].

Olympiodorus does not undertake that these orders were carried out, nor does he state this important historical fact as we would need him to state it. Rather, he seems concerned at the sacrilege and breaking of the safe-conduct; he may not have been the only one with such scruples. Socrates, the well-informed Novatian, says nothing of JJ's death. Sozomen (writing AD440 in Palestine and using the full version of Olympiodorus, who, as a young man could have met JJ and Orosius) gives quite a full account of the siege and 'clericatus', ending: *Κωνσταντινος δε ἁμα Ἰουλιανω τω παιδι παραπεμφθεις εις 'Ιταλιαν, πριν φθασαι κατα την ὁδον κτιννυταν*. This word, a remote passive variant tense of *κτεινω*, 'I kill' allows also the sense 'I would arrange to have killed if I could'.

I claim confidently that it is an open question whether JJ and John-George may have survived, with slight indications, from Olympiodorus, that this was indeed the outcome.

187.3 **Praetorian-elect** During the latter part of JJ's legitimized usurpation Honorius had made no such appointment.

188.1 **Carthage** Hodgkin (1880, I, p. 409) demurs at Olympiodorus' witness and is rebuked by Freeman (1886, p. 83). Here, probably, are the Romancers' 'heads on stakes' (Loomis 1959, p. 372 *et al.*)

188.2 **Orosius** His polemical 'Adversus Paganos', hurriedly written for Augustine is normally utilised as a major historical source for the period.

189.1 **Rufinus** Melania I's close friend and companion for 37 years in the East. Paulinus' descriptions of Melania the Holy Terror in his Ep. 29 as, *inter alia*, 'that most ***virile*** of Christians' are hilarious as well as touching.

189.2 **Sicilian Briton** Morris (1965, in *Journal of Theological Studies* N.S., Vol. XVI, Pt. 1, pp. 26–60) is persuasive and compelling reading. Myres (1951, p. 26) comments that de Plinval (1934) has succeeded in detaching the 'Pelagian' tracts from ascription to Fastidius and Agricola without successfully attaching them to Pelagius. Morris is, for the moment, definitive, and 'The Sicilian Briton' will fit John-George admirably. I have identified Fastidius for you as 'Cousin Vic' and Agricola as JJ/Pelagius. The tracts were written in Sicily, and certainly reached Britain and Ireland. Whether, as modern scholars furiously debate, they were the immediate cause of socialist and/or Bacaudic unrest in Britain is not the right question – *pace* Thompson (1977). St Ambrose's sermon 'de Nabuthe' (terrific stuff – do read it!) would have been sufficient to set off this whole train.

190.1 **Pelagius** See Comm. p. 287, 102.2.

190.2 **Holy Land** That's why the *Historia Meriadoci* (see Loomis 1959, pp. 473–6) will send young Walwanius (i.e. my Gawain) to Jerusalem. Both will go in time, but Gawain, *here*, is Pseudo-Gawain alias John-George.

190.3 **Boiling Spring** Vulgate Lancelot 243–8 in Bruce (1923, p. 354).

191.1 **Heraclea** Careful comparison of Pliny Jr. (Bk. III, Cap. IV) and Stephanus of Byzantium (De Galatia) with the map satisfies me that Heraclea is indeed St Gilles. The objections by De Vic and Vaissete (Paris 1730, Note XLVI–XI, i–iii) are based on negative evidence only.

191.2 **In the Palatinate** Prosper of Aquitaine for 413.

191.3 **St Gilles** There will be another St Gilles later. The Irish remember Merlin, *inter alia*, as 'Yellow son of White', *Gellius* son of *Albanus*. Think, too, of the 'gilles' of the Flanders carnivals, especially the 'gilles' and 'arlequins' of Binche.

192.1 **Perrons Merlin** There will be two more such 'pyramids' in Glastonbury Old Cemetery. See Loomis (1959, p. 390 and fn. 3, *et al.*).

192.2 **inscriptions** They read:

*Atáulpho Flávio póténtissimo*
*régi régum réctissí[ssi]mo*

*víctori víctor[um] ínvictíssimo*
*Vandálicae Barbári(e)i dépulsóri; et*
*Caesarea Placidiae animae suae:*

*Dominis suix clementissimis*
*Anatilii, Narbonenses, Arecomici,*
*optimis principibus in palatio posuerunt*
*Ob electam Heracleam in Regiae Majestatis sedem.*

To Ataulphus Flavius the most powerful:
King of Kings, the most upright:
unconquered conqueror of the conquered:
Expulsor of the Barbarians and Vandals.
And to [Galla] Placidia, she with the spirit worthy of a Caesar.
To their two most clement Majesties, and best
of Princes, the inhabitants of Narbonese
Anatilia and Arecomica have erected this
memorial in his palace, in gratitude that His
Majesty (Ataulphus) has chosen Heraclea (St
Gilles) as the capital of his Kingdom.

The metre *reveals* that the first six lines are in fact the words of a marching song made up during the recent campaign. It is tempting to suppose that Galla and Merlin were themselves responsible for the two amorous side panels which show (my translations):

(1) Bas-relief of Rome. Ataulfus on horseback bearing torch bears down on it to be stopped by Cupid with the words 'I do not permit you to enter. Rather than that Rome should burn, your own vitals shall burn with my fire. Thus I, Love, save the City, a mercy not welcomed by *all*'. [Not welcomed by whom? By Augustine?]

(2) Bas-relief of a turreted town (an 'artist's impression' of New Heraclea) with a palace in the middle. 'Had love not pierced his breast, Rome would be no more; Heraclea would not exist; the palace of the Flavii will see us gain, not the City [Rome] but the remaining world'.

In consigning this celebrated group of inscriptions to the ranks of the 'Falsae' (Falsae, p. 25, XXVI, no. 263) or forgeries, the learned editor (Hirschfeld) of CIL Vol. XII has reposed his great weight on De Vic and Vaissete – see Comm. p. 307, 191.1. These in turn rest the bulk of their arguments on the proposition (ignoring Jordanes and Orosius) that Galla Placidia married Ataulfus for the first and only time at Narbonne in 414. Rightly, they then say that there is too little time available (barely nine months) for an unrecorded dash eastwards into what was by then Constantius III's territory and the setting up of a 'capital' there, before Ataulfus' departure for Novempopulana, then Barcelona and death. This, and their other serious objections vanish as I now redate it for them; their other objections are trifling and explicable. They go too far in pleading Tillemont in aid. The most he does is to raise his eyebrows at the style. This is not the place to defend further my rehabilitation of this outstanding historical document. Read all about it in the respectable Bouche (1664, Vol. II, p. 157ff.).

192.3 **Arles** The wharves and granaries are on the Right Bank.

193.1 **latest laws** A cascade of laws against Manichees, Donatists and Pagans in

Africa poured from Ravenna between AD405 and 415, resulting in a state of near civil war there. In 410 Jovius persuaded Honorius to grant the Africans freedom of conscience, but a deputation of irate African bishops persuaded Honorius to revoke this. On 30 August 415 he issued a swingeing edict to Heraclian specifically against the Pagans. The dating of Cousin Vic-Publicola's death depends on the dating of Augustine's reply (Ep. 95) to Paulinus' second letter (Ep. 45) telling him of Publicola's death. Scholars such as Fabre and Reinelt have relied here on Goldbacher's dating of the former in CSEL (58.40). Goldbacher ties this to the anti-*Donatist* Council of Carthage of 14 July 410, but this should not in my view be taken as settled. Possidius' visit bearing Augustine's Ep. 95 is on record as resulting from troubles with disaffected **pagans** and would lie more kindly soon after the 30 August 415 edict, the pagans having become saucy during the 'liberty of conscience' phase, and resenting the new penalties. I would therefore date Ep. 95 to early 416, whence my redating of Cousin Vic's death in the palace at Caernarfon.

193.2 **Council of Carthage** Read all about Augustine and the Donatists in Farrar (1907, II, pp. 514–45). Worse still, read his own words in Migne, the latter now available selectively, and in translation, on the Internet.

193.3 **a Turcius** His father, *Turcius Auchenius Rufus*, is Wolfram's 'Tankanis'.

193.4 **bemoan to Augustine** Threaten to become a monk, Ep. 220, ibid.

193.5 **Aëtius** is Ga-lahault, Loholt II, le Haut Prince.

194.1 **coup d'état at Mainz** Prosper and Marcellinus say only 'in Gaul'. Orosius is silent. Idatius would 'top' them both at Narbonne. I think my version is likely.

194.2 **Dardanus** Claudius Postumus Dardanus. (In years to come Sidonius will denounce him as combining all the vices of Merlin, of JJ, and of Jovinus.)

194.3 **Umbria** By one Count Marinus, who himself was later topped.

194.4 **miscarry *en route*** Accepting, as I do, the first (albeit unconsummated) marriage at Forli I have to explain the subsequent negotiations for the return of Galla Placidia to Honorius and/or Constantius III. My reconstruction admittedly limps a bit here, but I think just about manages to get by.

195.1 **marvellous party** Amply described in the history books.

196.1 **assassin** Was his name 'Dobbius', as some scholars will say? Or have they misread the gloss *dubius*, indicating not the name of the assassin but that the success of the assassination was in doubt. I propose with complete confidence that Ataulfus survived.

197.1 **never ... again in this world** Rightly or wrongly, I have chosen to exclude from this reckoning the enigmatic Leontius, Galla's chamberlain at Ravenna prior to 423 to whom Honorius seems to have taken a dislike.

197.2 **in the grave** In the chapel of San Aquilino in Milan. The sarcophagus lid comes from Justina's sarcophagus opposite, taken over by St Aquilinus; and you can see well in Fig. 56 that it is by no means a good fit.

197.3 **Constantius III** Yes, he is Tristan's 'King Mark', and a 'Marcian' by birth.

197.4 **a fine husband** The Emperor Theodosius II in AD421. But she's not yet 15.

198.1 **Areopagus** Before AD814, Hilduin of Paris will dub Merlin 'St Denys' ( a good Sicilian name), and will rightly attribute to him the religious treatise of 'Dionysus the Areopagite'. See Comm. p. 271, 44.1.

198.2 **100 siliquae** This per the Paschal Chronicle Migne (PG XCII).

198.3 **first eight books of the Bible** Actually, the five books of Moses, plus Joshua, Judges and Ruth. She also tackled Zechariah and Daniel.

198.4 **all eternity to win** Merlin's still musing here on his great metaphysical work, the 'Pseudo-Dionysus'. H. O. Taylor (EB, 11th edn, text article), will write of this: '...lofty, apparently complete. Perhaps theological philosophic fantasy has never constructed anything more remarkable'.

198.5 **said earlier** Text p. 190.

198.6 **Pope Innocent ... orthodoxy** The differences between them are recorded in Paulinus' Ep. 37 to Victricius around Christmas 403 (see Comm. p. 196, 135.3) and Innocent's own fairly chilly Ep. II (Migne PL. 20 cols. 468–74 *et seq.*) sent after him to Rouen on 15 February 404 seemingly shortly after he had departed in something of a huff. He would seem to have been delated to Innocent by detractors in Rome as an Apollinarist heretic, and from lines 3–6 of col. 471 they may well have called him a 'people-pleaser' (Publicola). Innocent then summons him from Naples to Rome. Paulinus understands that he has cleared himself before Innocent of Apollinarism, although he personally plainly remains uneasy. He had also been hauled up before Innocent and Honorius himself for careless ordination of curiales and soldiers. In his letter Innocent reminds Vic cautiously of his own Petrine authority. He goes on to make rules for reception of *Novatians* into communion; for ordination of *monks*; for clothing and professing *nuns*. All these were matters in which Victricius was involved. His feathers must have been badly ruffled.

199.1 **publicola** The very thing Innocent had ticked him off about.

199.2 **provost** Latin *praepositus*, whence 'Pabo Post Prydein', *Papal*Archbishop, *Provost* of *Britain*, of Welsh Genealogy (see Bartrum 1966, Index). Rather Maccabee. For Prydein see also Comm. p. 318, 227.6.

199.3 **Primus** (First Consul) This title will in due course be held by John-George as 'Elaphius' in the Vita St Germani's second visit to Britain. I have already argued repeatedly that '*duumvir*' was represented by the Welsh '*eiludd*'. It is possible that '*eiludd*' is for '*uchel jud-ex*' ('*uchel*' from Greek ὐξηλος, ὐψηλος, meaning 'superior' or *primus*). Either way, '*Eiludd*' is the title here referred to; moreover '*eiludd*' transposes (in Welsh and Breton nomenclature), to 'Judhael', even 'St-judhael' which elides to Tudwal; and we shall encounter John-George in the Welsh genealogies as 'Tudwal II Tudclyd'; also, significantly, as 'King Ludd'.

199.4 **Perpetual Consulate** The letter is cited in Morris (1965) and Liebeschuetz (1967) from Caspar in (PL 1–3, 1867). The last Perpetual Consul had been the Augustus Vitellius in AD69.

199.5 **Protector** '*Protectores divini lateri*' were the Emperor's personally appointed bodyguard, chosen from the *scolani*, a young man's rank. The title here has a wider sense, as Cromwell knew. John will bear the title in due course as Vortigern III (Sir Bohort de Gannes, Sir Bors – see Bartrum 1966, Index). **As so often in Welsh, and other epic genealogy, the 'ap's' (son of) are intrusions.**

199.6 **Dorchester** See Comm. p. 294, 128.3.

201.1 **definition** In his three books of AD413 to Marcellinus.

201.2 **Jerusalem** Conjecture. We know only that he was in Palestine. He would hardly have been with Jerome at Bethlehem.

202.1 **letter to Demetrias** The text in Migne PL 30.3 col. 1099.

202.2 **appalling letter** Migne (PL. Ep. 185).

202.3 **on his horse** Chrestien will use this incident in his *Erek*, mistaking Merlin (*Erc*, Gereint-Gerontius, Ataulphus) for Sig*eric*.

203.1 **serving Rome well** As Orosius will write very shortly (in his Book VII, Cap. 42).

203.2 **Exuperantius** See N. Chadwick in *SEBH* 1954, pp. 223–4 and 230–1.

203.3 **to recover Britain** Scholars will rage furiously together as to whether or not there was a recovery of Britain in AD416/7, and the sources give a foothold to both camps. What seems to be overlooked is that Orosius, writing in the next year, gives an unmistakeable account of it in Book VII (Cap. 6) of his *Against the Pagans*. Please read it carefully. The points of comparison are (i) a short and virtually bloodless war, (ii) waged for a civilian Emperor by able generals, (iii) resulting from internal disturbances. Orosius invites us to compare 'period with period, war with war, Caesar with Caesar'. He is writing this piece at the close of AD417.

203.4 **at the end of 415** I have justified this re-dating in Comm. p. 308, 193.1.

203.5 **buried at Caernarfon** As St Peblig.

203.6 **panegyric or epithalamium?** Someone must have been doing them and Rutilius is present and competent. He could presumably choke down his paganism sufficiently to hymn Christian Emperors and Empresses as well as Claudian had been able to wear the mantle of traditional pagan verbiage. I strongly suspect that Rutilius Taurus is Sidonius' Cadurcan poet of Carm. IX, 1, pp. 277–88, and that it is from his lost works (see Comm. p. 266, 25.7) that the Romancers absorbed the characters of Pandion's Athens, Phoebus, Hermes, Orpheus and the Aloidae with so many other Classical allusions, all strikingly appropriate. Sidonius (Carm. XXII, 1, pp. 263–99) also describes stage performances of the Classical myths.

204.1 **marrying** Gawain **and her own son by him.** See text p. 246. Date, AD434. Honoria seduces, but does not marry Gawain Vassonius. She does marry his son Childeric Vassonianus (Guengazonein) by whom she becomes the mother of Clovis (see Gregory of Tours HF II, §12; see also Vita St Geneviève of Paris in Baring-Gould 1872 3/1). No wonder St Geneviève had a much questioned reputation among the Parisians until her heroic efforts in the siege of Paris by Alaric II won her belated acceptance.

204.2 **doubly prestigious** The suggestion is not mine but Duchesne's (*apud* Vacandard 1903, p. 154).

205.1 **Sicilian Socialist** Time, perhaps, to look up 'Seisyll' (Sicilian) in Bartrum (1966, Index). What do you make of the 'Three Legs of Man'? Obvious really: all Man's Roman conquerors/occupiers, from Count Theodosius on, hailed from Sicily, specifically (as Marcians) from Syracuse. 'Enceladus rides again, OK?' The 'three legs' are so depicted on the shield of Enceladus in his unsuccessful battle with the Goddess Athene, on the famous Agrigento Vase. I prefer my explanation to the latter-day Manx version, viz. that the Sicilianising heraldic arms of Man reflect no more than Alexander III of Scotland's wish to ingratiate himself with his brothers-in-law.

206.1 **Prefect of New Rome** Freeman is right; see Freeman (1887, p. 429 and fn. 35).

206.2 **reservoir ... Adrianople Gate** Still very much in evidence; now a football ground.

206.3 **Taurus ... Prefect ... 414** For the dating of Taurus' Prefecture see Tillemont (1701, V, pp. 626, 819).

206.4 **Morgan was dead** Nordic legend will make her *Grendel*'s enormous mother (Merlin being Gereint Æl-ianus), but she was only his stepmother. It will have Beowulf II slay her in her underwater palace (at Castel Maniace, Ortygia, Syracuse). Nordic legend has it wrong. Beowulf II, pseudo-Gawain/John-George (confused with 'my Gawain') 'straightened out' his 'larger-than-life' mother Elissa (spiritually), as you will see on text p. 233, *et seq*. Don't forget that JJ and Merlin are both 'Havelocks'; Hygelak (Havelock) is Beowulf's uncle. In Beowulf's mother 'Hygd' we must, with a phonetic effort, recognise Eudoxia; the author intended John-George but has described Gawain II. To the other Havelock (JJ), Hygd/Eudoxia also bears a son, 'Heardred' (Count Hardres of Romance) who is Aëtius the 'primrose-headed' (or broombush-headed).

206.5 **Theodoric, King of the Vizi-Goths** Gothic *Thiudriks*. He is *not* the Romance Dietrich of Berne (Verona), in whom many of my personae are conflated; nor is he – off my map – Theodoric the *Ostro-Goth*. He *is* Theodoric I, King of the Vizi-Goths, aka Walthar of Aquitaine, the 'Third Hostage'. The Romance of 'Waltharius' gives us, in total confusion, Walthar (Valteger; yet another Vortigern – this time of Aquitaine), 'son' of K. Alphue (Ataulphus-Merlin, but should be Alaric); Hagen II, a noble youth; and Ursula/Hildegund. King Gibich (sib-Ecke, still Merlin) King of the Franks withholds his son Gunthar (Gawain II). Take 'Waltharius' with much salt.

207.1 **she would not relinquish it** In 451 she'll 'marry' Uncle Heliodorus' son Theodosius (Theodosiolus) (see Appendix 4) who will then reign with her rather effectively as Marcian Augustus. Together, in AD451, they will give the Church the last great Ecumenical Council of Chalcedon.

208.1 **Minister of Munitions** We owe this titbit to the *Paschal Chronicle* (or *Chron. Alexandrinum*) (Tillemont 1738, VI, p. 39), and Migne (PG XCII).

208.2 **Eudokia Athenais** There will be a little problem for scholars here, as when she becomes Augusta she will coin as *Eudoxia* **II**. You have been warned.

208.3 **Kyriakos** i.e. 'Man of the Church'. ('H *'Εκκλησια του Κυριακου*, 'the Assembly of The Lord's People' or *ὁι κυριακοι*, was the ancient name for the whole body of Christians, i.e. of 'The Church'. Indeed, it is the *origin* of the name. Don't Caesar and Tacitus say the Germans knew Greek? Later scholars will derive 'Church' from the German '*Kirche*', and think they've got to the bottom of it.) Ref. Migne (PG XCII, col. 791).

208.4 **different after dark** The church historians will write that they only gave over prayer and hymn-singing to ply their needles and gold thread embroidering sacred vestments. Little time over to run an empire. Their only male companions, priests and eunuchs. A pretty tale. Secular, and more cynical, historians will write that Pulcheria had eyes only for her brother the Augustus, but that she had other lovers, notably Count Paulinus, and that Theodosius had him murdered out of jealousy. Either way, her affairs, and those of her sisters, were conducted with the greatest propriety, if we may so name discretion.

208.5 **Ninth District** See *Notitia Urbis Constantinopolae* (Seeck 1876, p. 237, line 7). Tillemont gives a valuable clue to the location of these regions (which has tended to baffle scholars) by translating them as 'arrondissements' on the pattern of Paris, and indeed of Old Rome. If you make them radiate anticlockwise from the Forum of Constantine (as Constantine I probably laid them out) it will all make sense.

208.6 **next time it'll be poison** Geoffrey of Monmouth (HRB, VIII.24) actually kills him off by poison. We know there are to be several more attempts on Aëtius' life, but we do not know if poison was Padusia's (Felix' wife's) weapon.

208.7 **our John ... up at the Convent** The Romancers will have it wrong here. Chrestien's Cligés *is* John-George, but he was 'cuckolding' (if that is the word here) the other Cligés (Theodosius II). ('Alis' is Arcadius by lamdacism, and the generations are confused.) At the Coven, John-George has been learning how to 'slay dragons' in the alchemical sense, and this will remain an absorbing interest for him. You can't 'make gold' unless you first kill the dragon. **Now** he's *Beowulf II* for real. The only problem (for the Beowulf author) is that John has got red hair. The fair-haired Beowulf is Aëtius.

209.1 **Faramund, from φαραγξ** See also next item. Vendryes (1925) strives with rather moderate success to identify him with Dathi (Nathi) King of Connaught, who is his son, but he gives us Forménus, King of Thrace (Formenius, Parmenus, Fer Menia, for *Vir Arminius*), which is not so wide of the mark.

209.2 **Pharaon Dandde** *Meleagris Numidiae*, the African guinea-fowl noted for its wattled **jowls** (see Bartrum 1966, Index; Ffaraon ap Brân). The 'Palamedes' (Löseth 1891, p. 447) gives MS variants [P]haroan, [Ph]araon (Aaron and cf. Aaron the 'Moor', Maurus in *Titus Andronicus*), Aryhoan, and Ariohan of Saxony, and brings him together with Leodagan (Leo tigernus). Elsewhere Löseth (ibid.) gives **Ferramon** (Faramund) and Syn**amon**. For 'jowls' see '*gulae*', Comm. p. 276, 58.4, p. 284, 82.6.

210.1 **Catacombs** See Comm. p. 259, 3.2. Merlin's tour of the catacombs is thrillingly described in the Romance of 'Palamedes', where 'Breus-Sans-Pitie' is shown the tombs of the ancestors of the Merovingians by Phoebus-Apollo(nius). The latter is Merlin 'Goldilocks': Aëtius is Palamedes, as will be explained in Book XIX.

210.2 **and his many other estates** He will justly earn the Romancers' epithet of 'Le riche Soudier': 'the Rich Soldier'. Indeed, his rival, Tristan (Boniface), will call him Aëtius-*Edatius*', 'Aëtius the covetous'. See Freeman (1887, p. 436, fn. 61). Scholars rightly conclude that these epistles are insufficiently prolix or moralising to be by Augustine himself. Why not Alypius?

210.3 **sneak** On John's socialism. Augustine (Ep 156/7).

210.4 **Too close, perhaps?** See Comm. p. 314, 211.6.

211.1 **Julyot (variously spelt)** Canner (1982, p. 33) cites Leland for 'Ulette', 'Uliane'. On p. 5 he gives 'Julitta'.

211.2 **evidence there for all to see** A whole class of Mediterranean imported pottery. Two rock-cut labyrinths. Churches, one remembered after St 'Martyriana' or Madron. (Martyriana: Canner (ibid.), App. II, gives Merthiane, Merteriane, Mertheriane, Mertheriana, Marthariane, Matheriane, Matheriana, Materiana.) The Exeter Bishop's Register (Canner, p. 15) for 2 June 1258 calls her church St Marcelliana's and I see no reason to follow those who would have this a scribal error. The churches of Tintagel and Minster were in my view erected, probably by John, in memory of St Marcelliana Mertheriana, *recte* St Marcella the Martyr, already identified as St Ursula.

211.3 **'Esplumeoir'** See Loomis (1959, p. 374) for Romance refs.

211.4 **Uther Pendragon** Uther, for Eleutherus (recalling Aëtius as the freed hostage);

Pendragon, for cavalry tribune, as explained in Book VII. In the Tintagel tales of the begetting of 'Arthur', Merlin plays himself. John-George plays 'Gorlois'. Ursula plays the little 'Grail Maiden' Elayne, for *Pelagiana.*

211.5 **Siegfried and Grane** Wagner has it wrong. It was not a special 'horse' but a very special '*mare*' that Brünnhilde there put at his disposal. Once again, '*O matre pulchra filia pulchrior*'.

211.6 **Grainne** The pursuit of Diarmait-Grainne is translated in Vol. III of the Transactions of the Ossianic Society, retold in Squire (1910, pp. 215–21). She is Ursula Gratiana IV, Ygrainne-Igerne, of Geoffrey of Monmouth's HRB. It is an unpleasant thought that she may have borne him a son 'Amr' who may have married Eugenia (see Comm. p. 302, 167.2).

211.7 **a Latin** The Latinus stones at Whithorn and Slaughterbridge also indicate someone of Latin origins, but for the latter see my generally sceptical view in Comm. p. 272, 47.3.

211.8 **classical historians** They will rely on Priscus, and maybe on Seeck's article on Carpilio in Pauly-Wissowa.

211.9 **redating them both** All agree that the dates of the earlier entries in the *Anglo-Saxon Chronicle* can hardly even be taken as indicative. I see no mischief in bringing Cerdic back to a birthdate in AD422. As to Coroticus, he is usually linked to 'Patrick' by the Epistle. I have now given you a birthdate for 'Patrick' of October AD409, and I propose that he excommunicates Coroticus c. AD448.

213.1 **battles in Saxony** Most notably in the *Livre d'Artus*, but the Arthurian Romances are all too full of them, and Nennius, and the *Song of the Saxons*. There will be a further campaign in AD426.

214.1 **Count** Augustine (Ep. 220) tells us this. Augustine is the counselling hermit 'Amytans', rightly named by the author of the *Prose Tristan* as St Augustine, though he wrecks chronology by getting the wrong St Augustine.

214.2 **advice ... eight years previously** Read what they said in Augustine's letter (220), still extant; refs in Comm. p. 318, 226.2.

214.3 **Southern Picts** or Di-caledonii (*decumani* Caledonii). He'll be their *defensor* and by and by much more.

214.4 **St Regulus or Rule** Here we have John-George. His *Vita*, summarised in Baring-Gould (1877) for 17 October should be read in full in the *Acta Sanctorum* for the same day. The inventive *Vita St Regulus* (Rieul) of 30 March (ibid.) also deserves a percipient glance.

214.5 **Diarmid** Dermot of the Love Spot (freckles) of Irish myth (see Comm. 211.6 above).

214.6 **Iona** Where he will leave a memory in 'relig *Oran*' (of himself as St Pol *Aurelian*)! This is not a long-shot; see text p. 245 and Comm. p. 327, 245.4. 'Saul the accursed' will become 'Paul', and he was ever an Aurelian in right of his father.

215.1 **Bishop Fastidius** *Fastidius* means 'haughty' in the non-pejorative sense of distinguished. Not 'proud' or 'arrogant' but 'auspicious', in its true Roman sense, is what you seek.

215.2 **John's letter** '*Honorificentiae tuae*': see Comm. p. 310, 199.4; Migne (PL. Sup 1, 1687).

215.3 **first invited tame Saxons** Per Nennius (Cap. 16) and again (less than 100 years) at Cap. 31.

215.4 **Tigernicus** See the Llan-y-Mawddwy stone ECMW 284 (another of Maelgwn II Gwynedd's revivalist efforts – or are they Merfyn Frych's?).

215.5 **Praetorian** One Agricola. See Apollinaris Sidonius (Ep., Bk. I, ii, II, xii).

216.1 ***tribunicia potestate*** This highly technical phrase again goes 'back to Livy'. It signified the right of the Consuls to call out (and thereafter command) the army. Augustus Octavianus never called himself more than *Princeps Senatu cum tribunicia potestate* which he had them regularly reconfirm to him. It means much more than 'Tribune'. (See also Cagnat in Egbert, 1896.)

216.2 **number of churches** The church dedications, and related place names, of South Wales alone amply demonstrate this. But the (putatively) 'Pre-Saxon' churches of Silchester, Canterbury, Richborough and Reculver are not, perhaps, irrelevant.

216.3 **St Maughold** Pronounced Maccul, or Mc Cool. Glorious Dad is Finn the First, Mac Cuill son of Agricola. Merlin is Finn II, 'Demna' (the *daimonic*), alias Fingal.

216.4 **Pre-Patrician** See MacNiocaill (1972, 2nd edn, 1980, pp. 22–4).

216.5 **by Merlin as St Sechnall** Here, at long last, is 'Sir Kay the Seneschal' *senex Calchas*, old Calchas the Seer, of the Proem and Book XII (often wrongly derived from *senex calchus*, and not wholly inappropriately since *Calchus* doesn't only mean servant or slave of man. As *Gottschalck* it means 'servant of God'); Merlin is also St Ail-be (*Ælius Benedictus*). Merlin was assisted by John-George as Sts Auxilius (for Achilles), Budoc, Kevin/Kieran, Declan (*dei colanus* – St Collen II).

216.6 **Ireland for Iona** In Ireland (where he is remembered as Tigernach the first) Irish myths tell us of his hagiographical struggles and conflicts with other Irish saints and personalities (Kieran, Diarmaid, Albin, Molais, Mo-Chonna, Frych). Those who have absorbed the nomenclature of I Merlin will recognise that these fights *are no more than John's struggles with his own conscience and, as often as not, his own unmanageable libido*. Tigernach's traditional area, i.e. John-George's, lies on the border of Ulster and Meath. It is the scene of the 'fight' of CuChulainn/John-George and Ferdiad/John-George. [Ferdinand means *recte* Vir Ordinandus, and John-George was not only 'fit to be Augustus' but actually became so: the other 'Ferdinand', i.e. Aëtius, was too proud ever to try for the purple.] As Baring-Gould (1872) for 9 June (condensing de Montalembert) points out, the first 40 years (to AD423) of St Columba's life have to be pieced together from 'a maze of confused and contradictory narratives', and only thereafter does Adamnan become serviceable. I feel free to contend, therefore, that John left Ireland for Iona in AD425, being at that time in his early forties.

216.7 **King Brude** Bridei Meilochon. See Bede, in Sherley-Price (1955). John himself is 'Britu' in Welsh sources, and 'Brutus' in Latin. He is also Maelgwn I, *μεγαλος κυων*, the great wolfhound, the 'man-wolf' or 'werewolf'.

216.8 **St Andrews** This truly remarkable exemplar of **late Roman art** is customarily assumed to be a late and unique flowering of Pictish art. Scholars have been content merely to dispute whether it is eighth, ninth, or early tenth century work. It is assumed to derive from (but surpass) the Hilton of Cadboll stone. Why not vice versa? The front slab, of which we are talking, has significant differences from the remainder of the 'shrine' in which it figures as an earlier and intrusive item. The 'Daniel figure' bears a marked facial resemblance to the coins of Joannes Augustus. He wears a short cape over his tunic, identifiable as the *paludamentum trabeatum* of an old-time fighting *Consul cum tribunicia potestate*. Just a bit formal for hunting? He bears the falcon (or maybe eagle) which the troubadour Bertran de Paris says he introduced into Arctois (Loomis 1959, pp. 394–5). He is bearing a large knife (not sword) or *Anelathus* (Hamlet), from which he will derive his Welsh names of 'Ossa gylellfawr' (or 'Offa') (see Comm. p. 325, 242.7). As to 'Offa', John-George is recognisably Offa of *Beowulf*; and he is 'Offa the First, of Angle' in the 'Vitae duarum Offarum' ascribed to Matthew Paris c. AD1250. (Aesop's Fable LXXXIV gives rise to John's own Welsh nickname of Garan Hir, 'the tall crane', and the tale describes with the utmost accuracy the principal scene to the right of the slab.) Note particularly, when you go to see it, the pendant cross on John's dexter lapel. John also wears gloves (maybe to conceal his artificial left hand), as required by Arnant-Guilhem de Marsan (in Loomis, ibid.). I see no satisfactory resemblance to the Breedon Angel. The Reculver column is much more to the point, **indeed perhaps very much** so. To clarify all this would require a separate monograph.

217.1 **Honoratus** Is he perhaps none other than 'Little Benedict' himself? See Comm. p. 282, 75.6.

218.1 **number of churches** as St Malo etc., Miles Gloriosus, St Samson, 'St Nicodemus' recalling Merlin as Joseph the Arimathean. Others commemorate their rich patroness St Melania the Holy Terror, and her, hardly poorer, granddaughter of the same name.

218.2 **guilty secret** Augustine (Ep. 220), says she bore Boniface a daughter, initially baptised as an Arian. See also text p. 223.

219.1 **an Augustus of the Blood** See the *Augustan Histories* (Elagabalus, Caps i–iv) or *Lives of the Later Caesars*, Birley 1976.

219.2 **deacon or priest** We left John at Arles in AD411 no more than a deacon. He may, however, be that 'restless and dissolute young man' rashly 'priested' in Edessa by Rabbula and Ibas; or that may have been another.

220.1 **provost** Not yet a 'Pope', Merlin will be only 'Vortigern II'.

220.2 **Melania** Surely not St Melanius, the perfectly authentic later Bishop of Rennes. Breton place-names are insistent on St Melaine (feminine), where Melanius would be St Melain (masculine).

220.3 **new Augustus** Olympiodorus, in Freeman (1887, p. 430, fn. 38), will describe him as the 'authentic' Augustus. One source (the 'Gallic Chronicle of 452' for AD423), by referring to the new Augustus as *Primicerius*, has been rashly taken by scholars as referring to that other John, *Primicereus Notariorum* in 408, who treated with Alaric and then treated with Ataulfus at Marseilles as Praetorian of Gaul. In fairness to Lérins (don't you think the contents of the Gallic Chronicle smack rather of Lérins than Marseilles?) I have made our John *Primicereus* (Secretary) to JJ in Book XIII (p. 153) which would validate the Chronicle. That was 12 years previous; John's coins (as displayed comprehensively in Spink 1994) will show a much younger man than John the Praetorian would have been, especially 1901, 1904, 1911. Indeed these latter show reasonable congruence with the St Andrew's slab portrait of John as St Rule.

220.4 **reunited with Titia** I have been in some doubt whether to retain the 'mother of John's second daughter' with him in normal wedlock. History and Romance alike are silent. She is *not* Nennius' Rowena ('Hengist's daughter'). The latter is, of course,

Eugenia/Antigone (see Comm. p. 326, 245.3) and we are faced with the unpleasant thought that, like Merlin, John too was guilty of daughter incest. Nennius combines this (Sec. 38) uneasily with Vortigern II (Merlin) having a son (Faustus) by his own daughter (Ursula). Here, I think, is the source of the confusion. But worse is to come. If my conjecture in App. 11 that John-George is Gildas' denounced 'Maglocunus' is correct, John murders Eugenia's husband, his own sister's son in order to wed Eugenia c.436 as her second husband. And Nennius tells us that 'Arthur the soldier' kills 'his own ... son' Amr. There is only one way, alas, in which 'Amr' can be at once John's son and his nephew. Thankfully, there is too little reliable information for us to reconstruct this appalling story in its entirety, but see Comm. p. 314, 211.6.

220.5 **10,000 Huns** Philostorgius (XII, 14) says 60,000 Huns, if the text is right. This seems to me excessive. 10,000 (a myriad), the fighting strength of two legions, was a normal Duke's command (hence Meriadoc, *myriad-dux*). See Comm. pp. 281, 73.2, 303, 171.1.

221.1 ***Ludd llaw ereint*** For Ei*ludd*, *duumvir*, a title he will get very shortly. See Comm. p. 310, 199.3. In Irish myth Luch*taine*, Lucius the *τεκτων*, the craftsman rehabilitates John Scraib*taine*, the cunning penman.

221.2 **couriers** Paulinus (Ep. 37). The estimable Candidianus was later to preside over the Council of Ephesus, which by exiling Nestorius was to send much of the *Liber Gradalis* astray. The Table of Contents of Marciana (MS 299) shows chapters which are no longer there. Here is the Romancers' 'Loss' of the Holy Grail.

222.1 **Wroxeter** Where the *Llywarch Hēn* cycle will remember him poignantly as 'Cyn-ddylan' (*Constans Julianus*). See Bartrum (1966, p. 91) [28 (e) variant reading F]. John is 'Dylan Son of the Wave' (Julian) of Welsh myth; also 'Fiachu (*vir Achilles*) Fermara' (Man of the Sea), 'Myrmidonian Achilles' (Eochu Mugmedon) of Irish myth.

222.2 **memorial church at Ravenna** St John Evangelist, the 'St John' being a play on John Cassian. The gateway has a later relief of Galla as Mary Magdelene, shown in Fig. 38. Her original very full mosaic inscription (here translated by Hodgkin 1880, I, p. 452) with portrait medallions, is now perished, but is recorded in Gruter (1048) and Muratori (1878), *apud* Clinton (1850, II, p. 126). It reads:

> To the Holy and most Blessed Apostle John the Evangelist. Galla Placidia Augusta, with her son Placidus Valentinianus Augustus and her daughter Justa Grata Honoria Augusta; in fulfilment of a vow for deliverance from peril by sea. 'Strengthen O Lord what Thou hast wrought for us; because of thy Temple at Jerusalem shall Kings bring presents unto Thee'.

Ten mosaic portrait medallions are then 'captioned' including (with commendable Christian meekness), her usurping nephew John-George Julianus.

224.1 **and write poems** Cf. the '*Llywarch Hen* cycle' etc., and more.

225.1 **Julian's strictures** In his *Contra Julianum*: six books of stumbling apologetics, c. AD429 (Migne, PL XLV col. 1049ff) attest a powerful and once noble intellect now in discreditable decay.

226.1 **forged letter** Aëtius' reputation will be besmirched for nearly 1500 years by this false accusation until he is cleared by Professor Freeman in 1887. Whoever wrote it, *pace* Freeman (1887), it would have been neither surprising nor discreditable if Aëtius did in fact write this letter.

226.2 **just read *this* letter** Translated in full in Hodgkin (1880, Vols I–II). Ep. 220 is in Vol. I at pp. 495–503. No one seems to read Hodgkin any more. A pity. An earlier generation of scholars treasured him, and were not ashamed to use him.

226.3 **Pictish** See Comm. p. 264, 20.2.

226.4 **Goidelic** The language of Romulus' North-pushing Romans (as opposed to Oscan and Etruscan). What we call 'Latin' today. See Comm. p. 278, 65.6.

227.1 ***agnomen*** Additional or 'nickname'. It is electrifying to find in the 'Labour Pains of the Ulaid' of the Ulster Cycle one 'Crunnine' (read Coronog, Conor), father of the twins (Genesius and Maximus) of Macha (Elissa the Atalanta of the Ardennes; Romance, Ardanata), described as 'son of **Agnoman**' (Gantz 1981, pp. 128–9). Classically educated *filid*? But of course.

227.2 **pretended … Flavian Gens** And genuine membership of the somewhat lacklustre Valerian Gens.

227.3 **Cuaran** For *coronatus*. Many many reverberations of Cuaran in Ireland and in the Havelok legends. Shakespeare will even give him a walking-on part in *King Lear*, when he would have been barely ten years old – or is this Merlin, still a few years from his laurel crown?

227.4 **headmaster** His 'fables' for them, very much in the manner of Aesop, will survive in Iolo MSS 1888, pp. 154–65, 560–76.

227.5 **unorthodox tinge** Prosper of Aquitaine (Bishop, Chronicler and dedicated anti-Pelagian), will write that 'Agricola's (i.e. JJ's) 'Pelagian' *writings* will start this year to corrupt the Church of Britain.

227.6 **Prytaneion** The Ancient Greek Civic Hall. Every community had one, where the councillors met and where the communal Vestal fire was maintained (see text p. 80 re. the centre of the 'Three Gauls'). New Rome still had one (per Notitia, CP Seeck 1876, p. 233) in the Fifth Arrondissement. No antiquarian anachronism therefore, the name was thus in current use in the 420s after nearly 1000 years. Not just the name but the ideas that went with it, and continued to do so into late Saxon times with 'Bret-walda' (or even better 'bretenan-wealda') as a title of honour.

228.1 **since 417** Year of Constantius III and Germanus' recovery of Britain.

228.2 **Diocletian** In his original division, the Eastern Empire had extended all the way up the Danube to where the Inn comes in at Passau (Bataviensis) and included not only Pannonia but Noricum, home of the Western Empire's sword-steel (and some gold). In the Romance of the Erle of Thoulouse, 'Erle Barnard' quarrels with 'Diocletian' about boundaries. This is the boundary in question.

228.3 **King Gundahar** Or 'Gwyn Tigernus'. Will they remember Merlin this time round as the dwarf King Laurin (*Lucius Aurelianus*)?

229.1 ***Imperator* Arthur** See text p. 240, and Comm. p. 323, 240.3. I remind you yet again that 'Imperator' is not synonymous with Augustus although some 'Arthurs' were both. Aëtius, proudly conscious not only of his noble birth but also of his bastardy, would never even try for the purple.

229.2 **campaign in the forests** Nennius will pick up some of the battles in his *Historia Brittonum*, and an unmistakeable account of the campaign is in the Romance *Palamedes* (MS 5243). Generations of scholars will struggle to locate them. Here's one clue: 'Mount Agned' is in Batavia (*Passau*), where one day Thomas à Kempis will write.

229.3 **Leprechauns** I thought I'd give you a reminder of the heading of Book II.

229.4 **the Guide** The English, when they come along, will write his deeds as '*Guy* II of Warwick'.

229.5 **CCAA (Köln)** She may also have resided at Mayen (Genovefaburg), often mentioned in Grimms' *Sagen*, esp. No. 539.

229.6 **grotesque dwarf Zercon** Alberich I (or Oberon) (de Boron's '*Bron* the rich fisherman/sinner'), is Merlin. Alberich II, *recte* 'Albinus', is John Hamlet, [R]**Ogier the Dane,** 'the Danish redhead'. If Merlin is, or shortly will be, Alberich I, Zercon will be mistaken by Wagner for Mime. John, of course, is *Wild Hagen* 'the hawk' (a mistake again here, this time in the saga genealogies – John is 'foxy'; Aëtius the 'aquiline' could be called hawk-like). Lots more about Zercon in the *Palamedes* (and in Priscus, *apud* Suidas).

230.1 **Dispargum** See Comm. p. 261, 12.1.

230.2 **Elsinore** Name with 'vibes'. What about the 'Elesa' of the Saxon genealogies; and 'Eliseg' of the Welsh pillar? Who's Elise the strong? Admiral John-George of course – see Bartrum (1966, Index).

230.3 **Tigernicus** (Irish Tigernach) Remembered by the Cambrians as Gurtheyrn Gwrtheneu, 'the *Antenorian*'. See Morris (1973, endnote 124.2), and Comm. p. 299, 153.3.

230.4 **say what I was** Will Romancers recall Merlin as the *Fisher-King*,'le Roi Pêcheur', 'Amfortas' (Ambrosius the Strong)?

230.5 **City of the Phoenix** Particularly Fénice the ambiguous heroine of Chrestien's Cligés.

231.1 **pantaloon** Do we see here Wolfram's *Malcréatiure*?

231.2 **Vitalis** See Comm. p. 287, 101.5, and a forest of Welsh epithets to prove it. See Bartrum (1966, Index) 'Bywyr Lew, Bywdeg' (*Bivatigus* and see the Trescawen Stone, Comm. p. 272, 47.3). The Trescawen Stone purports to record the tomb of 'Branwen' (Wagner's 'Bran*gäne*'); she is indeed Eu*genia*, and her pitiful and hallowed destiny will emerge later. She's FR*owena Flavia* (*Ulpia-Marciana*) *Eugenia*, **Ophelia II.**

231.3 **No time for men** If my very unpleasant suggestion implicit in App. 11 is inescapable, namely that John is Gildas' denounced Maglocunus, it would follow that Eugenia/Ophelia was already married, and the text would have to be rewritten to accommodate this further unpleasantness. See Comm. p. 316, 220.4.

231.4 **Gawain ... to Metz** As St (O)*Livier* of Metz, and also later as King *Bazon* (Vassonius) of Sedan and Toul, 'husband' of Honoria.

231.5 **Rothenburg ob der Tauber** This town preserves the tradition of Pharamond. I have an idea that this tradition has been transferred from Rottenburg-on-Neckar, (*Salmulocenae*, a Roman site), south-west of Tübingen at the foot of the Swabian Alps. Should we look here for the origins of the enigmatic and indeed hag-ridden principality of Salm?

232.1 **Grimms' *Märchen*** (*Sagen* No. 473) Think too of St Crispinian of Comm. p. 276, 60.1. The Crispiniani are remembered in sacred myth as 'shoemakers'. Indeed, that's just about all that is remembered about them.

232.2 **Burgundians** They become Nibelungs in the Nibelungenlied after the death of 'Siegfried' *recte* **Sigmund/JJ**. Previously the Franks (probably the Riparian Franks) had had the title.

232.3 **would one day record** So important, I will quote it, from Merobaudes Panegyric II to Aëtius (1, pp. 112–19 per Vollmer in Clover 1971, p. 66).

*nam claro genitore satus – sed forte parentem*
*caedibus Arctois et iusta sorte potitum*
*callidus et falsa tectus prece perculit ensis*
*mercatum vita leti decus: haut secus olim*
*pugnaces Fabii patria pro gente cadebant*
*et Decius, propero lucem qui fine refudit,*
*sed famam sine fine tenet, nam mortis amorem*
*pensat laudis honor ...*

I venture my own translation and comments: 'for he was born of a distinguished father; but it so happened that, amidst "Arctic" carnage, his father, a man worthy of a juster fate, was struck down by a sword cunningly cloaked in a false petition – thus purchasing with his life a glorious death. Even thus, once fought and fell the Fabii for the sake of their country; even thus, Decius won endless glory embracing death for love of honour'.

Merobaudes (who is Gawain II) has to tread delicately here before Aëtius himself and a knowledgeable audience. His description of the murder reminds us irresistibly of Kyriakos' attack on Aëtius outside St Sophia. The analogies of the Fabii and of Decius are carefully judged. All these heroes gave their lives in defence of the Plebs. They were all 'left-wingers', 'Fabians', *publicolae*. This is perhaps the moment to explain to you the last two fragmentary references to 'Quirinus' in *Paneg.* (II 1, pp. 195–6). They are to Aëtius – see text p. 210.

232.4 **experienced approval** Merlin, like Paul in Acts VIII.1, was 'consenting unto his death'. Did Merlin, too, feel the guilt thereof?

232.5 **wax bust** The wondrous talking head of the second Branch of the Mabinogion. Hippolytus (see Comm. p. 260, 7.6) tells the secret of the talking head of *Orpheus*. The secret survives, appropriately, with Pope Silvester II (Gerbert), Roger Bacon, and Albertus Magnus. Appropriately, since they were all into alchemy, indeed I suspect that Gerbert may be the alchemists' 'Latin Geber' (otherwise unidentified), 'author' of the *Summa Perfectionis Magisterii*, which he might have uncovered during in his student days at Ripoll (see Comm. p. 286, 100.3). It is curious that 'Walter Mapes' (Nugae, Dist IV, Cap. xi) singles out Gerbert for a not irrelevant eucharistic essay.

232.6 **Irish King slain in the Alps** He is the predecessor of Loegaire (Pelagianus) John-George (Dathi, Nathi). See Morris (1973, Vol. 1, p. 65) and Chadwick (1976, p. 85). This is not the place to 'rectify' early Irish History, which remains, despite Mac Niocaill's heroic efforts, just about where Geoffrey of Monmouth left British History. With the firm identifications and dating which I here supply, it is now no longer impenetrable. For tactical military reasons I have 'slain' JJ in the Swabian Alps but I have buried him in the Valaisan Alps, the *Alpi Penninae.*

232.7 **Sigurd ... Sigvrid** The sagas have father and son understandably confused, but they may now be successfully disentangled.

233.1 **de-bastardising** Here Peredur/Pryderi, of the Third Branch of the Mabinogion, bestowed his mother on Manawydan – Ædonius of Man, that's Merlin – in marriage, with the comment 'when she was in her prime none was ever fairer'. Oh how very true!

233.2 **Agri Decumates** So called because they were an Imperial Development Area with tax concessions, although, like so much else, modern scholars impugn this.

233.3 **Augsburg** *Augusta Vindelicorum* (the Romancers' 'Windsor'!).

233.4 **Bishop Salvius** He was certainly Bishop of Agaunum a few years later, but we may here be dealing with his unnamed predecessor. The letter to him (before AD449) of Eucherius of Lyons is our prime source for the legend of 'St Maurice and the Martyrs of the Theban Legion'. In itself this is but a *novella* on the theme of the legitimacy of Christian soldiering. 'The sword of the Lord and of Gideon', as it were. That there was a Martyrium containing the bodies of certainly two martyrs, archaeologists have demonstrated (notably L. Blondel, 1948). The letter to Salvius claims, as prime source for the *Passio*, Theodore (Theodul) Bishop of Octodurum, contemporary and associate of Ambrose, and friend of Victricius. This was when the cult of Martyrs in the West was at its peak and *Passio*'s were being written for them almost daily. Eucherius of Lyons could be Eucherius, Stilicho's and Serena's son. But Rettberg and Gieseler attribute the letter to another Eucherius of Lyons, one whom Ado in his martyrology describes as having two daughters, Consortia and Tullia, one who spent occasional periods as an anchorite. (For Constantia Consentia, Concessa, Consortia see text pp. 146, 150). It is not impossible that Merlin/Eucherius should be this author, as a sort of valedictory to JJ. We can see the ingredients, even the names – especially that of the II Trajani, the Theban Legion in which Glorious Dad had served – floating in Merlin's subconscious if we will. It does not matter too much, as the *Passio* cannot be taken as solid fact, however hard we try. The two (plus) original unknown martyrs are fact enough, as at Xanten.

233.5 **St Maurice-en-Valais** *Agaunum in Veragria*. A *vicus* of the *Tarnatae Nantuatum*. Here, maybe, you should look for the Romancers' 'Forest of Darnantes'.

233.6 **martyrs graves there** German legend will have Brünnhilde lay up Sigurd's body at Lorsch over against Worms. There is time for this. But 'Lorsch' means only a (Pachomian) convent. Copious references in the 'Prose Tristan' show that Agaunum was originally intended. The wry, rollicking, erudite author of the 'Tristan' – surely the Cervantes of his day – plainly had excellent sources. The references here are to Löseth (1891): p. 7, Cap. 8, 'La ville d'Albine'; p. 14, Cap. 17, 'la cité d'Albine *Archana*' (Acarne, Acharna, erroneously punctuated by Löseth – Latin name *Acaunum*); p. 17, Cap. 20, 'Albine'. I read all this as 'the alpine city of Agaunum', St Maurice-en-Valais.

233.7 **just the place for him** An unknown Cambrian Bard will write 'Anoeth bid, bedd Arthur' which will be very fancifully translated by the wilder Welsh scholars. The meaning is more simple. 'but hard to find, the grave of Arthur'. Hard, but not impossible. Where are **this** Arthur's bones (i.e. JJ's)? Mingled with those of the saints in the reliquaries of the Convent nearby.

233.8 **horse up that path** The citation is from the *Perlesvaus* (or Prose Potvin) in Sebastian Evans' splendid 'Gothicke' rendering (XXIV, 10/13). A strong-headed mule could probably make it up the path. So can you on foot. Services in Summer only.

234.1 **his prefect's job** The twelfth-century historian, Saxo Grammaticus, calls him *Frowinus Sleswicensium Prefectus*; it is Saxo, too, who names Hamlet 'Amlethus' which in turn reminds us of *Anelathus* of Comm. pp. 315–6, 216.8.

234.2 **cistern in the ruins** Merlin-Gundahar and his Burgunds were probably responsible for ruining it, on his earlier trip North to flog the Burgunds to Jovinus.

234.3 **inscription** See Plate 11. This sarcophagus is a key piece of evidence for the prosopological and genealogical identifications of this book. A photograph of this inscription, as it emerged from the soil, was sent to the great T. Mommsen who replied, on 27 July 1897, '*les personnages sont parfaitement inconnus ... les arbustes que vous dites sont des feuilles de lierre, qui, a l'époque Impériale, servaient pour la ponctuation. L'inscription est* ***certainement*** (my bold) *du IIIe siècle*'. There, till now, the matter has rested. (Quoted in P. Bourban 1901, 'Mélanges', t.II, p. 286.) Collart (1941, p. 24) still follows Mommsen. It is true that '*hedera distinguentes*' are commonplace from the latter part of the first century AD, and I think it is on this basis that Mommsen has elected an early dating. Nevertheless, in the Museo Gregoriano Cristiano in the Vatican, there are a large number of inscriptions – securely dated by their consulates to the fifth century – on view which display the same 'ivy leaf' punctuation. I mention No. 52144 in particular, but also 32027, 32001 and 32004. Maybe there was a fifth century revival of this usage. I regret that Mommsen should have lent his enormous authority to so perfunctory a judgement. Vassonius, as I explained in Comm. pp. 257, 1.5, 266, 25.9, is Gallic for *Nitonius* (Latin), and *Lohen* (Teutonic). There is another 'Nitonius' funerary cippus in the tower wall of the Abbey of St Maurice which, being hardly legible, I have left unexplained.

234.4 **diplomatic marriage** Shall we call her Theodorica? She will bear him a son, Gaudentius II, well recorded in the history books. 'Theodorica' will be vividly brought to life in Apollinaris Sidonius' panegyric for Majorian, but he does not name her, and scholars will go astray in identifying her as Count Marcellinus' and John of Antioch's Pelagia (see text p. 223), former wife of Boniface. John confirms that the latter (Galla) only became Aëtius' mistress.

235.1 **assist them theologically** Here, I think, we have the origin of Bede's much argued 'King Lucius' legend. If we think Merlin still, at bottom, something of an Augustinian, he might have had a hand in instigating Germanus' second visit. We are then left with the small problem of the 'Pope Eleutherus' to whom Lucius is supposed to have written. Bede does not quite call him Pope. He writes *Eleutherus vir sanctus Romanae ecclesia praeesset.* Nennius calls him *Evaristo*, which looks like an attempt at *Eucharisto*, or even Eucherius. The debate continues; and this is only my preliminary contribution to it.

235.2 **setting things to rights** His Vita tells us that Germanus visited Verulamium and committed a 'pious sacrilege' on St Alban's tomb, placing within it a 'mixed bag' of Saintly and Apostolic relics, thus thoroughly denationalising and 'Europeanising' this former focus of 'British' nationalism. To introduce additional relics was hardly 'sacrilege'. We may wonder whether Germanus did not at the same time remove all or most of Alban's remains; and whether John later reinterred them at somewhere like Whithorn as Bede and tradition will suggest.

235.3 ***Book of the San Graal*** Much of the latter will be dispersed with Nestorius (see below and see Comm. p. 317, 221.2). The Crusaders, especially the First Crusaders (Godfrey of Boulogne and Bouillon, Baldwin of Flanders, and Raymond of Toulouse), hopeful Swan Knights to a man, will go East in search of it. Whereupon, Plantagenet 'King Arthurs' will bemoan the loss of their best knights in this Queste, notably, Henry II, the Neo-Arthurian.

236.1 **Χαος** (Chaos) Chaos was the primal Greek (*and* Egyptian) God, representing matter in its original undifferentiated form. Chaos Χαος first coupled with Gaia Γη to produce Uranus 'Ουρανος, the physical Universe. The word 'gas' was invented by J. B. van Helmont, alchemist/transmutationist and (sceptical) disciple of Paracelsus. He describes it thus in 1648, in his *Ortus medecinae*: '*spiritus sylvestris* (because first obtained from charcoal) *"gas" sylvestre sive incoërcibile, quod in corpus cogni non potest visibile ... hunc spiritum, incognitum hactenus, novo nomine "gas" voco.*' And later, '*halitum illum "Gas" vocavi, non longe a Chao veterum secretum*'. 'I have called this name "gas", it being scarcely distinguishable from the "Chaos" of the Ancients'. All this is from the *EB XIth Edn, 1910*, text article 'Gas'. The same source, in text article 'Priestley, Joseph' describes how Priestley worked on the different sorts of 'air' πνευμα (van Helmont's gases). By heating 'spirits of salt' (Hydrochloric acid) he made hydrochloric acid gas. Then he boiled 'oil of vitriol' (sulphuric acid) and made sulphur dioxide. Then he followed Scheele in boiling fluorspar in vitriol and got silicon fluoride. Boiling 'spirits of hartshorn' (aquaeous ammonia) he made ammonia gas, which by electrolysis he separated into nitrogen and hydrogen; from the former he synthesised *Sal Ammoniac*. Finally, by heating red oxide of mercury (mercurochrome) **with a burning glass** he prepared oxygen. It was Faraday in 1823 who first liquified chlorine by means of an hermetically sealed bent glass tube (see Fig. 40) containing hydrate of chlorine. On heating one end of this, distilled chlorine appeared at the other end, the pressure created by the ever-expanding gases resulting in their partial liquification. Using the same hermetically sealed tubes he then liquified a number of gases, but failed with hydrogen and oxygen. Later chemists struggled by mechanical means to liquify oxygen; Berthelot (yes, it is he! Who else?) in 1850 failed to liquify oxygen at 780 atmospheres. Finally in 1895 a regenerative apparatus was devised which successfully liquifies oxygen, hydrogen, etc., and this was developed for industrial use. Discovering Faraday's 'hermetically sealed tube' in *Berthelot 1888* (sc. the *Liber Gradalis*), I have felt inspired and enabled to apply it, and the experimentation of which it forms part, to Merlin's work at the Convent of the Resurrection in Book X.

237.1 **Good Friday** Having identified Merlin as Irish legend's Conor Mac Nessa, son of Fiachtna (Finn Mac Cool), I have utilised the story of his death, in Spence (1913).

239.1 **Merobaudes** *Meropius-baudes*, 'the courteous bastard', also, 'Claudebaud', Claudius' bastard.

239.2 **Aunt Elizabeth** [Elizab]ETH-NI[tonia Avitiana; Elissa], whence the Cambrian 'Ethni Wyddel', 'Ethni the Goidel'. The Teutonic larynx translates [Elizab]ETH the heroine – and she was all of that – as 'ETH-hilde', whence 'Ethyllt', 'Yseult', 'ISOLDA'. The Romancers will conflate several heroines under the latter head; especially Galla Placidia, who could deserve the same phonetic treatment if, as cradle-Christian, she had been christened Elizabeth, thus becoming Isolda II.

240.1 **Aspar** With whom as an aide came Theodosiolus, Uncle Heliodorus' son; he is the future Emperor Marcian.

240.2 **Lady-in-Waiting** This plausible conjecture, and it is no more, would explain much of the otherwise murky proceedings.

240.3 ***tronçon*** Many Romance reverberations, particularly the commencement of 'La Vengeance Raguidel' (in Loomis 1959, p. 365) where the slain 'Irish King' (or Rivalen) is elsewhere called 'Trahans' meaning an Ulpian of the stock of the Emperor Trajan (see Comm. p. 258, 2.3).

241.1 **before she did that** A somewhat hagiographic account of a drunkard's vision in 'Gregory of Tours' HF, II, 7 is our only source for Galla-*Isolda*'s agony of mind for Aëtius as he set forth to improvise a coalition to confront Attila around the close of AD450, and Galla supposedly died on 27 November 450, just at that time – but it could have been the following year. Gregory seems to say she died in Rome, but Ravenna also had a church of the Apostles, and seems on the whole more likely. For Galla's credentials as Isolde II, Eth-hilde, see Comm. p. 323, 239.2.

241.2 **interrupted ... pen** Apollinarius Sidonius (Carm. IX, 1, pp. 293–5).

241.3 **latest lover** Wagner will call the latter 'Morold' (Romance 'Le Morholt' or Lamorat). Here he's Boniface *Ammoraldo*, the immoral. Take Augustine's word for it! (John-George is 'Morold of Ireland' for similar reasons.)

241.4 **political marriage** See Comm. p. 322, 234.4.

241.5 **Dalmatia** Leland, seeing an impression of Aëtius' signet ring will mis-supply Dacia for Dalmatia in reading the abbreviation 'D'. Leland ('Assertio': refs as given in Comm. p. 297, 136.3), gives a very full and precise description of this seal-impression, which he had plainly handled himself. He goes on to speculate that 'Dacia' (as he wrongly restores 'D'), is synonymous with 'Denmark'. A case of being sort of right for the wrong reason.

242.1 **Vic's old letters** N. Chadwick is content to dismiss this in *SEBH* (1954, p. 222, fn. 4) by simply writing (without argument adduced) 'I cannot accept the suggestion of A. Anscomb who seeks to identify him with the Victoricus ... of the Confessio Patricii'. I think her view probably results from her different 'Patrician' chronology, although as 'Patrick' only says he had a dream about one of Victoricus' letters the chronology can here remain open.

242.2 **St Ruadan the Red** Tautology. See Baring-Gould (1872, April, pp. 202–4). For the ample references to distillation you will need to read the full Latin *Vita* in the *Acta Sanctorum* for the same day, but Morris (1977, Vol. III, p. 413) has picked up one of the more hilarious bits.

242.3 **High Admiral** Many Romance reverberations here. Here's one you might miss: *Matroed* the opponent of Esplandian in the Amadis de Gaula series. For Matroed read Medraut, Mordred (the Great 'Red', Ross the Red, Daniel Fab Drem-rudd); i.e. Admiral John-George.

242.4 **Vic ... employing tame Saxons** Nennius (Giles 1847, HB, §11) gives some very well-judged dates, on all of which I have felt able to rely (save that Bridget's death is 46 years after Columkill's birth, not 6), Nennius states '*A primo anno quo Saxones venerunt in Britanniam usque ad annum IV Mervini regis, supputantur anni 429*'. The fourth year of Mervyn is AD838 which, less 429 years, gives us AD409/410 for the first coming of the Saxons. So good are the other dates here that this particular one simply cannot be ignored. **The ruler who invited them should therefore be Cousin Vic, as 'Vortigern I'.**

242.5 **Finn Benachus** The 'White-horned Bull' of Connaught (of the race of Constantius), in the 'Tain Bo Chuailgne', who deserts the flock of Mēdb (Elissa) to join her husband's, Ailill's (JJ's), flock. (Chuailgne, 'Queen', woman, is Greek *γυνη* in comical Irish spelling.) This may be a convenient moment to tell you that (Irish) 'Fergus' is for *Vir Augustus*. Of the Roman rulers of Ireland (Ri-valen, Rhi-wallon), only Maximus, JJ and John achieved this and they were all Ælian redheads. There were thus three Irish 'Fergus-es', being at the same time the three Irish 'Ross the Red's, their exploits conflated.

242.6 **Elafius 'the timid stag'** *Elafius regionis illius primus*, of the *Vita Germani*. Here is the Romancers' 'Coward Knight'. They have wrongly thought that John was timid, just because, in Viking helmet, he was 'stag-like' in appearance.

242.7 **golden opinions** 'Much to be Lauded' (Amlawdd). Students of Welsh genealogy will need to know that he is Amlawdd II (Hamlet to future readers). He is the Amloyd amwerydd, Afloyd cuaran, of Bartrum (1966, Index). Magnus Maximus is Amlawdd I of the *Vita Illtuti*, also in Bartrum. 'Hamlet' more probably derives from *Anelathus*, or 'gylellfawr' (Bartrum q.v. 'Ossa'), meaning 'Big Knife'. The latter is splendidly depicted on the St Andrew's shrine slab (Plate 12 and Fig. 37), and see Comm. p. 315, 216.8, showing Hamlet very much in action.

242.8 **scientific research establishment** What else are we to make of the explosion of pottery imports at Tintagel from the late fourth through the fifth centuries? (Thomas, building on Radford, in BAR.BS.102, 1982, pp. 20–30). Plainly there was an important and prosperous community there. Excavations continue.

242.9 **'Loss' of Britannia** '*De excidio Britanniae*'. This book has up to now relied scrupulously on Zosimus and other yet more contemporary sources, but we have no option now but to make some use of the extraordinary *Liber Querulus* ascribed to Gildas, and to the *Historia Brittonum* compiled by Nennius. These sources are therefore reviewed in App. 11.

243.1 **spirited battles** as Vortimer, Vortipor, Catigern (*dux bellorum*), and Gwyrangon (*vir Eugenius*), and even [B]*Rhio-catus*; all as per Nennius. One of these sea battles just may have given us the name 'Herne Bay' from 'Cuaran's bay', since Admiral John is also 'Herne the Hunter' of the St Andrews slab. John was not killed, as Nennius will claim; Nennius has thought the Reculver perron (see below), was funerary. (The inhabitants of Canterbury may well do the same in naming the 'motte' in the south-west corner of their Town Walls the '**Dane John**'.)

243.2 **Reculver** Some fragments survive in New Reculver church at Hillborough; more, and better, in the South ambulatory of Canterbury Cathedral.

243.3 **keep the Picts and Scots quiet** Nennius (HB 28 in Giles 1847), gives: *Vortigernus regnavit in Britannia; et dum ipse regnabat, urgebatur a metu Pictorum Scotorumque, et a Romanico impetu, necnon a timore Ambrosii.* I would translate '*Romanico impetu*' here as 'Romanising policy', and '*timore Ambrosii*' as 'respect for Germanus'.

243.4 **Panegyrics** See Clover (1971), in full, with translation.

243.5 **own bust in Poets' Corner** CIL6, no.1724, and Panegyric I fragment IIA, lines 2–3.

244.1 **Spring of that year** Titia's death like her life is conjectural.

244.2 **now John had done it too!** Here is the Coptic Tale of the 'Son of Armenios' (Loomis 1927, p. 335; see also Comm. p. 302, 167.2). For 'Armenios' read 'Arminius' (Herrman), representing JJ as Pharamund. Note particularly that, in the tale, 'Armenios' and his wife both die 'together' (AD 428 at St Maurice). The other correspondences in the tale, albeit jumbled chronologically, are precise.

244.3 **Dad himself** Don't forget that Merlin, too, is Ambrosius. Here is the explanation of the much quoted and much misunderstood 'Battle of Wallop'. I quote Nennius (per Giles 1847, p. 313, the penultimate paragraph of the Nennian Chronologies): *a regno Guorthigerni usque ad **discordiam** guitolini et Ambrosii anni* *sunt xxii, quod est Guoloppum id est* ***Catguoloph.*** 'Guitolinus' is John-George the Goidel/Gwyddel – not to be confused with 'Vitalis'/Merlin. 'Discordiam' is hardly a battle'. 'Cat-guoloph' I read as *catellus Ulpiae*, the son or 'pup' of Eugenia-Ophelia, namely 'Riothamus' (cf. Apollinaris Sidonius, Ep. Bk III, no. ix), well known to history as John Reith 'Gradlon II', the Breton hero of AD468/70 (see Morris 1973, pp. 90–3), to whom we can now assign a birthdate. I interpret 'Riothamus' as 'Ri-Jotham' and leave you to look up Jotham in 2 Kings XV.32–8 and 2 Chronicles XXVII.1–9, to get the full flavour of this allusion to a young son replacing his disgraced father. I do not at all believe in the so-called 'Battle of Wallop', and prefer my own very different reconstruction.

244.4 **denouncing ... in Biblical terms** Reminiscent, maybe included in, some elements of Gildas' '*Liber Querulus*'. The 'vibes' here are explored in App. 11.

244.5 **flag of rebellion** As Ti-bato (Theobald, Theo for Θεοδουλος, *deo colanus*, 'Declan', the 'bold', or, better, 'bagaud').

244.6 **skirmish of the Vicus Helena** Fully, indeed vividly, described in Apollinaris Sidonius Panegyric to Majorian (Poem V, 1, pp. 213–36). The site may be well recognised on the ground as 'Vieil Hesdin' in the Pas-de-Calais. It is far from impossible that this intervention by Aëtius to clear the *trajecti Britannicae* (Pas-de-Calais) may have left that *Insula Francii* or detached 'enclave' of Franks who have given their name to the Isle-de-France, although this could have been a later incursion under Childeric.

244.7 **Riothamus** See Comm. pp. 325–6, 244.3, above. He is the famous 'Rum map Urbgen' (Albinus-Eugenius) of Nennius HB (Giles 1847, p. 312), apostle/baptizer of Deira and Bernicia. He is thus 'Sir Bedivere II'.

245.1 **Night of the long Knives** Nennius (Giles 1847, §49), '*nimed eure saxes*' (*cultellos*). I hardly credit the slaughter of 300 British Councillors, but there was plainly a major diplomatic 'hiccup' at the signing ceremony. Such 'eleventh-hour' tactics are still with us today.

245.2 **AD442** The chronicle of Prosper of Aquitaine (Theodosii XVIII, AD441) gives: *Brittaniae usque ad hoc tempus variis cladibus eventibusque latae, in ditionem Saxonum rediguntur.*

245.3 **Sanctity** Her marvellous sarcophagus is still to be seen there, with an inscription which surely *must* be by Apollinaris Sidonius, by style and date. Not knowing where it is published, I give you my own transcription.

*Nobilis Eugenia praeclari sanguinis ortu*
*Quae meritis vivit hic tomolata* [sic] *jacit.*
*Exuit occumbens oneroso corpore vitam*
*Quo melius superis possit adire domos*
*Quae prudens anemis permansit pondere morum*
*Provida laudandum semper elegit opus.*
*Parcere jejunos gaudens festina concurrit*
*Esuriens epulas o paradise tuas.*
*Captivos opibus vinclis* [sic] *laxavit iniquis*
*Et pulsos terris reddidit illa suis*
*Meus intenta bonis toto cui tempore vitae*
*Actibus egregiis unica cura fuit*
*Quam sub olis labsam besseris inclita lustris*
*Condedit nic* [hic?] *lacremis φ Avi*[tiana] *piis.*

ϕ 'Avitiana' could well be Papianilla, wife of Apollinaris.

It is not irrelevant that local tradition at St Victor invests three of the fine fifth-century reused sarcophagi with names that may well have been brought to Marseilles by Eugenia herself. Indeed, their presence so far from their place of origin is otherwise more than odd. They are, three sarcophagi 'attributed' to: 'St Maurice [JJ] and his companions'; 'the companions of St Ursula'; 'Sts Marcellina and "Petrus" [Ursula and John]'. We may note also 'Sts Chrysanthus [Merlin] and Daria'; the latter tale is a typical 'Ocean College *novella*'.

245.4 **other saintly names** A selection only is given; serious scholars will consult Lobineau (1836), where they will not find the identifications too difficult in the light of this book.

Armagillus, armel, arthmael; Brieuc, brioc; Budoc; Cado, cadoc; Columbanus; Corentin, cronan; Defynog, devennec; Docmael; Edern, edeyrn; Eugenius; Fingar; Foirtchern; Guenole; Guirec; Gwinnear, Houarneau; Hulien, huon; Jacut; Jestyn; Jud.budocmael, judhael; Maudez; Machutus; Meriadoc, meriasec; Ninadh, ninian; Padarn, paternus; Pol-aurelian; Rhigath; Ronan; Servan; Suliac; Tudwal; Tu-tuarn; Ty-ssilio; Vener, vennec, vigner; Waroch; Winwaloe.

245.5 **Thank God I'm a Christian** That Merobaudes was in fact rather a good Christian we may deduce, not only from his poem '*De Christo*' – superior in style, orthodoxy and sentiment to his father's effort on the same lines (Vollmer's text in Clover 1971) – but also from his endowments of the Mantaniacum monastery (Clover *ibid.* p. 7) and possibly of Trogir in Dalmatia.

246.1 **King of the Scheldt** Tennyson's 'Shalott'. For the moment he, too, is 'C'il Sans Nom' or Guin*glain* of the Romancers. 'Glain' is the River Salm, a tributary of the Meuse, not too far away. But Glain (cf. Nennius' River Glein) is a common river name, meaning no more than 'clean' or 'fresh-flowing'.

247.1 **keeper of the Holy Grail after my death** As Abinadab the keeper of the Ark of the Covenant in I Samuel VII.1. When we see that Eleazar is the son of the biblical Abinadab we shall recognise them as 'Eliezer Pelagianus' in the Vulgate 'Queste', and as 'Aminadab', Grail keeper of the Vulgate '*Estoire del Saint Graal*'.

247.2 **in their covers** See Comm. pp. 294, 129.2 and 327–8, 247.5.

247.3 ***Book of Mary*** By this is intended 'Cleopatra's Papyrus' (Cleopatra-Mariamne, the Jewish Alchemist, inventor of the 'Bain Marie' and much else of significance to this book). See again the 'Melchinus' extract of Comm. p. 294, 129.2. (The Book of) 'Joseph' 'Αριμαθος is buried *juxta meridianum angulum oratorii ... super potentem adorandam Virginem, supradictus spherulatis*. For an example of thus personalising a Book as its author see Giraldus Cambrensis' *Itinerarium Kambriae* (Cap. VI.1). where the Archdeacon discovers 'Merlin Sylvestris' at Nevyn.

247.4 **wrote about the lodestone** Claudian cm. XXIX (Birt XLVII). The Irish and Manx will treasure the memory of Mannannan (Manawydan) who, by his magical arts, could sail when no others could put to sea. Centuries later, Guiot de Provins, the Crusader and Carer Monk, will write about the compass in his 'Bible Guiot'. Modern scholars who scoff at the old identification – and how they still scoff – have not, I suspect, read the *Bible Guiot*. Maybe they don't like Norman French.

247.5 **Calf** The Welsh *De Situ Brecheniauc* has Merlin/Bʀychan (*not* Brychan, who is John-George) actually buried there, not his altar. At this point I should make clear that, in what here follows, I claim licence to 'tell a story'. I do not contend that Merlin himself carved the 'Calf-of-Man Crucifixion' (now in the Manx Museum), any more than I claim that he penned all or part of *Codex Marciana* MS 299; or that JJ wrote the *Codex Spirensis*. The very similarity yet difference of the Athlone Crucifixion (compare Fig. 60) shows that both artefacts look to a common source. I would look to a metalwork original (probably by Merlin himself) and would infer a 'repoussé book cover for the *Liber Gradalis* similar to all the many Gospel and Psalter covers which survive.

247.6 **Nicodemus the Arimathean** We only need to delete one tiny conjunction from John XIX.39 to be able to conflate these two eminently conflatable characters, both Jews, but one bearing a Jewish name one a Greek, who plainly moved in the same distinguished circles.

248.1 **pictures speak** It is instructive to read the whole of 'Eireneus Orandus' Exposition of the hieroglyphical figures of Nicholas Flamel, in full, in Taylor (1976, pp. 125–33 and Plate 19). The strictly relevant paragraph is the first of p. 132, with its exposition of the double signification. It will be a test of my publishers' technical ingenuity whether we can make these pictures speak for you even better, in the manner of the Ancient Egyptians (See Comm. p. 271, 43.5). A videotape would serve well.

248.2 **Clonmacnoise** This reproduction is about half life-size, and has been reversed so as to agree with the other 'Merlin muances'. Comparison with the Conques 'A' of Charlemagne is not inapt.

**Figure 60**
Clonmacnoise 'Aludel' (reversed)

251.1 **muances** Mutations. 'Arthur' beholds the Divine Secret at Mass in five muances, in 'Perlesvaus Le Haut Livre du Graal' once known as the 'Prose Potvin' (see Nitze in Loomis 1959, p. 266).

251.2 **ask the right questions** Chrestien de Troyes, and Wolfram, alike make much of Perceval/Parsifal's failure to ask the key question (variously remembered). See Loomis (1959, p. 275).

252.1 **it remains** Not quite so; it is now in the Manx Museum.

253.1 **statue and inscription** (see Plate 18) The stump of the statue may still be seen *in situ*. The inscription, with a photograph (as discovered and read by A. Bartoli in the Roman Forum in 1946) is in '268 *Rendiconti della Pont. Accad. Rom. d'Archeologia – Vol.* xxii'. It reads:

> *[ne]c non et magistro militum per Gallias,*
> ***quas dudum [o]bjuratas***
> ***BELLO PACE*** *[sc.* 'Sieg Fried' *in Teutonic]*
> *victorias Romano Imperio redditit,*
> *magistro utriusq(ue) militiae et*
> *secundo consuli ordinario [sc. AD437]*
> *atq(ue) patricio semper reipublicae*
> *[i]npenso omnibusq(ue) donis militarib(us) ornato;*

*his [S]enatus Populusq(ue) Romanus*
*ob Italiae securitatem,*
*[q]uam procul, domitis gentib(us)*
*peremptisque [B]urgundionib(us) et Gotis oppressis,*
*vincendo praestit[it],*
*[i]ussu principum (duorum) d(ominorum) n(ostrorum)*
*Theodosi [II] et Placidi [Valentin]iani*
*p(er)p(etuorum) aug(ustorum),*
*in atrio Libertat[is],*
*quam [ille] [bene me]rens erigit, dilatat et tu[et]ur aeque,*
*st[atu]am conlocavit m[or]um probo, opum refugo, delatorum ut hostium inimicissimo, vindici libertatis, pudoris ultor[i].*

254.1 **Founder of the House of Wessex** I have referred above (Comm. p. 314, 211.9), to the scepticism with which the earlier dates in the *Anglo-Saxon Chronicle* should be treated. M. Julius Aëtius 2 Coroticus, *Comes Domesticorum* for Marcian Augustus from AD451, was born towards the end of AD421. A youthful hostage of Attila, then a Roman cadet under Duke Germanianus, 'draws the sWord from the stone AD446', as we have seen. A military appointment in North Britain could well follow, marred by his row with St Patrick and ensuing excommunication c. AD448. I would then propose his transfer to the Eastern Command, since we next hear of him in Pannonia in AD453 taking belated revenge on Attila and winning (AD454) the consulate at the nomination of the Emperor Marcian, his patron and kinsman. His final achievement was the siege of the *Mons Badonicus* AD491, and he must have died soon after.

* * *

This concludes the Commentary. **Gnomic** maybe. Terse to a fault. Many more references might have been given if space had permitted, particularly to Romance sources and Saga. It is rather a shame that it has to terminate at AD447 with the death of Merlin when so much of continuing interest was still going on. But this is Merlin's book and it must needs close with him.

# Appendix 1: The House of Constantius I, the Dynast

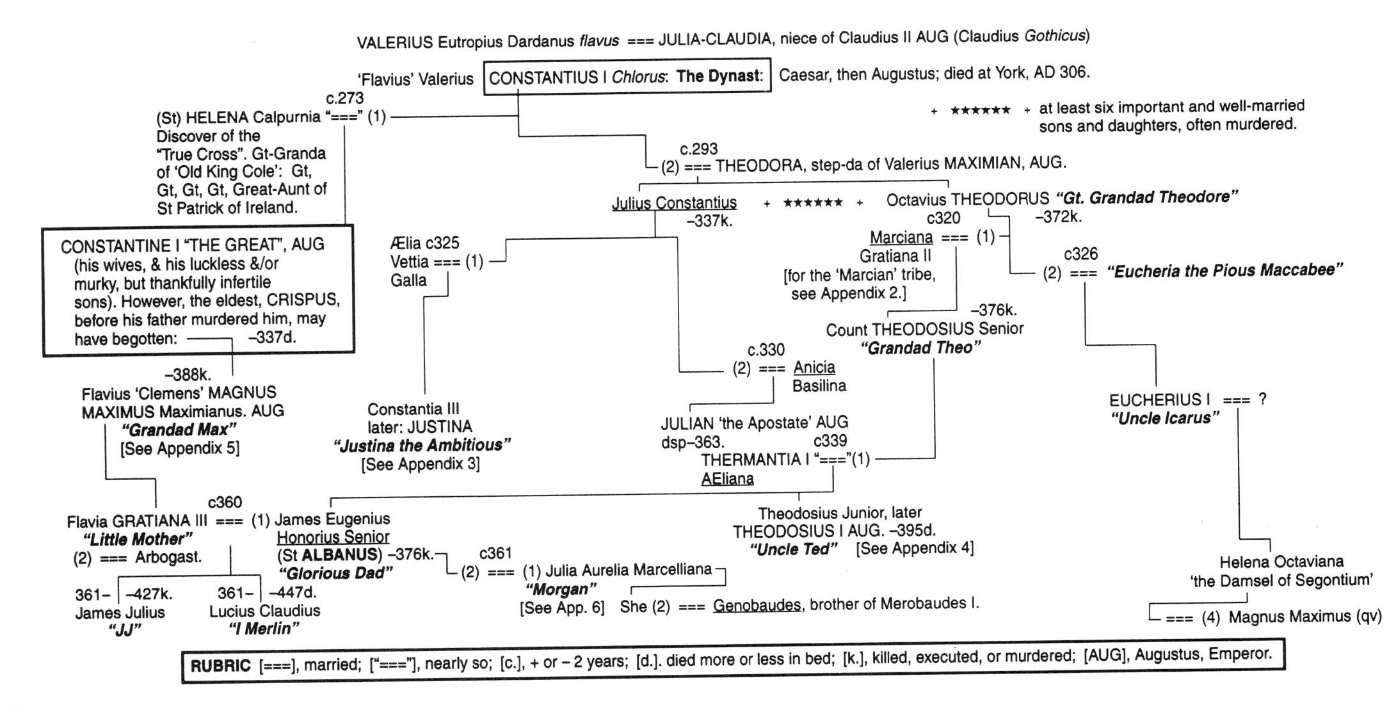

# Appendix 2: The House of Marcian (Ulpiani)

The family's descent from **Trajan** Augustus (or rather from his father of the same name), although unquestioned in antiquity, cannot now be traced. however the family emerges to fame in Thrace with:

FLAVIUS ULPIUS (OPELLIUS) MACRINUS 'FULVIUS', AUG 217/8: FOLLOWED BY MACRIANUS; THEN MARTINIANUS, 'TYRANNUS' OF THRACE 261. HIS SON MARCIANUS WAS HIS CAESAR IN 261.
WE COMMENCE WITH THE LATTER'S SON:

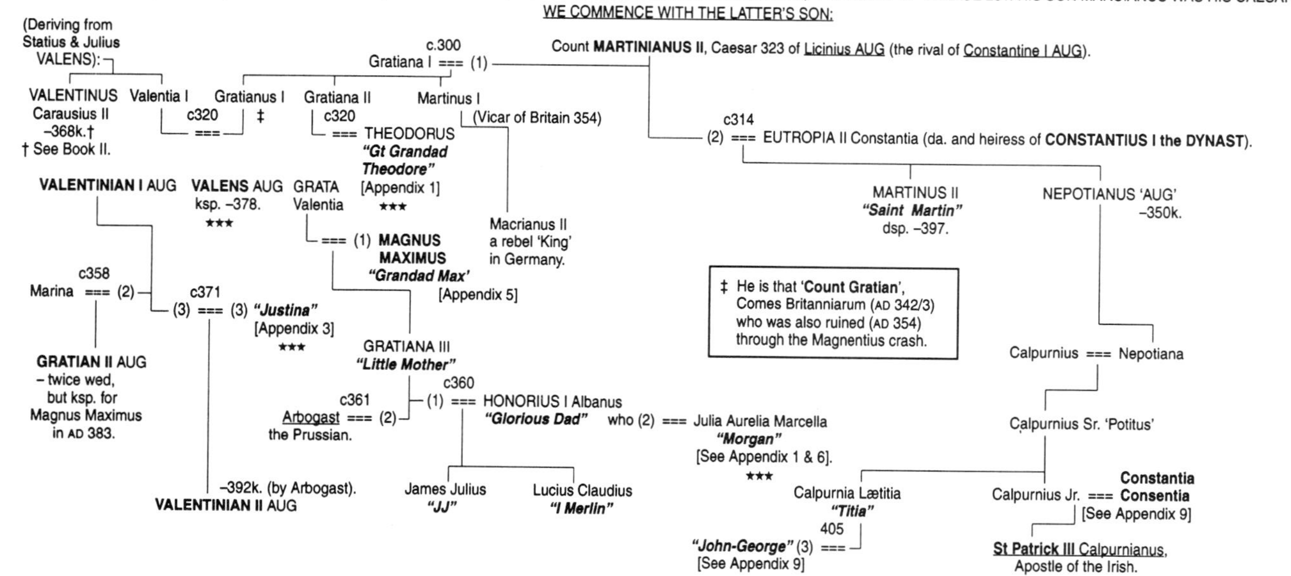

# Appendix 3: Great Aunt Justina, the Ambitious

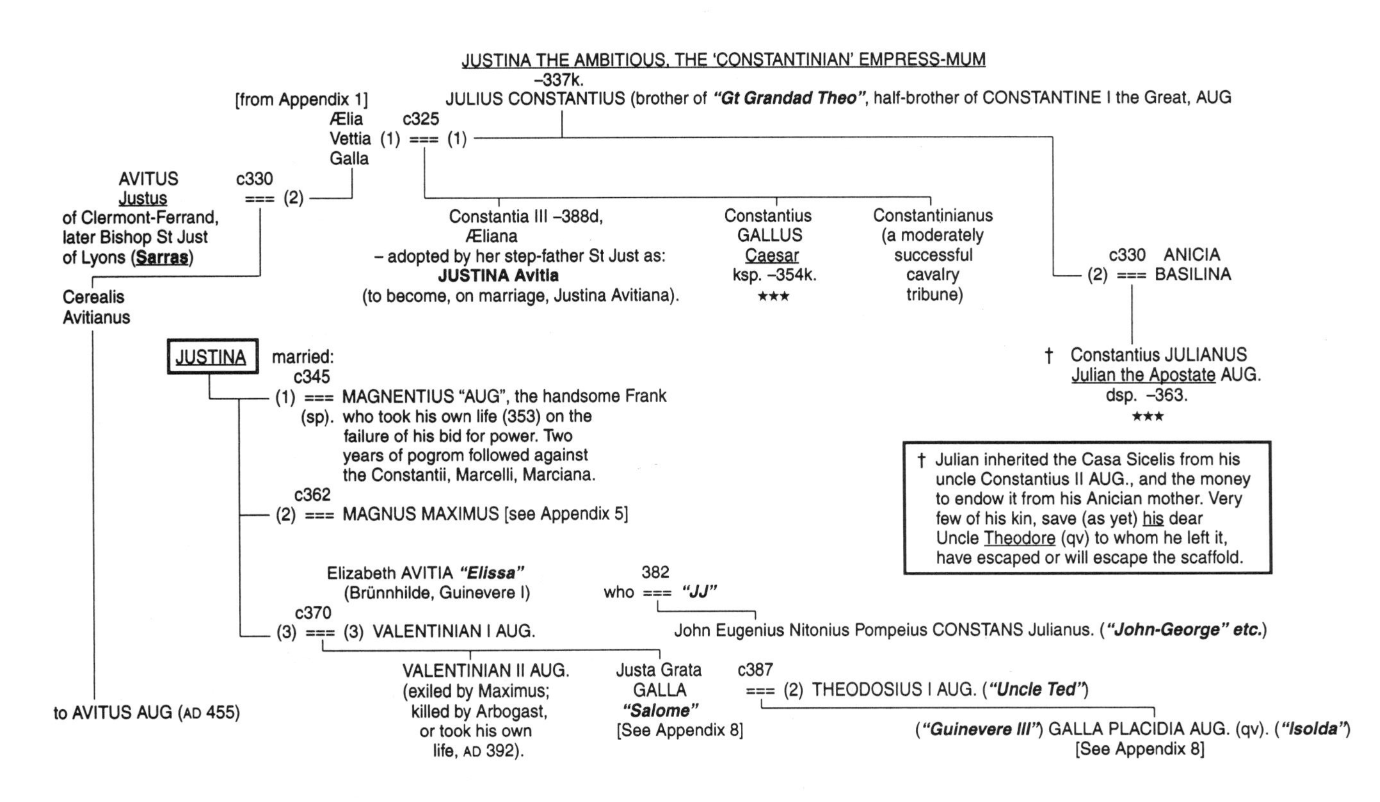

# *Appendix 4: Constantius I, the Dynast, continued*

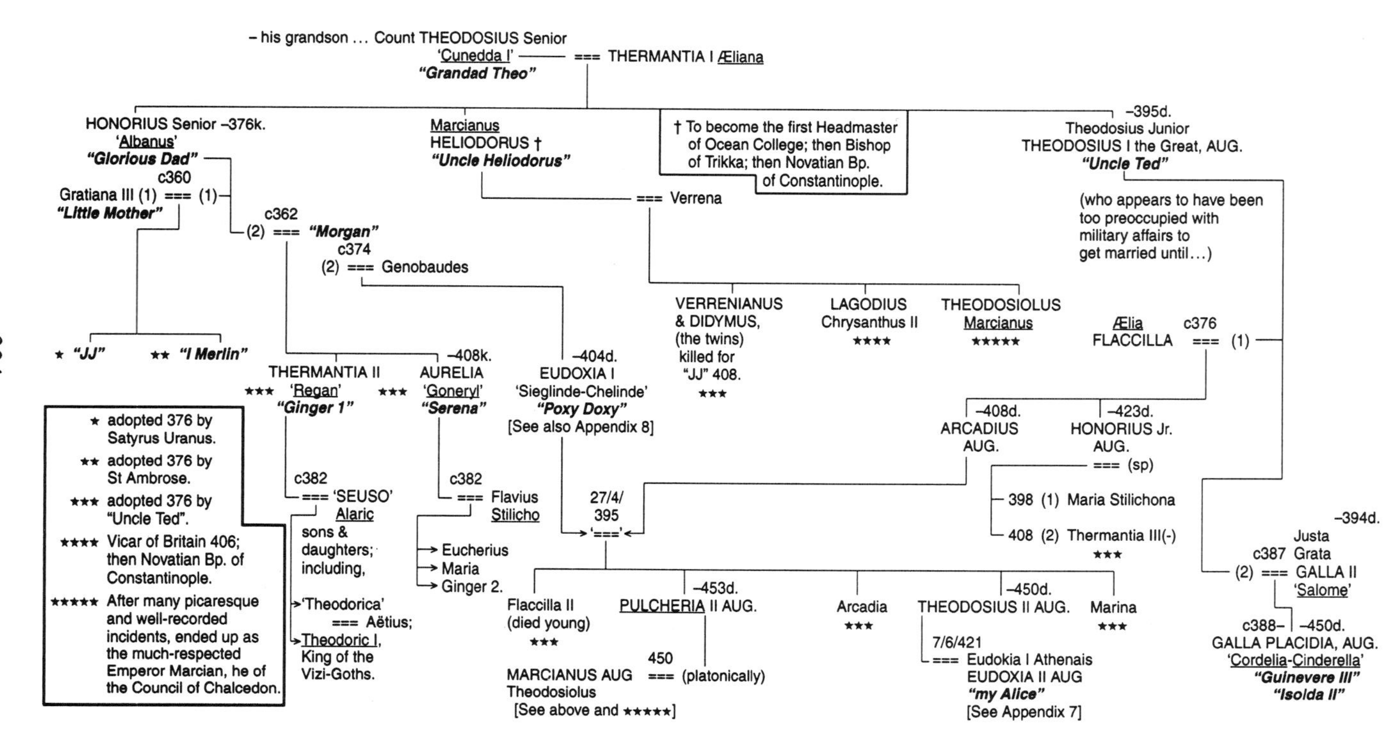

# Appendix 5: The House of Magnus Maximus

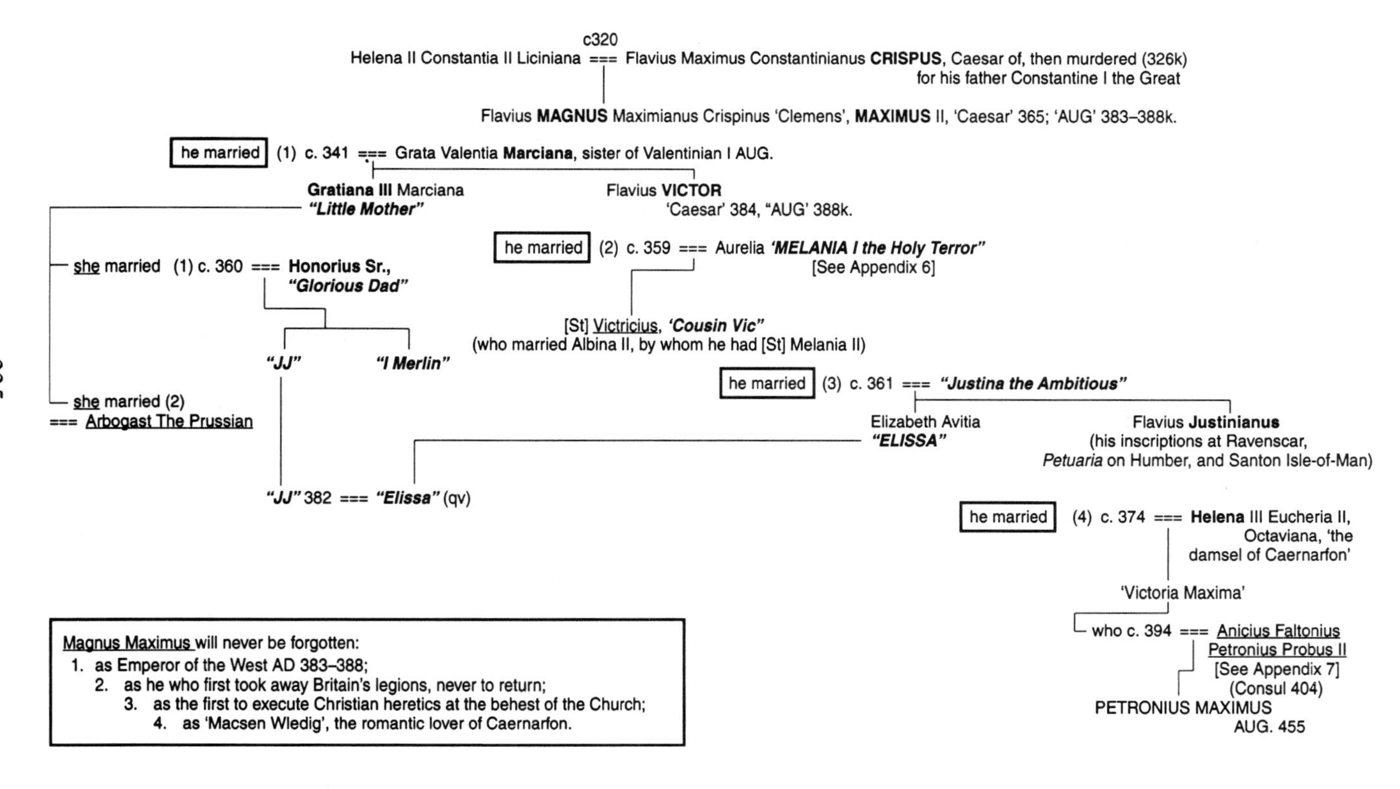

# Appendix 6: The House of Aurelius-Marcellinus

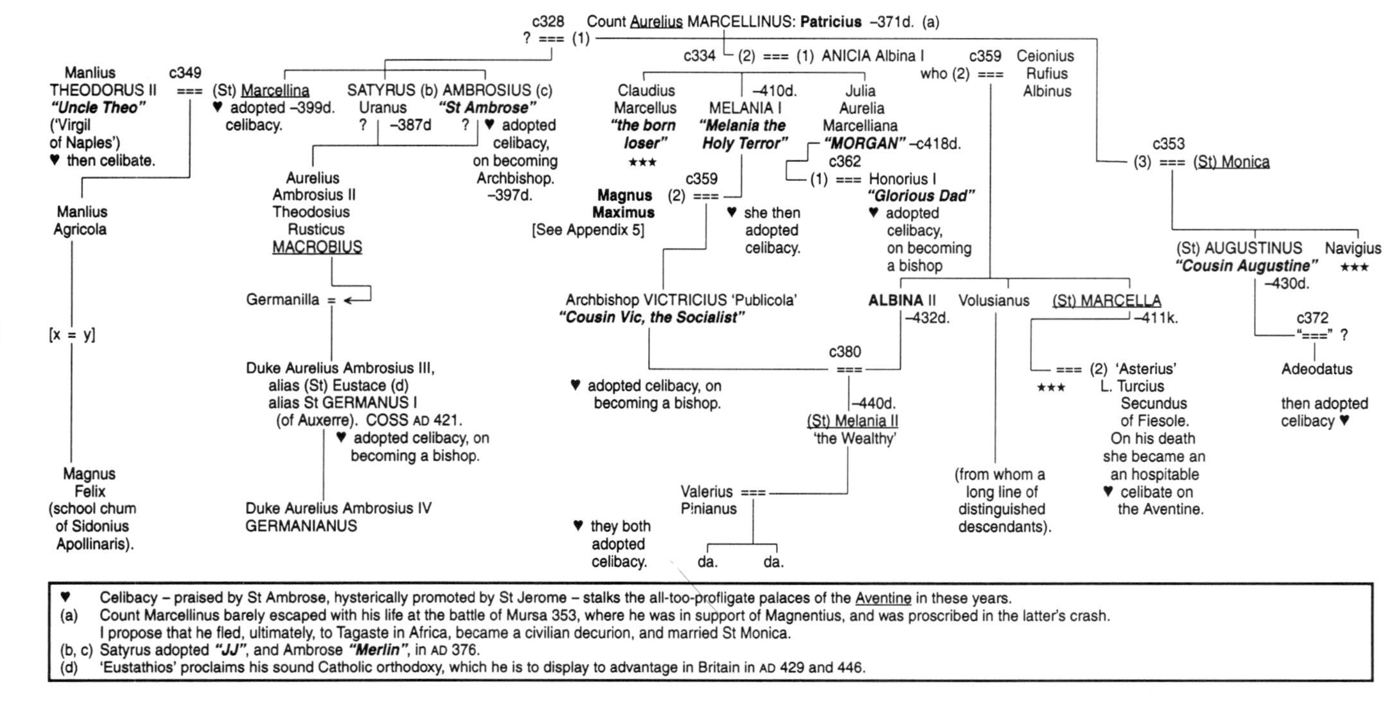

# Appendix 7: The Anicii-Faltonii

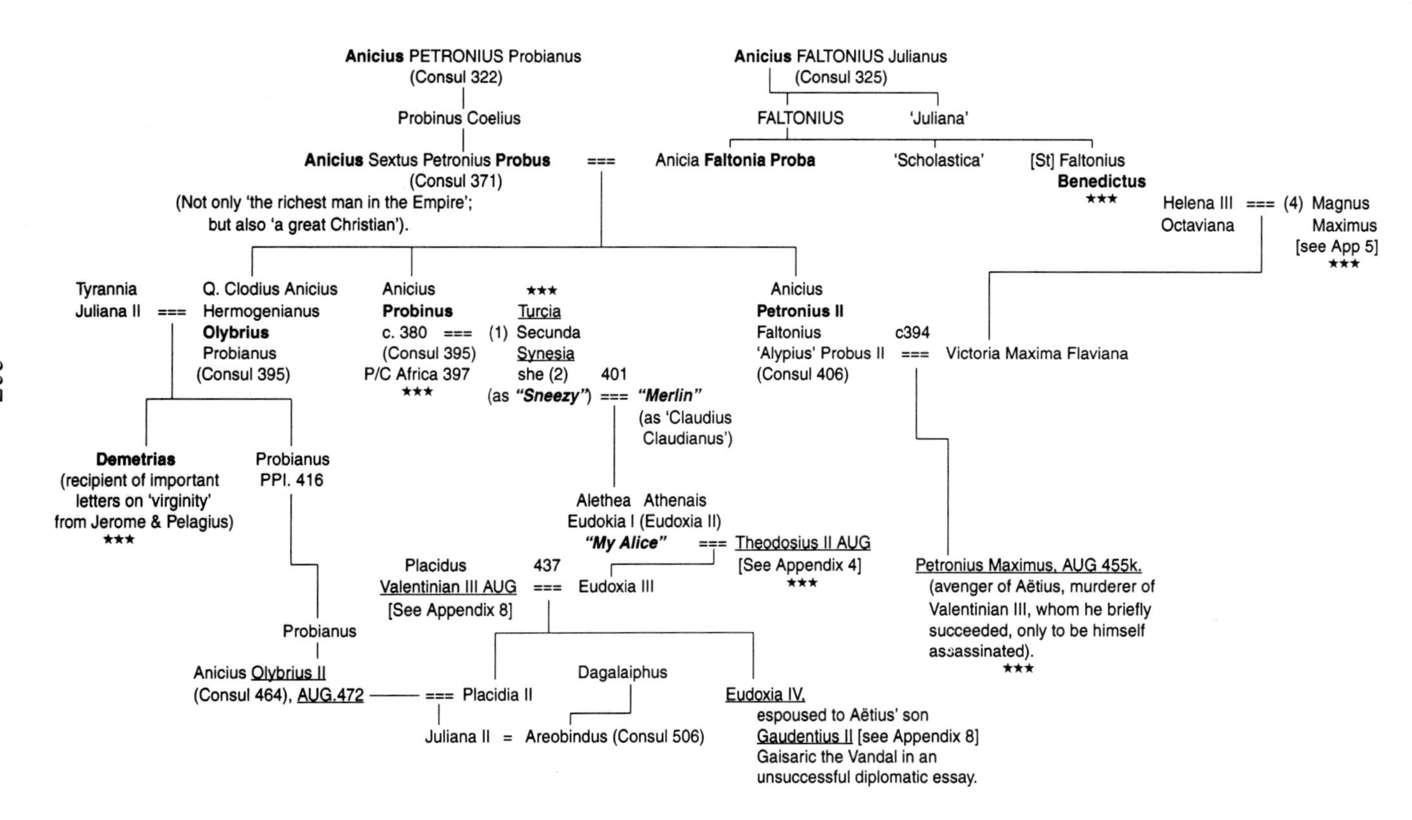

# Appendix 8: The House of Theodosius the Great

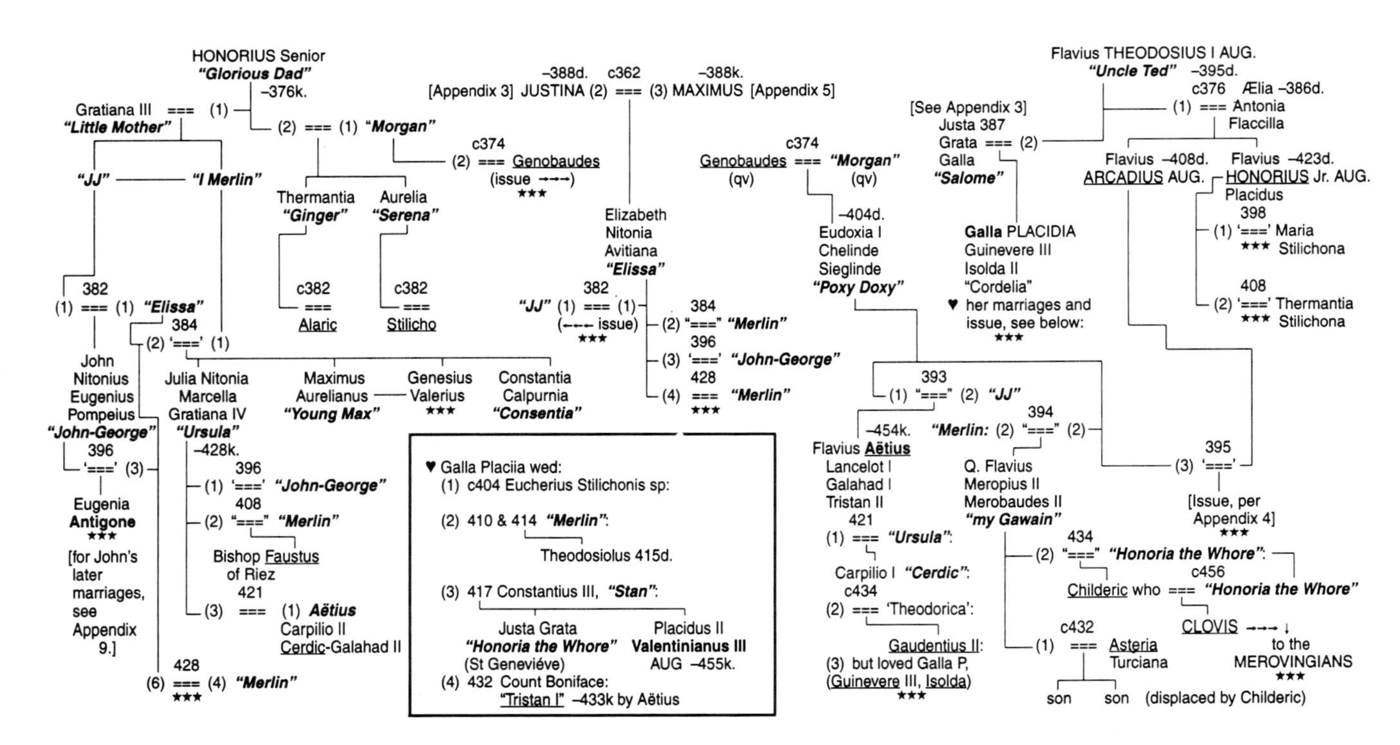

# *Appendix 9:* Et in Arcadia … Oedipus: *Some Later Arthurs and their Loves*

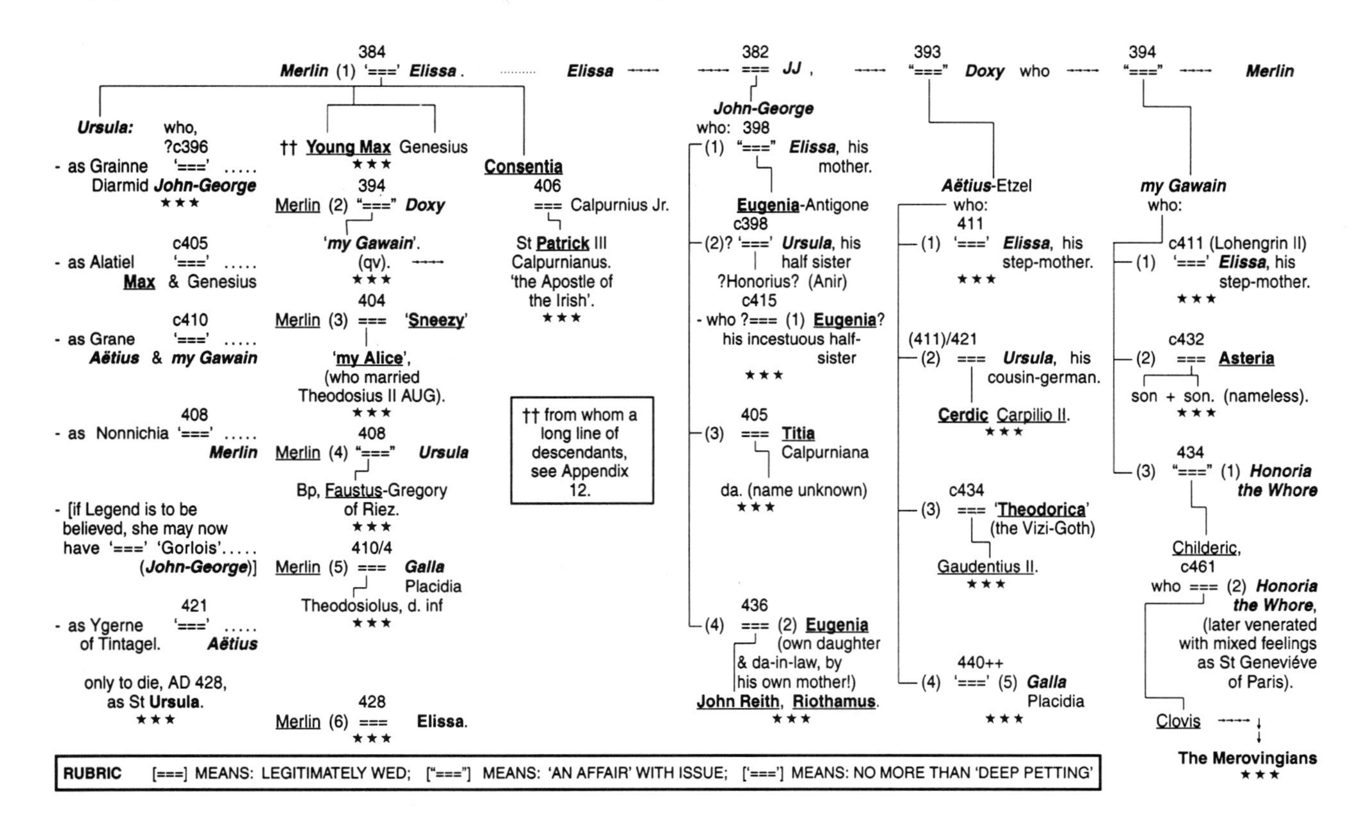

# *Appendix 10: Skeleton Key: The Heroes and Heroines of Myth and Legend Identified*

## WELSH LEGEND

1. Pwyll Prince of Dyfed is *JJ*.
2. Arawn is ***Merlin***.
3. Havgan is ***Grandad Max*** (Magnus Maximus).
4. Rhiannon is ***Little Mother*** (Gratiana III).
5. Gwri Gwallt Euryn is ***Merlin*** (Goldilocks/Taliesin).
6. Pryderi is ***John-George***, here confused with No. 5. Remember that he is also Gwrtheyrn gurtheneu (Vortigern). Say that aloud and you'll get 'Sir Bohort de Gannes, Sir Bors'.
7. Branwen is ***Elissa***.
8. Bendigeid Vrân is *JJ* (Custennin Bendigeit) is Seithenin the Drunkard (Saturninus, adopted son of Satyrus Aurelianus).
9. Manawydan is ***Merlin*** (Mannannan of the Isle of Man).
10. Matholwch is ***Merlin***.
11. Kicva (say it aloud) (*recte* Guinevere II) is ***Ursula***.
12. Gwynn Gloyw is ***Merlin***. He has little or nothing to do with Gloucester.
13. Math, son of Mathonwy, is ***Merlin***.
14. Goewin (say it aloud) is ***Ursula*** (Guinevere II).
15. Gil-vaethwy and Gwydion are both ***Merlin***.
16. Llew LLaw Gyffes is ***Merlin*** (Eucherius).
17. Gronow Pebyr is ***Merlin*** (Pebyr for presbyter).
18. Kilhwch (Cu-Lucius) is ***John-George*** conflated with ***Aëtius***. Both are sons of Kilydd, *JJ* Prince of Kelyddon (Caledonia/Apulia).
19. Goleudydd (aloud, Gladys) is ***Elissa*** daughter of Amlawdd I, ***Grandad Max***.
20. There is such a cornucopia of names in 'Culhwch and Olwen' that I cannot give them here, save to say that Olwen is ***Ursula***.

## IRISH LEGEND

Irish heroic characters tend to be reiterated in triple form, so I have here had to simplify. Their spelling, too, is subject to the wildest variations.

1. The Morrigan is ***Elissa*** (Morgan la Fée), Medbh (M Aev, from N Avitiana).
2. ***Merlin*** is Conor (Conchubor) mac Nessa, is Cormac I, is Cu Roi mac Daire, is Finn II, Démna (the daimonic).
3. ***Merlin*** is Cullen the Smith (Scolanus, St Collen I), is Crafttaine, Lughtaine. His 'hound' or 'pup' (see Welsh No. 18, above) is:
4. Cu Chulain (variously spelt), who is ***John-George***, Diarmid, Loegaire.

5. The sons of Turenn (T. Ulpianus, ***Glorious Dad***) are ***JJ*** and ***Merlin***; their exploits are remembered with fantastic accuracy in the legend.
6. The children of Lēr are as No. 5 above, plus Goneryl and Regan. They were turned into Novatians, not Swans, as I explain.
7. Ross the Red/Bôdb the Red/Fergus is/are (i) ***Grandad Max***, (ii) ***JJ***, (iii) ***John-George***. All redheads, all Augusti.
8. Deirdre is *Ursula*.

## BEOWULF

1. Beowulf the Elder is ***Glorious Dad***, is Ongentheow (Welsh: Owain Dantguin).
2. Ohtere is ***Merlin*** (Eucherius).
3. Hoc (Finn Folcwalda), is ***Merlin***.
4. Hnaef is ***John-George***, is Hengest the Jute.
5. Hildeburgh is ***Ursula***.
6. Grendel is ***Merlin***.
7. Sigemund is ***JJ***; his son Fitela is Flavius ***Aëtius*** (Hettel).
8. Hygelac (Havelock) is ***Merlin*** and also ***JJ***.
9. Hygd is *Doxy* (Eudoxia Bautonia).
10. ***Merlin*** is Waymund, is Edgetheow, Édgelaf, Eadgils, Eanmund; is Healfdene; is Herebald Hathkin (or v/v Herlekin Hathbad, Cathbad the bard).
11. Heardred is ***Aëtius***, is Beowulf the Orphan, Alexander the Orphan (confused with the next).
12. Hrothgar II (Ogier the Dane, Roger) is ***John-George***, Hengest/Hamlet.

## TEUTONIC & NORSE

### Gudrun Lay

1. Sigmund (Sigurd I) is ***JJ***.
2. Signy the First (Sigune), his 'sister' is ***Elissa***. She later weds Siggeir (Gereint) ***Merlin***, quondam K. of the (Vizi)-Goths.
3. Sigmund soon 'marries' Signy II ***Doxy***, who has 'changed shapes with a wise woman' (Morrigan la Fée) and bears, to ***JJ***, Sinf-jötli (Atli, Hettel, Etzel) ***Aëtius***.
4. Hjordis is ***Doxy*** (Eudoxia/Hygd) in yet another corruption. This time she bears, to ***JJ***, *Sigurd II*, who remains ***Aëtius***/Siegfried. (Note the confusions of Siguard and Sigvrid.) Hjordis next weds Alf-the-Viking (Ataulphus), ***Merlin***.
5. Grimhild is ***Elissa***. She 'weds' K. Giuki ***Merlin*** and bears him Gudrun (Gratiana), ***Ursula***.
6. ***Merlin*** is Giuki, Gibich (sib-Ecke), Lyngi, Loki (Lucius), Memer/Regin, Andvari, Fafner (the 'waffener'), Other, Heimir (Alprecht, Oberon, Aymery). *Doxy* (here Bekkhild, Brynhild's 'sister') bears, to Heimer, Alswid ***my Gawain*** (Merobaudes II).
7. Brynhild (prünk-hilde) is ***Elissa***.
8. Hogni is Hagen II, is ***John-George***. He is also K. Jonakr (Hartmut).

## Nibelungen Lied.

1. Aldrian is ***Merlin.*** He is only Uncle and foster-father of Hagen II Dancwart ('Dane-protector'), who remains ***John-George***, Hamlet.
2. Gunter I (Gundachar) is ***Merlin***, who is also Liudegast and Liudeger.
3. Siegmund (Sigurd I) is ***JJ***. He 'weds' Sieglinde ***Doxy*** (Hygd/Hjordis), who bears him ***Siegfried Aëtius*** (Sigurd II, Sinfjötli) as above.
4. Kriemhild (Grimhild II) is ***Ursula***. She bears, to Siegfried, Gunter III who is Cerdic/Carpilio II.
5. Dietrich is Theodoric I, K. of Vizi-Goths. son of ***Ginger*** and **Alaric.**

## Norse Eddas

1. Burnt Njal is **Earl** Briant, is ***JJ***. He shares his wife Bergthora/Hallgerda, ***Elissa***, with Gunnar (Gwyn Aurelius), Otkell, ***Merlin***. Gunnar's death harping (so like Amphion) is a conflation of both their ends. We meet Njal again in Irish legend, as Niall.
2. Wieland Smith is ***Merlin***, Fafner etc.

## Wagner

### *The Ring*

1. Alberich is ***Merlin.***
2. Fricka is ***Elissa.***
3. Wotan is ***JJ.***
4. Freia is ***Ursula.***
5. Fasolt is ***JJ.***
6. Fafner is ***Merlin.***
7. Loge is ***Merlin.***
8. Mime is ***Merlin.***
9. Erda is ***Elissa.***
10. Siegmund is ***JJ.***
11. Sieglinde is ***Doxy.***
12. Hunding is ***Uldin.***
13. Brünnhilde is ***Elissa.***
14. Siegfried is ***Aëtius.***
15. Gunter is here ***Merlin***, although Gunter II, ***my Gawain*** was also present.
16. Hagen is ***John-George.***
17. Gutrune is ***Ursula.***

### *Parzifal*

18. Gurnemanz is ***Merlin.***
19. Kundry is ***Elissa.***
20. Amfortas is ***Merlin.***
21. Parsifal is ***my Gawain.***
22. Titurel is ***Glorious Dad.***
23. Klingsor is ***Merlin.***

## *Tristan and Isolda*

24. Isolda is ***Galla Placidia***, confused here with ***Elissa.***
25. Brangäne is ***Eugenia***, here misplaced to keep ***Elissa*** company.
26. Tristan is here both ***Aëtius*** and Boniface.
27. Melot (Morhold) is here Boniface, with a dash of ***John-George.***
28. King Mark here is **Constantius III**, ***Stan the Inexorable.***

## *Lohengrin*

29. Lohengrin is ***Merlin*** (although ***my Gawain*** gets a serious look in as Lohengrin II). ***Merlin*** is also Salvius (Silvius) Brabo, eponymous founder of Brabant.
30. Elsa of Brabant is ***Elissa***, although ***Ursula*** gets a look in.
31. Friedrich of Telramund is ***Merlin.***
32. Ortrud is ***Elissa.***
33. 'Henry the Fowler' may be ***Merlin.***
34. Godfrey the 'Swan' (Novatian) is still ***Merlin.***

## ANGLO-NORMAN ROMANCE

1. Erek is ***Merlin*** Hercules, Harlequin.
2. Enid is Elizabeth Nitonia, ***Elissa.***
3. Ivain is ***John-George***, Cligés I.
4. Gawain is mostly 'pseudo-Gawain', ***John-George.***
5. Perceval is mostly Gawain II, ***my Gawain***, Merobaudes II.
6. Guinevere I is ***Elissa***. Guinevere II is ***Ursula***. 'Guinevere III' (wrongly so described) is ***Galla*** Placidia.
7. Lancelot is ***Aëtius***, is Gal-aäd the First ('Gâl' for 'Carl').
8. Galahad II is No. 7's son **Cerdic**/Carpilio II.

## MALORY

1. Uther Pendragon II is ***Aëtius.***
2. Igraine II is ***Ursula.***
3. King Bors is ***John-George***, 'Bohort-de-Gannes'/Vortigern.
4. King Ban of Benwick is ***JJ.***
5. Lionel is ***Merlin.***
6. Mordred is ***John-George.***
7. Guenever (II) daughter of Leodigrance is ***Ursula***, is Nimue.
8. 'Arthur' is a conflation of at least seven characters entitled to that name.

There are many too many names in these Romances to list more.

## CHANSONS DE GESTE

1. Charlemagne is **Constantius III**, ***Stan the Inexorable***, and subsequently ***Merlin.***
2. Amon is ***JJ*** (Amphion). He had two sons (***John-George*** and ***Aëtius***), not four.
3. Aymery of Narbonne is ***Merlin*** much reduplicated.
4. Garin of Lorraine, and Gerin of Chartres are ***my Gawain.***

5. Roland is ***Aëtius***; Oliver/Bego is ***my Gawain.***
6. William of Orange is ***Merlin.***
7. Amadis of Gaul is mainly ***JJ.***
8. Ganelon is ***John-George***, is Gamelyn, Grands Alains, Alains le gros, the great Irish wolfhound or werewolf, is (R)Ogier the Dane.
9. 'Floovant' is either of the *Gawains*, or rather both.

## SHAKESPEARE

### The Tempest

1. Prospero (Milanion) is ***Merlin.***
2. Antonio is ***Cousin Vic.***
3. Alonso is ***Merlin.***
4. Sebastian is ***JJ.***
5. Ferdinand is ***Aëtius.***
6. Miranda is ***Ursula.***
7. Caliban and Ariel are ***Merlin*** disguised.

### Two Gentlemen of Verona

8. Duke of Milan is ***Merlin.***
9. Valentine is ***JJ.***
10. Proteus is ***Merlin.***
11. Julia/Sylvia are ***Elissa.***
12. Eglamour is ***JJ.***
13. Launce is ***Aëtius.***
14. Outlaws are 'bagauds' in the Ardennes.

### Measure for Measure

15. Vincent (the Praetorian) is historical.
16. Lucio and Claudio are ***Merlin.***
17. Pompey is ***John-George.***
18. Isabella is ***Elissa.***
19. Juliet is ***Ursula.***

### Much Ado About Nothing

20. Don John/Pedro is ***John-George.***
21. Claudio is ***Merlin.***
22. Benedick is ***JJ.***
23. Leonato is ***Merlin.***
24. Hero/Beatrice/Margaret/Ursula are ***Ursula.***

### A Midsummer Night's Dream

25. Theseus (Tereus) is ***JJ.***
26. Lysander/Demetrius are ***John-George.***
27. Helena/Hermia are ***Ursula.***

28. Oberon is ***Merlin***, is Puck, Robin Goodfellow.
29. Titania is ***Elissa***.

## The Merchant of Venice

30. Gratiano is ***Merlin***.
31. Old Gobbo is ***JJ***.
32. Portia is perhaps ***Sneezy***.

## As You Like It

33. Most of the cast of *I Merlin* are evident here.

## Titus Andronicus

(the originals have never before been revealed)

34. Titus is **Stilicho**.
35. Saturninus ('Seithenin') is ***JJ***.
36. Aaron the Moor is ***JJ*** (*Araon Maurus*).
37. Tamora is ***Ginger*** (Thermantia).

## Romeo and Juliet

39. Paris (Alexander) is ***JJ***. ***Merlin*** is Hector (Alexander).
40. Romeo/Peter/John/Laurence/Tybalt are ***John-George***.
41. Gregory/Sampson are ***Merlin***.
42. Juliet is ***Ursula***.

## Pericles, Prince of Tyre

43. Antiochus/Pericles is ***Merlin***.
44. Thaliard is ***JJ***.
45. Simonides is ***Celerinus***.
46. Thaisa is ***Sneezy*** (confused with *Doxy*).
47. Marina is ***my Alice***.

## Hamlet

48. Claudius is ***Merlin***.
49. Hamlet is ***John-George***.
50. Fortinbras is ***Merlin***.
51. Polonius is ***Merlin***.
52. Laertes (son of 'Acrisius the needy') is ***my Gawain***.
53. Reynaldo is ***John-George***.
54. Gertrude is ***Elissa***.
55. Ophelia is ***Ursula***.
56. The characters in the 'inner play' are also right on the mark.

## King Lear

57. Lear is ***Glorious Dad*** conflated with ***Uncle Ted***.

58. Duke of Burgundy is **Stilicho.**
59. Duke of 'Cornwall' is **Alaric.**
60. Gloucester is ***Glorious Dad.***
61. Edgar/Edmund are ***Merlin.***
62. Curan is ***John-George.***
63. 'Fool' is ***Merlin.***
64. Goneryl is ***Serena.***
65. Regan is ***Ginger.***
66. Cordelia is ***Galla*** Placidia, Cinderella, Greidiol.

# Appendix 11: Gildas and Nennius – An Appraisal

## GILDAS VINDICATUS

Something is terribly wrong with this famous and, alas, indispensable work of which a version was available to Bede in AD731. Bede claims as his prime source Albinus, Abbot of St Peter and Paul Canterbury whence the oldest MS of Gildas derives. Two MS survive, both at Cambridge, one of which has the Preface and History, but not the Epistola; the other has the Epistola but only a truncated History, together with two differing Tables of Contents, neither according perfectly with the combined text as we now have it (for reference, I am using Giles (1847) text, since this is on my desk).

In his preface, 'Gildas', if indeed it be he (for he is only so named in glosses), admits to have had the work on the stocks for ten years, and there are internal signs of revision and amplification by the author. In particular, the Preface has a huge interpolated sermonette more in the style of the Epistola; and six more sermonettes in the same vein intrude into the History. It seems possible that on completing the later Epistola Gildas returned to his earlier modest attempt at history in order to 'beef it up' with some of his – by now, practised to overflowing – denunciatory religious fervour.

If we are right in this, the Epistola is up to ten years later than the main text. In the Epistola Gildas throws 30 pages (per Giles) of *Old* Testament jeremiad (and his style owes much to Jerome), at five named Kings; he then goes on to throw no less than 43 pages of *Old* and *New* Testament at the clerics of the day. His mastery of the Bible is complete. (Curiously he also quotes from Porphyry, the Neo-Platonist, whose works were banned by Theodosius II in AD448). His style is a somewhat barbarous example of fifth-century Latin, with good masters lurking in the background, but no current educated competition to cut him down to size. The Ireland of c. AD460+ would be a likely environment for his schooling; I date the siege of Badon, onto which 'Gildas' ambiguously ties his birthdate, as AD491.

The Epistola is curious in many ways. For a humble monk on an offshore island – perhaps Caldy, perhaps in Brittany – with still a passionate love for his homeland of Britannia, he shows quite extraordinary nerve in denouncing in such terms five living Kings of that country. Even with benefit of clergy and of sanctuary, his audacity is stunning, since the invective is plainly intended to reach the eyes of its targets, nay to shame them into mending their ways. If indeed it be his own, the pastoral love and sympathy he evinces is heroic. But he also shows, from his island fastness, an ongoing detailed intimacy with the most private peccadillos and secret crimes of these high-ranking men which implies close and continuing contact with them. Moreover, he addresses them as men and equals; albeit himself at most a Deacon, he writes to them as if a Patriarch. Finally, four at least of the Five Kings bear the names of one man only: John-George Vortigern III. Do we see here Vortigern's sinning children or grandchildren, proudly bearing the same dishonoured names?

All very odd.

The History, too, is odd. Save for the arrival of Christianity – with the earliest *Passio Albani* – Gildas knows, or at least writes, of no events between Boudicca and Maximus; 300 years of *Pax Romana* whistle by without comment. He disapproves strongly of British 'tyrants', yet Clodius Albinus, Carausius and Allectus get no mention. As he nears his own days the gaps recur. As a tyrant, Maximus comes in for criticism; but Marcus, Gratianus, and Constantine III pass unnoticed. He alludes darkly to the 'Rescue' of Britain in AD416/7, but – oddly for a supposed monk – does not mention St Germanus' two visits and the Halleluia victory, nor the damning of Vortigern. He has not heard of St Patrick, despite his Irish connections. He hasn't read Orosius, has not heard of Pelagius, nor of Saints David, Dubricius, Teilo, Columba, etc. Getting very near to his 'own time', he knows nothing of John Riothamus' gallant expedition from Britain to Armorica c. AD470 in support of the lawful Emperor Anthemius. We have little alternative to smelling a rat about the entire work. May I offer an alarming explanation?

There *was* one 'Patriarch' who did indeed visit Britain; who was the social equal and indeed close relative of the rulers he denounced; whose orthodoxy ('Ευσταθιος) was surely founded on massive orthodox biblical competence; who cared with glowing pastoral sincerity for the men he rebuked. His own biographer, Constantius, tells us it was St Germanus; and Nennius, whom we shall soon reach, tells the story of the Saint's 40-day mission against the aged sinful Vortigern. The Pillar of Eliseg is further evidence. Did Germanus leave some notes behind (or a disciple take them down) of his extended series of addresses *contra Vortigernum*? Did he vary the content appropriately, even as he varied the names of the addressee? And, could these notes have fallen into the hands of 'Gildas' at Caldy (per the important gloss in Josseline's text), or Steepholme (not so far from Llancarfan, where Caradoc of Llancarfan's Vita sends him; or even Llancarfan itself, where Caradoc has him overnight)? 'Gildas's theme is the moral regeneration of public life of Church and State in the Britannia of his day (whenever that was); the eloquent relics of Germanus' diatribes would have been useful grist to his mill. **My case rests.**

We return to 'Gildas's limp little History. For all its *lacunae* it makes good sense historically and chronologically – providing we transfer the first sentence of §17 (Giles 1847) to the commencement, or middle, of §25. §16 then runs happily on to the second sentence of §17. (I could annex a summary of the History to this Appendix with the dates duly inserted, but you will not now find it hard to insert them for yourselves.) I would draw your attention to some telling and convincing touches in 'Gildas's narrative. §11: Maximus has taken away not only the *comitatenses* and *tirones*, but also the *rectores*. §12: Fresh incursions by the Picts and Scots cause the Britons to repent of UDI and seek Roman aid (416/7) and a *legio* is sent (IInd Augusta?). 'A wall is built across the island from sea to sea'. At this point it is only fair to defend 'Gildas' against the sniggers of modern scholars. Scholars have always known that Septimius Severus is recorded in the *Augustan Histories* (Aelius Spartianus §18–1) as having built, or archaeologists would say rebuilt, Hadrian's Wall. And Nennius (Giles 1847) has Septimius Severus doing just this at §19; but he also mentions §24 *Octavus fuit alius Severus*, who is Marcus Gratianus Merlin. 'Gildas' has simply got the wrong Severus, and consequently wrongly dated him. Careless, rather than stupid. §14: (c. 425+) The Romans send *equitum in terra, nautarum in mari*; and the Countship of the Saxon Shore is revived. Watchtowers are built along the South Coast (one recently found on the East Hill at Hastings); a new earth wall (semi-privatised) is built in East Anglia (Fleam Dyke?). §23: (The first item is perhaps out of order; Nennius makes us think this was 'Cousin Vic', c. 410.) When many more *cyulis* come they are manned by Frisians. §25: the famous 'Duke Ambrosius Aurelianus' sentence is very densely written and needs meticulous punctuation before it will yield its full meaning. We may well infer that Duke (Ambosius Aurelianus) Germanianus is intended, and his father St (Eustachius Eustathius) Germanus was Consul Ordinarius in AD421. It was the Consular purple which he wore, not the Augustan purple. Well done 'Gildas'!

There is enough here for us to take 'Gildas Historicus' very seriously, with all his faults, and I have done just this in Books XVII–XX.

## NENNIUS VINDICATUS

Some recent scholars have offered the view that, far from being an artless compilation, 'Nennius', or at least the Preface thereto, is a work of virtuosic disingenuity wilfully fabricated to mislead. I must say it reads to me just as 'Nennius' describes it: *hanc historiunculam undecunque collectam balbutiendo coacervavi*. One could hardly put it better. The Latin is what one would expect from an erudite ninth century Welsh cleric, the contents chaotic – now Romantic, now pedantic, now folkloric, now antiquarian.

There remains an enormous amount of valuable stuff in it from disjunct sources, albeit the chronology is haywire. Nevertheless there is some excellent chronography dispersed among it, and I have dared to use this. Unlike Gildas, who is usable on his own terms, 'Nennius', rather like the *Gesta*, can only be used, if at all, when he has first been interpreted and rectified by reference to outside sources.

Maybe *I Merlin* will serve as a useful roadmap to 'Nennius'. By way of return, 'Nennius' has had only minimal influence on *I Merlin*.

# *Appendix 12: The Author's Genealogical Descent from Merlin*

| | | |
|---|---|---|
| Llywarch or Llowarch Hēn, *Merlin* | ↓* b. 361 | 'MERLIN' himself |
| Cadraut Calchfynydd, Yspwys 1, 'the man from Spain' | * b. 387 | 'Young Max', see text, Books VII onwards; enthroned 'Augustus' of Spain, 410–415. |
| Yspwys 2 Mwyntyrch | * b. c.414 | Settled in Cardiganshire as a miner, by Duke Ambrosius Germanianus 446 or 466. |
| Yspwys 3 Fychan, (Yspwch) | * b. c.441 | |
| Mynan Mor, (Eglwys ynad) [*St Beuno*] | * b. c.468 | |
| (M)Ælvyn Alexander 2 [Maelgwn Gwynedd] | * b. c.495 | The identification with 'Maelgwn Gwynedd' is insecure. |
| Einion | * b. c.522 | |
| Cyfnerth | * b. c.549 | |
| Tegawc (app. 4 generations unrecorded) | * b. c.576 | |
| Sandde, Alexander 3 = Celenion of Man | * b. c.711 | |
| Elidur | * b. c.738 | |
| Gwriad I of the Isle of Man, last 'Celtic' King of Man | * b. c.765 | His splendid cross at Maughold, Isle of Man. |
| Cadrod II | * b. c.795 | His elder brother was Merfyn Frych, King of N. Wales, and formerly also King of Strathclyde, to whom Nennius dedicates his work. |
| Cilmin Droetddū, of Dinas Dinllé, Gwynedd, (heartland of the Mabinogion). | ↑ ↓ b. c.822 | Chief of the Fourth 'Noble Tribe' of Wales and heraldic dynast of the Glyns, Guylemins, Gillmans, Salamans, etc. |
| Lleon. | ** | |
| Llowarch II | ** | |
| Iddig | ** | |
| Iddon | ** | |
| Dyvnant | ** | |
| Gwrydr | ** | |
| Ednowen | ** | |
| Rev. Ystrwyth of Caernarfon fl. c1225. | ** | Diplomatic agent of Llewellyn the Great. |
| Ierwerth Goch | ** | |
| Ivan | ** | |

| | | |
|---|---|---|
| Einion | ** | |
| Gronwy | ** | |
| Tu'dur Goch fl. c.1360; of Nantllé. | ** | Fought at Crécy and Poitiers. Awarded Nantlle and the west shoulder of Snowdon by the Black Prince. Married his cousin, the heiress of Glynllifon, and lived happy ever after. |
| Hwlkyn Lloyd of Glynllifon Park, Gwynedd Meredydd | ** | |
| Robert d. 1509 | ** | |
| Edmund Lloyd d. 1541 | ** | |
| William I Glynne of Glynllifon | ↓***/**↑ | Royal Commissioner to the 1567 Eisteddfodd. |
| Rev Richard Glynne, of LLanfaethlu d. 1617. | | Rector of Llanfaethlu in Anglesey. |
| Thomas I of London | *** | Merchant Taylor of London, 1601. |
| Rev Christopher Glynne or Glin d. 1668. | b. 1596 | Vicar of Burford throughout the Civil War. |
| Rev Robert II Glynne | *** | Rector of Little Rissington, Glos. |
| Robert III Maynard Glynn | *** b. 1673 | Salter, of Hatton Garden. |
| Sir Richard Glynn or Glyn, Bt. of Ewell. | b. 1713 | Glyn, the Lord Mayor; MP and Banker. |
| Col Thomas II Glyn Grenadier Guards | ↑*** b. 1756 | Fought in the US War of Independence and the Napoleonic Wars. |
| Rev Thomas III Clayton Glyn d. 1860. | b. 1789 | |
| Clayton William Feake Glyn d. 1887. | b. 1821 | Barrister and JP, of Durrington House, Essex. |
| Clayton Louis Glyn (= Elinor Sutherland) | b. 1857 | Elinor Glyn the novelist. |
| Margot Elinor Glyn (= Sir Edward Davson, Bt) | b. 1893 | |
| Sir Christopher Michael Edward Davson, Bt | b. 26.5.1927 | Author/redactor of 'I Merlin'. |

**Rubric**

- * Pedigree hesitantly constructed from Bartrum 1966.
- ** Pedigree delivered to Lewis Dwnn, Welsh Deputy to Clarenceux and Norroy in 1588, see *Welsh Visitations* II, p. 147.
- *** Pedigree prepared by Col. Thomas Glyn and his son. Continued, from family records, to the present day by the writer.

# BIBLIOGRAPHY OF AUTHORS CITED


**Acta Sanctorum**, see Bollandists.

**Alexander** (1973). *Beowulf*, trans. M. Alexander. Penguin Classics, London, repr. 1973.

**Amadis de Gaula**, in Spence (q.v.).

**Ambrose**, in Farrar and Migne (q.v.).

**Ammian** (fourth-century Roman historian). *Ammianus Marcellinus* Vol. 3, 1939: with translation by John C. Rolfe, Loeb Classical Library, William Heinemann, London, and Harvard University Press, Cambridge, Mass.

**Anderson** (1936). *Sidonius; Poems and Letters*, text and trans. W. B. Anderson, Loeb Classical Library, repr. 1980.

**Anderson** (1987). *The Ancient Secret; Fire from the Sun*, Lady Flavia Anderson, Thorsons, Wellingborough, Northants.

**Apocryphal New Testament**, see James (1924).

**Apollinaris Sidonius**, see Anderson (1936).

**Ardenne et Gaume** (1978). *Monographie* 12, 2nd Edn. Bruxelles.

**Ariosto.** *Orlando*, in Spence (1913).

**Ashe** (1960). *From Caesar to Arthur*, Geoffrey Ashe, Collins, London.

**Atkinson** (1956). *Stonehenge*, R. J. C. Atkinson, Hamish Hamilton.

**Augustine.** *Confessions*, trans. F. J. Sheed, Sheed & Ward, London.

**Bacon** (1960). *Digging for History*, E. Bacon, A&C Black, London.

**B.A.R.** (for British Archaeological Reports), 122 Banbury Road, Oxford. I make a number of citations from various numbers (identified in the Commentary) from the British Series.

**Baring-Gould** (1872). *Lives of the Saints*, S. Baring-Gould, 3rd edn. 1877 (entries by days).

**Bartlett** (1865). *History and Antiquities of Wimbledon*, reissued, SR Publishers Ltd, 1971.

**Bartoli** (1947), in *Rendiconti della Pontifica Accademia romana di Archaeologia* 22 (1946–7), pp. 267–73, Rome.

**Bartrum** (1966). *Early Welsh Genealogical Tracts*, P. C. Bartrum, University of Wales Press Board, Cardiff.

**Bateson** (1973). *Roman Material from Ireland: a reconsideration*, J. D. Bateson, Proc. Royal Irish Academy, Vol. 73 C, pp. 21–97.

**Bateson** (1976). *Further Finds of Roman Material in Ireland*, Bateson, Proc RIA (ibid.), 76 C, pp. 171–9.

**Bede**, see Sherley-Price (1955).

**Beowulf**, see Alexander (1973).

**Berthelot** (1885). *Les Origines d'Alchimie*, M. Berthelot, Paris.

**Berthelot** (1888). *Collection des anciens Alchimistes Grecs*, M. Berthelot, Georges Steinheil, Paris. Vol. I, Introduction, Vol. II, Greek text, Vol. III Traduction (French).

**Bewnans Meryasek** (1966). *St Meriasek in Cornwall*, Peniarth MS 105 1, 587–1099), R. Morton Nance and A. S. D. Smith, The Federation of Old Cornwall Societies, Marazion.

**Bible Guiot**, see Guiot de Provins.

**Birley** (1976). *The Lives of the Later Caesars*, trans. A. Birley, Penguin Classics, London and New York.

***Black Book of Carmarthen***. Facsimile edn, by J. Gwenogvryn Evans, Oxford, 1888.

**Blondel** (1948). *Les anciennes basiliques d'Agaune*, 'Vallesia' t.III, Sion, pp. 9–57, t.IV (1949) pp. 15–28.

**Boccaccio**. *The Decameron*, any edition.

**Bollandists**. *Acta Sanctorum*, Paris and Brussels, 1864 *et seq*.

**Bonedd y Saint**, in Bartrum (1966).

**Bouche** (1664). *Histoire de Provence*, H. Bouche, Aix-en-Provence, edn. Marseilles, 1784.

**Bouquet** (1738). *Recueil des Historiens des Gaules et de la France*, Martin Bouquet (the 'Maurist'), Paris. This collection conveniently assembles Zosimus and all the historians and chroniclers of the period, with much else, albeit using older texts. The 1869 reprint, made for the Bollandists, has a kindlier Greek font but lacks the splendid maps.

**Bourban** (1901). *Mélanges*, t.II Cap. III, pp. 285–7.

**Brachet** (1868). *Etymological Dictionary of the French Language*, A. Brachet, trans. G. W. Kitchen, Clarendon Press, Oxford, 1882.

**Braun** (1964); in *Livre des Promesses et des Prédictions de Dieu*, trans. René Braun, Sources Chrétiennes, 101–2, Les Éditions du Cerf, 29 Bd. de la Tour-Maubourg, Paris, CNRS sponsored.

**Brewer**. *Dictionary of Phrase and Fable*. Many editions.

**Bruce** (1923). *The Evolution of Arthurian Romance*, J. D. Bruce, Johns Hopkins University.

**Bury** (1897). Gibbon's *Decline and Fall of the Roman Empire*, edited, by J. B. Bury, Methuen & Co., London.

**Canner** (1982). *The Parish of Tintagel: Some Historical Notes*, A. C. Canner, pub. by the author, Camelford.

**C.I.L. XII**. *Corpus Inscriptionem Latinarum*, Vol. XII, 1888, Berlin.

***Camb. Med. Hist.*** (1911). Cambridge, Cambridge University Press.

***Canterbury Tales***, G. Chaucer, trans. N. Coghill, Penguin Classics, 1951.

**Carson and Kelly**, in *Proc. Royal Irish Academy*, Vol. 77, C, pp. 35–55.

**Cedrenus**. *Historiarum*, t.1. Paris, 1647, and in *Corpus scriptorum historiae Byzantinae*, Bonn, 1828–78.

**Chadwick, H. M.** (1899). 'Háva mál', 2nd poem of the *Elder Edda* [edach] in Old Icelandic, in H. M. Chadwick, *The Cult of Othin, an essay in the ancient religion of the North*, London, C. J. Clay, Cambridge University Press, 1899.

**Chadwick, N.** (1954), see *S.E.B.H.* 1954.

**Chadwick, N.** (1970). *The Celts*, Nora Chadwick, Penguin/Pelican Books, Middlesex.

**Chadwick, Owen**, in *S.E.B.H.* 1954.

**Chaucer**, see *Canterbury Tales*.

**Chrestien's Perceval.** *Perceval le Gallois*, ed. C. Potvin, Mons, 1866+; and see Loomis 1959.
**Claudian**, see Platnauer 1926.
**Cligés**, see Comfort 1914.
**Clinton** (1845). *Fasti Romani*, H. Fynes Clinton, Oxford University Press, Vol I.
**Clinton** (1850). *Ibid.*, Vol. II.
**Clover** (1971). *Flavius Merobaudes*, trans. and Comm. by Frank M. Clover, Transactions of the American Philosophical Society, N.S. Vol. 61, Pt. 1, Philadelphia.
**Colgan.** *Acta Sanctorum* (Hiberniae), Jan 1 to Mar 31, c. 1640.
**Collart** (1941). *Inscriptions Latines de St-Maurice et du Bas-Valais*, Paul Collart, Revue Suisse d'Art et d'Archéologie, Vol. 3, Nos 1–2, Birkhæuser, Bâle.
**Comfort** (1914). *Arthurian Romances by Chrétien de Troyes*, trans. W. W. Comfort, Everyman's Library, J. M. Dent, London.
**Courtier.** *Le Vrai Visage de Montgenèvre*, Michel B. Courtier, Reims, c. 1980+.
*C.S.E.L.* *Corpus Scriptorum Ecclesiasticorum Latinorum*, Vienna 1866+.

**de Boron**, see Loomis (1959).
**Decameron**, see Boccaccio.
**de la Halle** (1276), see Loomis 1959.
**De Vic and Vaissete** (1730). *Histoire Générale de Languedoc*, Claude De Vic and J. J. Vaissete, Paris.
**Doon de Mayence**, see *Enc. Brit.* XI, text article.
**Dream of Macsen Wledig**, see Mabinogion.
**Duff** (1934). *Minor Latin Poets*, text and trans. J. Wight and Arnold M. Duff, Heinemann, London, and Harvard University Press.

***E.B.*** XI Edn *Encyclopædia Brittanica*, XI Edn, Cambridge University Press, 1910.
***E.C.M.W.***, see Nash-Williams (1950).
**Egbert** (1896). *Introduction to the Study of Latin Inscriptions*, Jas. C. Egbert, Longmans, Green & Co, London.
***Emperor Octavian*** (*Romance of the*), see Spence (1913).
**Erle of Thoulouse**, see Spence (1913).
**Esplandian**, see Spence (1913).
**Eucheria's Journal**, see Wilkinson (1971).
**Eunapius**, *apud* Photius, see Clinton (1845, 1850).
**Evans** (1887). Sir Arthur Evans in Numism, Chron., s.3 (7).

**Fabre** (1948). *Essai sur la chronologie de l'oeuvre de Saint Paulin de Nole*, Paris.
**Farrar** (1907). *Lives of the Fathers*, Frederic W. Farrar (1889), edn. 1907, Adam & Charles Black, London.
**Floovant**, Geste of, see Guessard (1849).
**Freeman** (1886). *Tyrants of Britain, Gaul, and Spain*, E. A. Freeman, in English Historical Review, Vol. I, pp. 54–85.
**Freeman** (1887). *Ibid.*, Vol. II, pp. 417–65.
**Frere** (1974). *Britannia*, Sheppard Frere, Sphere Books Ltd, London. (Cardinal edn. first published 1967.)

**Gallic Chronicle 452.** Pseudo-Prosper, or (*quondam*) 'Prosper Tiro'. In full in Bouquet 1738.
**Gantz** (1981). *Early Irish Myths and Sagas*', trans. Jeffrey Gantz, Penguin Classics, Middlesex.
***Gawayne and the Grene Knight***, in Loomis (1959).
**Geoffrey of Monmouth**, see Thorpe (1966).
***Gesta Romanorum***, see Swan (1891).
**Gibbon**, see Bury (1897).

**Gildas**. *Prefatio, de Excidio, Epistola; Liber Querulus*, text in Giles (1847), Translation in Giles (1841).
**Giles** (1841). *Gildas and Nennius*, trans. J. A. Giles, James Bohn, London.
**Giles** (1847). *Historical Documents Concerning the Ancient Britons*, ed. J. A. Giles, George Bell, London. (Comments as for Bouquet 1738.)
**Giot** (1982). *Saint Budoc on the island of Lavret (Brittany)*. P.-R. Giot, in Pearce (1982).
**Giraldus Cambrensis**, see Williams (1908).
**Goldbacher**, see *C.S.E.L.*
**Golden Legend**, see Jacobus de Voragine.
**Grattius**. *Cynegetikon*, see Duff (1934).
**Gregory I**. *Dialogues*, in Migne PL.
**Gregory of Tours**, see Thorpe (1974).
**Grimm** (1850). *Vorlesung über das Verbrennen der Leichen*, Jacob Grimm, Akademie der Wissenschaft, Berlin.
**Grimms Sagen** (1981). *The German Legends of the Brothers Grimm*, ed. and trans. Donald Ward, Institute for the Study of Human Issues Inc., USA and Davison Publishing Ltd (Millington), London.
**Guiot de Provins**, *aliter Guyot. Works* (in French) ed. John Orr, Manchester University Press, 1915.
**Guessard** (1849). *Floovant* (chanson de geste), first published, M. M. F. Guessard and H. Michelant, F. Vieweg, Paris. (A translation by F. H. Bateson, Loughborough, 1938, not seen by me.)

**Hare, Augustus**. *Walks in Rome* 12th edn. (undated), George Allen, London.
**Hartman von der Aue**, see Loomis (1959).
**Hatto** (1965). *The Nibelungenlied*, trans. A. T. Hatto, Penguin Classics, 1969 revision 1979 edn.
**Hatto** (1980). Wolfram von Eschenbach, *Parzival*, trans. A. T. Hatto, Penguin Classics, 1980.
**Havelok the Dane**, see Sands (1966) (full text), and Spence (1913).
**Helinandus**, in Migne PL.
**Hippolytus**, in Migne PG; and Miller (1851), Oxford.
**Hodgkin** (1880). *Italy and her Invaders 376–476*, Thomas Hodgkin, Clarendon Press, Oxford (Vols I and II).
**Holder** (1896). *Alt-Celtischer Sprachschatz*, t.i (1896), t.ii (1904), Alfred T. Holder, Leipzig.
**Horace**. *Odes*, any edition.
**Hunter-Blair**, see *S.E.B.H.* (1954).

**Idatius**, see Bouquet (1738).
**Innocent**, see Migne, PL 20.
**Iolo MSS 1888**. *A selection of Ancient Welsh Manuscripts*, Welsh MSS Society, Foulkes, Liverpool, 1st edn, 1848.
**Irish myth**, see Squire (1910) and Gantz (1981).

**Jacobus de Voragine**, see Ryan and Ripperger (1941).
**James** (1924). *The Apocryphal New Testament*, M. R James, 1975 edn. Oxford University Press.
**Jerome**, in Migne, citations in Farrar (1907) and Clinton (1845, 1850).
**John of Glastonbury**, see Lewis (1955).
**Jordanes**. Getica, in Mommsen, Mon. Germ. hist. auct. antiq.
**Jornandes**, see Jordanes.

**Kent** (1957) J. P. C. Kent in Numism. Chron. (6) xvii, pp. 78–83.
**Kipling**. *Puck of Pook's Hill*, any edition.

**Languedoc**, see De Vic and Vaissete (1730).
**Larousse** (1959). *New Encyclopædia of Mythology*, Hamlyn, London.
**Latin Geber**, in *E.B.* 9th edn., text article *Geber*.
**Leland** (1544). *Assertio inclitissimi Arturi Regis Britanniae*, London 1544, and see Mead (1925).
**Le Nain** (1701, 1738). *Histoire des Empereurs*, t.V and t.VI, Le Nain de Tillemont, Rollin fils, Paris.
**Levinson** (1940), in Antiquity, pp. 280–91.
**Lewis** (1955). 7th edn, *St Joseph of Arimathea at Glastonbury*, Lionel S. Lewis, James Clarke & Co. Ltd., London.
**Liebeschuetz** (1963). *Did the Pelagian Movement have Social Aims?*, W. Liebeschuetz, Leicester, in 'Historia', Vol. 12.
**Liebeschuetz** (1967). *Pelagian Evidence on the Last Period of Roman Britain?*, W. Liebeschuetz, Leicester, in Latomus, Vol. 26.
**Lindsay** (1970). *The Origins of Alchemy*, Müller, London.
**Livy**. *Ab Urbe Condita Libri*, Books I–X at least (reissued for Q. Aurelius Symmachus by the Nicomachi, AD396), any edition.
**Llywarch Hēn** (1935). *Canu Llywarch Hēn*, ed. Sir Ifor Williams, Cardiff.
**Lobineau** (1836). *Les vies des Saints de Bretagne et des personnes d'une éminente piété qui ont vécu dans cette province*, c.1720, Dom Guy-Alexis Lobineau (the Maurist), edited and revised by L'Abbé Tresvaux, published by Méquignon Jr., Faculté de Théologie, Paris.
**Lombard-Jourdan** (1989). *Montjoie et saint Denis*, Anne Lombard-Jourdan, Presses du C.N.R.S., Paris.
**Longfellow** (c.1850). *The Golden Legend*, Henry W. Longfellow, any edition.
**Loomis** (1927). *Celtic Myth and Arthurian Romance*, R. S. Loomis, Columbia University Press, New York.
**Loomis** (1956). *Wales and the Arthurian Legend*, R. S. Loomis, University of Wales Press, Cardiff.
**Loomis** (1959). *Arthurian Literature in the Middle Ages*, ed. R. S. Loomis, Clarendon Press, Oxford.
**Löseth** (1891). *Le Roman en prose de Tristan (etc.)*, E. Löseth, Paris.

**Mabinogion**, any edition (but I prefer Lady Charlotte Guest's Everyman edition for the intriguing Notes).
**MacNiocaill** (1972). *Ireland before the Vikings*, G. MacNiocaill, Gill & Macmillan, Dublin.
**Manitius**, see *Cambridge Medieval History* 1911.
**Marcellinus**, Comes, see Bouquet (1738) and Tillemont (1701).
**Marciana MS.299**, see Berthelot (1888).
**Marie de France**, in Loomis (1959).
**Margary** (1957). *Roman Roads in Britain*, Vol. II, Ivan D. Margary, Phoenix House Ltd, London.
**Matarasso** (1969). *The Quest of the Holy Grail*, trans. P. M. Matarasso, Penguin Classics, 1981 edn, Middlesex.
**ME Romance**, see Sands (1966).
**Mead** (1925). Leland's *Assertio*, trans. R. Robinson, ed. W. E. Mead, Early English Text Society, Vol. 165, Oxford University Press.
**Melchinus of Avalon**, see John of Glastonbury.
**Merobaudes**, see Clover (1971).
**Migne PL**. *Patrologia cursus Latinærum*. J. P. Migne, Paris from 1844+. (Innocent's letter to Victricius follows V's *Liber de Laude Sanctorum* in PL t.20; Augustine (Ep. 185) is t.33, col. 793 *et seq.*).

**Mommsen**, see Bourban (1901).
**Morris** (1965). *Pelagian Literature*, John Morris, in Journal of Theological Studies, NS, Vol. xvi, Pt. 1, April 1965, pp. 26–60.
**Morris** (1973). *The Age of Arthur*, John Morris, 1977 edn. in 3 Vols, Phillimore & Co. Ltd., Chichester.
**Myres** (1951). Journal of the Roman Society, Vol. 50/51, Vol. 50, p. 26.

**Nash-Williams** (1950). *The Early Christian Monuments of Wales*, Cardiff.
**Nennius**, as Gildas (q.v.).
**Nibelungenlied**, see Hatto (1965).
**Notitia Dignitatum**, see Seeck (1876).

**Olympiodorus** (*apud* Photius), in Clinton (1845) and Bouquet (1738).
***Ordnance Survey***. *Map of Roman Britain*, 3rd edn, 1956.
**Orlando**, see Spence (1913).
**Orosius**. *Adversus Paganos*, trans. I. W. Raymond, Columbia University Press, New York, 1936.
**Ovid**. *Metamorphoses*, any edition.

**Pacatus**, in Clinton (1845).
**Palamedes**, the Romance of, see Löseth (1891).
**Palmerin d'Angleterre**, see Loomis (1959) and Spence (1913).
**Paton** (1926). *Les Prophecies de Merlin*, Lucy Allen Paton. M.L.A. monograph Series, London.
**Paulinus**, see Walsh (1967).
**Pauly-Wissowa**. *Real-Encyclopädie der Classischen Altertums Wissenschaft*, Berlin, 1894, *et seq*.
**Pearce** (1982). *The Early Church in Western Britain and Ireland*, ed. Susan M. Pearce, B.A.R. British Series 102, Oxford.
**Perlesvaus**. *The High History of the Holy Graal*, trans Sebastian Evans, Everyman Edition, London.
**Philostorgius**, in Clinton (1845) and Bouquet (1738).
**Pindar**, *Odes*, any edition.
**Platnauer** (1926). *Claudian*, text and trans. M. Platnauer, Loeb Edition, Harvard University Press and Heinemann, London.
**Pliny**. *Natural History*, any edition.
**Priscus**, in Hodgkin (1880).
**Procopius**, Loeb edn., 1914/15.
***Prose Tristan***, see Löseth (1891).
**Prosper of Aquitaine**, in Bouquet (1738).
**Ptolemy**, in Bouquet (1738).

**Reinelt** (1904). *Studien über die Briefe des Heiligen Paulinus von Nola*, Breslau.
**Rettberg and Gieseler**, see Baring-Gould (1872), 22 September.
**R.C.H.M.** *Anglesey* (1937).
**Ricemarchus** (Rhygifarch), d. 1099; see Wade-Evans (1944).
**Rodwell**, see Pearce (1982).
***Romance of King Horne***, see Sands (1966).
**Rutilius Namatianus**, see Duff (1934).
**Ryan and Ripperger** (1941). *The Golden Legend of Jacobus de Voragine*, trans. Granger Ryan and Helmut Ripperger, 1969 edn., Arno Press, New York Times, New York.

**Sands** (1966). *Middle English Verse Romances*, ed. Donald B. Sands, Holt, Rinehart & Winston, Inc., New York.
***S.E.B.H.*** (1954). *Studies in Early British History*, N. Chadwick and ors, Cambridge University Press.
**Seeck** (1876). *Notitia Dignitatum*, ed. Otto Seeck, Weidmann, Berlin.
**Seeck** (1894), in 'Philologus'.
**Shakespeare**, any edition.
**Shelton** (1981). *The Esquiline Treasure*, Kathleen J. Shelton, British Museum Publications Ltd, London.

**Sherwood Taylor** (1976). *The Alchemists*, F. Sherwood Taylor (Heinemann 1952), 'Paladin' Granada Publishing Ltd., St Albans.
**Sherley-Price** (1955). Bede's *History of the English Church and People*, trans. L. Sherley-Price, Penguin Classics, London rev. edn. 1968, repr. 1970.
**Société Dinantaise de Recherches.** *A propos d'un bronze d'époque romaine retrouvé à Falmignoul-Dinant*, K. and V. Pizinger, Arnould, Dinant, Bulletin, May 1979.
**Socrates**, in Bouquet (1738) and Clinton (1845).
*S.O.E.D.*, *Shorter Oxford English Dictionary*, 1968 edn.
**Song of the Saxons**, see Spence (1913).
**Sozomen**, in Bouquet (1738) and Clinton (1845).
**Sparey-Green**, in Pearce (1982).
**Spence** (1913). *A Dictionary of Mediaeval Romance and Romance Writers*, Lewis Spence, George Routledge, London.
**Spink** (1994). *The Roman Imperial Coinage*, Spink Ltd, London.
**Squire** (c.1910). *Celtic Myth and Legend*, Charles Squire, Gresham Publishing Co. Ltd., London.
**Sutherland** (1954) in Numism. Chron. 6–5.
**Swan** (1891). *Gesta Romanorum*, trans Charles Swan, George Bell & Sons, London.
**Synesius**, in Berthelot (1888) and Sherwood Taylor (1976).

**Tain Bo Chuailgne**, in Squire (c.1910).
**Thomas** (1963). *The Interpretation of the Pictish Symbols*, in the Archaeological Journal, Vol. CXX for 1963.
**Thomas** (1981). *Christianity in Roman Britain to AD500*, Charles Thomas, Batsford, London.
**Thomas** (1982) in Pearce (1982).
**Thompson** (1977). *Britain AD406–410*, E. A. Thompson, in *Britannia*, Vol. 8, pp. 303–18.
**Thorpe** (1966). Geoffrey of Monmouth's *History of the Kings of Britain*, trans. Lewis Thorpe, Penguin Classics (1968 edn.), Middlesex.
**Thorpe** (1974). Gregory of Tours's *History of The Franks*, trans. Lewis Thorpe, Penguin Classics 1979, Middlesex.
**Tillemont** (1701) (Vol. V), see Le Nain.
**Tillemont** (1738) (Vol. VI), *ibid.*
**Tonnelat**, see Larousse (1959).

**Ussher** (1639). *Britanniae Ecclesiarum Antiquitates*, James Ussher, Dublin, also in Complete Works (Vol. V), Elrington, Dublin 1864.

**Vacandard** (1903). *Saint Victrice*, E. Vacandard, Paris.
**Van Millingen** (1899). *Byzantine Constantinople*, Alexander Van Millingen, John Murray, London.
**Van Millingen** (1912). *Byzantine Churches in Constantinople*, *ibid.*, Macmillan, London.
**Vendryes** (1925). *Pharamond in Irish Tradition*, J. Vendryes, in 'Mélanges, Ferdinand Lot', Paris 1925 (also Geneva 1976, pp. 743–67).
**Vita of St James of the Tarentaise**, in Baring-Gould (1872).
**Volsunga Saga**, in Spence (1913).
**Vulgate Estoire**, in Loomis (1959).
**Vulgate** 'Queste', *ibid.*, and see Matarasso (1969).

**Wade-Evans** (1944). *Vitae Sanctorum Britanniae et Genealogiae*, text and trans. A. W. Wade-Evans, University of Wales Press Board, Cardiff.

**Walsh** (1967). *Letters of St Paulinus of Nola*, trans. P. G. Walsh, Longmans, Green & Co., London, Vol. II.

**Walter Mapes**. *Nugæ*, ed. M. R. James, 'Anecdota', Oxon, 1914.

**Waltharius**, see Hatto (1965) and Spence (1913).

**Weir** (1980). *Early Ireland, a Field Guide*, Anthony Weir, Blackstaff Press, Dundonald, Belfast, N. Ireland.

**Whithorn Volume 1950**. Proc. Dumfries & Galloway Nat. Hist. & Antiq. Socy, Vol. xxvii, pp. 46ff.

**Wilkinson** (1971). *Egeria's Travels, newly translated with supporting documents and notes*, John Wilkinson, SPCK, London 1971.

**Williams** (1908). Gerald of Wales' *Itinerarium Kambriae*, trans W. Llewellyn Williams, Everyman Edition, J.M. Dent, London.

**Williams** (1937). Sir Ifor Williams in R.C.H.M. *Anglesea* (q.v.).

**Williamson** (1965). Eusebius' *History of the Church*, trans. G. A. Williamson, Penguin Classics, London.

**Wolfram von Eschenbach**, see Hatto (1980).

**Zosimus, Count**, in Bouquet (1738) and Clinton (1845).

**Zosimus of Panoplis**, in Berthelot (1888) and Sherwood Taylor (1976).

# INDEX OF PERSONAL NAMES

**Note:** Major page references in **bold**. Illustrations in *italics*. Numbers (in brackets) refer to the notes in the Commentary (pp. 257–329). Pages 331 to 351 refer to the Appendices (1–12). ***Major characters thus***, per the Dramatis Personae pp. xxix–xxx.

# INDEX OF PLACES

**Note:** Major page references in **bold**. Illustrations in *italics*. Numbers (in brackets) refer to the notes in the Commentary (pp. 257–329). ***Major characters thus***, per the Dramatis Personae pp. xxix–xxx.

# SUBJECT INDEX

**Note:** Major page references in **bold**. Illustrations in *italics*. Numbers (in brackets) refer to the notes in the Commentary (pp. 257–329). ***Major characters thus***, per the Dramatis Personae pp. xxix–xxx.

Indexes prepared, along author's guidelines, by Mary Orchard and Richard Raper of: INDEXING SPECIALISTS, 202 Church Road, HOVE, East Sussex BN3 2DJ. Tel: 01273 738299. www.indexing.co.uk